VHF/UHF Handbook

Second Edition

Edited by Andy Barter, G8ATD

Radio Society of Great Britain

Published by The Radio Society of Great Britain
3 Abbey Court, Priory Business Park, Bedford, MK44 3WH

First published 1997

Second edition published 2007

Reprinted 2008

ISBN 9781-9050-8631-8

Publisher's note

The opinions expressed in this book are those of the authors and not necessarily those of the RSGB. While the information presented is believed to be correct, the authors, the publisher and their agents cannot accept responsibility for the consequences arising for any inaccuracies or omissions.

Cover design: Dorotea Vizer, M3VZR

Production: Mark Allgar, M1MPA

Typography: Andy Barter, K M Publications, Luton

Printed in Great Britain by Latimer Trend & Company Ltd of Plymouth

Acknowledgements

The articles in this handbook have been supplied by radio amateurs from around the world. The editor would like to thank the following people and organisations for their contributions:

Bob Hicks, W5TX

David Worboys, M0ZLB

Dragoslav Dobricic, YU1AW

E Chicken, MBE, BSc, MSc, CEng, FIEE, G3BIK

Geoff Pike, GI0GDP

Lyle Johnson, KK7P

Matthias Bopp, DD1US

Martin E Meserve, K7MEM

Ole Nykjaer, OZ2OE

Ron Taylor, G4GXO

Ross Wilkinson, G6GVI

Steve Kostro, N2CEI

Uwe Kraus, DJ8DW

Wolfgang Schneider, DJ8ES

Zeljko Bozic, S52ZB

CQTV Magazine

DUBUS Magazine

OZ Magazine

PW Magazine

QST Magazine

RadCom

Silicon Chips Magazine

UKW Berichte Magazine

VHF Communications Magazine

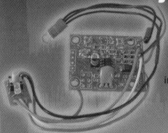

Contents

This is the second edition of the VHF/UHF Handbook. It has been substantially updated since the first edition to make it a true 21st century edition. There are so many changes that it is impossible to itemise them all but suffice to say that all of the text has been checked and where appropriate it has been revised to make it as up to date as possible.

Since the first edition The Internet has become a way of life for many of us, where possible I have included postal addresses and telephone numbers so that references can be followed up without using The Internet but it has to be said that this is becoming more difficult.

The objective of the handbook is to introduce the main information needed by radio amateurs wanting to use the VHF/UHF bands. There are many practical designs included that I hope will encourage readers to construct their own equipment, this is the only real way to understand the principles involved and further the use of the bands. It is very important that radio amateurs continue to use the VHF/UHF bands because there are many com-mercial organisations looking at our frequency allocations with longing eyes. It is very true that we must use the frequencies or loose them

Many of the articles require a PCB, the artwork in this book is not reproduced to exact size, so if you are going to make you own PCBs please take care to scale the artwork correctly. I recommend that you take an easier option because most of the authors can supply PCBs and I have included contact details where possible. Many of the contacts are email addresses or web sites, unfortunately these have a habit of changing, they were current at the time of editing (June 2007). If you have difficulties with PCBs, finding components or contact details please contact me and I will try to help.

Andy Barter, G8ATD, Email: andy@vhfcomm.co.uk

Introduction to VHF/UHF

 ntroduction to VHF/UHF

What is VHF/UHF?

The electromagnetic spectrum cannot be infinite due to limitations imposed by the finite age of our universe and because there is only a finite amount of energy in the universe. Nevertheless, the range of frequencies at which something, somewhere, is happening is immense. The (relatively) much smaller range of frequencies used for deliberate communication is still too big to contemplate all at once.

VHF (very high frequencies) is the name given to the 30 to 300MHz part of the electromagnetic spectrum. UHF (ultra high frequencies) is the name given to the 300 to 3000MHz part.

The whole of the 'radio' part of the electromagnetic spectrum is divided into a series of named ranges. The boundaries between ranges are at 3, 30, 300, 3000MHz (or not quite exactly at 100, 10, 1, 0.1 metres wavelength). Fig 1.1 shows the broad picture of the electromagnetic spectrum. Fig 1.2 focuses on the part of the spectrum used for radio communications.

The boundaries were just chosen arbitrarily at nice, round, numbers. Nothing abrupt happens at them. It is well known that there are differences in the propagation characteristics of radio signals of different frequencies, but these are caused by the environment – our atmosphere and terrain – rather than being direct consequences of the frequency of the signal. As a result of changing weather

Table 1.1: VHF/UHF amateur bands in the IARU regions.

Band (MHz)	Region 1	Region 2	Region 3
50 - 54	UK 50-52MHz	Yes	Yes
144 - 146	Yes	Yes	Yes*
146 - 148	No	Yes	Yes*
220 - 225	No	Yes*	No
430 - 440	Yes*	Yes*	Yes*
902 - 928	No	Yes*	No
1240 - 1300	Yes*	Yes*	Yes*

* Shared band

and upper-atmospheric conditions, the frequencies where changes in propagation effects occur are not fixed. They can move by at least a factor of 10, and the changes may be abrupt or gradual. Without any fixed natural landmarks, any fixed divisions have to be arbitrary. Any attempt to fix boundaries based on the different technologies we use would fare no better, as they too would shift as new technologies evolve.

30 to 3000MHz is still a very large chunk of spectrum, and while someone studying propagation may be interested in the whole of it, most amateur interest naturally focuses on the bands where our licences permit us to transmit. Table 1.1 shows the worldwide VHF and UHF amateur bands.

The border with microwaves

Although the formal definition of UHF extends up to 3000MHz, traditionally some of the higher-frequency part of the range has been considered to be 'microwaves' and treated separately, with its own technologies, literature

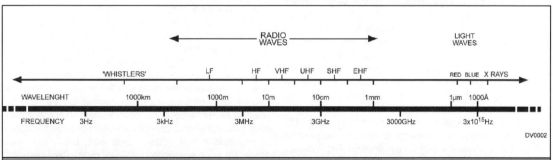

Fig 1.1: The electromagnetic spectrum.

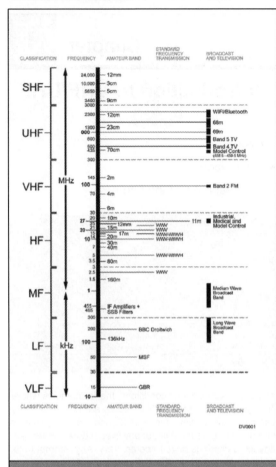

Fig 1.2: Amateur bands in relation to other services.

Progress is rarely smooth, and the frantic development of centimetric radar in the 1940s was a sudden jump to much higher frequencies than had ever before been used. It opened up a gap in the VHF/UHF region where available techniques were much less advanced than those used at both lower and higher frequencies. Subsequent advances have filled in the gap, and the whole of the VHF/UHF range is now fought over as prime territory for many different uses. Modern semiconductors, surface-mount components, and stripline techniques allow printed circuit type construction to be used well into microwave territory. The 1296MHz amateur band used to be considered to be a microwave band, but advancing technology has meant that techniques used at 144 and 430MHz can now be used at 1296MHz, so it is now firmly in the UHF fold. The appearance of commercially made equipment for this band has reinforced this. There is a still higher UHF band at 2310MHz, but it is currently thought of as being a microwave band even though it's definitely in the UHF range. Technology continues to advance and the 13cm band at 2310MHz may eventually be poached from the microwave people.

The border with HF

Radio signals do not halt obediently at national borders, so the governments of the world have long been forced to meet in order to plan the usage of the electromagnetic spectrum. The level of chaos that would result without meticulously detailed planning is a powerful incentive. Even those nations who frequently refuse to sit around the same table send their representatives, who sit down and get on with some good, pragmatic compromising. The ITU is the overall international co-ordinating body for all communications, covering wired and optical fibre systems as well as radio. The CCIR is its main committee on radio matters. The large spectrum management meetings are called the World Administrative Radio Conferences (WARCs), and are usually given a year number suffix. WARCs are not held regularly, but are called when there is sufficient need. The amount of information gathering and planning needed to put together proposals for such meetings mean that several years notice is normally given, though it may be less if the amount of spectrum scheduled for review is limited. WARC79 was a major one which reviewed the entire spectrum and gave us three new HF amateur bands. In the late 1980s it was realised that the use of the radio spectrum was changing very rapidly so the format and frequency of these meetings was rationalised, they are now called just WRC conferences and take place every 4 years with various sub committees to discuss specific topics. The HF-VHF boundary, at 30MHz, is the major breakpoint in this planning process. Signals below 30MHz are treated as if they could propagate over the entire planet, and thus need to be co-ordinated globally. Those above 30MHz are treated as if long-distance propagation is rare, and so need only relatively local co-ordination. This is rather simplistic and fails to take into account the large variations in propagation that occur in this area, but it has been made to work reasonably well to date. Consequently, changes to the plans above 30MHz can be made readily

and specialists. The word 'microwave' does not feature on the HF, VHF, UHF, SHF, EHF etc scale. It's really an older name from an earlier nomenclature of the spectrum and overlays part of UHF upwards, right up to infra-red light. It doesn't have any definite frequency boundaries, but you will find that contests, specialist groups and specialist publications have drawn their own (sometimes different) arbitrary lines and class everything higher in frequency as 'microwaves'.

Historically, microwaves were treated separately from the rest of radio technology because of the very different techniques that had to be used at such frequencies. Waveguide structures, dishes, horns, klystrons, and cavity magnetrons made up the armoury of the microwave engineer. Active devices were unusual in that the dimensions of their internal components were chosen to be resonant at their intended operating frequency. Conventional radio techniques of the time were simply not capable of approaching these frequencies. Lumped components and pin-based valves worked well into the VHF region, while microwave components had an effective limit to how low a frequency they could be made for; imposed simply by what physical size could be tolerated.

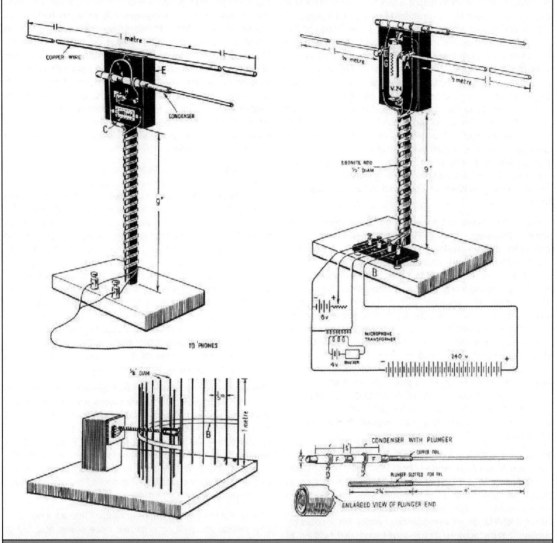

Fig 1.3 Marconi's 2m receiver and transmitter, made in 1919, which demonstrates the production of a beam using a parabolic reflector.

by more frequent and smaller meetings than the global-scale ones that have to be called to make decisions below 30MHz. Above 30MHz, the ITU regulations give a lot more freedom for individual administrations to create their own variations to suit their particular countries. In the UK, these freedoms can be seen in the existence of the 4m and 6m bands as well as the old Class B licence.

Prehistory

Faraday, Oersted, Gauss and others had discovered that there was some sort of relationship between electric charge, motion and magnetism. They had performed a variety of experiments and evolved a number of theories, but there was something missing. The ideas of forces that acted at right angles to motion and action at a distance seemed bizarre compared to classical mechanics. James Clerk Maxwell set out to tidy up the theories, and produce

something simpler that would collect them all together and cover all the known phenomena. Between 1864 and 1873 he published four very small equations that did just that. They were written in partial-differential form, in a dialect of mathematics he had learned at Cambridge. They were quite general and covered all conditions, but when they were used to study what would happen if an electric charge was oscillated, they predicted something new. They predicted that it would cause a pair of moving waves, one of electric field, the other of magnetic field, to radiate away from it. They also predicted that the waves would be in phase with each other, moving at the same speed, the speed of light. They showed that the two fields would be oriented at right angles to each other, and be transverse to the direction of propagation. The concept of electromagnetic waves had been born.

Theory is fine, as far as it goes, but experimental

verification does a lot to help make it believable. The first experiment looked like a disaster. Maxwell had thought of how sound waves are carried in air, and how waves of the nautical sort are carried in water, and proposed that there had to be a medium that carried electromagnetic waves. It was called the ether. Michelson and Morley devised a neat experiment in 1881 to prove the existence of the ether. Surprisingly, it proved that the ether did not exist. This destroyed the concept of any sort of carrier medium for electromagnetic waves, and caused a great upset that eventually resulted in the theories of relativity. It did not destroy Maxwell's equations, though. They described moving waves, irrespective of whatever they did or did not move in. Maxwell's equations similarly survived the theories of relativity, and are still believed to be generally valid today.

Heinrich Hertz set out to make some electromagnetic waves. Michelson and Morley had needed waves of extremely short wavelength to make their experiment practicable, and had chosen light (wavelength about 0.0005mm). Hertz wanted to show the relationship with electricity and used a gapped metal ring which he excited with a spark. His receiver was a second gapped ring which would spark across its gap if it was close enough when the transmitter was excited. Using amazingly simple apparatus, he showed that electromagnetic waves did indeed travel at the speed of light. He demonstrated polarisation and the fact that the electric and magnetic field components lay in orthogonal planes, transverse to the direction of motion. With different-sized rings he made signals of different wavelengths, and showed that a similar-sized receiving ring was needed to be able to detect a signal.

Many people believe that radio started on long wave, and only much later expanded into the VHF, then UHF, regions. This is completely wrong! Hertz had chosen to make his apparatus a comfortable size for bench-top experimentation. His early experiments were at UHF, about 800MHz, as a consequence. Just for fun, it could be argued that because Hertz's receiver produced light as its output, then the first-ever radio link was in fact UHF television. Admittedly, it was only of one pixel resolution, but at least its intensity could be varied!

Hertz had no interest in long-distance communication. He had been inspired by the work of Helmholtz and Maxwell, and had produced the necessary experimental support for their theories. 'Action at a distance' was no longer dubious, it was demonstrable. Hertz's work, in its turn, was the inspiration for others. Marconi saw great possibilities in developing Hertz's laboratory toys. After a start at UHF, radio technology entered a period of rapid evolution with antennas getting higher, power levels getting higher and frequencies getting far lower.

History

The history of the development of long-wave communications and broadcasting, followed by the revolutionary discovery of the capabilities of short waves is widely known and often repeated. Comparatively unknown, per-

haps simply lost in the tumult of new LF/HF developments, people were experimenting at even higher frequencies. In 1919, Marconi was experimenting at 150MHz, pushing the limits of what valves could then do. He used dipole antennas with the oscillator and detector placed right at their centres, and used parabolic reflectors to form the emission into a narrow beam. Also in 1919, Barkhausen discovered that ordinary, cylindrical anode, triodes could be made to oscillate internally. Frequencies up to 900MHz could be created under very peculiar bias conditions, with the anode slightly negative and the grid at a high positive voltage.

In 1920, Hull applied a strong magnetic field to a simple diode valve. He could make the electrons spiral out from the cathode to the anode because their trajectories were bent by the magnetic field. With a strong enough field, the anode current cut off as the electrons went into circular orbits. With anode current flowing, useful oscillation could be achieved to several hundred megahertz. A later refinement, splitting the cylindrical anode into two pieces with separate connections, made it much easier to extract a signal from the valve, and the magnetron was born. George Jessop reported that one commercial type was capable of 50W output at 144MHz. This was before strong, compact, permanent magnets had been developed, so early magnetrons were rather unwieldy; just recall the loudspeakers of the period with their huge permanent magnets or large field-coils.

The discovery, by amateurs, that the short waves were not after all useless, but instead were dramatically better than long waves for long-distance communication, made people wonder what might be found at still higher frequencies. If a move to higher frequencies produced wonderful results, then maybe going still higher might produce still.. people had to try it. It was not long before commercial use of the short waves started. This fuelled the development of improved valves for high-frequency use.

One proud tradition of amateur radio: 'Give an amateur a new device and he'll soon extract more power and higher frequencies from it than the designer ever thought possible', goes right back to the beginning. HF ionospheric propagation had been explored with signals coaxed out of valves intended for LF use. Small 'short-wave' triodes with the electrode connections brought straight out of the bulb to avoid the stray capacitance and inductive coupling of conventionally based types proved useful up to 50–70MHz.

All valves were very expensive in this period, so minimising the number needed was a very high priority. A typical transmitter would have been a pair of triodes configured as a push-pull oscillator, while super-regenerative receivers provided the necessary sensitivity with the minimum number of valves. Wire antennas were used, based on those used at lower frequencies.

In Japan, Yagi and Uda were experimenting with arrays of dipoles and had discovered the ability of non-driven dipoles to reflect or direct the signals from a driven one. From this, in the late 1920s, they developed the Yagi-Uda array, much better known as the Yagi antenna. The ability

Fig 1.4: An early 2.3GHz klystron oscillator and receiver.

of this new antenna to concentrate the radiated power in a narrow beam made up for the difficulty of generating appreciable power at higher frequencies, though only in the direction it was pointed. Marconi experimented with Yagi antennas and special valves at 500MHz and proved that communication beyond the visible horizon was possible. Up to this time, VHF and UHF signals had been assumed to behave like light, and the first sign of a flaw in this belief helped to stimulate increased interest in these frequencies.

Commercial research is done with a view to eventual profit. Academic research is done with a view to the publication of new knowledge. Both have to justify their existence; there has to be some possible outcome that can be explained to the controllers of their sources of funding. We amateurs are free to explore where our interests take us. We may not have industrial strength budgets to spend, but we do have a unique level of freedom. In the late 1920s, SSB was invented by a telephone company as a means of multiplexing several telephone channels onto one wire. It was considered to be esoteric and rather fragile in view of the quality of cable it needed to make it work acceptably. Nobody thought that a radio connection could be good enough to carry it until amateurs demonstrated reliable intercontinental SSB contacts. Earlier, it was the sheer number of amateur stations, their geographic diversity and their operation at all hours that allowed the totally unexpected propagation effects of HF to be discovered.

The amateurs exploring VHF were developing new techniques and setting new records. Almost everything that could be thought of was being tried. The small size of efficient VHF antennas must have made trials from aircraft seem natural. One VHF DXpedition of 1935 ran an extensively equipped 5m station at the top of Snowdon and logged a 205 mile contact with Romford, Essex.

Higher frequency bands were tried and techniques were developed to suit them. Coaxial cavities and trough lines gave the frequency stability needed to get results on 112MHz. 'Acorn' valves like the 955 triode appeared and were pressed into service up to 500MHz. Their extremely direct electrode connections and small size made them ideal.

War

The 1939–1945 period saw some of the most intense development of radio and electronics ever. The skills of the radio amateurs were quickly put to work as operators, technicians, instructors and researchers. Because of the amateur's insatiable desire for long-distance contacts, much of the commercially made equipment for the amateur market represented the state of the art. The American Hallicrafters S27 receiver covered from 28 to 142MHz and proved to be the only available instrument that could be used in the hunt for the first VHF radio navigational aids that had been revealed in notes from crashed aircraft. According to an unsubstantiated legend, the entire stock of S27s at Webbs Radio, Soho, was bought up by an RAF signals officer; on credit! One lesson learned from this was that even line of sight frequencies can be used over large distances when one station is on a highflying aircraft, without needing any help from unusual propagation. The navigational beams were simple extensions of the Lorenz landing aid that had been developed in the mid 1830s. The ILS system still in use today is a direct descendant. The possibility of making directional antennas of convenient size made the VHF part of the spectrum the natural choice for beam-type navigational systems. Throughout the war a cat-and-mouse game of progressively more sophisticated navigational systems and their subsequent countermeasures was played. Perhaps we ought not to get too focused on the interesting technology of it all; we must always remember that these 'games' were literally deadly to people on both sides. As fast as new valves could be developed to make high power at higher frequencies, radar moved up in frequency to take advantage of the increased directivity of the antennas that could be made in the available space. Night fighters were larger than their daytime equivalents and had arrays of Yagi beam antennas pointing forwards from their noses. Imagine a respectable 2m or 70cm moonbounce array bolted to the front of an aircraft! Ground-based radar could detect nocturnal bombers, and could direct fighters to their rough location, but the fighters needed their own radar to close the remaining distance.

In the late 1930s, a system of electronically scanned television had been developed at EMI to challenge Baird's mechanically scanned system. This had created a whole

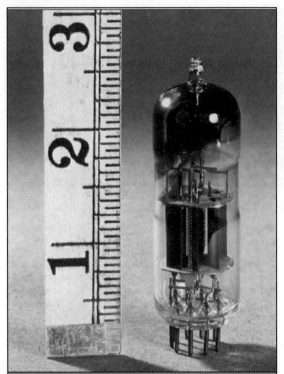

Fig 1.5: Manufacturers introduced smaller and smaller valves for VHF mobile radio, such as this 6W double tetrode (Mullard QQV02-6), but all transistor technology was already on the way.

new sort of electronics: sawtooth 'timebase' oscillators, cathode-ray tubes, pulse amplifiers, synchronisation and triggering circuits. Previously the only signals that anyone had had much experience with had been sine waves, speech and modulated sine waves. Britain's lead in the strange new circuits of electronic television was a great help to the radar pioneers. Because several megahertz of bandwidth were needed to transmit what was then called 'high-definition' 405-line television, operation in the deserted parts of the VHF band was inevitable. Not only did television create the signal-processing circuits needed by radar, but it also created the high-power VHF transmitter technology. After the war, radar repaid its debts because the new valves and circuits that had been developed for it gave a flying re-start to the infant TV industry.

Ships' masts are the obvious mountings for sea-borne radar antennas, and for an uninterrupted view, the radar antenna has to go on top. This means that the size of the antenna has a large effect on the stability of the ship as well as on its visibility. Rayleigh's criterion from optics works for all wave phenomena, so the Royal Navy was able to estimate what angular resolution it needed, and what size of antenna it could tolerate, in order to decide on the minimum frequency they needed. They commissioned a team at Birmingham University to develop radar at 3000MHz. This was a huge step from the existing systems which had been in the 30, 50 and 200MHz regions. Radar requires very high peak power pulsed transmitters and the increase in frequency required a step far beyond the limits

of any known technology. One group at Birmingham based their work on the klystron valve that was known to be able to oscillate at 3GHz, but they could not achieve anything like the power output needed. Instead, the klystron was to prove useful as the receiver local oscillator. In one of those jokes that Nature sometimes plays, John Randall and Harry Boot were working on the Barkhausen-Kurz oscillator (the mis-biased triode described earlier) to develop it as the receiver local oscillator. Eventually, they gave up hope of getting enough power to drive a mixer, or good enough frequency stability, and switched their attentions to the split-anode magnetron. This was at least known to be capable of moderate power, although the frequency stability was known to be poor.

Randall and Boot attacked the frequency stability issue by replacing the simple split anode with a solid block of copper, drilled to make a group of resonant chambers, sized for the wanted frequency. Their prototype had six resonator cavities, each linked to the central cavity by a slot. It was reputed to have been made by using the cylinder of a revolver as a drilling jig. It burned out their dummy load and easily produced several hundred watts, close to the intended frequency. Permanent magnets had been greatly improved by this time, and the quest for a receiver LO had produced a marvellous high-power transmitter. Small, robust, and efficient, the cavity magnetron was simply ideal, and could easily produce peak powers of many kilowatts in pulsed radar duty. Klystrons, which had started out being groomed for the power output job, made great LOs for superhet receivers. Centimetric radar had arrived, right at the upper limit of UHF

Just after the war, many people were using beam antennas, crystal-controlled transmitters and superheterodyne receivers. The first trans-American contact had been made at 50MHz, showing that VHF was sometimes anything but 'optical'.

War surplus

At the end of hostilities, the immense military organisations could not be dismantled instantly, and time was needed for the world's economies to change back to peacetime activities. Military service and rationing continued for several years in some countries. Huge quantities of hardware became surplus to requirements. Cryptographic equipment and other highly secret things were stockpiled or were carefully destroyed to protect their secrets, but tremendous amounts of communications equipment and components were sold off. Disposable incomes were very low before the economies recovered, so technical treasure could only be sold for a tiny fraction of its original cost. It took until the middle of the 'sixties for the flow of war surplus goodies to dry up – there was simply so much of it. In the space of a couple of decades we had gone from it taking many weeks worth of the average income to buy one valve, to amazing devices, being sold by the tea-chest-full, at disposal prices. Large numbers of people had been trained as makers, operators and repairers of all manner of communications and radar equipment. They, too, had become surplus to require-

Fig 1.6: Transistorised power amplifier stage using an MRF646 transistor capable of delivering up to 40W at 2m.

ments. Suddenly dumping large quantities of people or things onto an open market is usually a precursor to disaster, but in this case the things and people were complementary and were just what the emerging civilian markets needed. Radar experience was very appropriate to television, and the work done in developing CRTs and wide-band valves was not wasted. Many home-brew TV receivers were founded on the VCR97 electrostatic CRT and the EF50 VHF pentode. Most amateurs were primarily interested in HF activities, so the demand created a scale of prices, with radios like AR88s at the top, then down through the HRO, CR100, BC348, R1155 etc. The 19 set tank radio was one of the bargain-basement jobs, and although it had a crude VHF transceiver built into it, the VHF section was usually unceremoniously ripped out to make space for an audio amplifier. The period of home-brew television construction created a market for some VHF bits and pieces, but it was relatively short lived as commercially made televisions became available. Perhaps black and green pictures on 5in screens just didn't fit in with the entertainment needs of other members of households? Specialised VHF or radar equipment and components went for junk prices. No true amateur can ever turn down something for nothing or even close to nothing, so a lot of strange things wound up in the hands of people who then wondered what they could do with them. In addition to the dispersal of all this bounty, there was the dispersal of the knowledge to go with it. There was a big influx into the hobby caused by some of all those highly trained people looking for an outlet for their curiosity. Many of them had been involved with VHF/microwave technology. With advanced components and knowledge the records previously set on the VHF/UHF bands were highly vulnerable, and new frequencies with no records had become accessible. The 144 and 432MHz bands were allocated in the late 1940s, virgin territory for new explorers. As had happened earlier on short waves, it was the creation of a large number of stations spread across the world, operating at all hours, looking for long-distance contacts, which led to new discoveries. Two American stations made the first moon-bounce contact in 1953. One bunch of radio astronomers-to-be tried to use the surplus mobile radar unit they had obtained to detect their own lunar echoes. They included Bernard Lovell, and they went on to build the Jodrell Bank radio telescope. Terrestrial propagation studies got a

boost in 1957, the International Geophysical Year, with the opening of GB3IGY, the first of the VHF beacons. The potential of meteor-scatter and sporadic-E propagation were beginning to be discovered. In 1959, a sporadic-E opening gave contacts between the UK and Italy. In America, 400 miles was achieved on 1.3GHz, then California and Hawaii were linked on 220MHz. Records and 'firsts' were there for the taking.

The rise and rise of the transistor

A typical VHF/UHF stations in the 1950s and early 1960s consisted of a crystal oscillator, multiplier and PA chain as the transmitter, with a crystal controlled converter ahead of a standard HF receiver as the tunable IF. Contacts were made by CW, AM or FM. In the 1960s, commercial VHF transceivers became commonplace in emergency services vehicles, with utilities, and with taxi firms. There had been experiments with mobile 'two-way' radio much earlier, on HF and VHF, but this was the full scale deployment of private mobile radio (PMR). The PA stages of this PMR equipment still used valves with smaller and smaller valves developed such as the QQV02-6 (Fig 1.5). Successive generations of PMR mobiles were rapidly developed, as new types of transistors became available, capable of supplanting the valves. An example is shown in Fig 1.6, a complete power amplifier stage, not much larger than the QQV02-6, using an MRF646 power transistor capable of delivering up to 40W on 2m. Many of these PMR sets found their way into amateur hands when they were prematurely pensioned off to make way for each successive smaller and cooler replacement. An example of such a PMR set is the Pye Vanguard shown in Fig 1.7, these and similar equipment can still be found in many shacks as the FM chat station. It was not difficult to re-crystal some of them for 144MHz, though some people who acquired 'lowband' units had to put in a lot of work rebuilding their RF stages to convert them into 'high-band' units. Up to the appearance of this equipment, anyone who wanted to operate mobile had to build their entire station. On HF, the arrival of the transistor coincided with the rapid growth of high-power short-wave broadcasting, so the sudden worsening of the ability of receivers to handle nearby big signals was rather badly timed. It took over two decades to make up for this great step backwards, and to be able to make semiconductor-based HF receivers that were in no way inferior to the best of the

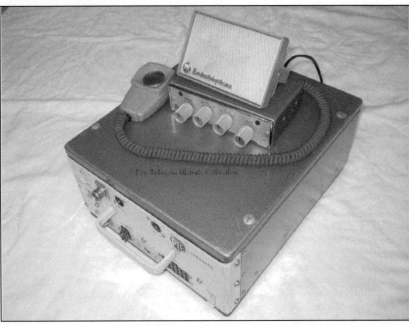

Fig 1.7: An example of PMR equipmet, a Pye Vangaurd from The Pye Telecom Historic Collection.

valved units. On VHF/UHF, conditions were more favourable, receivers were not being 'tenderised' to the same extent, and semiconductors offered progressively lower noise figures, a great boon where noise limitation was far more likely than overload problems. In 1961, just four years after the first-ever artificial satellite, Sputnik-1, the first amateur satellite, Oscar 1, was launched. It transmitted telemetry on a low-power beacon in the 144MHz band. Later amateur satellites offered communications facilities for short periods. While these were marvellous advertisements for the hobby, and a great deal was learned from them, satellite operation in the 1960s was very much a minority interest. Many people listened to them, but only the very dedicated built the multiband stations with azimuth elevation mounted antenna arrays needed for two-way working through something that might only last weeks, if it made orbit at all. It was Oscar 6, which was launched in 1972 and survived for four years, that broke the pattern and showed that satellite DX was a long-term proposition. Four years was more than long enough for the exploits of the pioneer users, and the details of how to follow their lead, to reach print and become general knowledge.

I the early 1970s SSB working on 2m was given a boost

with the arrival of the Belcom Liner 2 (aka the KLM Echo 2) shown in Fig 1.8. It had many faults in terms of performance but that did not stop it's popularity, for many amateurs it was their first experience of SSB on 2m and it gave many the opportunity to work DX that they had only dreamed of before. Of course rigs with better performance appeared very quickly such as the IC202 and the FT290 and FT790 but at the time the only other method of using SSB on VHF and UHF was to use a transverter on the output of a standard HF transceiver, some of the most popular transverters came from Microwave Modules and were the true "black box", see Fig 1.9.

Enter the 'big three'

In Japan, amateur radio had long been practised by a much larger fraction of their population than had been the case in the West. This proved to be a fertile market for the evolution of a number of fiercely competitive manufacturers, each large enough to support mass-production methods. Once their home market approached saturation, they looked to exports for further expansion. The Western manufacturers never knew what hit them. The radio amateurs in the West were abruptly confronted with shiny, new, feature-packed radios at much more affordable

Fig 1.8: The Belcom Liner 2 (aka The KLM Echo 2). Many amateurs first experience of SSB on 2m.

Fig 1.9: An example of a Microwave Modules 70cm transverter.

Fig 1.10: A Yaesu FT817, 160m to 70cm amateur band transceiver.

prices than ever before, and the move from home-built to purchased equipment was fully underway. The first equipment from Japan concentrated on HF SSB operation and rode the change from AM to SSB on those bands. Soon afterwards, the Japanese companies started to export their VHF models. The VHF bands had never before been served by specifically manufactured equipment, and affordable off-the-peg radios were an attractive alternative to scratch-building or modifying surplus PMR equipment. The range of VHF and UHF equipment available from the big Japanese manufacturers has developed over the past 35 years, everything from base stations covering up to 23cm, transceivers with facilities for satellite working and hand held transceivers with up to 4 band operation. They have continually pushed the technology forward with more facilities built into smaller and smaller boxes at prices that most amateurs can afford. If you cannot afford the latest technology there are plenty of last years model on the second hand market. The current trend is towards the

Fig 11: A 144MHz Direct Digital Synthesiser (DDS). The DDS IC is at the top of the PCB with an MMIC amplifier at the bottom left.

multi band, multi mode transverters such as the Yaesu FT817 (Fig 1.10), this covers all amateur bands from 160m to 70cm and is small enough to use as a portable station. Chapter 4 has a review of the current commercial equipment available and has designs for those who want to build their own equipment.

Components Galore

For radio amateurs who want to build their own equipment there are an amazing number of components available to produce very high specification transmitters, receivers and test equipment. The mobile phone market has been largely responsible for the development of components to fuel the demands for smaller and smarter. The result is the availability of components suitable for amateurs to use in VHF and UHF equipment such as the Monolithic Microwave Integrated Circuit (MMIC) that can be used as a building block much like the Operational Amplifier (OA) is used at low frequencies. The manufacturing techniques like surface mount have changed the way that amateurs can build high performance receivers and transmitters. Surface mount devices (SMD) give much better performance at VHF and UHF frequencies, they do require a special skill when building equipment but with care even the smallest components currently available can be used. The design techniques available to the radio amateur have also changed because many CAD programs developed for commercial use are available as free downloads from The Internet, these are usually restricted in some way but can solve many problems that would otherwise have taken many hours of head scratching to sort out. Digital techniques also form part of modern equipment. Direct Digital Synthesis (DDS) of signal sources is commonplace; single chip solutions are available from companies like Analog Devices [1]. A DDS 144MHz source is shown in Fig 1.11, this is a surface mount design with DDS chip at the top of the PCB and an MMIC at the bottom left. Micro controllers can be used to add facilities to equipment, suppliers like Microchip [2]. These controllers are easily programmed with much sample software available for amateur radio applications on The Internet.

Fig 12: Belgian and Dutch radio amateurs exchanging TV pictures via the British repeater GB3LO.

Repeaters

The amateur world was awash with affordable, commercially made, 2m band FM transceivers. Some were retuned, re-crystalled commercial PMR sets, others were purpose made for the amateur market. The 144–146MHz band had been fairly popular for local natter using AM PMR equipment, but the switch to FM accompanied a big increase in occupancy. The majority of PMR sets had been designed for mobile or portable operation, and the Japanese manufacturers produced portable and mobile models. To enhance the coverage of all these mobiles, an extensive network of repeaters has been built. With the part of the 145–146MHz bandplan assigned to repeaters pretty much full, most new repeater development has shifted to the 430–440MHz band. Not all repeaters are FM, just the majority, so the rarer SSB and TV repeaters are especially interesting. The repeaters have acted as magnets for a very small number of disaffected people who try to jam them. This is antisocial, illegal, and damages the reputation of the hobby. Their motivation seems to be a mixture of wanting to annoy people so that they can listen to the resulting anger, and of wanting to get attention. If you do encounter a repeater jammer, the best advice is to do nothing that acknowledges their existence in any way. Do not rise to any taunts. Any sign whatsoever that they have been noticed seems to encourage them. Quietly log the times, the signal strength on the input frequency (and direction, if possible) as this may later help. Never discuss such things on the air as this may either encourage them or tip them off. Ultimately, Ofcom has the power to prosecute, leading to confiscation of equipment and fines. Finding the perpetrator is only part of the problem; sufficient evidence has to be collected in a way that is admissible in court. All this work goes on behind the scenes, and all that is ever seen is a small piece in the news columns of RadCom magazine announcing the result of a court case. The number of jammers is very small indeed (though they try to make as much nuisance as possible), and the number of prosecutions indicates an excellent clean-up rate. Some have tried jamming while mobile, but now their vehicles are at risk of confiscation. Based on the number of QSOs and the number of users, the repeater network is very successful. Very few of the QSOs may contain matters of

Fig 13: The Phase 3C amateur radio satellite being packed for transit to the launch site.

direct importance to amateur radio, but they are useful indirect tools that allow the communities around them to organise various activities.

The 6m band

The creation of a 6m band in the UK came as a large surprise, and was solid evidence that the DTI looks favourably on the Amateur Service. This part of the spectrum was freed up when the 405-line TV broadcast system was closed down and, although it is assigned as an amateur band in the Americas, in our region it is not. The first amateur use was by a few stations with special licence variations as an experiment. Part of the experiment was to investigate the effect on French TV that was still active on low VHF. As the French TV service had coped with our old 405-line TV transmitters, each blasting out many kilowatts across the same band, some care over our power output and antenna configurations ensured a satisfactory demonstration of co-existence. The experiment turned into a permanent new band. It is ideally situated, with interesting propagation effects to be explored with more and more countries getting access to this band. It can give truly amazing contacts and with the coming increase in the sun spot cycle should give much pleasure over the next few years.

Data modes

The radio-teleprinter techniques used on HF have always been directly applicable on VHF, but the appearance of mass-market home computers in the 1980s prompted widespread exploration of new possibilities. Just using the computer to simulate the function of a classic electro-mechanical teleprinter may not look like a bold step

Fig 14: The moonbounce antenna at GM4JJJ.

once the only way of handling slow-scan and facsimile images. The UHF and microwave bands offer the space needed to carry a conventional TV signal. TV repeaters have also been built. Digitised images can be treated just as any other data files and sent by the normal data modes.

Space

There are amateur satellites acting as very-wide-area repeaters for SSB, while some provide images of the Earth and others carry packet mailboxes. Send your long-distance email up when the satellite is over you, and the recipient can read it when the satellite passes over him or her. Astronauts and cosmonauts have taken out amateur licences, and taken up amateur transceivers. There have been many contacts with Mir, The Space Shuttle and The International Space Station. One group onboard Mir actually did their exam in space to get their licences before the end of their mission, and had equipment sent up on a routine supply rocket. Amateur radio has become a popular hobby with spacemen and spacewomen everywhere. It is probable that most future missions will have some amateur radio content. As part of the first-ever amateur operation from orbit, Owen Garriott also sent slow-scan TV images of the interior of The Space Shuttle in the 2m band. Average VHF stations were sufficient to receive these. Few of us will get the chance to try radio actually in orbit, but we can all be Earth stations if we wish and join in the funding, design and development of future amateur satellites.

The present and the future

History is not 'bunk', it is simply inaccessible, and we can neither visit it nor change it. Living in the present, we can see the past clearly, yet our influence is over a future that we cannot see. This seems like a recipe for disaster. Given the unfair advantage of the certainty of the past over the uncertainty of the future, it is easy to believe that most of the wonderful things have already been done, and that there is little left worth doing. This is very probably not so; such things have been said for centuries by people who ought to have known better. Amateur radio is now quite a mature interest and, with the advances in communications in general, it must now look not at all magical to the layman. One of the greatest challenges of the future must be the attraction of new people. The future holds great threats to the survival of the hobby, especially on VHF/UHF. In the 1980s, the liberalisation and privatisation of telephone companies in various countries has led to a boom in radio-based communications services that is still continuing. The analogue mobile phone networks are dead and gone with the digital networks replacing them. Public appreciation of the relative security of their conversations on different types of telephones can only increase. Some companies are trying to sell mobile phones not just as mobile devices, but also as alternatives to wired phones in homes. The network of wires leading from the telephone exchanges to their subscribers is something that cannot be duplicated to allow free-market choice without astronomical cost, so there are plans for competi-

forward, but the reduction of size, noise and weight in a domestic environment did a lot to increase the numbers of people prepared to try RTTY. The X.25 protocol of the packet-switched data technology, used in some parts of the public telephone network, was modified for use on the air (AX.25) and grew into the packet radio network. The originators of X.25 never considered it suitable to be deployed over links made out of simple speech-type radios, but amateurs love making the unexpected work. To the basic packet radio network, bulletin board servers have been added, offering news and electronic mail facilities. Specialised bulletin board servers have been linked to make the DX clusters which rapidly distribute news of interesting band openings or the appearance of rare stations. They may be a mixed blessing, for while the news of a band opening can stir up activity on that band, the 'spots' of rare stations do tend to create beautifully synchronised pile-ups; though mostly on HF! The packet format is well suited to VHF/UHF conditions, and does not work anywhere near as well when tried on HF.

Image modes

Slow-scan TV works well on VHF/UHF and, compared to HF, the clearer channels give less interference on the pictures. Once again home computers have made things much easier and have replaced the long-persistence CRTs, photographic drum printers and scanners that were

tive phone networks using fixed radio links to homes and businesses. Add in the growth of cordless telephones, cordless burglar alarms, remote control devices, WIFI computer networks and car key-fob transmitters, and it can be seen that the demand for space in the RF spectrum is accelerating dramatically. Proposals for global spectrum allocations for use by low-orbit satellite-to-person communications have included requests for the reassignment of all our prime VHF and UHF bands. The idea of a wristwatch phone that will work anywhere on Earth (or in nearby space) with everyone having a single personal telephone number, without geographic codes, is now very close to being achieved. Such progress cannot and should not be stopped, but nor should it be allowed to simply destroy other services. Amateur radio above 30MHz is facing the most severe threats ever. To fight these pressures we need to be able to demonstrate large numbers of people regularly using all the bands, and we need to be able to make good presentations of the value of the continued existence of these amateur bands.

Things to do

There are plenty of things waiting to be done that will advance the individual and/or the hobby. On 2m or 70cm FM, there are new people to be welcomed and encouraged. This could range from informal help when requested, to organised on-air tuition for novices in your area. The voice repeater network is still expanding but it is fairly mature now. The receiver sections of many repeaters are suffering from overload from adjacent paging transmitters, so a high-dynamic-range receiver design would solve many problems. Some groups are experimenting with solar or wind powered repeaters to take advantage of low-cost isolated sites, and also with linking groups of repeaters. A few ATV repeaters already exist, but more of them would stimulate TV evening nets. DXing can be done via sporadic-E openings, meteor-scatter or moonbounce. The moonbounce station at GM4JJJ is a typical medium-sized installation for the 144MHz band, with four long-boom Yagis driven by a pair of 4CX250B valves at about 900W, allowed by a special experimental licence. A small moonbounce station might have a single long-boom Yagi fed from a 100W solid-state amplifier. There are big league stations with monster antenna arrays that can make CW contact with small stations, or SSB contacts with medium stations. Occasionally some amateurs get the temporary use of a really big dish and moonbounce contacts become possible for quite modest stations. The packet network is there to be explored, but it is now bound by two limitations. Our licence conditions covering message content and purpose prevent it becoming open to full Internet traffic, because of the wide-open nature of that network. More open to being fixed is the speed limitation forced by channel bandwidths originally planned for narrowband FM speech. The progressive replacement of the network with high data-rate microwave links could yield a great improvement in network capacity and response speed. There is very little activity on the higher and microwave bands other than during contests. On the 'use it or lose it' principle, we need to devise attractive new uses for these bands. TV and fast data links

are obviously suited to the great bandwidth available, but what other possibilities are there? In a market flooded with commercially made equipment, there is still a place for home construction. Much of the commercial gear tries to do everything at the cost of doing nothing particularly well. If you want a competition-grade system, think in terms of masthead pre-amps and home-made transverters into HF transceivers, if not entirely home-built transceivers. Much commercial equipment has been compromised; the current fashion for wide receiver coverage has made the receiver sections of many transceivers resemble scanners, with a subsequently increased likelihood of inter-modulation and overload problems from out-of-band signals. Hand-held transceivers have responded to market demands for smaller size, longer battery operation, as well as wide range scanning. The tiny 'rubber duck' broadband antennas are very inefficient, but the receivers have been compromised by their wide range and low power consumption design goals, such that the use of any better antenna risks overload problems. Much better performance can be got from a radio specifically optimised for amateur-band-only use. One approach would be to convert one of the cheap ex-PMR handhelds that appear at all rallies. It would be unfashionably big, but it would also be tough enough to knock nails in with and would also maintain a QSO under conditions that would overload something more fashionable. Kitchen-table construction can still produce things that can outdo the big firms if the constructor targets his specific needs and tolerates a less 'consumer' appearance.

Welcome

Well, that's a brief introduction to the VHF/UHF bands, a place of threat and opportunity. It offers wide open spaces in which to try out things that no-one has yet thought of, and it offers many known activities that may still be adventurous for the individual. The Brendan Trophy still awaits the first transatlantic 2m QSO. Anyone fancy a QSO with the first manned mission to Mars?

References

[1] Analog Devices web site: http://www.analog.com

[2] Microchip web site: http://www.microchip.com

Getting Started

etting started

OK, you've done it! The pass certificate for the examination is in your hand and you are ready to post it off for your licence but while you wait for your callsign you will be thinking of where to start and with what.

You may have spent some time listening to the bands as a short-wave listener and have a pretty good idea of where your interests lie but there are those who do not have this preconceived idea of their immediate future.

The best place for your first stop is your local radio club – if you are not sure where your nearest club is located then a phone call to the RSGB or a visit to their web site [1] will give the required details of dates, times and contacts. Most clubs give newcomers a hearty welcome and this will be your chance to talk to other amateurs about what they prefer. Many clubs have a club station where you can get 'hands on' experience of some of the available transceivers and get some answers to those difficult questions. Many of the local amateur radio retail outlets will also offer advice but remember that they may be tempted to push the higher-profit radios your way.

Transceivers

The first real decision is which transceiver to obtain. There are many on the market but which one is best for you? Should you go for a hand-portable ('hand-held'), or a more expensive base unit to sit on the table at home? Would a mobile unit be preferable and should it be just for FM or for SSB and CW use too? Which bands do you want?

The questions are easy to ask but much more difficult to answer, and of course the answers will be constrained by the money you have available for the hobby or the units you are willing and able to build. There are some example designs in the Transmitters and Receivers chapter for those who want to build their own equipment. If you are going to buy your equipment, let's take a look at each in turn – it should be noted that all comments made here refer to the 2m band but are also applicable to all VHF and UHF bands too, from 6m upwards to the microwave

bands. There is a table in the Transmitters and Receivers chapter showing the current new commercial equipment available.

A great percentage of radio amateurs own a 'hand-held' transceiver – most are on the 2m (144MHz band) but some are only for the 70cm (432MHz), There are also dual-banders for 2m and 70cm or triple-banders for 2m, 70cm and 6m. They are typically FM only and will only give an output power of about 1W when run from the supplied battery. (Some may give higher power when run from 12V, though.)

These hand-helds can be used while walking the dog, while you are strolling around the local rally or even while mobile or sitting in the armchair at home. When in use out walking, the 'rubber duck' antenna supplied with the transceiver will be used – these are helically wound in most cases and will radiate a signal (of sorts). For base use or in a mobile environment some form of outside antenna will be beneficial. It must be remembered that the 1W output of these rigs will be heavily attenuated if poor-quality coaxial cable is used. Even in short lengths a good proportion of the signal can be wasted. Having said that, a good antenna can make all the difference to any radiated signal, but more of that later.

So, we have our hand-held radio clipped to our belts or in a pocket. It will prove very useful, but not so good for longer-distance contacts except perhaps through a repeater or when standing on the top of a hill. Many of these repeaters also require slightly more power than the typical hand-held can deliver.

There are many, many hand-helds available on the market, both new and used. It all depends on what you require of your rig, how much you can afford or more importantly how much you are willing to spend. If this is your main interest then a call into the local shop or a browse through the adverts in a few magazines will point you in the right direction.

The older type of thumbwheel-tuned type such as the IC2E has been used by many amateurs over the years. There are even a few modern look-a-likes available too.

They are simple, easy to use and above all cheap. The more modern type of hand-held with its built-in processor may at times make you feel that you need a degree in programming to understand the way they work.

If your interest lies in longer distance contacts you may wish to consider something a little different. While FM is a good chat mode for stations fairly close to each other it is not as efficient as single sideband working for longer distance contacts. In this mode the carrier is removed and thus more of the available power is used to concentrate the voice into a narrower bandwidth than FM.

Single sideband is a much more efficient way of using the available spectrum when conducting a contact – the FM signal is typically 12kHz wide, while the SSB signal is typically only 2.5kHz. Thus the output power of the transmitter is more efficiently used. It is because of this that an SSB signal will be heard over a greater distance and stations that would be impossible to work when using FM can be contacted with ease when using SSB.

So, which transceivers are available for SSB and FM working? Without doubt the most famous of all the simple, low-power transceivers ever built were the FT290R and the FT790R from Yaesu. This is not meant as an adverse comment about all the other manufacturers, but these rigs stand out. Throughout the late 1970s, the 1980s and the early 1990s almost every amateur owned one of these at one time or another. They were used mobile, portable, at home, and on planes and ships – truly versatile rigs. It is true that they only gave 2.5W out on 2m or 1W on 70cm but they worked and worked very well.

These radios gave the newly licensed amateurs their first taste of longer distance working (DX) on VHF/UHF and the addition of a small linear amplifier made the chance of those 200km-or-more contacts a distinct possibility. Like all good things the early FT290R was superseded by a Mk 2 version which in many people's opinion never came up to the standard of its elder brother.

So, in the case of the hand-held transceiver, the advantages are: portability, low weight, ease of use (mainly), and low power consumption. The disadvantages are: low power output, the need to recharge the batteries, and the ease of losing the set if you are not careful.

The trusty hand-held with its 1W of power may seem very basic, but under certain conditions can work very long distances; the chapter on propagation should be studied in detail to give more information on this. Suffice it to say that I have worked from my house in Folkestone, Kent to Paris, France on FM with 'flea power' – just 2W into a vertical antenna. On VHF you should be able to work all over Europe with a couple of watts of CW.

Let's look a little more closely at the larger transceivers available for base use. These typically run off a mains supply but after the introduction of the EMC regulations in

1996 most of the big manufacturers changed over to transceivers that required an external 12V supply.

During the late 1970s and the early 1980s the champion VHF rig was the FT221R. This transceiver was used by most of the big contest groups and when fitted with the famous replacement muTek front-end became the 'be-all and end-all' of contest rigs. These transceivers changed hands at huge amounts of money. Because of trends they have become less popular. These rigs didn't have too many bells and whistles but did work extremely well. They had analogue tuning too; no digital frequency readout here. The advantage for us now is that because of these supposed disadvantages the transceiver is considered 'old hat'. The value has dropped considerably but they still work very well when compared with modern equipment. The later contest radios didn't become classics like the FT221R did, but some became firm favourites. The Icom IC251E and the later IC271E were also very good and the later IC275E was used by many contest groups. Yaesu produced the FT726 which could be used on 6m, 2m and 70cm, this was followed by the FT736 which also had a 23cm option. In more recent years the multi mode multi band transceiver has become popular, offering all modes on all amateur bands from top band to 70cm. These come in all sizes from the "I can't believe you can get all that in such a small box" FT817 from Yaesu [2] or IC-706 from Icom [3] up to the larger FT897 and FT847 from Yaesu or IC-7000 from Icom. These rigs are amazing because they cover all the bands but the performance is often compromised especially for the VHF/UHF receivers. There are also some more specialised base station rigs such as the IC-910H that is designed for the VHF/UHF enthusiast. The serious VHF/UHF operators often opt for a good HF only transceiver driving a good transverter such as those available from Kuhne Electronics in Germany [4], this gives the best performance on the VHF/UHF band plus all of the functions of a good transceiver.

For those who wish to have only a simple, inexpensive FM rig for VHF/UHF the ex-PMR (private mobile radio) types are an invaluable source of cheap rigs. Most will require some work to get them onto the amateur frequencies but many of these modifications have been published in the amateur press. Chris Lorek, G4HCL, has published a profusion of them. His *PMR Conversion Handbook* (and its predecessor, *Surplus 2-Way Conversion Handbook*) gives many. These transceivers may be found at silly prices at your local rally. There are always a selection available if you look around.

These days, there is a profusion of rigs that can be used by the newly licensed, the only proviso being whether your interests lie in only FM local contacts and/or SSB with longer-distance contacts, packet use with the radio connected to your computer or even the receiving and transmitting of ATV (amateur television). There is of course a world of difference in the way the various modes are operated. There is usually a huge difference in cost, too. The multitude of transceivers available will baffle most, but eventually one will stand out above the rest.

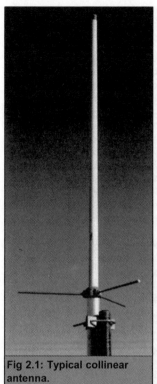

Fig 2.1: Typical collinear antenna.

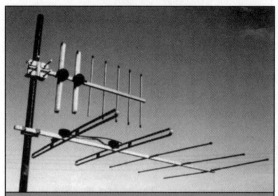

Fig 2.2: Vertically and horizontally polarised antennas on the same mast. The upper one is a vertically polarised 70cm antenna, the lower one is a horizontally polarised 2m antenna.

Listen to what the locals say about it and try to listen to other owners of the same model. See what they think about it. Are they happy with their purchase?

Reviews of current and older transceivers are always available. Finding which magazine did the review will not be difficult as they generally all do a review of each one. Read the reviews and see what they say. Be careful and read between the lines – sometimes a lot can be said by what is *not* written about a radio.

So, we have discussed the basic radios that you may consider. There is much more than this of course. The old adage of "if you can't hear them, you can't work them" makes sense.

If the long-distance station (DX) is inaudible at your station then you will never work him. What can be done to remedy this situation?

Choosing an antenna

No matter how much you spend on your shiny new or dusty second-hand transceiver it will always be improved by a better or more suitable antenna.

By now the newcomer should have a vague idea of where his or her main interest lies – if it is for local chatting on the FM simplex channels on VHF/UHF then even a modest outside antenna will give the transmitted (and received signal) quite a boost.

Many amateurs keep their antennas in the loft of the house, while others prefer to have them on the roof. Whichever you choose, the higher the better.

The standard quarter-wave antenna will radiate an omni directional signal, that is a signal of the same strength in all horizontal directions. This is what we need for our hand-held. Convention has it that when using FM the antennas will be vertically polarised. This means that the radiating element will be in an up/down configuration. Don't assume that the antenna must always have the feeder at the bottom. There are circumstances, such as when the antenna is fitted under the eaves of the house, that it can be fitted with the feed point at the higher point

and the antenna is then 'hanging upside down'. This will not make for any difficulties in transmissions – the antenna will still work very well. Fig 2.1 shows a typical collinear antenna.

By looking at the roofs of houses around us we will see several antennas used for the reception of TV. Most of these types are called *Yagi beams*. These have directional properties in that they 'fire' the signal in one particular direction to the detriment of other directions. So, if that repeater you wish to access is too far away for the omni-directional antenna, put up a beam. Remember, for FM it should be mounted so that the elements are vertical and for SSB work it should be mounted horizontally. Do not do as one operator I know who mounted the Yagi pointing to the sky and wondered why his signals were not so strong! Fig 2.2 shows both vertically and horizontally polarised antennas.

You don't have to have two antennas if you swap between these two modes. You can buy antennas specially made for the job, where a single boom has two sets of elements running along it, one for vertical and the other for horizontal polarisation. You will need either two lengths of feeder to the shack and a switch box to select the polarisation required or you may decide to have a relay at the antenna and just a single line of feeder to the radio.

Of course the gain of any beam antenna works on receive as well as transmit. While we mention 'gain' in an antenna it must be remembered that if we supply an RF power level to an antenna of, say, 10W, there is no way that this antenna can increase this 10W level to a higher power level. What it can, and does, do is 'steal' a little of this power from one (unwanted) direction and push it in another direction. We still have 10W being radiated from the antenna but not in every direction. Look at Fig 2.3. It can be seen that the loss of apparent power in one direction can give an apparent increase in another. In this case the 'loss' is to the rear of the beam and the 'apparent' gain to the front.

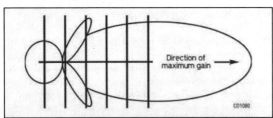

Fig 2.3: Yagi beam antenna showing direction of maximum gain.

For those who prefer to sit and chat on the simplex FM frequencies then some form of vertically polarised antenna will be required. This may be simply a vertically mounted dipole, a simple ground plane or a collinear array. For those who need to get a bit further in one particular direction then a beam may be required. The photograph (Fig 2.4) shows a typical antenna system.

The biggest and best antenna that can be put up is the one to go for. A careful look at antenna design will give guidance on which one will suit your particular location. But initially look for one that has a good forward gain and a good front-to-back ratio. This means that it radiates most of the signal towards the front and little from the rear. This front-to-back ratio is important as sometimes you may have a strong station behind you and by turning the beam a little you may be able to null them out. (Again, check the antenna chapter for more information.)

On VHF and UHF, although most will start out with just one beam, the wish to add another may come later, especially on UHF where many stations use two or more. A pair will increase the forward gain from the antennas by as much as 2.5dB. It has other advantages too. The receive capability will increase too as the gain of the antennas works both ways. If they are *stacked*, that is one mounted above the other, the radiation pattern will be narrowed in the vertical plane. This may help stop any potential EMC problems.

Having bought the antenna it is not the end of it all – some means of turning it must be found. The local TV shop may well have a cheap rotator for sale in the window but these are usually intended for small TV beams only. They may last a year or more with a small VHF beam but it would be much better to get a proper rotator capable of handling the loading. The instructions that come with the antenna should tell you its wind loading. The rotator used should be capable of handling this.

How is it all going to be held up in the air, though? The dream of most amateurs is the 60 or 80ft tower with a cradle of antennas bunched at the top. Of course, some of us can get these up, but often neighbours and the local planning authorities don't see towers as much of a thing of beauty as we amateurs do. Many will use a chimney lashing kit to bolt a short stub mast to the chimney. The small rotator carrying the beam will be safe with this. But just for safety, how about using a double lashing kit and making sure, especially if a pair of antennas are intended?

Fig 2.4: Typical VHF/UHF antenna system featuring two 2m, two 70cm and one 23cm beam.

If you do intend to erect a pair of beams, it is no good siting them a foot apart – they must be set the correct distance apart to get this 2.5dB gain. Check out Chapter 5 – 'Antennas and transmission lines' for more on this subject.

Antennas don't have to be out in the open of course. Many estates have restrictions on mounting antennas on houses above the eaves or the ridge line. All is not lost. Many operators use a small rotatable beam in the loft. If a rotatable one cannot be fitted, consider a pair of delta loops at 90° so you can select one or the other. The radiation pattern will be off the side of each. Not perfect but again a signal will be radiated.

Many amateurs use scaffold poles to mount the antennas. One easy way to do this is to beg, borrow, or buy two poles, one of about 2m and one of 7m in length. The shorter one is concreted into the ground and used as the support for the longer one. A hinged scaffold clamp is used and thus the whole can be lowered for work to be carried out on the antennas. If guy ropes are used even two poles maybe used. See Fig 2.5. Even unwanted windsurfer masts can be pressed into service but these should be used with care when brackets are bolted on.

Feeder

There is no point in putting a good-quality vertical antenna

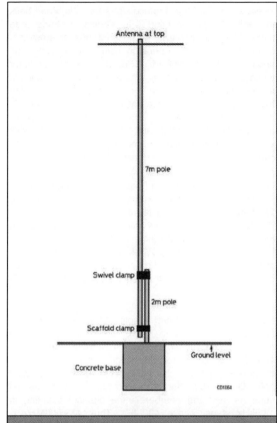

Fig 2.5: Using scaffold poles to mount antennas.

are only required from time to time.

One essential item when putting the antennas up is either a directional power meter or a VSWR (voltage standing wave ratio) bridge/meter. The intention of these is to measure the effectiveness of your antenna(s). Our requirement is that the minimum amount of power is returned to the transmitter. The directional power meter can be used to measure this actual amount of returned power. The VSWR (usually abbreviated to just 'SWR') bridge/meter will enable the user to measure the ratio of power levels in the system. Usually we try to tune for an SWR of unity or 1:1. This is often unobtainable, so anything under 2:1 will be acceptable.

The power supply to drive all this amount of equipment will be an essential item. The small 5A CB power supplies found cheaply are often not regulated to the extent we require. I have seen many trip into 'over-voltage supply', causing problems to the transceiver.

It may seem an extravagance but I would recommend buying the biggest power supply you can afford. It should be capable of delivering a very stable 13.8V under load. It is no point having a supply that 'sags' to 11V on load. A good one that will deliver 20A will suffice until a bigger one comes along. There are two types of such power supplies available, linear and switching. A linear power supply is preferable, it uses a large mains transformer so will be heavy and more expensive. Switching type power supplies will be smaller and cheaper than the equivalent linear supply but may cause interference problems.

Another essential is an accurate clock or watch. The type that relies on Rugby MSF time clock signals for accuracy is an excellent one. Some operators even have a pair in the shack, one with CET (Central European Time) and the other with local time.

The standard microphone supplied with the transmitter will almost certainly provide good audio on the transmitted signal but a base (free-standing) microphone may prove beneficial and permit some hands-free use. The log book and notes can then be completed during the contact. Later on a complete headset (earphones and incorporated microphone) may be used with a foot switch to give totally hands-free operation.

If you are intending to use Morse, you can use a hand key, these can be used to provide good-quality Morse code for long stretches but this takes practice. A good electronic keyer with a twin paddle can provide easy sending without fatigue over long periods. The only things that move with the keyer are your two fingers. With the hand key the whole arm from elbow to fingers move. Remember, when wiring your paddle and learning to send, that convention has it that the thumb sends the dots and the finger the dashes!

The transceivers we have discussed so far have been run

up in the air and using a coaxial feeder such as RG58U. This feeder has a loss of 4.65dB per 100ft at 100MHz, so if your transmitter gave out 1W, and assuming no other losses, only about 200mW would be radiated from the antenna. By changing to a better feeder these losses can be reduced by a huge amount. The 'common or garden' RG213 has a loss of 1.9dB at 100MHz per 100ft, about a third of that of the RG58U. See Chapters 5 and 12 for more data on coaxial cables.

The benefit of choosing good-quality feeder is obvious. There are many types available on the market today, ranging from the very expensive Heliax type to the cheaper, but still very good, Pope H100 and Westflex. Remember that, although the transceiver gives you the results of the signal and the beam radiates it, it is the feeder that gets it to the rig and the connectors that join them together.

The station must be thought of as a whole, not as separate parts. If one part fails, the whole will fail.

Other equipment

Several other items of equipment will be found in most amateur shacks. Some of it will be essential, some may be just useful. Some may be borrowed from friends if they

'barefoot', i.e. without the addition of any form of amplifier to boost the transmitted or received signal. There are three types of amateur when it comes to amplifiers:

Those with a 'big mouth and no ears' (big linear transmit amplifier and poor reception facilities)

Those with 'big ears and no mouth' (no big transmit amplifier but perhaps a masthead preamplifier). This is a much better configuration.

Finally, there are those who have both a 'big mouth and big ears'. These are the full contest-style stations who have possibly full legal output power available with multiple antennas and a masthead receive preamp.

Many commercial linear power amplifiers incorporate a preamplifier. While these will help a little with low signal levels they also tend to amplify the noise on the feeder too. The best place to fit the preamp is at the masthead where it amplifies the signal at the antenna and passes it to the receiver.

Most commercial linear power amplifiers are excellent but several will have been 'got at' by previous owners. Always check the signal quality of your new amplifier before going on the air and *never try to overdrive it*.

Where to put it all

So, the antenna(s) are up in the air and we have a pile of other bits in their boxes; where in the house is the best place to operate from? This will very much depend on the space you have available and the amount of equipment you have accumulated.

For the VHF and the UHF station feed length may be a little critical and the attic a good place to consider. Remember though that if it is in the attic sleeping children may hear your signals and during the summer it may get very hot.

Many operators use a spare room for the shack; others prefer a garden shed. Wherever you put your equipment make sure it is safe from burglars and away from small hands when not in use.

Remember, if you plan to operate for any length of time, that the operating position should be comfortable. There is no point in entering a contest when you have to sit awkwardly. Set up the desk so that each item is within reach without stretching. The most-used items such as the tuning control should be closest to hand.

Operating techniques

For ease of use the whole of each amateur band is split into segments, and a list of these can be found in the *RSGB Yearbook* and other publications. On VHF and UHF in the UK we keep the bottom section for moon-bounce (or *EME* as it is known from 'Earth-Moon-Earth')

where amateurs try to bounce signals off the Moon back to Earth. The next section is for dedicated Morse code users. There are separate sections for those interested in meteor scatter (MS) operation using Morse code and another for those using MS SSB. The next section is for those using SSB in normal terrestrial modes. A small all-mode section is followed by the packet section, the beacon subsection and the FM simplex channels and finally the satellite section. There are also sections for amateur TV (ATV), QRP activity, and many more. Let's look a little more closely at a couple of these. (Check the current *Yearbook* for more details of the band plans.)

In the UK the main 'calling frequency' for FM work on 2m is known as 'S20' (simplex channel number 20). It is on 145.500MHz (on 70cm it is 433.500MHz and known as 'SU20'). Operators should use the established calling frequencies to only make initial contact and agree another frequency to move to (QSY). Don't stay and chat on the calling frequency even if the band appears dead. Keep all conversation on calling frequencies to an absolute minimum.

For FM use the 2m band is split into 12.5kHz channels, the letter 'V' is used to identify the channels, and the number is the channel, counting in 12.5kHz steps, above 145.000MHz. So 145.500MHz (still known as S20 from the time when 25kHz channel spacing was used) is called 'V40'. On the 70cm band the letter 'U' is used for channel numbers, and the number is the channel counting in 12.5kHz steps, above 430MHz. Thus 433.500MHz is 'U280' (still known as SU20 from the time when 25kHz channel spacing was used). The current band plan for 70cm uses the even numbered channels with 25kHz bandwidths allowed.

In some areas such as London it may be difficult to find a clear channel but in the outer regions it will be easy.

On SSB, the calling frequency is 144.300MHz and this has often been the cause of contention. In the old days, it was the norm to call CQ and state that you were 'tuning high (or low) for a contact'. Modern rigs have very stable VFOs and this practice has now vanished.

Most UK and European mainland amateurs listen on 2m at 144.300MHz, 6m on 50.150MHz and 70cm on 432.200MHz for an opening or the band to liven up. Again, if one of these frequencies is used to establish a contact then a move away, to a clear frequency, should be made immediately to complete the contact.

We have covered part of the band plans and learnt to move away from the calling frequency, but what actually is a valid contact? If I hear a station calling CQ such as:

"CQ CQ CQ, from HB9FAP"

and I answer with:

"HB9FAP, you're 59, roger? "

He then replies with:

"Roger roger, you're also 59 here, name Fabio, QSL?"

Is this a valid contact? No, of course not – let's look at this once again, only this time done properly . . .

"CQ CQ CQ, from HB9FAP"

"HB9FAP, you're 59 from G0BPS"

" G0BPS from HB9FAP. Many thanks, you're also 59. My name is Fabio. G0BPS from HB9FAP"

In this case both callsigns have been given by both parties so there can be no confusion. In the first instance he may have been answering another station, not you. In the latter there is no mistake at all who he is talking to. A valid contact is where both callsigns have been exchanged and also signal reports in the usual RS(T) configuration. In some cases, especially on VHF and UHF, the designated worldwide locator should be given too. This comprises a set of two letters, two numbers and two letters. For example, for G0BPS is JO01OC.

Contests are a great way to make some longer distance contacts on all bands, but before jumping in listen for a while and find out just what information is being exchanged. On some contests the exchange of region may be required, in others your county or even your age. In most, though, it will be a signal report and a serial number. Your first contact in the contest will be 001 (zero zero one) and increase one by one from there. In most VHF/UHF contests the worldwide locator will also be required. You may well hear something like:

"DJ5VE from G0BPS, you're 59085 in JO01OC. QSL?"

and followed by "73 and good luck".

Above all, listen before jumping in – you'll be VERY unpopular if you ask the other station what information he requires if he has a pile-up going.

Never, never . . .

There may also be the occasion where you may hear a station calling CQ but in a specific direction. On the VHF/UHF bands you may hear a Dutch station perhaps calling "CQ Oscar Kilo or Sugar Papa, CQ Oscar Kilo or Sugar Papa" (calling Czech Republic or Poland). It means that the station wants to speak to Czech and Polish stations *only*.

I have often heard newly licensed stations hearing this type of call and then calling the Dutch station. They do *not* want to hear from you; if they did they would be calling CQ G! The station calling a specific CQ as above *only* wants a call from that specific area. If he wanted just anyone he would call CQ (a general call for a contact), or CQ DX for distant stations. On the VHF and UHF bands DX is relative; for those who have never worked further than the next county, the next country will be DX. However, for those who can regularly work 400–500km on a flat band, only a 500km+ contact will be considered by them to be DX.

The basic rule is *never* to call a station that is calling a specific CQ *unless you are in that country or area he is calling.* If you do answer them from a closer area, expect the proverbial 'flea in the ear'!

Often the station calling CQ OK or SP etc will be 'big', i.e. running full legal power to several rotatable antennas, mast-head preamp, quality feeder etc. Your 10W to a five-element or so antenna does not make you DX, but if he slips up and just calls CQ you can justifiably call him.

Remember a band devoid of signals does not mean that the band is flat. It just means that there are no operators; often there are people just listening for someone like you to call CQ. So, a short CQ call may well bring forth a station that may surprise you.

One of the most misunderstood controls on many rigs is the 'clarifier'. This control is often referred to on HF as the 'RIT' (receiver incremental tuning). Its purpose is to enable the operator to move the receive frequency away from the transmit frequency.

Often we hear two newly licensed stations meeting and agreeing to move to, say, 144.330MHz. Both change frequency so that the dial on their rig shows this frequency and call each other. It is most unlikely that the true frequency of each rig exactly matches the other so the two stations are not *netted* (on the exact same frequency). In with the clarifier . . . and they can hear each other now. We now have in effect a duplex contact with both receiving on the other's transmit frequency which differs to their own.

The simple answer is to agree who will call who when you arrive at the agreed frequency. The other person should listen and use their ears to get to the frequency that makes the other station sound right. Ignore the tuning dial. It may well show '144.332' but if both stations avoid using the clarifier they will both be on the *same* frequency and be operating in a simplex mode or, as we say, 'netted' to each other. Best of all, ignore the clarifier except for very exceptional occasions.

Talking English

Having established a contact you will wish to exchange some information. Remember that if you bumped into a stranger at a party you would introduce yourself perhaps with: "Hello, my name is Dick and I live in Folkestone". How many times do we hear on the air "Personal here is Harry, QTH is Lyminge" or similar? You wouldn't talk at the party like that so why on the air? Use plain English and avoid the royal 'we', e.g. "We are running 100 watts . . ." when the operator is alone in the shack. The use of Morse abbreviations on the air should also be avoided – they were designed to speed up CW communications and should remain there. The exception to this rule, perhaps, is the use of 'QSL' when referring to the contact confirmed card!

When passing the contact to the other operator do so clearly - listeners may want to know who is there, especially if you have hooked a rare one. "HB0QS from G0BPS back to you" or similar will suffice. If you are both a clear, strong signal with each other, i.e. 57 or so, then you may wish to avoid phonetics, but if conditions are difficult it may be beneficial to both to give full callsigns in phonetics. Stick to the proper ones too. The oddball ones may help in rare occasions but most operators' ears are tuned to the correct ones and can pick them out of the noise.

The pile-up

If you happen to hear a huge amount of noise on one frequency it will be almost certain that a rare station has appeared on the bands. This can provide you with two options. Sit on the frequency and shout your call in amongst all the others and hope, or . . . cheat!

Tune around the edges of the pile-up listening carefully as you go. Very often the loudest rare station will have another from the same area who is not so strong but is also audible. Those in the pile-up won't hear them, but those tuning the edges will snap up the rare one and grin as they pass the noise again.

If you do decide to go for the pile-up the first thing is to listen, listen and then listen. Unless you are running a 'big' station the only option is to get all the information you need such as callsign, locator and possibly their name first. When you have this information you can try for the contact.

Many times we hear an operator in the pile-up calling the DX station, getting answered and then asking for his callsign first. Oh dear . . . We say listen and listen again; is the DX station working simplex or on *split frequencies*? (That means calling CQ on one frequency and listening a little higher, or lower, in frequency.) If they are working 'split' *never, never* call him on his transmitting frequency; the wrath of all and sundry will fall upon you if you do. A transceiver with twin VFOs is essential if the other operator is working 'split'. Never try to work them by tuning between the two frequencies – it just won't work.

Having found his listening frequency, which may even be a small section of the band, you may then call him. If you are competing with some high power stations then skill, not power, will be required. Listen for the style of his operating. Yes, I know this requires a lot of listening, but I get more hits than misses with my calls by listening

carefully first. Having established his rhythm give your callsign quickly and just once without giving his. It will be assumed that all are calling the DX station. Try and find the gap between all the others. I know this will be difficult but that is the reason for listening so much first.

If the full call doesn't work try just giving the last two letters of your callsign; use phonetics and call twice in a gap. "Papa Sierra, Papa Sierra" is my way. Often the DX operator will call back "Papa Sierra again". You can then give his callsign and yours, his report and your locator and name. Do not give your station details etc unless they are asked for. You will get his information and then maybe just "73 . . . QRZ?" without waiting to see if you got the information. A good operator will do a check though and often give his callsign, locator and QSL manager where appropriate.

QSL cards are often exchanged to confirm contacts. It is not essential that you send a card for every contact made. Often you may see written that "a QSL is the final courtesy of a QSO". If you want a QSL card to confirm the contact, say so, asking politely, and you will probably get one. However, if you have worked that square many times you may not want it again, so say so. It is not essential to exchange cards for every contact – they should be treated for special use only, not as a matter of course for each contact.

Many stations that hold or use rare callsigns may prefer to use a QSL manager – this is usually a friend who is willing and able to handle the large amount of cards arriving for the DX operator and enable them to spend their time on the air rather than filling out cards. If a manager is given it is usual to use that route.

If a card is required by the direct route then it is usual to enclose one or two IRCs (International Reply Coupons) which are available from the Post Office (these may not be accepted by all countries, so check first). You may instead prefer to use a 'green stamp' – the name used by all amateurs throughout the world for a one US dollar bill. Needless to say, from one UK station to another a stamped, self-addressed envelope (SSAE) will usually suffice.

QSL cards can be a pleasure – I have received many delightful ones in full colour but most are on thin card and quite plain. This is fine because I only need to have confirmation of the new square – it doesn't have to be a work of art. Talk to the members at your local club and ask them what they have on theirs.

Check out the adverts and send for samples. These will give you a fair idea of what you may wish to see on yours. As a minimum it should show your callsign, name, your locator, your power used, QSL PSE/TNX. You may also wish to add your address, your WAB information and your latitude/longitude. Simply add any information that you think the other operator may find interesting. See the typical QSL card shown in Fig 2.6.

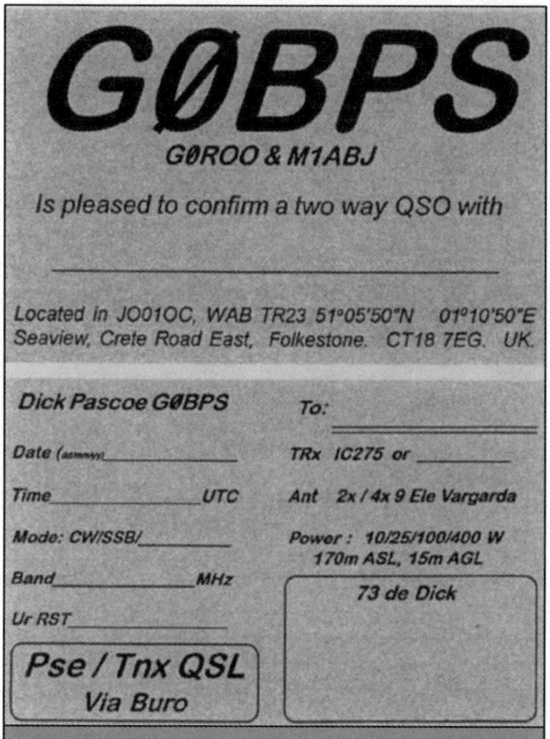

GØBPS

GØROO & M1ABJ

Is pleased to confirm a two way QSO with

_____

Located in JO01OC, WAB TR23 51°05'50"N 01°10'50"E
Seaview, Crete Road East, Folkestone. CT18 7EG. UK.

Dick Pascoe GØBPS   To: _____

Date (_____   TRx IC275 or _____

Time_____UTC   Ant 2x / 4x 9 Ele Vargarda

Mode: CW/SSB/_____   Power : 10/25/100/400 W
                                        170m ASL, 15m AGL
Band_____MHz
                            73 de Dick
Ur RST_____

Pse / Tnx QSL
Via Buro

Fig 2.6: Front and rear of a typical double sided QSL card.

Single-sided cards are fine – double sided ones will cost much more. Check out your local printer too. They will often prove to be quite competitive when compared to those advertising in the magazines.

Finally, the best advice I ever heard for the newcomer to the bands is: "Listen, listen and then listen some more".

Repeaters

A large number of repeaters are scattered across the UK and these are usually on the 2m and 70cm bands. Repeaters are just a way of getting your signal a little further. They are typically set on a high site with a range dependent on the others in the area. Each repeater is on a different frequency from others nearby. They will require either a short 1750Hz tone burst of usually about 400 milliseconds or CTCSS tone access. This is a sub-audible tone that 'opens' the nearby repeater for you to make a call. Each one will have a different CTCSS tone to stop operators opening those repeaters not required.

European repeaters in the 2m band use a 600kHz offset between the transmit and receive frequencies, and in the UK the user transmit frequency is the lower of the two. For example, the repeater outside Folkestone in Kent is GB3KS (Kent South) with an input frequency of 145.025MHz and a repeater transmit frequency of 145.625MHz. On 70cm the offset is 1.6MHz and on 23cm it is 6MHz except for ATV where it is variable (see the current _Yearbook_ for details).

Repeaters were first set up to enable mobile stations to have contacts but of course base stations can also use them. However, it is courteous to let any mobile station use take preference over base station use.

Often there will be gatherings of users in the mornings and evenings as amateurs travel to and from work.

There will be times during enhanced conditions when it may well be possible to chat through other repeaters. During one memorable opening a UK station was chatting to a Danish station through a UK repeater. Often stations in the Midlands will be able to access Southern repeaters. The use of CTCSS will help to stop this.

So far we have discussed terrestrial repeaters, but the amateur also has access to satellites that are solely for amateur use. These sometimes require two radios. Check the chapter on satellites for more information on these.

Finally, you may also hear the request for a QSL card for a repeater contact. You may of course exchange cards but they will not be accepted for any awards or contests. Why? Because you have been in contact with a repeater, not the other station direct.

Mobile operating

For those who do not have the facilities for an operating position in the house a parking spot with a good take-off can provide hours of fun. Just because you are operating from a vehicle doesn't mean that you are restricted to FM only. Lots of fun can be had with the mobile whip on the gutter when using SSB. Yes, we know that the preferred polarisation for SSB is horizontal, but the difference between vertical and horizontal is only about 3dB.

What about your mobile whip? Will it lift out of the base and hang sideways, horizontally? Many do, and by rotating the whip around the base you can have a slightly directional antenna. Yes, it is cheating but it does work – try it!

Before I had an antenna on the roof of the house I would often take to the hills with a small beam antenna on a short pole attached to the side of the car and the roof rack. I would point the beam and call CQ either on FM or SSB from my old FT290R. Only 2.5W out but I could have hours of fun. I well remember taking to the hills at one of the better VHF/UHF spots in a country lane for one of the QRP contests, never dreaming that I would some years later buy a house only a few hundred yards away on that same lane.

Logging

Although it is no longer a condition of the amateur radio licence to keep a log, it is advisable to keep a log for your own reference. Before the advent of computers, and their acceptance, all logging was done on paper. Many would keep a rough scrap of paper beside the operating position

AMATEUR RADIO STATION LOG

DATE	TIME (UTC) start	finish	FREQUENCY (MHz)	MODE	POWER (dBW)	STATION called/worked	REPORT sent	received	QSL sent	rcvd	REMARKS
2 Nov '88	0800	0810	3	J3E	20	GM5ABC	59+10	59+5			Bert
"	0811	0820	145	F3E	16	G7XYZ	57	56			Terry first G7
"	0825	0830	14	J3E	20	CQ					No reply
"	1725	1735	145	F2D	16	GB7XYZ					Local packet mailbox
"	1740		Station closed down								
4 Nov '88	1030		/P	from 73 Antenna Lane, Squelch-on-Sea							
"	1031	1036	50	J3E	10	G10XYZ	55	56			Jim, Bridgetown
"	1036	1045	50	J3E	10	G7XYL	58	58			Anne, N° Squelch-on-Sea. QRM
"	1205	1215	433	F3E	13	G2XYZ	46	47			
"	1220		Station closed down								
5 Nov '88	0945		/P	from 73 Antenna Lane, Squelch-on-Sea							
"	0950	1005	144	J3E	16	GB2GUY	56	56	✓		Catherine Fawkesville
"	1010	1015	144	A1A	16	G05ZZZ	542	541	✓		QSB! QSL via WF9XYZ
"	1526	1530	144	A1A	16	G7CW	579	589			Good keying!
"	1535		Station closed down and dismantled								
7 Nov '88	1810	1902	435	C3F	10	G7ZZZ	P3	P3			Ted, first ATV contact!
"	1930	1945	21	J2B	16	VK2ABC	559	569	✓		RTTY, Sid at Bandedge
"	1946	2005	21	J2B	16	ZL3ZZZ	569	559	✓		1st ZL on RTTY
"	2010		Test for TVI/Harmonic Radiation - Nothing noted								
"	2020		Station closed down								
8 Nov '88	1735	1737	7	J3E	20	CQ					
"	1738	1805	7	J3E	20	G70ZZZ	58	58			Nobby - chatted about G5RV ant
"	1930	1945	51	F3E	10	G0SIX	55	55			Allen, wanted W198 ref.
"	1950		Station closed down.								

NOTES

Fig 2.7: Typical hand written log page.

and make notes as time went past. They would then write up the log in a nice neat hand after the operating session was over.

A paper log must not be loose leaf, must be indelible, and must contain a certain amount of information. The minimum requirement is that you record: date, time, callsign of station worked or called, CQ calls made, frequency and the mode of transmission used.

Many, if not all, operators prefer to add to this essential list by including the reports exchanged, the power level used, the name of the other operator, and whether a QSL card has been sent and/or received. Fig 2.7 shows a typical written log page.

There are many advantages in using a computer logging program, they will give you immediate access to previous contacts with the same station so that you will know the name of the operator without thumbing through the pages of a paper log. The other useful piece of information available is the beam heading for a station, if you have recorded the locator for the station last time you worked, so you can easily turn your beam to the right direction. If you are operating in a contest the computer log comes into its own, it gives immediate duplicate checking, it handles your serial numbering and finally it will produce an electronic log to submit after the contest. Most contest organisers prefer an electronic contest entry because it makes their life easier. There are many computer logging programs available, see [5], [6], [7].

References

[1] RSGB web site, http://www.rsgb.org

[2] Yaesu web site, http://www.yaesu.co.uk

[3] Icom web site, http://www.icomuk.co.uk

[4] Kuhne electronics web site, http://www.kuhne-electronics.de

[5] G0GJV logging program, http://www.goodey.org.uk

[6] Super-Duper logging program, http://www.ei5di.com

[7] TACLog, http://rudius.net/oz2m/taclog/

Chapter **3**

Propagation

In this chapter :

- Recognising VHF/UHF modes of propagation
- Tropospheric propagation
- Meteorological units
- Causes of Tropo DX

- Signal strengths and ranges attainable
- Tropospheric scatter propagation
- VHF sporadic E
- Amateur auroral studies
- Trans-equatorial propagation
- Meteor trail propagation

T his chapter has been updated for the second edition of the handbook to reflect some of the latest sources of information on propagation. The Internet provides a wealth of information not even dreamt about when the propagation chapter was originally written by R G Flavel, G3LTP for the VHF/UHF Manual series. One of the best sources of information now is The radio propagation page [13] from The Propagation Studies Committee of The RSGB.

There may be much more information available these days but the underlying theory and measurement techniques remain the same and are described in this chapter.

In the early 1920s communication engineers decided that wavelengths of less than 200m were useless for serious message handling; so they generously gave them all to amateur operators. This was an action they were soon to regret, for by the end of 1923 two amateurs using a wavelength of about 100m had carried out two way exchanges with another in France. The following year, transatlantic working was becoming quite commonplace down at 100m, using considerably less power than the 'big boys' were needing on their medium wave circuits.

The authorities acted swiftly and predictably. They called a conference. At the end of it the amateurs found that they had lost their entire gift apart from a sequence of harmonically related bands; 80, 40, 20, 10 and 5m.

Amateurs began to progress their way through the list of assigned bands, tackling each in turn when it became practicable by the state of the art. Their professional counterparts were surprised to find that each time they seemed to work longer ranges with lower powers, all the way to the 10m band. Beyond that were 'ultra short waves', and there their luck appeared to run out. The 5m band really did seem to be a desert, with little prospect of any DX working at all.

Then came the war. Amateur activity ceased but many future amateurs were fortunate enough to acquire a solid grounding in radio communications while serving in the armed forces, where they had been able to use up-to-date (and expensive) commercial equipment rather than the customary pre-war homebrew.

A lot of that sort of equipment came on the market after the war at knock down prices that people could afford. Many post war amateurs began their activities using modified war surplus gear and they were eager to find out just what it was capable of doing, given a free rein. At that time everyone started off with an interest in propagation, whether they admitted to it or not. A good proportion of those took it very seriously indeed.

In the UK, television swallowed up the old 5m (56MHz) band. So, in a way, everyone venturing on to VHF and UHF after the war, was starting with a clean slate. In the years that followed they discovered that many of the features of propagation that they were taking for granted were things that rocked the foundations of previously held textbook theories. They were working far greater distances than their limited power should have allowed; they worked paths crossing mountain ranges that, at VHF and UHF, should have been blocked completely by the terrain; they were finding that the ionosphere could, on occasion, reflect signals of up to at least 200MHz; about four times higher in frequency than had been expected; and amateur experiments had revealed an unexpected mode of propagation, trans-equatorial, that had stimulated a wide range of interest, particularly among broadcasters. They had projects covering a variety of other modes, including auroral, meteor trail, moonbounce and propagation via field-aligned irregularities, all active on a truly international scale and all producing results which would have been unobtainable by other means.

As a result the Amateur Service enjoyed a rewarding relationship with professionals in the field of propagation research. But, although the two sides were working towards the same end, their reasons for doing so were

Table 3.1: Conversion between the old locator system and the IARU locator for main squares.

Longitude (first QTH locator letter)

1st IARU letter	1st IARU figure									
	0	1	2	3	4	5	6	7	8	9
I	—	—	—	—	U	V	W	X	Y	Z
J	A	B	C	D	E	F	G	H	I	J
K	K	L	M	N	O	P	Q	R	S	T

Latitude (second QTH locator letter)

2nd IARU letter	Second IARU figure										
	0	1	2	3	4	5	6	7	8	9	
M	Q	R	S	T	U	V	W	X	Y	Z	South
N	A	B	C	D	E	F	G	H	I	J	
O	K	L	M	N	O	P	Q	R	S	T	
P	U	V	W	X	Y	Z					
P					A	B	C	D			North

Examples:
1. To find QTH locator equivalent to IARU locator JN18. Enter longitude table with first letter (J) and first figure (1) to find first letter (B). Enter latitude table with the second letter (N) and the second figure (8) to find the second letter (I). Required locator is BI.
2. To find IARU locator equivalent to QTH locator GP. Record indicated IARU first letter and the first figure (J-6-). Find second letter (P) within the boxed section of the latitude table. Record second letter and second figure (-O-5). Combine. The required IARU locator is JO65. Refer to the text for the use of the letters outside the boxed section.

poles apart. To an amateur a 'tropo opening' is like a heaven sent reward for eating up all his spinach, whereas to a professional it signals a period of frustration, when co-channel interference creates interruptions in his data flow, patterning or breaking up of his television signals and dents in his reputation for reliability. Despite that, both groups were interested in knowing such things as: "When?", "For how long?", "Where?", "To what extent?" and those were just the sort of questions that amateurs found themselves in an ideal position to answer.

Sadly, those golden periods of close co-operation are becoming less frequent nowadays. There are basically three reasons for that. One is that the professional research interest has moved beyond the VHF and UHF parts of the spectrum to much higher frequencies, well outside the province of this handbook, where point-to-point working involves extremely narrow pencil beams. Our large and dense networks of potential observers can contribute little to that sort of situation. Secondly, many of the former problems have been avoided by the routing of commercial traffic through satellite transponders. Thirdly, professional and commercial organisations are cutting back on expenditure to such an extent that research requirements are currently being shelved unless they can show an immediate financial return against the investment supporting them.

That last consideration affects our activities also. To analyse our own original signal records in terms of cause and effect we need an ongoing supply of solar and geophysical data from official sources. In the past we have been very fortunate in being able to get what we need either on an exchange basis or through various 'old boy' networks. But now, in many cases, such information has to be paid for and some of the rates are extremely high. As a result, amateurs are gradually being priced out of individual research. In that we are not alone; amateur meteorologists face a similar situation and frequently voice their frustration in that respect.

The RSGB has done a lot to remedy this situation with the advent of The Propagation Studies Committee in 1976. In particular The radio propagation page [13] is a wonderful source of information.

Our field of interest

The term 'radio wave propagation' really covers two objectives. The first is to determine the nature of the mechanism involved in getting signals from point A to point B, the second to explain the route in terms of physical quantities. To do this may require some knowledge of meteorology, the Earth's magnetic field and even of events taking place on the Sun. There will be one or two close encounters with mathematics, but surely nothing more complicated than is needed for GCSE level mathematics.

In the context of this handbook we are supposed to be concerned only with those amateur bands that fall between the lower limit of VHF (30MHz) and the upper limit of UHF (3GHz). But the various modes of propagation do not sit easily within those confines and, at some time, you should take a look at the wider picture that includes frequencies below (HF) and above (SHF etc) where similar principles apply but the end results may be very different. For example, there are several references to the ionosphere in this chapter but we shall not be concerned with the part it plays in everyday world-wide communications.

Long, long ago, the Ancients believed that the world had been formed on the top side of a disc, carried, it was said, on the back of a giant turtle. From the propagation point of view that would have simplified things considerably. Many of our problems stem from the fact that we live on the surface of a sphere. Electromagnetic radiation (which includes, among other things, visible light and radio waves) travels in straight lines so, if their rays are to be persuaded to follow the curvature of the Earth, they must get themselves bent by some means in order to achieve any significant distance and remain near to the ground. Fortunately for everyone concerned with radio communications, Nature has thoughtfully provided four alternative ways of getting beyond the horizon: reflection, refraction, diffraction and scatter. We shall see how they operate later on.

As you turn the pages you may be surprised to find references still to the 'old' form of QTH locator. That is not something left over from the last edition of the VHF/UHF Handbook that ought to have been edited out. The so-called 'squares', 1° of latitude by 2° of longitude, which happen to be common to both the old and the current systems, represent a network of areas which are ideally sized for the needs of propagation research. Although the IARU Maidenhead locator (which is worldwide in coverage) has replaced the QTH locator, many research workers continue to use the two letter designators when it comes to report storage and analysis. There are two good reasons for that, one being that only four characters serve to define a path instead of eight, the other that it is easier to familiarise oneself with a single grid of 26 × 26 lettered squares than it is to deal with six or seven grids of 10 × 10, even though the areas covered turn out to be much the same. A simple conversion between the two locator systems at the basic square level is provided by Table 3.1.

A word of caution, however. For locations at latitudes below 40°N (roughly the heel of Italy) and above 66°N (the north end of the Gulf of Bothnia) there is an ambiguity because the lettered squares repeat. But that is easily resolved by reference to the callsign of the station concerned. No trouble if you are doing it manually, but a point to watch if you entrust the job to a machine.

Recognising VHF/UHF modes of propagation

At frequencies above 30MHz (following the definition of the terms 'VHF' and 'UHF') propagation by the regular layers of the ionosphere takes place but rarely and then generally only around times of maximum sunspot activity.

The usual mechanism governing the day-to-day performance between two Earth based stations has its origin in the lower part of the atmosphere, at rarely more than 4 - 5km above the ground. Tropospheric propagation is descriptive of this mode and the fundamental properties of the air which have the most influence are the vertical distributions of temperature and water vapour, both of which tend to decrease with height and, in so doing, cause elevated radio rays, such as might otherwise escape into space, to bend back down towards the ground, and to reach it beyond the normal visible horizon. At times, when dry warm air overlays cool moist air, usually in the presence of an anticyclone, ranges extend dramatically and signals from distances up to about 2000km may be expected. At the same time the strength of nearer signals may be enhanced, effects which extend throughout the VHF and UHF parts of the radio spectrum. During a tropo opening, as it is often called, signals generally rise slowly, accompanied by a progressively slower rate of fading. At peak strength, fading may be absent altogether. A long period of enhancement generally ends when a cold front reaches one end of the transmission path.

Tropospheric scatter depends on the presence of small scale refractive index irregularities and dust or cloud particles in a relatively small volume of the atmosphere towards which both the transmitting and the receiving antennas are directed. High power is required at the transmitter and good signal-to-noise performance at the receiver. Scattered signals are weak, spread in frequency by up to 1kHz either side of an unmodulated carrier, due to the differing motions of the scattering particles, and several rates of fading may coexist, often giving the impression of a rough modulation. The rate at which intelligence may be sent is limited by blurring, introduced by the range of signal path transit times possible within the upper and lower limits of the scattering volume.

At the top end of the UHF band atmospheric absorption effects become noticeable, for beyond 3000MHz, in the SHF part of the radio spectrum but outside the scope of this book, attenuations due to oxygen, water vapour and precipitation (rain, snow etc) become increasingly important. These affect not only transmission paths that are wholly within the troposphere, but paths originating within and terminating without; ground to satellite, EME etc; although there the effects tend to diminish with increase of beam elevation as the length of that part of the path which contains the absorbers and attenuators decreases.

Although many textbooks still imply that the ionosphere has little effect at VHF and above, a number of very important events have their origin there. Nearly all of them are associated in some way with the level around 100km above the ground, which is generally occupied during the day by the regular E layer.

Of these the most important is Sporadic E, which radio amateurs have studied particularly at 144MHz for many years, despite the fact that its presence there, according to our professional colleagues, ought to be impossible. In 1980 the Amateur Service was invited to contribute to a symposium on Sporadic E held at the Appleton Laboratory, and it was clear that at that time the amateur activities concerning this mode of propagation came as a surprise to many of the distinguished authorities present. It is now acknowledged by them that such a mode does exist at frequencies that may exceed 200MHz for short intervals of time, although the feeling is that it may not be Sporadic E at all but an entirely different mechanism as yet unidentified. In this chapter, it will still be referred to as Sporadic E (or E_s) until such time as its true identity is discovered. VHF Sporadic E signals generally begin suddenly and unpredictably (hence their name), bring in stations from distances of 1000 - 2000km at excellent strength and clarity for periods of up to several hours, and then, with a rapid decline, they cease. The duration of an opening decreases with increasing radio frequency, the higher frequencies starting later and finishing sooner than the lower ones. During the event the locations heard gradually progress from one area to another. Sporadic E events at VHF within Europe are generally confined to the months of May to August.

Operators living in southern Europe make use of another VHF mode, which depends on the presence of field aligned irregularities (FAI) in the distribution of free electrons in the ionosphere at E layer heights (around 110km). It has a similar seasonal variation to VHF Sporadic E but differs from it in that signals do not follow

Table 3.2: Working frequency bands of various VHF and UHF propagation modes (MHz, unless shown otherwise).

Aurora	50, 70, 144, 432
F2 layer	50
FAI	144
Meteor scatter	50, 70, 144, 432
Moonbounce	50, 144, 432, 1.3GHz, 2.3GHz
Sporadic E	50, 70, 144
TEP	50, 144
Tropospheric	50, 70, 144, 432, 1.3GHz, 2.3GHz
Troposcatter	70, 144, 432, 1.3GHz, 2.3GHz

the direct path between stations but appear to originate from a scattering volume which is often situated near to the Swiss Alps or close to other mountainous areas at about the same latitude.

Another ionospheric mode is associated with the appearance in the northern sky of the aurora borealis (or 'Northern Lights'), which is caused by the interaction of streams of charged particles from the Sun with the Earth's magnetic field. Signals reflected from the very mobile auroral E curtains, which usually accompany visual displays often seen in the Northern Isles and the north of Scotland but less frequently further south, are readily recognisable with their characteristic tone, variously described as "rasping", "ringing" or "watery", and the fact that beam headings for optimum signal strength are commonly well to the north of the great circle path joining the two stations in contact.

Short lived trails of ionisation due to the entry into the Earth's atmosphere of small particles of solid matter (seen at night as shooting stars) can be responsible for meteor scatter, where two stations, usually widely spaced, can establish contact in intermittent bursts ranging in duration from several seconds down to periods which afford little more than occasional 'pings' of signal. Meteor scatter signals should be looked for at times of meteor showers, which are listed later in this chapter. Duration of meteor reflections and their frequency of occurrence decline with increasing frequency. Meteor scatter propagation has been used professionally at operating frequencies of between 30 to 40MHz for communication purposes.

Trans-equatorial propagation (TEP) is usually confined to paths in which transmitter and receiver are situated approximately equal distances either side of the magnetic equator (e.g. the Mediterranean area and Zimbabwe). 144MHz openings seem to require high solar flux and low geomagnetic index; frequency spreading is apparent at 144 and 432MHz, with flutter fading, often giving the signals a quality similar to that of signals reflected from the aurora. On the Zimbabwe to Cyprus path openings were centred on 20:00 local time at Cyprus. It is believed that extensions to TEP via E_s or tropo may be possible.

For many years any involvement of the F layers of the ionosphere with TEP was disputed but it now seems likely that some, if not all, of the extreme ranges that have been recorded may have come about as a result of double

reflection at those heights, without intermediate contact with the ground.

Without question there is an involvement of the regular F2 layer at 50MHz around the peak period of the solar cycle. There should be no difficulty in recognising such signals because they ought to bear all the characteristics of normal DX working at HF. At the appropriate time the likelihood of regular layer propagation at 50MHz and the paths concerned should be signalled in monthly ionospheric prediction tables.

Diffraction is a mechanism that is associated with signal paths that cross sharp mountain ridges (it is sometimes referred to as knife edge diffraction). At the ridge a small degree of bending occurs, acting in the direction towards the ground. It is the likely reason for the ability of near mountain stations to work out over seemingly impossible paths. However, it may be difficult to rule out assistance by tropospheric refraction, particularly for places where the mountain crest supports a blanket of snow which may be undergoing sublimation, that is, going directly from the solid state to vapour. As a rule, signals may be considered to have been diffracted when they have travelled along a path which has crossed a mountain ridge and similar contacts have been possible between the same two stations on a fairly regular basis.

Table 3.2 shows a summary of the bands in which the various VHF and UHF modes play a part in propagation.

Tropospheric propagation

The propagation of light

It may be found helpful to begin this study of tropospheric propagation by considering first some comparable aspects of the propagation of light. In most cases the analogy is a close one because radio and light are both forms of electromagnetic radiation, differing only in wavelength (or its inverse, frequency). However, light has the advantage of being readily detectable by its direct action on one of our senses and most of us have had many years of experience working with it. We do not usually think of a torch bulb as being a transmitter, nor our eyes as being receivers but they are nevertheless, and all the perturbing effects to which a radio wave is subjected within the troposphere have their visual counterparts with which we are very familiar already.

A beam of light normally travels in a straight line unless something is done to deflect it. This can be brought about by reflection, as in a mirror or from the surface of a still pond, refraction, when light passes from one medium to another causing a straight rod in water to appear to be bent, or by scattering as from the dust in a shaft of sunlight. Certain frequencies can be made to suffer attenuation by inserting one or more filters in the path of the beam, and a very important filter which occurs naturally is provided by a layer of ozone in the upper atmosphere which prevents harmful amounts of ultra-

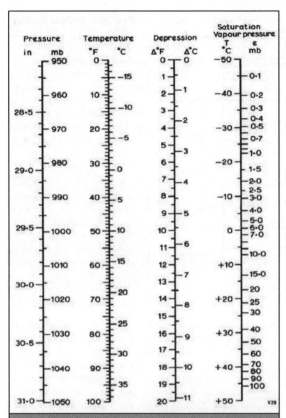

Fig 3.1: Conversion scales based on the following expressions:
(a) Atmospheric pressure: inches and millibars. 29.53 inches Hg = 1000mb.
(b) Temperature degrees Fahrenheit and Celsius. (°F) = 9/5 (°C) + 32.
(c) Depression of wet bulb or depression of dew point. (Δ°F) = 9/5 (Δ°C).
(d) Saturation vapour pressure, e, in millibars, given the ambient temperature in °C. See "vapour pressure" paragraph for an expression for e.

violet light from destroying life on Earth. Mist and fog are visible counterparts to attenuation and scatter.

It will be seen later that most tropospheric radio events of any importance are manifestations of refraction. In terms of light it is refraction which provides the lens with its well known properties, whereby light leaving one medium, such as air, and entering another, such as glass, suffers a deflection. A Dutch scientist named Willebrord Snell discovered in 1621 that the sine of the angle made by the incident ray with respect to the normal, divided by the sine of the angle made by the refracted ray with respect to the normal, was a constant for a given pair of media. The property possessed by each of the materials involved is known as the refractive index, and Snell's constant (sin i/sin r) is equal to the inverse ratio of the refractive indices of the two media.

Changes in refractive index also occur in the atmosphere, due to variations in density, usually as a result of the juxtaposition of two unmixed layers differing greatly in temperature, or due to the presence of a steep gradient of temperature within a single layer. This is the origin of the optical mirage. When air near the ground is heated, as over hot sand in the desert or sometimes along a straight road, a line of sight directed downwards is refracted upwards, giving an unexpected (and usually unsuspected) view of the sky which appears as a shimmering pool some distance ahead. Conversely, where cool air underlies warm air a line of sight directed slightly upwards is bent down, so that objects which are in reality well beyond the normal horizon appear to be on it, or even above. There was a famous occasion in 1798 when the whole of the French coast from Calais to Dieppe became visible one afternoon from the cliffs near Hastings.

Effects such as these are even more pronounced at radio frequencies because the radio refractive index contains a term which is dependent upon the amount of water vapour present, and this is a parameter which is subject to considerable change in the lower atmosphere in both space and time.

The radio refractive index of air

There are two basic methods used to determine the refractive index of air; one is to measure it more or less directly using a device called a refractometer, the other is to derive it from other, more readily accessible, measurements of atmospheric functions.

Refractometers are beyond the scope of the radio amateur. They are usually airborne or tethered balloon borne devices constructed and operated by large research organisations. They depend on the fact that the resonant frequency of an open microwave cavity is a function of the dielectric constant of the air within it, and that this is also a function of refractive index.

The more common method is to use upper air soundings of pressure, temperature and humidity provided by meteorological services all over the world, generally on a twice daily basis, at midnight and midday GMT. This information is obtained from cheap and simple balloon borne telemetry devices called radiosondes, which have been in regular use since shortly before the Second World War.

The radio refractive index of the air, symbol n, is a quantity which is only very slightly higher than unity, but the difference between, say, 1.000345 and 1.000300 is all important in propagation studies and may have a profound effect on the path of a radio wave. To bring out this importance, and to simplify subsequent calculations, it is usual to subtract 1 from the refractive index value and then multiply the remainder by one million. This quantity is given the symbol N; in mathematical terms $N = 10^6(n - 1)$.

Before demonstrating how N values may be calculated from meteorological data it will be advisable to define the

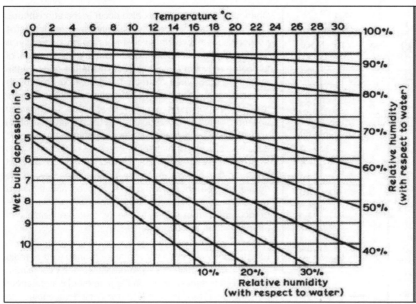

Fig 3.2: Percentage relative humidity as a function of temperature and wet bulb depression.

Meteorological units

Pressure

According to international agreement the current unit of pressure is the hectopascal (hPa), which is equivalent to a force of 100 newtons per square metre. However, the United Kingdom Meteorological Office (who provide most of the weather observing and forecasting services in this country) have shown themselves to be strangely reluctant to adopt the name 'hectopascal' in their dealings with the public, preferring to stick with the millibar, which has exactly the same value. To avoid confusion that practice will be followed here but at some time in the future you may have to start getting used to the new name. Your home barometer probably still has a scale that is calibrated in inches, which is a relic of much earlier days when air pressure was measured by balancing against it a column of mercury and reporting its height. The units are related such that 29.53 inches of mercury are equivalent to a pressure of 1000 millibars or 1000 hectopascals. For ground level values Fig 3.1 provides a rough conversion. Whole millibars are sufficiently precise for most propagation purposes.

Pressure decreases with height in an approximately logarithmic manner. Near the ground the rate of change is about 1mb in 10m, but this should not be presumed to extend over too great an interval because the relationship is actually a function of temperature also.

In meteorological studies it is customary to use pressure rather than height as a measure of vertical displacement and it will be found very convenient to carry over this practice into propagation work, because the physical processes of the atmosphere are a function of pressure,

units involved, and, in some cases, to show how they can be obtained from measurements made at home.

not of height, and any attempt to make them otherwise will complicate normally convenient relationships beyond belief. It requires some adjustment of ideas, not the least being that height is traditionally measured upwards from the ground, whereas pressure is measured from the top of the atmosphere downwards. But the radio wave, once launched on its way from the transmitting antenna, encounters nothing that can be identified directly with height. It 'sees' changes in air density and refractive index, which are themselves functions of pressure, temperature and water vapour content. Height, as such, is not one of the natural properties of the atmosphere, and that is why aircraft altimeters, which appear to measure it, have to be set to read zero at sea level before the pilot attempts to land, for they are really barometers carrying an approximate scale of feet or metres instead of an accurate one in millibars.

Very roughly indeed a pressure level of 900mb may be considered as being equivalent to a height of 1km and the 700mb level as being approximately 3km. Exact equivalents in respect of a given place and time form part of the basic meteorological data used in analysis work.

Temperature

In scientific work temperatures are generally expressed in degrees Celsius (°C, formerly known as Centigrade) or in kelvin (K). Strictly, kelvin are degrees Celsius plus 273.15 but for our purposes the constant may be rounded off to 273 in order to keep the working figures as whole numbers.

Relative humidity

This is a measure of the amount of moisture present in a sample of air, expressed as a percentage of the total amount which could be contained at the given temperature. It can be obtained from the readings of two identical

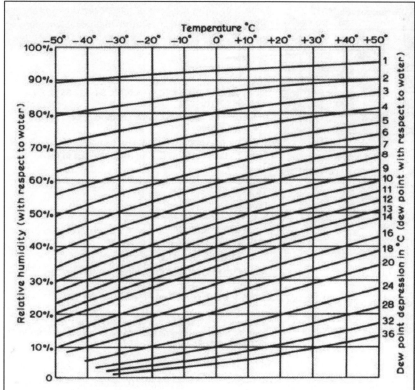

Fig 3.3: Percentage relative humidity as a function of temperature and dew point depression (may be used to convert radiosonde data published in the "wrong units").

thermometers, one of which has its bulb surrounded by a muslin wick moistened with distilled water.

They should be well sited in the shade, and preferably enclosed in a properly ventilated screen. The difference between the two readings is the depression of the wet bulb, and the percentage relative humidity can be found from Fig 3.2. If the thermometers are calibrated in degrees Fahrenheit it is better to convert their difference using the scale of Fig 3.1(c) than to find the difference of two converted figures.

Dew point

If a sample of air containing a given amount of moisture is allowed to cool it will be found that the wet bulb depression decreases until eventually both wet and dry bulb thermometers read the same. The relative humidity will have become 100% and the air is said to be saturated. The temperature at which this occurs, the dew point, is therefore another way of expressing the amount of water vapour contained in a sample of air. Most upper air reports nowadays show this as dew point depression, the difference between the dry bulb temperature and the temperature to which the air would have to be cooled in order to reach saturation, but some still refer to percentage relative humidity. The chart, Fig 3.3, can be used to make a conversion either way.

Vapour pressure

The water vapour present in a sample of air exerts a

contribution of its own to the total atmospheric pressure. The scales of Fig 3.1(d) show saturation vapour pressures corresponding to a wide range of temperatures, but it has to be admitted that the scale is a difficult one to interpolate. The relationship between temperature and saturation vapour pressure is a complex one and in the past most calculations have involved the use of tables. Recently, however, a number of organisations have tried to find an acceptable approximation, making use of an expression which is within the capabilities of a 'scientific' pocket calculator. The following, which is due to Parish and Purtnam of NASA, has been used elsewhere in this chapter for the machine calculation of refractive index:

$$e_s = T^{-4.9283} \times 10^{(23.5518-(2937.4/T))}$$

where e_s is saturated vapour pressure in millibars and T is the air temperature in kelvin.

When the air is not saturated the appropriate value of vapour pressure, e, can be found from the relationship:

$$e = e_s \times u$$

where u is the relative humidity expressed as a decimal (e.g. 72% = 0.72), or, more usually nowadays, from the dew point Td or the dew point depression, D (where $T_d = T - D$), using the expression:

$$e = T_d^{-4.9283} \times 10^{(23.5518-(2937.4/T_d))}$$

where T_d is in kelvin (°C + 273) which will be found to be the most practical form for use with a calculator or computer. Of course, the same trick of using the dew point

29

Table 3.3: Minimum duct thickness for the VHF and UHF amateur bands.

Band (MHz)	λ_c (m)	Minimum thickness (m)	Approximate millibar equivalent
50	6.00	317	31
70	4.29	263	26
144	2.08	176	17
432	0.69	96	9
1296	0.23	52	5
2300	0.13	38	4

to find the actual vapour pressure as if it was a saturated vapour pressure may be performed on the scale of Fig 3.1(d) to provide the required value of e.

The calculation of N

The basic equation is:

$$N = \frac{77.6}{T}\left(p + \frac{481e}{T}\right)$$

where p is the atmospheric pressure in millibars, e is the water vapour pressure in millibars and T is the air temperature in kelvin. It is often more convenient to expand this into:

$$N = \frac{77.6p}{T} + \frac{3.733 \times 10^5 \times e}{T^2}$$

because it then separates conveniently into a 'dry' term, corresponding approximately to the optical value of refractive index, and a 'wet' term which contains all of the contribution due to the presence of water vapour. The values which result from these expressions are known as refractivities, but they are often referred to simply as N units.

The degree of ray bending which results from refractive index changes can be assessed by calculating the decrease over unit height change. The normal gradient from the ground may be regarded as being approximately -40N/km. Should it become -157N/km the curvature of the ray becomes the same as that of the Earth, while gradients greater (i.e. more negative) than -157N/km result in ducting, where the waves travel for great distances, confined within a relatively shallow range of heights, suffering alternate refractions at the steep lapse layer and reflections from the ground.

Provided that well marked contrasts in refractivity exist above and below a ducting layer it is not essential for the ground to be involved at all. Once signals have been trapped in an elevated duct they may travel considerable distances without being receivable by stations on the ground below the transmission path. The waves eventually leak out of the duct at some point where the necessary conditions are no longer being fulfilled.

For efficient duct propagation the wavelength concerned must be less than a critical value λ_c, such that:

Table 3.4: Computer or calculator program to obtain radio refractive index, N, from basic meteorological data.

S = Store
R = Recall from store

Load stores with constants:
S1 = 273, S2 = 2937.4, S3 = –4.9283, S4 = 23.5518, S5 = 77.6, S6 = 4810

Input data for each level to be computed, pass to the indicated stores:

Enter p = pressure in millibars (or hectopascals). To S7 (p)

Enter t = temperature °C. Add R1 to convert to kelvin. To S8 (T)

Enter D = dew point depression °C. Subtract from R8. To S9 (T_d)

Program
1. Evaluate vapour pressure, e
   R9^{R3} * 10$^{(R4-(R2/R9))}$ To S10 (e)
2. Evaluate radio refractive index, N
   R5 (R7 = R6 * R10 / R8) / R8

Round off the result to the nearest whole number.

Test
When p = 900, t = –3.0 and D = 8, then N = 272

Note: A step-by-step calculator program (based on the TI58/59 calculator but easily adapted to suit any similar programmable scientific calculator) may be found in the fourth edition of the *VHF/UHF Manual*, p 2.5.

where D is the duct thickness in metres.

$$\lambda_c = 1.9 \times 10^{-4} \times D^{1.8}$$

Table 3.3 shows the minimum duct thickness and the approximate equivalent pressure difference in millibars, centred on 850mb, the pressure at a typical ducting height. The figures cover all the VHF and UHF amateur bands.

The following example of a calculation directly from basic meteorological data may be found useful:

p = 900mb, T = -3°C (= 270K), dew point depression = 8°C.

From this the dew point must be -11°C (= 262K) and the corresponding vapour pressure from Fig 3.1(d) is 2.6mb. Hence:

$$N = \frac{77.6 \times 900}{270} + \frac{3.733 \times 10^5 \times 2.6}{270 \times 270} = 259 + 13 = 272$$

Table 3.4 outlines a skeleton program to calculate radio refractive index N from basic meteorological data entered sequentially for each of the available levels. It should be readily adaptable for any type of scientific programmable calculator or a computer. Whole number answers are adequate for propagation studies and there is nothing to be gained by trying to make the results seem more precise than the data can support. Before undertaking extensive calculations make sure that the test figures yield the result shown.

Causes of Tropo DX

Having established a method of obtaining refractive index

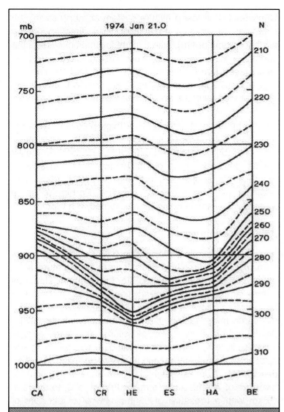

Fig 3.4: Cross section from SW England to Central Europe at midnight (0000GMT) 21ˢᵗ January 1974, drawn in terms of conventional refractive index N. The vertical scale is in terms of pressure. 700mb = 3km approximately. CA = Camborne, CR = Crawley, HE = Hemsby, ES = Essen, HA = Hannover, BE = Berlin.

values from standard meteorological upper air observations it is a natural progression to apply that knowledge to a study of the atmosphere during a well marked tropo-

spheric 'opening'; probably the main reason why radio amateurs take an active interest in this mode of radio propagation. For that purpose, consider the situation late in the evening of 20 January 1974, when continental Europe was 'wide-open' to the UK. This is a good example of a notable winter event and, as will be seen, it has been used to illustrate various aspects of a single occasion, as is shown in Figs 3.4, 3.5 and 3.6.

Fig 3.4 shows a cross section of the atmosphere up to 700mb (about 3km in terms of height), from Camborne in SW England to Berlin. The isopleths join levels having equal values of refractivity, scaled in N units. There is no mistaking the concentration formed in the lower part of the diagram. This indicates a steep fall of refractive index with height and is in the correct sense to cause the return to earth of rays which would otherwise have been lost in space above the horizon. Superrefraction of this sort produces bending towards the earth in the case of both ascending and descending rays. Because there is a normal tendency for refractive index to decrease with height, this effect is nearly always present in some degree and this accounts for the fact that radio communication at VHF and UHF is usually possible beyond the visible horizon. The presence in the lower atmosphere of a layer in which refractivity decreases very rapidly with height, as in the case being considered, is always accompanied by enhancement of signal strengths and an increase in working range. However, in the case where very narrow beamwidth antennas are used at both ends of the path, received signal strengths may fall, due to energy being deflected away from a path which has been optimised under conditions of normal refractivity.

From a cross section, such as Fig 3.4, it would be quite possible to calculate the probable paths of rays leaving a transmitting antenna at various angles of take off, using Snell's Law, as with optical ray tracing, but this is an exercise which is probably outside the needs of most amateurs. It should be noted that the values of refractivity

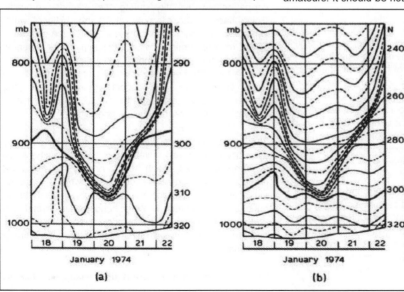

Fig 3.5: (a) Time section showing isopleths of potential refractive index, K, Crawley, 18ᵗʰ - 22ⁿᵈ January 1974. (b) Time section showing isopleths of radio refractive index, N, Crawley 18ᵗʰ - 22ⁿᵈ January 1974.

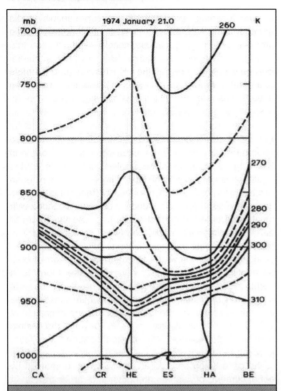

mb   1974 January 21.0   K
700   260

Fig 3.6: Cross section from SW England to Central Europe, at midnight (0000GMT) 21st January 1974, drawn in terms of potential refractive index, K. Compare with Fig 3.4 and note here how the steep lapse layer contains the same values along the length of the path.

at ground level reveal little of the situation above. For that reason the only really effective study of tropospheric propagation phenomena involves the acquisition of upper air meteorological data.

The atmosphere in motion

It does not require a great deal of experience on the VHF and UHF bands to realise that all the big 'openings' to the Continent occur during periods of high atmospheric pressure. Indeed, some amateurs look upon an aneroid barometer in the home as being their guide to the state of the bands. However, whereas good conditions are accompanied by high pressure readings, high pressure is not always accompanied by good conditions. Why should that be? The answer lies in an appreciation of the role played by vertical motions in the atmosphere.

In general, rising air becomes cooler and more moist, while descending air warms and becomes more dry. Air is sometimes forced into vertical motion by the topography in its path; it rises when it flows over hills and it descends into valleys. However, the present context mainly concerns vertical motion associated with the two main types of pressure system.

Consider first a low pressure system or 'depression'. Air circulates round it in an anticlockwise direction (in the northern hemisphere), with a slight inclination towards the centre, creating an inward spiral which leaves progressively less room for the volume of air in motion. There is only one escape route available, and that is upwards. So low pressure systems are associated with rising air.

On the other hand, anticyclones (high pressure systems) are characterised by light winds blowing clockwise round the centre but with a slight deflection outwards. As the air spirals outwards fresh quantities must be available to maintain the supply and the only source is from aloft, resulting this time in a downward flow. So high pressure systems have descending air associated with them.

Adiabatic changes

Air in vertical motion changes in both volume and pressure (they are directly related) and in temperature also, although there need be no gain or loss of heat. This may appear at first to be a contradiction in terms, for heat and temperature might be thought to be alternative names for the same thing. In fact, heat is a quantity which can be distributed either over a small volume to provide a large increase in temperature, or spread over a large volume to appear as a small increase in temperature. Thus 1kg of air descending from a height of 3km may begin with a pressure of 700mb and a temperature of -5°C, to arrive at 1.5km with a pressure of 850mb and a temperature of 10°C with no change of heat being involved. Such a process is adiabatic, and it is an important principle in meteorology.

A homely demonstration of it at work may be found in the case of the bicycle pump, the barrel of which gets hot in use due to the air inside having been compressed.

When the air is anything other than dry another apparent paradox links the amount of water vapour and the corresponding humidity during the adiabatic process. Going back to the example, at 700mb 3.78g of water vapour would have been sufficient to produce saturation (100% relative humidity) in the 1kg sample of air, whereas at 850mb the same amount would give only 41.5% relative humidity because air at 10°C could hold 9.1g of water vapour. So, air descending adiabatically gets warmer and drier, although the actual amounts of heat and water vapour remain unchanged.

The action is reversible but only up to a point. Ascending air is accompanied by increasing relative humidity, which at some stage will reach 100%. Any further lifting will result in the appearance of liquid water, which will appear either as cloud or larger droplets, which are likely to fall out of suspension as rain. When condensation occurs, the rate of cooling is altered by the appearance of latent heat, and the precipitation will alter the amount of moisture in the sample of air.

No such considerations affect descending air once its

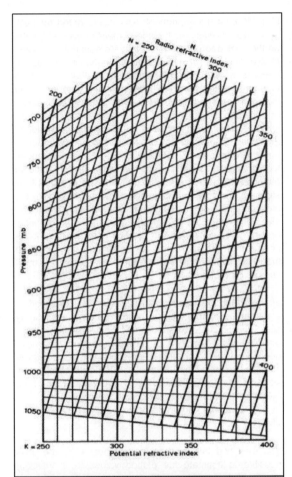

Fig 3.7: Refractive index plotting/conversion chart. Ordinate: pressure (mb). Abscissae: (vertical) potential refractive index, K; (slant) radio refractive index, N.

from time to time, all with the intention of minimising this effect, leaving emphasis on the features that are of most interest to the propagation engineer.

Opinions have varied on the best way to do this. Most methods proposed have involved some form of model atmosphere and the calculation of departures from it, resulting in complex exercises for which a computer is advisable. Another disadvantage has been the difficulty of recovering the original values of refractive index from the final data (should they be required elsewhere, or at a later date). The method to be described was first proposed in 1959 by Dr K H Jehn of the University of Texas, who does not seem to have taken advantage of the full potential of his suggestion. Curiously, little has been done outside amateur circles to exploit its usefulness; it involves a unit known as potential refractive index (K).

It may be obtained from upper air meteorological sounding data in just the same way as has been described for N units, the only difference being that each sample of air, whatever its true level may be, is presumed to have been transported adiabatically to a pressure of 1000mb before the calculations are made.

The advantages of this form of normalisation are considerable. By adopting a procedure which imitates the natural process of the atmosphere, applying, for example, to the large mass of air which subsides from aloft within an anticyclone, each level of air is effectively labelled with a value of potential refractive index which remains with it during any adiabatic change.

The effect may be seen particularly well in time sections, such as that of Fig 3.5(a), which shows how the potential refractive index pattern varied from day to day at a single station, Crawley, over a period which included that eventful evening of 20th January 1974.

There is no mistaking the extensive tongue of warm, dry, subsiding air associated with an anticyclone and the steep lapse refractive index layer built up where it meets the opposing cool, moist air underneath.

Towards the right and left edges of the diagram may be seen evidence of rising air which is associated with two depressions, which preceded and followed the period of high pressure. These potential refractive index isopleths are very sensitive indicators of vertical motion in the atmosphere, and the patterns on cross sections and time sections take on an interesting three dimensional aspect when viewed in conjunction with surface weather charts.

It is interesting to compare the potential refractive index time section of Fig 3.5(a) with the corresponding section drawn in terms of conventional radio refractive index, N, Fig 3.5(b). Note first that there are fewer lines on the potential refractive index diagram, indicating that the normal fall off of refractive index with height has been considerably offset. At the steep lapse layer, the concen-

relative humidity has fallen below 100%, although there will have been alterations to the rate of change of temperature if liquid droplets of water have been evaporating, again on account of latent heat.

If the sample of air is taken adiabatically to a standard pressure of 1000mb the temperature it assumes is known as the potential temperature of the sample. It follows from this that potential temperature is a quantity which remains constant during any adiabatic change: conversely, a change is an adiabatic one if it is associated with constant potential temperature.

Potential refractive index

Referring back to Fig 3.4 it will be seen that, quite apart from the region of interest referred to earlier, there is a general background of fairly regularly spaced isopleths which represent the normal fall off of refractive index with height. A number of modifications to the standard procedure for calculating refractive index have been proposed

tration of isopleths has been greatly emphasised in Fig 3.5(a) but it is important to notice that this has not been at the expense of accuracy in indicating either the height at which the effect occurred or its vertical extent.

Because air undergoing adiabatic changes has been shown to carry its value of potential refractive index along with it, no matter what its level, it should not be surprising that the boundary layer across the whole of Fig 3.5(a) is formed of basically the same set of K values irrespective of changes in pressure (or height). Fig 3.5(b) shows that the same is not true for conventional refractive index. This is not to suggest that the N values are wrong, but rather to point out that they do not share this very useful attribute of coherence independent of height which appears in diagrams like these. That the same is true of cross sections may be seen by comparing Fig 3.6 with Fig 3.4.

If values of atmospheric pressure are known (as they always are when radiosonde data have been used) a simple relationship exists between potential refractive index and N. This leads to the conversion chart shown in Fig 3.7, which may also be used as a plotting chart, having the property that an ascent plotted in terms of one of the units may be read off in terms of the other by using the appropriate axes. In this way the potential refractive index values may be converted to N units for ray tracing purposes, or compared with N unit profiles produced elsewhere.

Alternatively, use may be made of the following expressions:

$$N = 0.00731 \times p^{0.712} \times K$$

and

$$K = 136.8 \times p^{-0.712} \times N$$

which may be performed without difficulty on a scientific pocket calculator.

Although this conversion provides a way of obtaining potential refractive index it is usually better to calculate values directly from the radiosonde data. A method of doing that using a calculator or computer will be found in Table 3.4.

Acquiring current upper air meteorological data

A much quoted Victorian lady, Felicia Hemans, began her poem 'Casabianca' with the words "The boy stood on the burning deck / Whence all but he had fled". Those two lines rather neatly sum up the situation as regards the present availability of upper air meteorological data. Gone are the Morse, RTTY and facsimile broadcasts which used to keep us supplied with current information within an hour or so of the measurements being taken. Gone, too, are the printed daily records that appeared a few days later giving copies of the coded messages. And gone, never to return, are the microfiche summaries that would have served us well had they continued. All that remained

in 1997 when this handbook was last updated for easy public access was a daily page of machine plotted graphs on the back page of the European Meteorological Bulletin (EMB), published by Deutscher Wetterdienst who, as the name suggests, run the national weather service in Germany. Since then the Internet has expanded at an incredible rate and the EMB is available to access online or on a quarterly CD ROM. Details can be found on the web site [1], as an example a 7 day online subscription in 2006 was €6.88, a 31 day online subscription was €30.45 and the quarterly CD ROM was €59.68. The European Meteorological Bulletin was available at the National Meteorological Library in London until 2001 when they stopped taking the publication because it converted to the electronic form described above. Unfortunately when The Met Office moved to Exeter [2] in 2004 all of its historical records were converted to microfiche and are only available in that format. Things are better after that because the library can supply sets of upper air data, for a small charge, on request.

In the EMB, the aerological diagrams are displayed in eight panels, each panel containing two diagrams side by side, making 16 diagrams in all. Each diagram shows machine plotted graphs of temperature and dew point depression plotted against pressure for up to three stations, identified by the use of differing symbols. The size of each diagram is such that temperature runs from -40°C to +30°C in 61mm, dew point depressions from 0°C to 30°C in 26mm and pressure from 225mb to 1000mb in 76mm.

You may find this hard to believe but, with care, it is possible to estimate the plotted values to a sufficient degree of accuracy to be able to provide meaningful cross sections and time sections for propagation studies.

Frequently you will find that temperature and dew point depression turning points do not occur at the same pressure level. Remember that you need all three values to calculate refractive index so you will have to use the plotted curves to interpolate where necessary.

The published selection of up to 48 stations (occasionally one or two are missed) provides excellent coverage over Europe, as may be judged from Fig 3.8, which needs to be studied in conjunction with Table 3.5. All the diagrams show soundings made at 12UT.

Fig 3.8 may be used to select the upper air stations most appropriate to a given signal path, which could be overlaid using the latitude and longitude scales. It will be found an advantage to extend your cross section beyond the strict limits of the path, if possible, because two additional soundings help in drawing in the refractive index lines.

Why not use historical upper air data?

Every researcher feels instinctively that he or she has to work with the latest information available. That is fine if what you need for analysis is easily come by. But when it

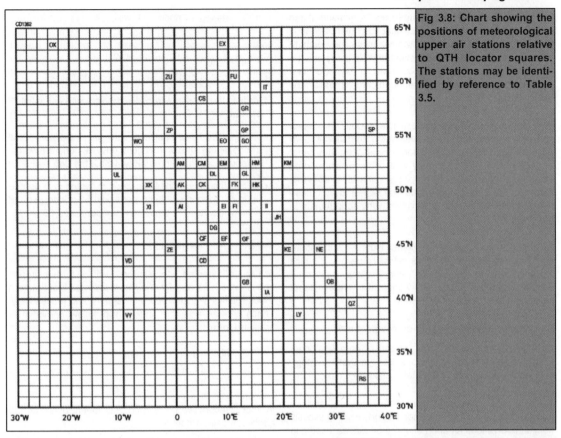

Fig 3.8: Chart showing the positions of meteorological upper air stations relative to QTH locator squares. The stations may be identified by reference to Table 3.5.

is in short supply or priced as if it were gold dust it makes sense to consider a more practical alternative.

The monthly VHF and UHF report columns of Radio Communication and (especially) the quarterly European report sections in the German magazine DUBUS [3] regularly contain details of unusual or exceptional signal

Table 3.5: Upper air sounding stations used in 1997 for The European Meteorological Bulletin.

QTH locator	IARU locator	Station number	Station name	Country	Height ASL (m)	QTH locator	IARU locator	Station number	Station name	Country	Height ASL (m)
OX	HP83	04018	Keflavik	Iceland	54	EX	JP43	01241	Ørland	Norway	7
UL	IO41	03953	Valentia	Ireland	14	FI	JN58	10868	München	Germany	489
VY	IM58	08579	Lisboa	Portugal	105	FK	JO50	10548	Meiningen	Germany	453
VD	IN53	08001	La Coruna	Spain	67	FU	JP50	01384	Oslo	Norway	204
WO	IO64	03920	Long Kesh	N Ireland	38	GB	JN61	16245	Roma	Italy	21
XI	IN78	07710	Brest	France	103	GF	JN65	16044	Udine	Italy	53
XK	IO70	03808	Camborne	England	88	GL	JO61	10486	Dresden	Germany	232
ZE	IN94	07510	Bordeaux	France	61	GO	JO64	10184	Greifswald	Germany	6
ZP	IO95	03240	Boulmer	England		GP	JO65	06181	København	Denmark	42
ZU	IP90	03005	Lerwick	Shetland	84	GR	JO67	02527	Gotenborg	Sweden	155
AI	JN08	07145	Trappes	France	161	HK	JO70	11520	Praha	Czech Rep.	304
AK	JO00	03882	Herstmonceux	England	52	HM	JO72	10393	Lindenberg	Germany	104
AM	JO02	03496	Hemsby	England	14	IA	JN80	16320	Brindisi	Italy	10
CD	JN23	07645	Nimes	France	62	IT	JN88	11035	Wien	Austria	209
CF	JN25	07481	Lyon	France	240	IT	JO89	02465	Stockholm	Sweden	14
CK	JO20	06447	Uccle	Belgium	104	JH	JN97	12843	Budapest	Hungary	139
CM	JO22	06260	de Bilt	Netherlands	15	KE	KN04	13275	Beograd	Serbia	203
CS	JO28	01415	Stavanger	Norway	9	KM	KO02	12374	Legionowo	Poland	96
DG	JN36	06610	Payerne	Switzerland	491	LY	KM18	16716	Athens	Greece	15
DL	JO31	10410	Essen	Germany	161	NE	KN34	15420	Bukarest	Romania	
EF	JN45	16080	Milano	Italy	103	OB	KN41	17062	Istanbul	Turkey	33
EI	JN48	10739	Stuttgart	Germany	311	OZ	KM69	17130	Ankara	Turkey	891
EM	JO42	10238	Bergen	Germany		RS	KM73	40179	Bet Dagan	Israel	35
EO	JO44	10035	Schleswig	Germany	48	SP	KO85	27612	Moskava	Russia	156

Note: In the QTH locator column an underlined letter signifies that care is needed to avoid ambiguity.

events, and have done for many years. Very few of those events have been properly analysed. So, why not look back 30 years or so to a time when the radiosonde network was much more extensive than it is today and the information was readily available? Twice a day, 00UT and 12UT, or, if you go back far enough, four times a day: 00UT, 06UT, 12UT and 18UT.

Why not consider going back to two periods of intense scientific interest the world over; the International Geophysical Year, 1957 and the International Quiet Sun Years of 1963 and 1964? Extremely well documented records covering a wide range of disciplines still exist in scientific libraries. The likes of the efforts that were put into those two periods will never be seen again. Why not put them to good use?

By changing your objectives Mother Hubbard's cupboard could be replaced by Aladdin's cave. To parody a notice which used to be common in general stores before the war; if you don't see what you want in the window, come inside and ask for something else.

Discontinued sources of meteorological data

Until 31 December 1980, the source of data from nine British and Irish upper air stations was the Daily Aerological Record, published by the Meteorological Office.

There was a companion series, dealing with surface observations, the Daily Weather Report, which gave six hourly observations for each of about 50 places located in all parts of the British Isles.

Those two publications had a very wide circulation in their time and copies may still be available in some specialised libraries in various parts of the country. They, and similar publications from other parts of Europe, are available at the National Meteorological Library in Exeter [2] on microfiche.

Extracting the data

If you are fortunate enough to be able to access the messages circulating on the global network you will need to know that they are headed by an alphanumeric indicator which reveals the type of information concerned and the country or area concerned. Upper air messages are split into two or more parts, not all of which are of interest in the present context. Printed copies may be similarly split, but the identifiers may have been edited out by then.

The first message, headed with a prefix beginning 'US' (e.g. USUK for British stations, USFR for French stations etc) and/or by the group 'TTAA', relates to observations at specific levels of pressure. The station number is generally the second of the numerical groups.

Next, look for a group beginning 99. This and the one following are in the form:

99ppp TTTDD

where:

- '99' indicates that the ground level data follows

- 'ppp' is the pressure in whole milibars with the initial '1' omitted for 1000mb and over.

- 'TTT' is the air temperature in degrees Celsius. If the tenths figure, the third figure one, is odd, the whole number is negative (i.e. 046 = 4.6°C, but 045 = -4.5°C)

- 'DD' is the dew point depression in tenths of a degree up to 5°, then in whole degrees with 50 added (e.g. 46 = dew point 4.6° below air temperature, 66 = 16° below).

Codes 51 – 55 are not used.

At regularly spaced intervals there will be further groups beginning 00, 85 and 70, indicators showing that the data which follows are for 1000, 850 and 700mb respectively. These groups and the ones which follow immediately have the form:

    00hhh TTTDD...85hhh
    TTTDD...70hhh
    TTTDD

In more recent years 925mb has been used as an additional standard level.

'hhh' is the height above sea level of the pressure level in metres, omitting the thousands figure. For 1000mb this becomes a negative number when the pressure at sea level is below that value, this is indicated by adding 500 to the code figure (i.e. 675 = -175m). The missing first figure is 1 for 850mb and either 2 or 3 for 700mb, whichever puts the value closer to 3000m. 'TTTDD' has the same significance as before.

The second message is headed with an indicator beginning 'UK' (e.g. UKUK, UKFR etc) and/or the group 'TTBB', signifying that it relates to turning points in the temperature and dew point profiles. It is the more useful of the two because it contains everything necessary for propagation studies, apart from the relationship between pressure and height for the particular ascent. As before, the station number is generally second of the five figure groups in the message. To decode the remainder, point off succeeding groups in pairs that begin with the figures 00, 11, 22, 33 etc. The pairs have the form:

    NNppp TTTDD

where:

- 'NN' enumerates the data points. '00' always signifies local ground level.

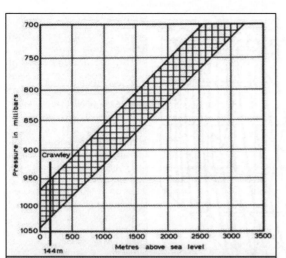

Fig 3.9: Relationship between pressure and height between the surface and 700mb, assuming an average contribution from temperature and humidity.

- 'ppp' is the pressure, in millibars, at the level of the observation, with the initial 1 omitted if the value exceeds 1000.

- 'TTTDD' contain the temperature in degrees and tenths and the dew-point depression, coded as before.

For most tropospheric propagation studies there is little point in going beyond the level at which the pressure has fallen to 700mb, unless it is to interpolate a refractive index value for 700mb in order to provide a uniform 'top' to a cross section.

In a radiometeorological study it is quite likely that all the work will be carried out in terms of pressure rather than height, not only for convenience because that is the form adopted in the radiosonde messages, but because the radio wave, once launched, does not 'see' changes in height but rather changes in air density, a quantity closely related to pressure. In the atmosphere, height, which seems so easy to understand on the ground, becomes a complex function of the integrated effects of temperature and humidity, and of the value of pressure at station height.

There are two ways of finding the heights corresponding to the various pressure levels reported in the Part 2 message. The more accurate, though time consuming, way is to plot the ascent data on a standard tephigram (obtainable from HMSO, where it is known at Metform 2810B) and then to follow the instructions given on the form. Alternatively, and this may well be accurate enough for the present purpose, refer to Fig 3.9, which assumes an average vertical distribution of temperature and dew point, leaving the height a function only of surface pressure. The diagram is used as follows:

- Find the station height from Table 3.5 and draw a

vertical line at the corresponding value on the horizontal scale. (Crawley, at 144m ASL, which appears in many of the examples used in this chapter, including this one, is no longer operational. Its place for observations over south-east England has been taken by Herstmonceaux.)

- Find the point where that vertical line intersects a horizontal line appropriate to the reported value of ground level pressure.

- Through that point lay off a line which maintains a constant proportion of the space between the two sloping lines. (An overlay of tracing paper is useful here.)

- Approximate heights corresponding to given pressures may now be read from the horizontal scale.

This diagram may be used also to interpolate between the height values reported in the standard level message.

Full details of all the codes used in meteorological broadcasts will be found in [4] and [5]

The Tephigram

Meteorologists usually plot radiosonde ascent data on a rather complex thermodynamic chart known as a Tephigram, (which may be used as a means of calculating potential refractive index) and a knowledge of its properties will help to achieve an understanding of the processes involved in the atmospheric movements we have been considering. Fig 3.10 shows an outline diagram, including a set of K lines which will be explained in the next section. Reference should be made to the small inset diagram which identifies the various axes as they appear at the 1000mb, 0°C intersection:

- P–P   are isobars, or lines of constant pressure.

- T–T   are isotherms, or lines of constant temperature.

- D–D   are lines of constant moisture content, which are followed by the dew point as the pressure alters during adiabatic changes.

- A–A   Are lines of constant potential temperature, followed by the air temperature during an adiabatic change.

- W–W is a saturated adiabatic, which marks the temperature changes followed by ascending saturated air (only one is shown here in order to simplify the diagram as much as possible).

Both temperature and dew point are plotted with reference to the T–T lines.

An example of the use of the Tephigram will help to emphasise the points which have been made earlier in the text. Consider Fig 3.11(a) which shows two points on the 900mb line, representing a temperature of -3°C and a dew point of -11°C. If that sample of air is taken to a pressure

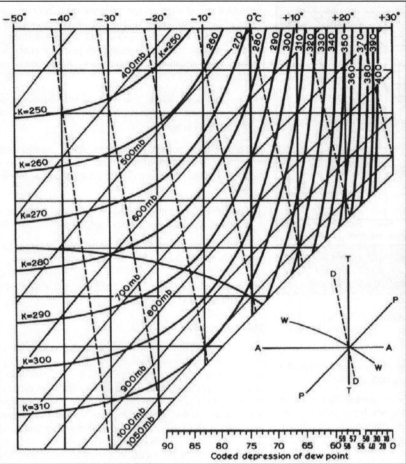

Fig 3.10: Skeleton tephgram (a meteorological temperature entropy diagram) showing the position of additional curves, labelled K = 250 to 450, used for direct graphical calculation of potential refractive index values from published radiosonde measurements. For practical use it is recommended that the curves should be transferred to a standard full sized tephigram.

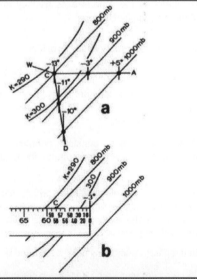

Fig 3.11: Alternative methods of determining values of potential refractive index from reported measurements of pressure, temperature and dew point depression, using the tephigram modified in Fig 3.10. (a) Intersection method. (b) Using scale of coded dew point depression values.

of 1000mb adiabatically, the temperature will follow the horizontal line CA, and the dew point will follow CD. At 1000mb the temperature becomes +5°C (by definition the potential temperature), and the dew point becomes -10°C. Lifting would cause the temperature and the dew point to come closer together, and they would become coincident at the point C, which is known as the condensation level, where condensed droplets of water begin to appear as cloud. Further lifting will cause the temperature to follow one of the saturated adiabatics such as CW, instead of an extension of AC, due to the liberation of latent heat.

Obtaining potential refractive index values

Potential refractive index values may be obtained in one of four ways, the method to be used depending on the resources available.

- From the expression:

$$K = \frac{77.6}{\theta}\left(1000 + \frac{4810000e}{p\theta}\right)$$

where p is the pressure in millibars at the level of observation and the potential temperature in kelvin:

Table 3.6: Computer or calculator program to obtain potential refractive index, K, from basic meteorological data.

S = Store
R = Recall from store

Load stores with constants:

S1 = 273, S2 = 2937.4, S3 = -4.9283, S4 = 23.5518, S5 = 77.6, S6 = 4810, S7 = 0.288, S8 = 1000

Input data for each level to be computed, pass to the indicated stores

Enter p = pressure in millibars (or hectopascals). To S9 (p)

Enter t = temperature °C. Add R1 to convert to kelvin. To S10 (T)

Enter either:

D = dew point depression °C. Subtract from R10 to S11 (T_d)

or t_d = dew point temperature, °C. Add R1 to convert to Kelvin. To S11 (T_d)

or U = relative humidity, expressed as a decimal. To S12 (R_H)

Program

1. Evaluate vapour pressure, e
   Either (a) If dew point or dew point depression has been entered:
   R11^{R3} * 10$^{(R4 - (R2/R11))}$ To S13 (e)

   or (b) If percentage relative humidity has been entered:
   R10^{R3} * 10$^{R4 - (R2/R10)}$ * R12   To S13 (e)

2. Evaluate potential temperature
   R10 * (R8/R9)^{R7} To S14 (θ)

3. Evaluate potential refractive index, K
   R5((R6 * R8 * R13)/(R9 * R14)) + R8/R14
   Round off the result to the nearest whole number.

Test
When p = 900, t = -3.0, either D = 8 or t_d = -11.0, or U = 53/100 = 0.53 then K = 293.

Note: A step-by-step calculator program (based on the TI58/59 calculator but easily adapted to suit any similar programmable scientific calculator) may be found in the fourth edition of the *VHF/UHF Manual*, p2.14.

$$\theta = (T_{°C} + 273) \times \left(\frac{1000}{p}\right)^{0.288}$$

e is the saturation vapour pressure at the dewpoint temperature.

Example: p = 900mb, T = -3.0°C, dew point depression = code 58 = 8°C below -3.0°C = -11.0°C, then:

$$\theta = 270 \times \left(\frac{1000}{900}\right)^{0.288} = 278.3$$

and from Fig 3.1(d):

e = 2.6mb (at -11°C)

whence K = 292.8.

- Using a programmable calculator or computer. Table 3.6 outlines a program which provides K values directly from pressure, temperature and either dew point de-

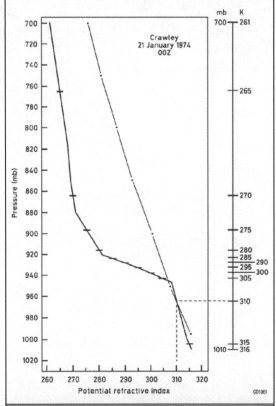

Fig 3.12: Potential refractive index profile from Crawley, 21st January 1974, at 0000GMT. The spaced values along the vertical line on the right have been used in the construction of both Fig 3.5 and Fig 3.6. The thin sloping line shows "normal" K values for the second half of January (see Table 3.8, line B).

pression, dew point or percentage relative humidity.

- Using a full sized Tephigram based on Fig 3.10 and a two line construction. The curved potential refractive index lines labelled K = 290, K = 300 etc are so placed that the required value of K may be read at the intersection of the dry adiabat through the temperature point and the moisture content line through the dew point, plotted on the appropriate isobar. These points are shown on Fig 3.11(a) at -3°C and -11°C (900mb), as in the previous example. The lines drawn as indicated intersect at the point C which, when referred to the K lines, gives the answer directly: K = 293.

- Alternatively, the scale labelled 'coded depression of the dew point' may be transferred to the edge of a card and used horizontally on the diagram as shown in Fig 3.11(b), with the right hand index against the point on the diagram defined by the temperature and pressure. The required K value is read against the coded dew point depression (58, signifying 8° depression). The scale is the projection on to a horizontal of depressions along an isobar, using the slope of the moisture content lines. This method is strictly correct only on the right hand side of the diagram and the method would suffer

Table 3.7: Seasonal variation of radio refractive index N at Crawley. Six years combined data, 1972-7.

Half month period		Sfc N	Sfc P	950 N	900 N	850 N	850 H	800 N	750 N	700 N	700 H
JA	A	318	1001	297	278	260	1465	244	227	213	3001
	B	314	995	296	278	261	1407	244	228	213	2929
FE	C	313	991	296	278	261	1381	245	228	214	2909
	D	315	1002	294	276	259	1468	244	228	213	2995
MR	E	313	999	294	276	259	1444	243	227	213	2966
	F	313	1000	294	276	259	1455	243	228	213	2984
AP	G	312	997	294	277	262	1434	245	229	214	2958
	H	313	1002	294	278	261	1480	244	227	212	3014
MY	J	316	997	297	280	263	1443	246	229	214	2879
	K	319	1000	298	281	262	1483	244	228	213	3035
JE	L	321	1001	300	282	263	1497	245	228	213	3059
	M	326	1001	304	285	265	1510	247	230	213	3091
JL	N	330	1001	306	287	267	1513	247	230	213	3098
	P	331	1000	308	288	269	1503	249	231	214	3096
AU	Q	331	1001	307	288	268	1519	248	229	213	3102
	R	330	1001	306	287	266	1518	246	228	212	3098
SE	S	327	1000	305	285	265	1495	246	229	213	3067
	T	327	999	304	284	265	1479	246	228	213	3041
OC	U	323	997	302	282	262	1455	244	227	213	3014
	V	323	1000	300	280	260	1475	244	227	212	3030
NV	W	320	998	299	281	262	1448	245	228	213	2990
	X	315	998	295	277	260	1439	243	227	213	2968
DE	Y	316	998	296	278	261	1441	244	227	213	2973
	Z	318	1002	296	278	261	1469	243	227	212	3006
Overall six year mean		320	999	299	281	263	1468	245	228	213	3015

a progressive loss of accuracy towards the left (because the moisture content lines are not parallel), were it not for the fact that the dependence of K on dew point diminishes at low temperatures.

From profile to section

Once the calculations have been made all the information necessary to draw a profile will be to hand.

A profile, such as the one shown in Fig 3.12, reveals immediately the presence of warm, dry, low refractivity air overlying a ground based layer of air which is cool, moist, and of high refractive index. The more abrupt the boundary between them, the more nearly horizontal will the transition appear on the diagram, and the more pronounced the bending experienced by the radio wave. Some of the occasions when conditions have been most favourable for DX have occurred during periods when there has been anticyclonic subsidence aloft with a contrasting depth of wet fog at the ground.

In some cases the refractive index profile is all that is required. It is much more rewarding, however, to combine it with others in order to make a section.

The first step is to project the pressures at which regular values of K occur across to a vertical line, as shown in the diagram. The spacings which result can then be transferred to form part of a time section for the station in

question (Fig 3.5), or a cross section for a given path (Fig 3.6); the one profile forms part of both diagrams.

The additional work involved in this type of exercise is amply justified by the sense of continuity which results. Thus the time section shown in Fig 3.5 reveals in a single glance far more about the formation and eventual dissipation of a subsidence boundary layer than could be gained by a prolonged study of the 10 separate profiles which were combined in its construction.

'Normal' values of N and K

It is in the nature of things that refractive index studies, requiring as they do a considerable amount of calculation and detailed graphical work, are carried out on an infrequent basis, as and when periods of interest come to light.

It means, inevitably, that a sense of continuity is lacking whenever an in depth study is undertaken. It means also that researchers usually see only abnormal conditions and few of them can be bothered to do similar exercises when nothing out of the ordinary has been occurring.

The situation is further complicated by the fact that there is a marked seasonal variation in values of refractive index near to the ground, making it difficult to compare, say, a February event with one that occurred in July, unless one has access to information showing the sort of values that

Table 3.8: Seasonal variation of potential refractive index K at Crawley. Six years combined data, 1972-7.

Half month period		Sfc K	Sfc P	950 K	900 K	850 K	850 H	800 K	750 K	700 K	700 H
JA	A	318	1001	308	300	292	1465	286	279	275	3001
	B	315	995	307	300	293	1407	286	280	275	2929
FE	C	315	991	307	300	293	1381	287	280	276	2909
	D	315	1002	305	298	291	1468	286	280	275	2995
MR	E	313	999	305	298	291	1444	285	279	275	2966
	F	313	1000	305	298	291	1455	285	280	275	2984
AP	G	313	997	305	299	294	1434	287	281	276	2958
	H	313	1002	305	300	293	1480	286	279	273	3014
MY	J	317	997	308	302	295	1443	288	281	276	2979
	K	319	1000	309	303	294	1483	286	280	274	3035
JE	L	321	1001	311	304	295	1497	287	280	274	3059
	M	326	1001	315	307	298	1510	290	282	275	3091
JL	N	330	1001	317	309	300	1513	290	282	275	3098
	P	331	1000	320	311	302	1503	292	283	276	3096
AU	Q	331	1001	318	310	301	1519	291	281	274	3102
	R	330	1001	317	309	299	1518	289	280	273	3098
SE	S	327	1000	316	307	298	1495	289	281	274	3067
	T	327	999	315	306	298	1479	288	280	274	3041
OC	U	324	997	313	304	294	1455	286	279	274	3014
	V	323	1000	311	302	292	1475	286	279	273	3030
NV	W	321	998	310	303	294	1448	287	280	274	2990
	X	316	998	306	299	292	1439	285	279	275	2968
DE	Y	317	998	307	300	293	1441	286	279	274	2973
	Z	318	1002	307	300	293	1469	285	279	273	3006
Overall six year mean		321	999	310	303	295	1468	287	280	275	3017

might be considered 'normal' in each of the two cases.

It might seem that monthly mean refractive index values could be obtained by putting mean monthly temperature and mean monthly dew point data into the computer program in place of individual ascent figures. An inspection of the skeleton Tephigram, Fig 3.10, will explain why that will not work. The temperature (T–T) and dew point (D–D) scales are straight line functions whereas the refractive index lines have a pronounced curvature which changes character across the chart. Mean figures of refractive index have to be obtained from daily refractive index values, not from means of the basic meteorological data.

That explains the origin of Tables 3.7 and 3.8, which were obtained from 4380 consecutive radiosonde ascents reduced to refractive index and potential refractive index spot values. They represent six years of real time data gathering from 1972 to 1977 and are, so far as is known, the only statistics available for either index in terms of atmospheric pressure instead of height. They appeared first in IERE Conference Proceedings No 40 (July 1978), to which reference should be made for further details and for other results of the study.

In this chapter refractive index and its distribution in the atmosphere are looked at from a meteorologist's viewpoint, having regard to the fact that the radio wave, once launched, is acted upon by atmospheric pressure, atmos-

pheric temperature and the varying amount of moisture in the air through which it passes. Height, as such, does not come into the basic equations at all and only appears in expressions for refractive index gradients because radio engineers feel that they must have a fixed scale firmly anchored to the ground. Statistics based on specific pressure levels eliminate one of the variables and provide results that are in the right form for comparison with day-to-day radiosonde measurements.

For an example of the use of the annual statistics consider Fig 3.12, in which the thicker line shows potential refractive index values plotted against pressure for one of the profiles used in the examples of cross sections and time sections. The fine line shows the mean values for the time of year and it should be clear that the low values of potential refractive index encountered above 940mb have been the result of air subsiding from above. During an adiabatic change potential refractive index remains unchanged so a parcel of subsiding air brings its original value down with it but, remember, the same is not true of conventional refractive index, N.

Strictly, these statistics are valid only for south east England, but they provide a useful indicator for adjacent areas, for which there are no comparable figures.

Signal strengths and ranges attainable

The effect of the boundary layer on signal strength

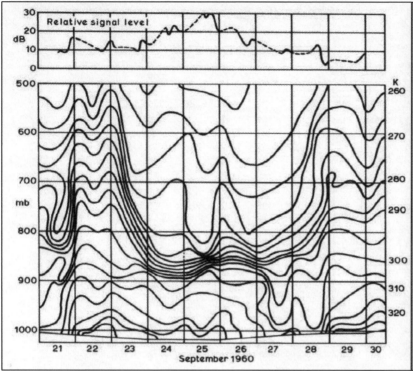

Fig 3.13: Potential refractive index time section, Crawley 21 - 30th September 1960, together with a record of signal strengths, obtained on a chart recorder located near Reading, from VHF TV transmissions originating at Lille in France. Note that the highest signals occur when the steep lapse layer is most pronounced, and a sudden drop occurs as the anticyclone is replaced by a low pressure system. With acknowledgements to J Atmos Terr Phys, Pergamon Press.

The time section is an ideal way of comparing a series of upper air soundings in terms of refractive index because, once you know the signs, you can see at a glance periods of rising or subsiding air and the formation and dissipation of steep lapse layers of the sort that lead to periods of anomalous propagation, or 'openings' as amateur operators prefer to call them.

Fig 3.13 illustrates very clearly the way that VHF signal strengths rise during a week of anticyclonic subsidence. When this diagram was originally prepared there was a television station transmitting on 174MHz, located at Lille, in northern France. G3BGL, located at a site just to the west of Reading, used to monitor the strength of the sound carrier using a pen recorder, with the object of compiling statistics for a 300km VHF path (this was before the time that we had beacon transmissions on the amateur bands). The television station operated every afternoon and evening.

The potential refractive index pattern is typical of an anticyclonic opening. The bottom boundary of the isopleths shows that ground level atmospheric pressure reached a peak during 24 and 25 September. The 'inverted pudding basin' centred on the 22nd heralded the commencement of subsiding air, a feature which was to make its presence felt over the next six days. Note the way that the signal level rose as the subsidence boundary layer formed, then lowered and intensified. The highest signals appeared when the gradient was steepest, on the 25th. After that the gradient slackened and the received signal strength fell. On the evening of the 28th a cold front arrived and

destroyed, by mixing, all traces of the boundary which had given the good conditions. A low pressure system moving in is responsible for the rising isopleths of the 29th. The radiosonde station at Crawley was very close to the mid point of the transmission path.

It is a point worth emphasising that this one time section shows, at a glance, all the significant information contained in 20 consecutive refractive index profiles.

The subsidence boundary layer may be thought of as being a battlefront. It comes about as a result of descending warm dry air coming up against cool moist air stirred up from the ground. If the two opposing forces are nicely balanced the layer stays where it is and intensifies. If subsidence increases or the turbulence decreases the boundary falls and may even reach the ground. If that happens the good conditions immediately drop out.

If the low level turbulence increases the boundary will rise and will eventually be lost through mixing. When conditions are at their best it is the contrast between the two opposing air components which is all important. Given warm dry subsiding air from aloft in an anticyclone you cannot do better than find yourself surrounded by wet dripping fog.

At their best, tropospheric 'openings' are productive of ranges considerably in excess of conventional textbook expectations. Using an analysis of extreme range signal reports it has been shown that if 1000km can be exceeded at 144MHz there is a strong probability that 1500km or further will be reached, for there is a pronounced peak in

Table 3.9: European VHF and UHF distance records as at mid 2006. Data supplied by SM6NZB.

Band	Propagation mode	Station A Callsign	Locator	Station B Callsign	Locator	Mode	Date	Distance km
50MHz	Tropo	ZS6Y	KG33VW	ZS1AGF	JF96FG	?	24/10/1999	1238
	Aurora	ES2QN	KO29DJ	TF3MLT	HP94	SSB	12/09/2000	2335
	Sporadic E	5B4FL	KM64TV	W4UDH	EM53AG	CW	09/07/2004	10528
	Meteor	G4IGO	IO80NW	SV1OE	KM17VX	?	12/08/1990	2542
	EME	F6FHP	IN94TR	ZL3NW	RE66HO	JT65A	03/03/2006	19441
	F2	ZL3VTV/1	RF73KD	EH7KW	IM67XI	SSB	03/04/2001	19921
	TEP	IK0FTA	JN61GV	KH8/N5OLS	AH45DQ	CW	08/04/2001	16920
	Aurora Es	OH5LK	KP30ON	OX3LX	GP36NP	CW	01/07/1990	3748
70MHz	Tropo	OZ1DJJ	JO65HP	G0IUE	IO81WJ	SSB	02/08/2003	1084
	Aurora	EI7IX	IO53FT	OZ3ZW	JO54RS	SSB	27/07/2004	1367
	Sporadic E	EI3IO	IO63WF	5B/G1JJE	KM64ES	SSB	29/07/2001	3640
	Meteor	OZ1DJJ	JO65HP	EI3IO	IO63WF	SSB	12/08/2003	1242
	Aurora Es	OZ1DJJ	JO65HP	CU8OA	HM49KL	CW	03/06/2006	3668
144MHz	Tropo	G4LOH	IO70JC	RW1ZC/MM	IL10GF	SSB	07/08/2005	3487
	Aurora	PA3EKK	JO32HA	UA4ANV	LO44	CW	10/05/1992	2724
	Sporadic E	OE1SBB	JN88FF	RI8TA	MM37TE	SSB	21/07/1989	4281
	Meteor	GW4CQT	IO81LP	UW6MA	KN97VE	CW	12/08/1977	3101
	EME	EA5SE	IM98IL	ZLIIU	RF64VR	JT65B	24/10/2005	19453
	TEP	I4EAT	JN54VG	ZS3B	JG73	CW	30/03/1979	7784
	Iono. Scatter	DF9PY/P	JO30JF	SM2EKM	KP05UW	CW	09/06/1989	1947
	Aurora Es	DK3BU	JO33NO	UA1ZCL	KP78TX	CW	25/08/1987	2254
	FAI	SP4MPB	KO03GS	EA2AGZ	IN91DV	SSB	13/06/2000	2110
432MHz	Tropo	G0FYD	IO83LS	EA8BPX	IL18SK	SSB	08/08/2003	3019
	Aurora	EI5KF	IO51RT	S51ZO	JN86DR	CW	20/11/2003	1883
	Meteor	SM3AKW	JP92AO	UA9FAD	LO88DA	CW	12/08/1999	2141
	EME	G3SEK	IO91IP	ZL3AAD	RE66GR	CW	12/03/1989	18970
1.3GHz	Tropo	EA8XS	IL28GA	G6LEU	IO790ME	SSB	29/06/1985	2617
	Aurora	SM3AKW	JP92AO	SM5QA	JO89WJ	CW	11/04/2001	358
	EME	PA0SSB	JO11WI	ZL3AAD	RE66GR	CW+SSB	13/06/1983	18773
2.3GHz	Tropo	SM0SBI	JO99CF	F5HRY	JN18EQ	CW	10/12/2004	1560
	EME	ZS6AXT	KG33VV	NU7Z	CN87ST	CW	13/06/1999	16475
	Rain Scatter	I4CVC	JN54WH	OE5VRL/5	JN78DK	CW	17/06/2001	495

the distribution at that range. Similarly, if 750km can be exceeded at 432MHz, there is a good probability that 1200km or further will be reached. Histograms showing these findings are included in a paper [6] which should be used as a reference for further details.

Table 3.9 gives details of maximum confirmed tropospheric ranges for the six VHF and UHF amateur bands, as at the middle of 2006.

EME (Moonbounce)

Earth-Moon-Earth contacts are, as the name implies, contacts made using the Moon as a reflector. It goes without saying that high power and accurate aiming of a narrow beam are essential requirements.

The paths are line of sight to and from the Moon but

tropospheric refraction effects could affect the performance at low elevation angles. Distance (around the Earth, transmitter to receiver) records are made and broken but they are a function of geometry rather than geophysical influences. All VHF and UHF bands apart from 70MHz have been used. Europe to New Zealand has been achieved on 50, 144, 432MHz and 1.3GHz.

Free space attenuation

The concept of free space attenuation between isotropic antennas, or basic transmission loss, Lb, provides a useful yard-stick against which other modes of propagation may be compared. It is a function of frequency and distance, such that

$$L_b = 32.45 + 20 \log f + 20 \log d$$

Table 3.10: Free space attenuation in dB for a given frequency and distance.

Frequency (MHz)	Distance (km)								
	50	100	150	200	300	400	500	750	1000
50	100	106	110	112	116	118	120	124	126
70	103	109	113	115	119	121	123	127	129
144	110	116	119	122	125	128	130	133	136
432	119	125	129	131	135	137	139	143	145
1296	129	135	138	141	144	147	149	152	155
2300	134	141	143	146	149	152	154	157	160

Table 3.11: Troposcatter path loss on a smooth earth.

Frequency (MHz)	Distance (km) 50	100	150	200	300	400	500	750	1000
70	47	49	53	55	61	69	75	91	109
144	50	52	55	58	64	72	78	94	112
432	55	56	60	62	69	76	82	99	116
1296	59	61	65	67	74	81	87	101	121
2300	60	63	67	70	76	83	90	106	

where f and d are expressed in megahertz and kilometres respectively. Table 3.10 provides a representative range of values against distance for various VHF/UHF amateur bands.

Tropospheric scatter propagation

Tropospheric scatter propagation depends for its effectiveness on the presence of dust particles, cloud droplets and small scale irregularities in radio refractive index within a volume of the atmosphere which is common to both the transmitting and receiving antenna beam cones. The height of the bottom of this common volume is a function of distance between the stations concerned owing to the effect of the curvature of the earth. Typical heights are 600m for a 100km path, 9000m for a 500km path. Path losses increase by about 10dB for every degree of horizon angle at each station so that a site with an unobstructed take off is an important consideration.

Only a very small proportion of the signal energy passing through the common volume will be scattered, and only a small proportion of that will be directed towards the receiving station. Therefore the loss in the scattering process is extremely large and the angle through which the signal ray has to be deflected is an important characteristic of a troposcatter path; for best results it should be no more than a few degrees.

J N Gannaway, G3YGF, has made a critical study of the losses in tropospheric scatter propagation, which appeared in RadCom August 1981, pp710-714, 717. It should be consulted for a fuller discussion of the mode than can be given here. A more recent article appeared in The UK Six Metre Group (UKSMG) magazine in 1996 [15].

Table 3.11 shows the path losses between two stations on a smooth earth, expressed as decibels below the free space values, for VHF and UHF amateur bands. (Free space losses have been given earlier in Table 3.10) To these values must be added losses depending on characteristics of the sites; height, distance to the first obstruc-

tion, antenna coupling losses etc; and variables depending on seasonal and weather factors.

Table 3.12, which is taken directly from the work cited, shows the theoretical range that could be expected under flat conditions and from good sites, with the equipment shown against each of the amateur bands. The ranges are for a 0dB signal-to-noise ratio in a bandwidth of 100Hz, representing a weak CW signal; for SSB these ranges should be reduced by 130km on each band.

For distances approaching 1000km the equipment requirements are comparable to those needed for propagation by moonbounce.

Because signal path transit times vary with height of scatter within the common volume a 'blurring' occurs which limits the maximum speed of transmission of intelligence; narrow beams have the faster capabilities.

Ionospheric propagation at VHF and UHF

Regular layers

The regular layers of the ionosphere play only a small part in the properties of the VHF bands and, according to current thought at least, none at all at UHF and above. Around the time of sunspot maximum and for perhaps a year or two after, there are occasions when maximum usable frequencies exceed 50MHz and cross band working with North American amateurs becomes possible. The most favourable times for transatlantic contacts at 50MHz occur when the solar flux is high and the magnetic index is low, but the required conditions do not persist for long. On 8 February 1979 G3COJ and WB2RLK/VE made the first 28/50MHz transatlantic contact since 1958. On the other hand, when conditions are good, they are often very good. EI2W, the only 50MHz licensed amateur in northern Europe at the time, succeeded in working 40 states of the USA on 50MHz during 1979 - 80. Such contacts are made via the F2 layer. It is unlikely that transmissions above 30MHz would ever be propagated by the regular E layer. In the tropics some occasional periods of activity around noon in maximum sunspot years may be possible, using

Table 3.12: Theoretical performance between good sites under flat conditions.

Frequency (MHz)	Path (dB)	Range (km)	Transmitter power (W)	Noise figure (dB)	Antenna	Antenna gain (dB)
144	240	870	100	3	2 x 16 ele. Yagi	18
432	247	790	100	3	2 x 25 ele. loop Yagi	22
1296	258	760	100	3	2 x 25 ele. loop Yagi	24
2304	262	720	50	3	6 ft dish	31

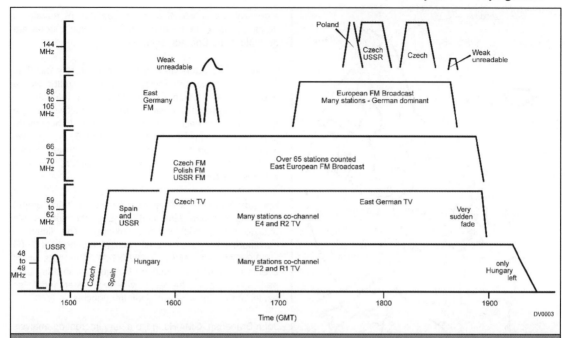

Fig 3.14: Frequency versus time for a major Sporadic E event recorded on June 10th 1980 at GM4IHJ, Saline, Fife

the F1 layer.

The current (2006) European record distance for 50MHz regular F2 layer propagation is 19,921km set by ZL3VTV/1 (RF73KD) and EH7KW (IM67XI) using SSB on 3rd April 2001.

Any propagation at VHF which may take place via the regular layers of the ionosphere will have a very strong dependence on the solar cycle.

Non-regular ionisation

Contacts at VHF and UHF are occasionally possible via ionisation which may take the form of sheets, clouds, mobile curtains or long narrow cylinders. Most of these forms are active around E layer height, but they are not directly associated with the regular layers.

Some effects, those involving the equatorial ionosphere, for example, may take place at F layer levels. The varieties which will be dealt with here are Sporadic E, auroral E, trans-equatorial propagation and meteor scatter.

VHF Sporadic E

As has been mentioned before, there is some question still regarding the nature of VHF sporadic E. The reason is that Sporadic E at HF has been known about and recognised since the earliest days of ionospheric sounding in the 1930s but what radio amateurs refer to as Sporadic E; typically extending to the 144MHz band and

beyond; just does not show up on ionosondes. Even those times when HF Sporadic E does appear on the record it does not display characteristics which would be sufficient to support reflections well into the VHF band (over 200MHz has been reported).

For many years VHF Sporadic E was regarded with scepticism by professionals but its reality has now been accepted, largely due to the weight of evidence provided by amateur observers in a truly international project co-ordinated by the International Amateur Radio Union. For many successive years the co-ordinator, the late Serge Canivenc, F8SH, collected and collated reports from all over Europe to provide day-by-day summaries, which were submitted to CCIR, the International Radio Consultative Committee (now a section of the International Telecommunications Union).

The project is ongoing and the collection of reports showing which paths are open (and when) remains a task ideally suited to amateur observers. There are many groups of amateurs carrying out this task, two of the best places to look at the results are in DUBUS magazine [3] and the DF5AI net [16] run by Dr. Volker Grassmann, DF5AI.

In its conventional form Sporadic E consists of horizontal sheets about 1km thick and some 100km across, usually at a height of 100 - 130km. Clouds form in an apparently random manner, although there is an obvious preference for certain times and seasons. They do not behave consistently for, whereas some sheets may travel across continents for several hundreds of kilometres, others remain almost stationary. It has been claimed that there is

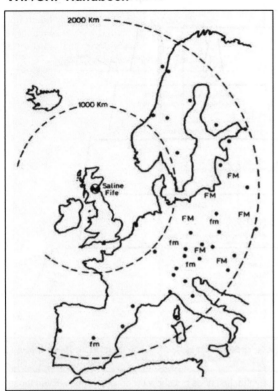

Fig 3.15: Stations received via Sporadic E at GM4IHJ.

a general tendency for them to drift towards the equator at about 80m/s. Both scattering and reflection modes are possible in the Sporadic E layers.

Above 30MHz, paths via E_s ionisation are rarely less than 500km. The maximum single hop range is limited by the geometry of the system to about 2000km and double hop from a single sheet is relatively rare because it would have to exceed 500km across in order to be able to accommodate the two points of reflection. Two hop E_s propagation is more likely from two separate sheets, separated by less than 2000km, when the possible maximum range is extended to 4000km.

Sporadic E at VHF is seasonal, nearly all of it (in Europe) occurring between May and August, although events outside that period are not unknown. The times of maximum activity are generally within the periods of 07:00 – 13:00GMT and 15:00 – 22:00GMT. The duration of events is an inverse function of frequency; that is, for a particular occasion the event will begin later and finish earlier at the higher of two given frequencies.

John Branegan, GM4IHJ, gave a very interesting analysis of the VHF Sporadic E event of 10 June 1980, as observed from Saline, Fife (Fig 3.14). This demonstrated very clearly how the longest opening; over 4½ hours; appeared on a 48 - 49MHz monitor, with progressively shorter periods on each of the other frequency bands

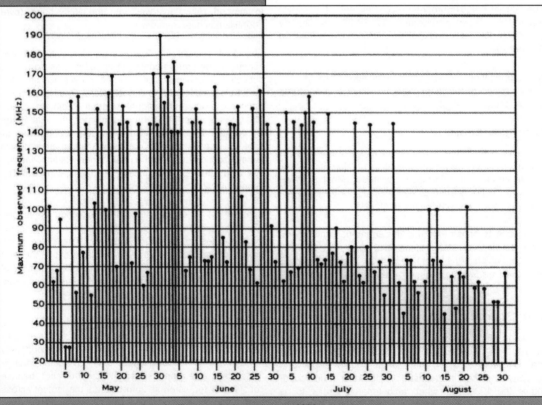

Fig 3.16: VHF Sporadic E activity in Europe during summer 1979.

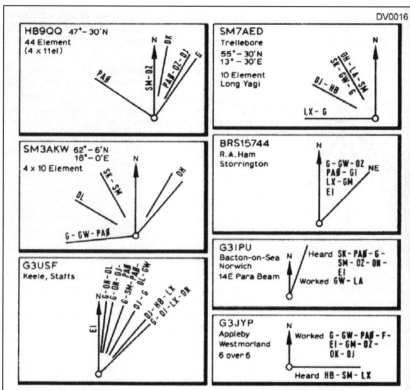

DV0016 Fig 3.17: Beam headings recorded by certain operators during the aurora of 8th March 1970.

checked. At 144MHz the event was confined, for the most part, to half an hour either side of 1800GMT. GM4IHJ had also produced a map showing the location of stations which have been positively identified during E_s openings (Fig 3.15). The symbols 'FM' and 'fm' indicate stations in the 70MHz and 100MHz FM broadcast bands respectively, while black dots are Band I TV stations around 50MHz. It may be seen that all the stations received were between 1000 and 2000km distant.

That being so and, assuming a reflection height of 100 - 130km, the geometry of the path certainly lends support to account for the claimed record distances worked during E_s events (Table 3.9). Clearly, in the case of 70MHz and 144MHz double hop is feasible, though probably not from a single cloud of ionisation. But, in the case of 50MHz, over 8000km in four hops seems to be stretching credibility a mite too far. Yet this report does not stand in isolation. In the DUBUS magazine [3] for the first quarter of 1997, the 50MHz E_s Top List showed claimed distances in excess of 4000km (theoretical double hop) in 36 entries out of a total of 81. If the reason for that is known it does not seem to have received very wide publicity.

The maximum frequency at which Sporadic E has been observed in the European area was found to have been 203MHz, recorded by F8SH on 9 July 1974. It is not known if anyone else has continued his work in routinely seeking a maximum frequency, but it seems certain that 200MHz is reached but rarely and for periods of very short duration.

Several Sporadic E warning nets; some radio, some making use of telephone 'chains'; are in operation in various parts of Europe such as The Dxrobot, Gouda, based in The Netherlands [7]. This web site gives real time information on several types of propagation and can send you an email or SMS when a specific type of opening is occurring. With their help a random network, several hundred amateur stations may get on the air in a very short time. A careful computer analysis of their collected reports, which need consist of no more than time, band, callsigns and QTH locators, is sufficient to provide details of the size, shape and movement of the areas of ionisation responsible.

Amateur auroral studies

The radio aurora at VHF probably represents the field in which radio amateurs can do most to contribute to present knowledge of radio propagation and the behaviour of the high atmosphere under the influence of solar emissions. A co-ordinated network of stations extending over a continent, each station equipped with nothing more complicated than a well maintained receiver and operated by a person able to read and log callsigns, QTH locators and accurate times, can establish the existence and movement of areas of auroral ionisation on a scale that is impossible to achieve by any other means. The addition of steerable antennas and two way communications increase the value of the observations still further, for these enable the location of the auroral reflection point to be established.

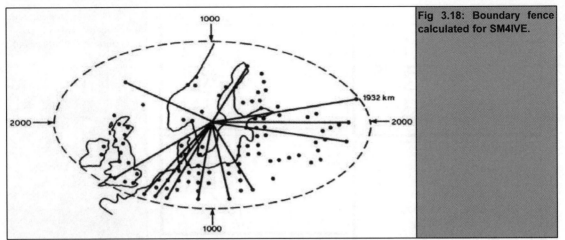

Fig 3.18: Boundary fence calculated for SM4IVE.

The geometry of the path is such that no two pairs of stations will reflect off exactly the same point on the radio auroral curtain so a number of near simultaneous observations from a random network of stations can yield detail of an area of ionisation; it's position relative to the Earth's surface and the direction of its main axis. If the process is continued throughout an auroral event, analysis of successive periods will reveal the motion of the ionisation in both space and time.

Unfortunately the aurora does not present itself as a perfect reflector placed perpendicularly to the surface of the Earth. Its vertical alignment tends to follow the curvature of the geomagnetic field so that a reflection from a relatively low altitude will appear to be above a point on the ground farther north than a reflection at a greater height. The reflection height is a function of the position of the two stations relative to the surface of ionisation, but the vertical and horizontal beam widths of most VHF antennas are such that a large number of alternative paths are possible without change of beam heading, although not necessarily at maximum strength. There is much to be learned from a study of accurate times and bearings of maximum signal taken as near simultaneously as possible from the two ends of a transmission path. Those stations equipped with two axis rotators, such as are used for satellite working, can contribute further by rotating in both azimuth and elevation for maximum signal.

From the foregoing it will be clear that, in general, the beam headings in the horizontal plane depart considerably from the great circle directions between the stations. When amateur auroral studies began in earnest in the 1950s it was commonly supposed that all stations had to beam their signals towards the north in order to make auroral contacts. During the International Quiet Sun Years (1963 - 4), when the GB3LER experimental beacon station was first set up beside the magnetic observatory at Lerwick, the beam direction for auroral studies was set at first towards 10° west of true north and nearly all reports of reception via the aurora came from Scottish stations.

A change was made to 25° east of true north, and this brought in reports from many parts of the Continent. That is not to say that 25° east of true north is an optimum direction, even for Lerwick. It is now known that beam headings can vary considerably during an aurora, and from one aurora to the next. No hard and fast advice can be given on this point, other than to suggest that an occasional complete 360° beam swing during an auroral event may produce results from an unexpected quarter, even when much of the activity appears to be concentrated in one fairly constant direction (Fig 3.17).

Charlie Newton, G2FKZ, who was for many years the IARU co-ordinator for amateur radio auroral studies, has established that, for any given station, there is a well defined area within which auroral contacts are possible, and he has shown that the area is a function of the magnetic field surrounding the Earth. He has called the perimeter of this area the boundary fence and has demonstrated that its shape and extent varies as different locations are considered as origin. As an example, Fig 3.18 shows the boundary fence calculated for SM4IVE (at HT68D); it is approximately elliptical, 2000km from east to west, 1000km from north to south. The large dots on the map indicate the centres of QTH locator lettered squares containing stations heard or worked by SM4IVE via the aurora, the lines are not signal paths; they serve only to indicate the line-of-sight directions and distances to some of the more distant stations. At any particular time during an event only a small part of the area shown will be accessible to SM4IVE, but the audible 'patch' will move during the progress of an aurora and may differ considerably from one aurora to the next, although all the stations worked will lie within the boundary fence. For stations farther east the area of accessibility is larger; for stations to the west and south it is smaller. Stations in Great Britain suffer from the disadvantage that there are no stations within the western half of the boundary fence.

There is a fairly close correlation between the occurrence of radio aurora and the three hourly indices of geomagnetic activity; the greater the magnetic field is disturbed, the further south the event extends. During the Interna-

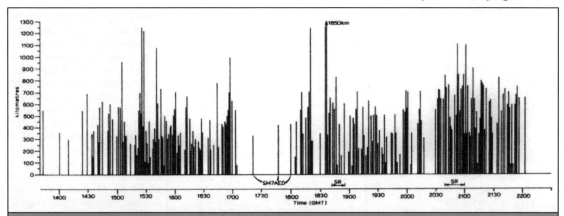

Fig 3.19: Times and distances for all stations heard or worked, based on logs submitted for the 8th March 1970 study. Note the pauses and the bunching of the longer range contacts. The periods marked "SR" indicate when a radar at Sheffield University recorded radio aurora to the north west.

tional Quiet Sun Years attempts were made to relate motions of the visual aurora at Lerwick to aurorally reflected signals from GB3LER as received on the Scottish mainland, but the results suggested that, on a short time scale, the two phenomena behave almost independently, although they must stem from a common cause. At times the visual aurora appeared to the south of Lerwick and forward scatter off the back of the beam was suspected on more than one occasion, although the point was never proved by turning the antenna because it was not accessible enough to be moved at short notice.

A study of pen recordings of signals from GB3LER, via the aurora, to Thurso on the Scottish mainland suggested that it was not the peaks of a geomagnetic disturbance that gave the strongest reflections, but rather the fastest rate of change in the components describing the instantaneous field, as recorded by the observatory magnetoeters.

Every radio auroral event seems to be unique in some respect but there are characteristic patterns that regularly recur. The weaker or diffuse events, which are often only detected by northern stations, move little and slowly. They are often found to relate to minor irregularities on the magnetometer trace, known as bays, when the geomagnetic field deflects for a short while and then gradually resumes its normal diurnal pattern.

An intense auroral event typically opens suddenly with the appearance of signals having a characteristic 'flutter' tone from stations situated to the north or north east. This often occurs in the early afternoon and contacts from European stations 1000km or more distant are likely. After perhaps two to three hours of activity it ceases and many operators unused to the mode may conclude that the event is over. The more knowledgeable stay on watch, and frequently their patience is rewarded by the appearance of a second phase, usually more rewarding than the first. The motion of the active region often follows the same general movement as the first phase, but reaching several hundred kilometres further south. Finally, when the event

seems to have reached a peak, perhaps by late evening, all the activity suddenly ceases as though somebody, somewhere, has 'pulled the big switch' and gone off to bed (Fig 3.19).

Table 3.9 shows the maximum distances which have been worked by auroral reflection on three bands at VHF and two at UHF. It must be pointed out that these distances represent the great circle path between stations, not the path followed by the signals, which is considerably longer.

There is a tendency for a major radio auroral event to recur after an interval of slightly more than 27 days. That is because the event has come about as a result of a disturbance on the Sun, and in that interval an active region has made a complete circuit of the Sun as seen from the Earth, and is in more-or-less the same position again. That position, at the time of the event, is generally about one day past central meridian passage (CMP), or, say, 13° west of the centre of the visible disc.

It is convenient to be able to record the dates of auroral propagation events in some way that links them to the rotations of the Sun. The chart shown in Fig 3.20 does just that. The vertical axis shows longitude on the Sun, L_o, following a sequence begun at Greenwich Observatory nearly 150 years ago. The horizontal axis is, in effect, a measure of where the Earth is around its orbit, passing through 000° at the time of the vernal equinox, 20th or 21st June. The sloping broken lines serve to connect a series of dots, each representing the date on which the indicated longitude, L_o, passed the centre of the disc of the Sun, as seen from the Earth, at 12UT. The sloping lines form a raster such that, if the diagram were to be rolled so as to make the top edge (L_o = 360°) and the bottom edge (L_o = 000°) coincident, they would form one continuous helix.

The chart may be used to record any event suspected of having a connection with events on the Sun. A horizontal trend corresponds to the rotation period of the Sun relative

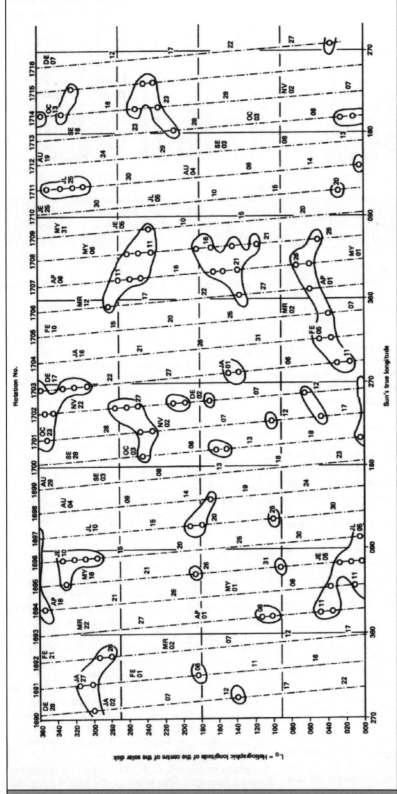

Fig 3.20: Days with reported radio aurora during 1981-2.

to the Earth; a trend of 45° (in the sense bottom left to top right) corresponds to the rotation period of the Sun relative to the stars. Known dates of radio auroral events are currently included in the propagation news section of the GB2RS news bulletin service of the RSGB, and the patterns which emerge provide a useful guide to probable active and quiet periods up to about a month ahead. Fig 3.20, which shows the days when radio aurora was reported by UK stations during 1981 - 2 should be compared with Fig 3.21, which shows the days when the magneto-meters at Lerwick recorded a disturbance of 5 or more on the conventional scale of geomagnetic K units. It will be seen that there is a close relationship between the two patterns and this confirms the usefulness of the Lerwick data when dealing with the analysis of radio auroral events taking place in the region of north-west Europe.

Monitoring auroral propagation

In a contribution to the March 1977 issue of RadCom, Peter Blair, G3LTF, gave practical advice on monitoring distant VHF transmissions, which can be used as a guide to the onset of auroral propagation events on the amateur bands. Many of his remarks were directed towards observers living in the south of England, but his methods were applicable to other locations, provided that suitably placed transmitters can be found. What is required is a signal from a northerly direction in the low VHF region, for this will go auroral before the effects reach 144MHz. These requirements used to be met by one of the Band I BBC TV sound transmitters. There are now 50MHz and 70MHz amateur beacon transmitters which may well serve the purpose. Two which operate at 100W and are suitably placed are GB3LER (IP90JD) on 50.064MHz and GB3ANG (IO86MN) on 70.020MHz.

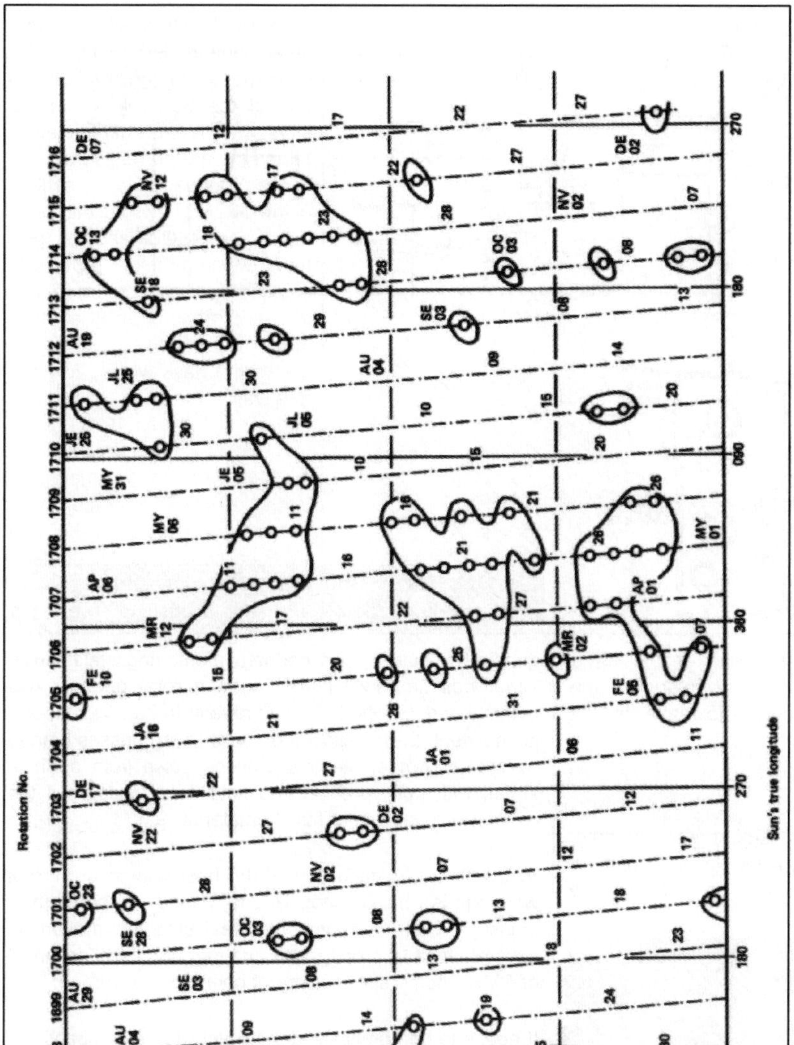

Fig 3.21: Days when Lerwick K figure was five or greater during 1981-2.

The suggested equipment for the aurora monitor is relatively simple. The antenna consists of two elements: radiator 95in by 3/8in, reflector 105in by 3/8in, spacing 30in, mounted 18 to 20ft off the ground, pointing north. This feeds a crystal controlled converter, such as the one shown in Fig 3.22 and Table 3.13, which uses any convenient crystal which will produce an IF of around 7MHz. After alignment in the usual way the circuits should be peaked on the desired signal when the opportunity arises. The two outputs are at around 7MHz; one is intended for a simple fixed frequency receiver, the AGC voltage of which drives a recording meter through a suitable DC amplifier. When correctly tuned, the 144MHz trap prevents the converter from being blocked in the presence of a local transmission.

Fig 3.23 shows the appearance of some typical auroral signal recordings. According to G3LTF a sudden (say within two minutes) onset of the auroral enhancement usually indicates that the effects will reach 144MHz within 10 - 15 minutes. A more gradual onset might herald a delay of up to about 30 minutes. It is rare for the effect not to reach 144MHz at all once it has been detected on the monitor. The equipment may also be used as an indicator for 70MHz but the respective time delays are considerably reduced.

The monitor should be left running during the day from about midday onwards. If you are unable to attend during the afternoon you may come home to find evidence of earlier activity. This should alert you to expect a second phase, and perhaps a third, later on. Where a more-or-less continuous watch is impracticable, the most fruitful times for checking the monitor are mid afternoon, early evening and around 22:00 local time. It should not be overlooked that a broadcast transmitter being monitored

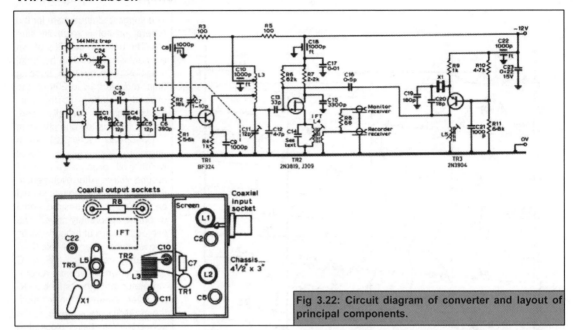

Fig 3.22: Circuit diagram of converter and layout of principal components.

may close down each day at the end of the day's programmes, but this is no real disadvantage of the method as it is unusual for an aurora to make its first appearance after midnight.

Auroral warning networks

In the past, very effective auroral warning networks have been organised, both in this country and on the Continent, using the public telephone systems. The warnings are generally initiated by a northern monitoring station who either has firm evidence that an auroral opening has commenced, or who has good reason to believe that one is imminent. Each recipient of the warning passes it on to at least two other stations, working down from north to south, with built in checks to hold the procedure if the event is a small one or fails to materialise.

At the time of writing one of the best source of auroral warnings is The Dxrobot, Gouda, based in The Netherlands [7]. This web site gives real time information on several types of propagation and can send you an email or SMS when a specific type of opening is occurring.

It needs to be emphasised, however, that the capabilities of the system are such that a large scale aurora can stimulate a level of activity amounting to several hundred transmitters being brought on the air during the early stages of the event. This cannot be matched anywhere outside the Amateur Service and offers a unique opportunity to put the service's talents to good use by doing no more than reporting its successes as soon as possible after the event.

Trans-equatorial propagation

An aspect of research in which radio amateurs can justifiably claim to have played a major part is in the field of trans-equatorial propagation, TE or TEP for short. From its discovery just after the Second World War (between stations in Mexico and Argentina, reported in QST for October 1947) to the present day, amateurs have provided almost all the raw material for subsequent study. Some dedicated operators have spent 30 years or more setting up series of carefully controlled experiments designed to test theories proposed or to provide fresh material for consideration. For a particularly useful survey

Table 3.13: Component list for converter.

C1, C4	6.8pF ceramic	R1	56k
C2, C5	12pF tubular	R2	18k
C11, C24	trimmers	R3, R5	100
C3, C16	0.5pF ceramic	R4, R9	1k
C6	390pF ceramic	R6	82k
C7	1-10pF tubular	R7	2.2k
	trimmer	R8	68
C8, C10	1000pF	R10	4.7k
C18, C22	feedthrough	R11	6.8k
C9, C21	1000pF ceramic		
C12	4.7pF ceramic	All 1/4W or 1/10W carbon	
C13	33pF ceramic		
C14	22pF (to suit IFT L4)		
C15	3300pF disc ceramic	TR1	BF324
C17	0.01µF 15v	TR2	2N3819, J309
C19	180pF ceramic	TR3	2N3904
C20	18pF ceramic		
C23	0.22µF 15v		
L1	10t 3/8in ID 18 SWG enamelled wire, close wound, tapped 2t up		
L2	As L1 but tapped 4t up		
L3	11t 3/8in ID 18 SWG enamelled wire, close wound, tapped at 1t and 5t from cold end		
L4	IF transformer appropriate to crystal chosen		
L5	6t 20 SWG on 1/4in slug tuned former (for 65MHz crystal)		
L6	9t 1/4in ID spaced wire diameter		

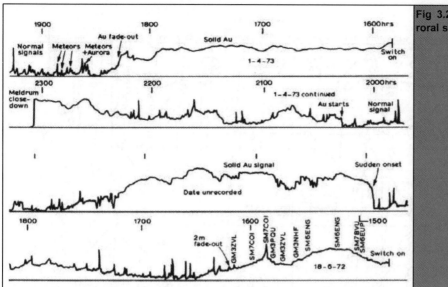

Fig 3.23: Some typical auroral signal recordings.

of progress to date of circuits between Europe and southern Africa, reference should be made to [7]. Some of the areas of the world which have contributed to the present knowledge of the mode are shown in Fig 3.24, where it will be seen that a prime requirement appears to be that the transmission path shall have the magnetic zero dip equator (a) approximately at its midpoint and (b) nearly normal to it. The placing of the KP4/ZD8 path with respect to the change of direction of the zero dip line over the Atlantic Ocean area is particularly interesting evidence in support of requirement (b).

The mode was first observed on 50MHz. Subsequent work has used 28, 50, 144 and 432MHz. During years of high sunspot activity the reliability of a TE path is considerable. On 50MHz the peak time during an opening was found to be 18:45 - 19:00. At 144MHz, using 100W RF into 16 element long Yagis, openings between Europe and southern Africa have lasted for up to two hours, centred on 20:00 local time in Cyprus; high solar flux and low geomagnetic activity seem essential. Detrimental effects of geomagnetic storms are less evident at 50 and

28MHz than at 144MHz. Fig 3.25 shows the days on which TE signals were observed at 144MHz, plotted on a solar rotation base map, which reveals some tendency towards 27 day recurrences, particularly around the time of the equinoxes. On the American paths, peak occurrences at the equinoxes were noted.

On the Zimbabwe/Cyprus path there was a decline at that time, thought by ZE2JV and 5B4WR to be a peculiarity of the path connected in some way with the southern Africa magnetic anomaly which gives rise to high dip angles at the southern end.

The previous record distance, for a TEP contact, of just under 8,000km was doubled to 16,920km on 8th April 2001 by IK0FTA and KH8/N5OLS.

Fading and chopping occur on the signals at rates which increase with transmission frequency. Slow chopping on 28 and 50MHz sometimes makes it almost impossible to read Morse code. At 144MHz the chopping rate is much faster, making the signal sound rough with an apparent

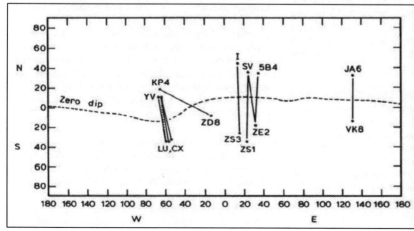

Fig 3.24: Areas of the world where trans-equatorial propagation has been observed.

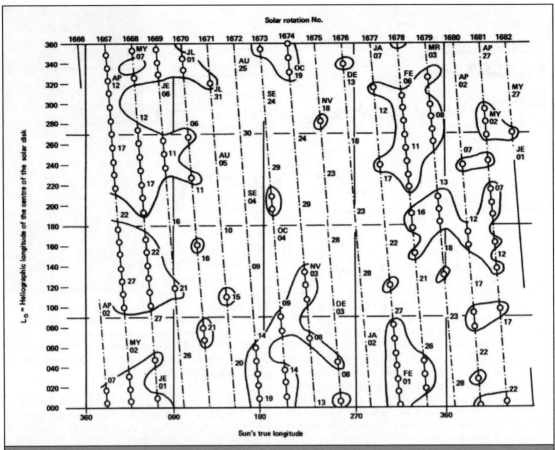

Fig 3.25: Trans-equatorial propagation. Reception of ZE2JV by 5B4WR (144.166MHz), 16:30 - 19:00 GMT between 1st April and 31st May 1978.

raw AC note. Frequency spreading has been observed to 2kHz or more. The character of the signals may change considerably from day to day and from hour to hour in a random manner. Under the best of conditions 144MHz SSB is just intelligible. At other times the spread is so wide and the flutter is so rapid that no beat note can be obtained with the received signal, which then appears merely as a change in the background noise. At 432MHz the Zimbabwe beacon operated by ZE2JV was heard in Athens by SV1DH and SV1AB between 18:16 and 18:30GMT on 20 March 1979, and on 13 May 1979 by 5B4WR. Their comments were that the signals were rougher than on 144MHz and spreading more in frequency.

Time delay measurements made in both directions along the Zimbabwe/Cyprus circuit showed afternoon intervals which at times corresponded with two hop F2 layer propagation, but evening delays took about 10% longer, which may have been due to an extra ray path distance of some 600km each way, or was in some way a function of the propagation mechanism. There appears to be no difference in delay time between 28MHz and 144MHz TE; although the character of the received signals differ on account of differences in fading rate.

Table 3.9 shows the European distance records for trans-equatorial propagation as they stood in the middle of 2006. The mode does not normally extend into UHF.

Meteor trail propagation

Propagation is also possible on an intermittent basis by means of scatter from short lived trails of ionisation which appear as a result of small particles of solid matter entering the Earth's atmosphere and becoming heated to incandescence by friction. They are usually accompanied by streaks of light, popularly known as 'shooting stars'. These meteors (strictly the term applies only to the visible streak, although most writers use it as though it refers to the object itself) fall into two general classes, shower meteors, which follow definite and predictable orbits, and sporadic meteors, which follow individual paths and are present at all times.

Both the ionisation and the visual display occur simultaneously at heights of around 85 to 120km. Most of the objects responsible are no bigger than a grain of sand and they burn up completely in the upper atmosphere. Occasionally larger ones survive the descent and examples of some which have reached the ground are to be seen in museums, where they are referred to as meteorites.

Table 3.14: Calendar of the main meteor showers.

Start	Dates of Maximum	End	Name	Comparative rate +	Transit Time	Transit Elevation
Jan 01	Jan 03	Jan 06	Quadrantids	6	09	90
Apr 19	Apr 21	Apr 24	April Lyrids	3	04	70
May 01	May 05	May 08	Eta Aquarids	3	08	40
Jun 10	Jun 16	Jun 21	June Lyrids	2	01	70
Jun 17	Jun 20	Jun 26	Ophiuchids	2	23	20
Jul 10	Jul 26	Aug 15	Capricornids	2	01	20
Jul 15	Jul 27	Aug 15	Delta Aquarids	4	02	30
Jul 15	Jul 31	Aug 20	Pisces Australids	2	02	10
Jul 15	Jul 30	Aug 25	Alpha Capricornids	2	00	30
Jul 15	Aug 06	Aug 25	Iota Aquarids	2	01	30
Jul 25	Aug 12	Aug 18	Perseids	5	06	80*
Aug 19	Aug 21	Aug 22	Chi Cygnids	1	21	90
Oct 16	Oct 21	Oct 26	Orionids	4	04	50
Oct 20	Nov 08	Nov 30	Tauids	3	01	60
Nov 07	Nov 09	Nov 11	Cepheids	2	20	80*
Nov 15	Nov17	Nov 19	Leonids	2	06	60
Dec 07	Dec 14	Dec 15	Geminids	5	02	70
Dec 17	Dec 22	Dec 24	Ursids	1	08	60*

+ Each step on the comparative rate scale represents a factor of 2.
* Above northern horizon.

Numbers vary during the year from a maximum in July to a minimum in February, with a ratio of about 4:1. There is a marked diurnal variation, due to the combined motions of the Earth's rotation and its movement around the Sun, leading to a maximum at 06:00 local time and a minimum at 18:00.

The initial trail of ionisation is in the form of a long, thin, pencil like cylinder, perhaps 15 to 20km in length. As soon as it is formed it begins to expand radially and to move with the various motions of the air through which it passes. The length of time when the trail is capable of supporting communication is generally very short, often less than a second, although longer persistences of a minute or more occur from time to time. The durations (and the frequency of occurrence) decrease with increase in signal frequency.

Considerations of phase coherence lead to an aspect sensitivity which favours radiation meeting the trail axis at right angles. Because of this only a small part of any trail acts as a reflector and the orientation of the trail relative to the antennas is of considerable importance because it determines the height and position of the main reflection point. Meeting the right angle requirement from both ends of a transmission path demands that the trail must lie in such a way that it is tangential to an ellipsoid of revolution having transmitter and receiver antennas at the focal points, and if ionisation is to result this condition has to be met at a level which is within 80 and 120km above the ground. It follows that large numbers of meteors enter the Earth's atmosphere along paths which can never satisfy the tangent condition within the prescribed limits of height and in consequence do not contribute to propagation along a given path.

These requirements suggest that it is unwise to direct very narrow beam transmitting and receiving antennas (to be used for meteor scatter work) along the strict line-of-sight between the stations. The only trails which can be tangential to the ellipsoid of revolution in that direction are those lying parallel to the ground, and this is an unlikely attitude to be taken up by a solid body entering the Earth's atmosphere from interplanetary space. The most likely beam directions lie a few degrees to one side or the other of the direct transmission path (both antennas must be deflected towards the same side, of course), and the optimum headings may have to be determined by careful experiment. Where the antennas are less directional the great circle path between stations may be found to give best results. Because little is likely to be received along the direct path heading, the acceptance angles of the antennas may be wide enough to include the longer but more likely paths on both sides.

The short bursts of signal which result from MS (meteor scatter) can best be observed on stations situated 1000 to 2000km away. In southern England several hundred examples per hour used to be heard carrying signals from the 40kW FM broadcast transmitter at Gdansk, Poland on 70.31MHz.

Table 3.9 shows the European VHF and UHF distance records by meteor scatter in the middle of 2006. It is interesting to note that the records are often set on the same date (but in different years) for each of the four bands. August 12 is the date on which the Perseids shower reaches a peak.

A very detailed treatment of the subject was published in the February 1975 issue of RadComm, under the title 'VHF meteor scatter propagation'. In it J D V Ludlow, GW3ZTH, has given details of suitable equipment for receiving and recording signals propagated by this mode, and has provided a practical method of calculating beam headings and optimum times in respect of particular showers. For those wishing to follow up the relevant theory there is a very useful list of 25 references in the article. The other good sources of information on Meteor scatter propagation are, The Propagation Studies Committee of The RSGB [13] and DF5AI Net, Amateur Radio Propagation Studies [16].

Table 3.14 gives a summary of the main meteor showers likely to be of use to stations in the northern hemisphere. Full details, including times of transit and the directions from which the trails appear to radiate (an effect of perspective) appear on The British Astronomical Association web site under the meteor section [9]. DUBUS magazine [3] also has a list of the meteor showers for the following 3 months in each quarterly magazine.

Commercial use is made of meteor scatter propagation, particularly at high latitudes where it provides a hedge against the effects of polar cap absorption. The best known system is the Janet Project of the Canadian Defence Research Board, which is described by G W L Davis and others in Proceedings of the IRE December 1957. Another, and later, application of the technique was seen in the 'Snonet' meteorological meteor burst system for collecting observations from remote sensors. Information recorded on magnetic tape at normal speed was played back (and transmitted) in the form of high speed bursts when a monitor on a slightly different frequency showed that a path was open.

In more recent times the availability of satellite channels has weakened the attraction of meteor scatter for commercial data communications. On the amateur bands, however, interest continues to grow and very detailed logs from stations all over Europe appear in every quarterly issue of the German DUBUS magazine [3]. For example, issue 3/96 contained 15 closely packed pages of reports, followed by two pages of operating procedures for meteor scatter QSOs, as adopted by IARU, Region 1. It is a very useful source of data for research purposes.

Two other similar propagation modes are popular with radio amateurs, these are lightning scatter and aircraft trail, a discussion of both can be found on the DF5AI net [16].

Satellite propagation experiments

A number of amateurs have suggested propagation experiments using satellites in ways that were not envisaged as part of the basic projects.

Pat Gowen, G3IOR, made use of Oscar 7 and Oscar 8 in its Mode A transponder configuration (145MHz up, 29MHz down) as a guide to conditions on 144MHz. Good tropospheric conditions were indicated by severe attenuation of one's own returned signal, with deep and rapid fading when the satellite was just above the horizon. Brief and rapid 'pop-ups' of signal before and after predicted times of access were caused by scintillation of 144MHz uplink as it passed through tropospheric ducts. Sporadic E

effects were similar, but they may have taken place at quite high elevations. Fading suggested the presence of multiple diffraction paths in the ionosphere. Aurora caused marked degradation of tone on returned signals from some of the northern stations, often specific to small areas.

This topic was brought into prominence in connection with 136MHz aircraft-to-satellite-to-ground communications, 250MHz military satellite applications and global positioning systems working around 1.2 to 1.6MHz. (See, for example a paper by Dr J Aarons in IEE Conference Publication No 411.)

John Branegan, GM4IHJ, kept a regular check on where satellite scintillation occurred on polar paths and used it to define the instantaneous location of the auroral oval to provide an estimate of the total electron content along the satellite line of sight. In this way, very high electron densities were observed at heights above the normal 110km auroral reflection zone, considered capable of scattering frequencies of up to at least 250MHz. GM4IHJ, G3IOR and several Alaskan stations all heard double signals on 144MHz satellite transmissions, the second signal some 750Hz from the nominal frequency, sometimes with an auroral tone.

G4DGU and SM6CKU investigated the idea of using a large low orbit satellite as a passive reflector. The relevant theory suggested that the total path length loss might be about 10dB better than moonbounce. There were problems; low orbit satellite orbits soon decay and they could not be predicted with accuracy. There were very high Doppler shifts involved. At 432MHz signals are likely to appear first 12kHz high, shifting down at about 1kHz per second to become 12kHz low, six to eight seconds later, when signals disappear. Despite these difficulties, however, a four second burst of SSB from G4DGU had been received by SM6CKU, 10dB over noise, off a Cosmos third stage launcher. The transmitter used was of 400W PEP into an array of eight 17 element Yagis. The receiver had been coupled to an 8m dish.

Solar/geophysical connections

Precursors

The relationship between events on the Sun and the associated effects in the Earth's ionosphere has been dealt with at length in the propagation chapter of the Radio Communication Handbook. Suffice it to record here that the main solar events of interest to VHF and UHF operators are solar flares, radio bursts and emissions of high-energy protons. Solar flare effects appear in three time scales. Within about eight minutes of a major flare suitably placed on the Sun, electromagnetic radiation brings about increased D region ionisation, sudden cosmic noise absorption (SCNA), short wave fadeout phenomena (SWF), sudden phase anomaly of ELF signals (SPA), sudden enhancement of atmospherics at LF (SEA), sudden frequency deviation at LF (SFD), and noise bursts (not all of these will be detected in one particular

Table 3.15 Solar rotation calendar, 2004 - 2010.

2004		2005		2006		2007		2008		2009		2010	
2012	JA13	2025	JA02	2039	JA18	2052	JA08	2066	JA25	2079	JA13	2092	JA01
2013	FE09	2026	JA29	2040	FE15	2053	FE04	2067	FE21	2080	FE10	2093	JA30
2014	MR08	2027	FE25	2041	MR14	2054	MR04	2068	MR20	2081	MR09	2094	FE26
2015	AP04	2028	MR25	2042	AP10	2055	MR31	2069	AP16	2082	AP05	2095	MR25
2016	MY01	2029	AP21	2043	MY08	2056	AP27	2070	MY13	2083	MY03	2096	AP22
2017	MY28	2030	MY18	2044	JE04	2057	MY24	2071	JE09	2084	MY30	2097	MY20
2018	JE25	2031	JE14	2045	JL01	2058	JE21	2072	JL06	2085	JE26	2098	JE16
2019	JL22	2032	JL11	2046	JL28	2059	JL18	2073	AU03	2086	JL23	2099	JL13
2020	AU18	2033	AU08	2047	AU25	2060	AU14	2074	AU30	2087	AU20	2100	AU09
2021	SE14	2034	SE04	2048	SE21	2061	SE10	2075	SE26	2088	SE16	2101	SE05
2022	OC12	2035	OC01	2049	OC18	2062	OC08	2076	OC23	2089	OC13	2102	OC03
2023	NV08	2036	OC28	2050	NV14	2063	NV04	2077	NV20	2090	NV09	2103	OC30
2024	DE05	2037	NV25	2051	DE12	2064	DE01	2078	DE17	2091	DE07	2104	NV26
		2038	DE22			2065	DE29					2105	DE24

The rotation numbers follow Carrington's series. The quoted date shows the first day on which a new rotation value of L_0 appears at 12UT.

event). Within an hour of the appearance of the flare, high energy corpuscular radiation is likely to cause polar cap absorption (PCA) of anything from 20 minutes to 20 hours duration, which may extend to VHF. Some 20 - 40 hours after the flare, low energy corpuscular radiation brings about magnetic storms, ionospheric storms and auroras, which may persist for more than a day.

The probability that this chain of events will lead to a magnetic storm and an aurora is greatest when the solar activity occurs when the region concerned is near, but slightly beyond, the central meridian.

There is a tendency for solar events to recur after periods of approximately 27 days, as has been discussed in connection with auroral propagation. Table 3.15 shows the starting dates of all solar rotations between 2004 and 2010 calculated in continuation of Carrington's photo heliographic series, using a method described by the Belgian amateur astronomer Jean Meeus in the journal Ciel et Terre.

Solar and geophysical data

There still remains much to be learned about the relationship between events on the Sun, their corresponding effect on the Earth's magnetic field and VHF/UHF radio propagation via the ionosphere as in sporadic E, auroral E and other similar 'openings' on the amateur bands. This is an interesting field for individual research but it requires access to basic solar and geophysical data. Three useful sources are suggested here.

The first, the easiest to obtain, is supplied by the brief summary of solar and magnetic trends over the previous week, together with a forecast covering the week to come, which is compiled from authoritative sources and included each week in the RSGB GB2RS news bulletin. These are transmitted according to a schedule published regularly in RadCom or available on The RSGB web site [11]. The summaries are compiled by Neil Clarke, G0CAS, who also edits a monthly 16 page booklet, which he calls SunMag

[10], containing tables of relevant data, together with graphs and diagrams, as appropriate. An explanation of the terms used may be obtained by post from RSGB Headquarters or through the RSGB Web Page [11].

The second source of information is by far the most detailed is to be found in the publication 'The Weekly', produced in the USA by the Environmental Data Service of the National Oceanic and Atmospheric Administration (NOAA) [12]. This is available in pdf format for each week from 1997 and include daily values of K_p, C_i, C_p, A_i, and other magnetic data, including an inferred interplanetary magnetic field indication derived from satellite observations.

The third source ought to have been the data broadcaster GAM1, which was to have been operated by the Amateur Service to provide daily messages containing various solar and geophysical information obtained from 'official' sources, such as Meudon Observatory, Paris, and Boulder, Colorado. Table 3.16 shows the format of summary messages that used to be available 'over the air' (but no longer, unfortunately). It will serve here to indicate the type of information it was hoped to cover. After years of trying it now seems that we cannot get the authorities to allow the service to go ahead in the way we had hoped. All was not lost, because this information and much more is available from The Propagation Studies Committee of The RSGB [13]. This is a wealth of information on all aspects of propagation.

The June 1997 issue of RadCom carried a reference to Solar Warning and Real time Monitor (SWARM) software, over the years this has become Space Weather Information Monitor (SWIM) [14] which provides current real time solar and geomagnetic data.

Geomagnetic data

Solar events and associated ionospheric disturbances are of less direct interest to the VHF/UHF operator than are geomagnetic variations, which correlate well with auroral events and, though to a lesser extent, with E_s and TE.

Table 3.16: Format of a typical GEOALERT message.

```
GEOALERT CCCNN DDHHMMZ
9HHDD 1SSSG 2FFFB 3AAAE 4//// 5MMXX
QXXYY nnijk (QXXYY nnijk . . .)
(Plain-language details of major optical
flares and tenflares)
8hhdd 7777C QXXYY degree of activity . . .
(Plain-language forecast of activity)
SOLALERT JJ/KK MAGALERT JJ/KK
```

Note: There is no fixed length to a GEOALERT message, groups being repeated as often as necessary.

Key

CCCNN	Originating centre (MEU = Meudon, WWA = Boulder); serial number of message
DDHHMMZ	Date and time of origin of message; Z = GMT.
9HHDD	Indicates that various daily indices follow, for 24 hours ending at HH hours on DD day of month.
1 SSSG	Indicates sunspot number, SSS, and number of new groups observed, G.
2FFFB	Indicates 2800MHz solar flux value FFF, and number of important bursts.
3AAAE	Indicates geomagnetic activity, AAA = A_k value; E = events (0 = no events, 1 = end of magnetic storm, 2 = storm in progress, 6 = gradual storm commencement, 7 = sudden storm commencement, 8 = very pronounced sudden storm commencement).
4////	Indicates cosmic ray data (not used on Meudon message).
5MMXX	Indicates flare counts: MM = daily total of M flares, XX = daily total of X flares.

Then follow groups identifying active regions on the Sun:

QXXYY	Q = Quadrant of the Sun (1 = NE, 2 = SE, 3 = SW, 4 = NW), XX = degrees of longitude, YY = degrees of latitude, relative to the centre of the Sun's visible disc.
nnijk	nn = total number of flares in active region indicated; i = number of flares greater than importance 1; j = number of M flares; k = number of X flares (in region QXXYY).
8hhdd	Indicates 24-hour forecast follows, starting at hh hours on dd day of month.
7777C	Indicator, C = types of observation used in forecast (1 = solar radio, 2 = partial solar optical, 3 = optical and radio, 4 = all, plus solar magnetic measurements).
QXXYY	Positions on the Sun, coded as before.
JJ/KK	Days of month between which the solar or magnetic alerts apply

Table 3.17: K figures for Lerwick.

0	0 to 10	5	140 to 240
1	0 to 20	6	240 to 400
2	20 to 40	7	400 to 640
3	40 to 80	8	640 to 1000
4	80 to 140	9	1000 or more

who take part in the Society's auroral observation work, which forms an important part of its Propagation Studies programme.

The terrestrial magnetic field at the Earth's surface is not constant, but is subject to both long term and short term variations in intensity ranging from periods of centuries or more to hours, minutes or even less. The transient variations are small in comparison to the total field; they are measured in gammas, which are equal to 10^{-5} gauss, the force being determined in terms of three components mutually at right angles, either in the directions X (geographic north), Y (east) and Z (vertically downward), or H (horizontal intensity), D (declination) and Z.

The main variometers at Lerwick record H, D and Z photographically on a sheet of sensitised paper approximately 40cm by 30cm, on which all three traces appear side-by-side, together with timing marks every five minutes, and suitable baselines. The present sensitivities are such that H changes of 3.45 gamma, D changes of 0.94 minutes of arc (corresponding to 4 gamma at right angles to the meridian) and Z changes of 4.35 gamma move their respective traces by 1mm. A system of prisms ensures that any trace which approaches the edge of its section of the chart appears again from the other side, thereby extending the effective width so as to be able to handle the widest excursions.

The traces exhibit two features, one a fairly regular diurnal 'background' change due to solar and lunar effects, the other a superimposed irregular, and often violent, variation, the extent of which depends on particle radiation from the Sun. It is necessary to examine initially a large number of traces obtained during magnetically quiet periods in order to be able to assess the appearance of the 'normal' diurnal curve, which has the form of a shallow letter 'S' on its side, and allowance has to be made for season, solar flare effects and certain decreases which follow a magnetic storm. The sum of the highest positive and negative departures from the 'normal' curve are converted into a quasi-logarithmic scale of K figures, where the actual values for the lower limit of each number vary from one observatory to another depending on the magnetic latitude. For Lerwick the scale is given in Table 3.17.

At other observatories the ranges are proportional, and may be found from the value assigned for the lower limit of K = 9, which will be quoted as being either 300, 350, 500, 600, 750, 1000, 1200, 1500 or 2000 gamma.

Using this K scale, the degree of activity is described for each directional component of the force during 8 three

These are comparisons which fall within the scope and capabilities of interested radio amateurs, but many find it difficult to extract the necessary elementary information from conventional manuals on the subject.

In the studies carried out on auroral propagation by the RSGB the region of interest is admirably represented by a knowledge of the performance of the magnetometers at Lerwick Observatory, Shetland, which location, at over 60° north latitude, often experiences spectacular displays of visual aurora. Valuable experience was gained there during the International Quiet Sun Years, 1963 - 4, when the GB3LER beacon transmitters were set up nearby and direct comparison of results against the magnetometer records became possible. The remainder of this section is intended to provide an introduction to the subject to those

hourly periods of each day, and the highest of the three numbers for each period are grouped in two sets of four digits, separated by Greenwich noon, beginning with the period 00:00 to 03:00 GMT.

A combination of K figures from 12 widely spaced observatories (of which Lerwick is one) results in the planetary K index, K_p, prepared monthly by the Committee on Characterisation of Magnetic Disturbances at the University of Göttingen, Germany, which is often preferred to single station data in analytical work, particularly in connection with the ionosphere or when purely local effects are unwanted. The normal 0 to 9 scale is expanded into one of thirds by the addition of suffixes, e.g. 2-, 2o, 2+, 3-, 3o, 3+ . . .

A daily magnetic character figure, C, has been in use for over half a century, each observatory subscribing a figure descriptive of their assessment of the day's activity: 0 if it was judged quiet, 1 if it was moderately disturbed or 2 if it was very disturbed. The individual figures are rarely used, but an index C_i, the average to one decimal place of C figures from a worldwide network of collaborating observatories, provides a convenient classification of daily activity. Another, apparently similar, character figure, C_p, is prepared directly from the K_p indices but, although its derivation is so different, it rarely differs from C_i by more than 0.2. To simplify machine tabulation the scales are sometimes expressed in terms of yet another, known as C_9, which uses whole numbers from 0 to 9 in place of the decimal range from 0.0 to 2.5.

The sum and arithmetic mean of the 8 three hourly K figures provide further expressions of daily activity which are simple and convenient to obtain. They are not ideal, however, because the K scale is a logarithmic one (as is the decibel scale), and the arithmetic average gives the logarithm of the geometric mean and not the logarithm of the arithmetic mean. To take an extreme example, consider the two series 1111 1111 and 0000 0008, both of which give a sum of 8 and a mean of 1; the first would be representative of a quiet day, whereas the second would be considered a highly disturbed day. For this reason it is preferable to turn each K index back into an equivalent range, a_k, on a linear scale, by using the corresponding values:

K	0	1	2	3	4	5	6	7	8	9
a_k	0	3	7	15	27	48	80	140	240	400

which may be summed and meaned arithmetically to represent activity over a period. It should be noted that the same table used for all observatories, irrespective of their actual K scales so that the resulting standardised figures are not the true gamma ranges, although those may be approximated from them, if required, by the use of a factor (which in the case of Lerwick is 4). The daily amplitude A_k is the average of the eight values of a_k for the day. In the case of the two examples cited above as leading to the same K figure sum, the first, 1111 1111, gives an A_k of 3, whereas the second, 0000 0008, produces an A_k of 30,

thereby reflecting the vastly differing states of activity.

A similar, but expanded, scale relates the planetary three hour index K_p to the three hourly equivalent planetary amplitude, a_p:

K_p	0o	0+	1-	1o	1+	2-	2o	2+	3-	3o	3+	4-	4o	4+	5-
a_p	0	2	3	4	5	6	7	9	12	15	1	22	27	32	39

K_p	5o	5+	6-	6o	6+	7-	7o	7+	8-	8o	8+	9-	9o
a_p	48	56	67	80	94	111	132	154	179	207	236	300	400

The daily equivalent planetary amplitude, A_p, is the average of the eight values of a_p for the day.

Accurate time recording

When selected frequencies need to be monitored for propagation studies, some form of recording is essential so that the operator can attend to more productive things. It also results in a semi permanent set of observations which can be transcribed and analysed as and when convenient.

Stereo cassette recorders provide a useful method of recording. The machines are relatively cheap because they are mass produced and, as the tapes may be used again and again, running costs are low, particularly when compared with pen recorders using paper charts. The stereo facility provides the user with two synchronised (but entirely independent) channels, one of which may be used for signal data, the other for timing signals originating from one of the standard time and frequency radio transmissions.

For some purposes it is sufficient to record no more than the presence of the selected signal at a known time and for this the recorder may be connected to the output of the receiver in the conventional way. When an indication of the signal strength is required it is advisable to use some form of voltage-to-frequency or analogue-to-digital conversion before recording from either the AGC line or a special detector giving a suitable time constant. This avoids the effects of differences between recording and playback, including the quality of the tape, from affecting the measurements.

Sometimes, to make more effective use of tape and to simplify the task of data reduction, discontinuous recording may be adopted. This can take the form of sampling, where, say, five minutes in every hour are transferred to tape and the transport mechanism is halted between times, or by causing the tape to stop automatically in the absence of signals for more than a selected period. Both of these practices complicate the provision of radio time signals from the best known sources, such as those which share 2.5, 5, 10 and 15MHz, because only minute and second intervals are available with no indication of absolute time.

MSF, Rugby, on 60kHz, carries time every minute in the form of a 0.5 second burst of pulse code modulation

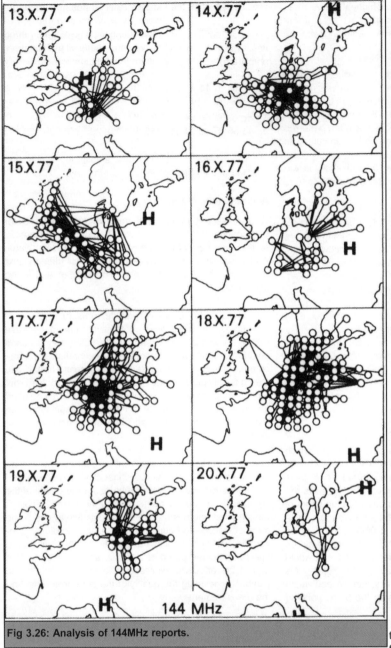

Fig 3.26: Analysis of 144MHz reports.

Finally, if you are using a computer as a real time logging device, or to sample signal strengths through a suitable interface, then the internal clock is, or should be, a useful source that may be accessed along with the incoming data. But check it against a source known to be accurate before you rely on it.

Amateur networks and further research

It is hoped that the preceding pages of this chapter will have left the reader with the feeling that there is still much to be learned about radio propagation at VHF and UHF and that organised groups of amateurs are particularly well placed to further our understanding of the physical processes involved in almost every mode other than direct line of sight.

There may never have been such an opportune time to put forward fresh evidence of the extent to which guidance given by such authorities as ITU and URSI to intending users of frequencies above 30MHz seriously underestimates the range and frequency coverage of the various modes in this part of the spectrum. The professionals acknowledge that such discrepancies exist and are looking to the Amateur Service for raw material that will help to bring present theory more into line with what is happening in the world outside.

There is a continuing need for long term studies of over-the-horizon transmission paths, particularly those involving beacons. This type of work demands a degree of involvement that can be expected from only a very few individual amateurs, although it provides a very interesting project for a club, particularly one associated with an educational establishment, provided that continuity may be assured over long holiday periods and there is sufficient overall supervision to maintain the stability and calibration of the equipment.

immediately before the minute indicator to which it refers. This could be recorded, together with successive one second 'ticks' on one channel of a stereo recorder.

Nowadays very accurate time is a very cheap commodity. An analogue clock with a built in decoder locked by radio to an atomic standard may be bought for under £25 from one of the big radio and electrical component chain stores.

For rapid access to a reliable time source try any teletext page from a terrestrial television station.

Enough has been written already to show the value of studies which make use of a very high volume of simple reports from stations covering a large area. The mere fact that contact was made on a specified band, at a certain

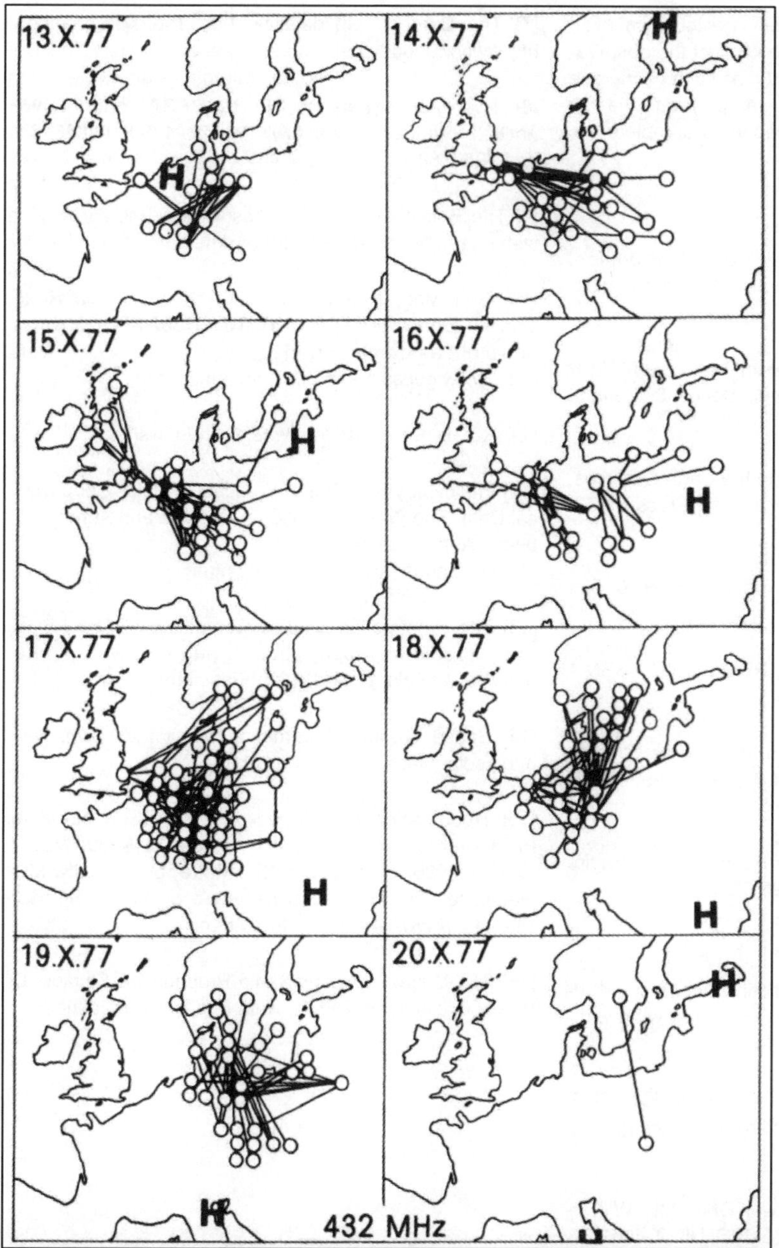

Fig 3.27: Analysis of 432MHz reports.

known that reporting amateurs were active in most parts of Europe during the whole of the period shown, and nearly all of them were within the boundaries of a very large anticyclone for a large proportion of the time, yet only a certain well defined area was experiencing long range anomalous propagation at any one time. That area is shown in the original paper to be where the steep gradient boundary has formed between air of low refractive index, over air of high refractive index. Although subsidence is present elsewhere the sharp boundary is not present either because the turbulence in the lower atmosphere is too weak, allowing the low refractive index air to reach ground level, or too strong, causing mixing at the interface and a consequent weakening of the gradient.

Observe how, in the course of the event, the centre of the anticyclone, marked with a letter 'H', moves from day to day, and how the axis of the really long range paths rotates so as to maintain a broadside on aspect relative to it. These paths form a chord across the curvature of the isobars (which had to be omitted from the diagrams in order to simplify them). In the last two maps the change in direction due to the approach of a fresh centre is of interest.

Another conclusion to be drawn from the maps is that the area of enhancement is approximately the same at both frequencies, although the two sets of reports used are entirely independent of one another. Individual path lengths differed within the area, however, being roughly half as far again at 144MHz as compared to 432MHz.

time, between two stations identified by callsign and QTH locator, is of little more than passing interest to either of the operators concerned. But when hundreds of such reports are collected and processed a powerful research tool emerges, and one, moreover, that is peculiar to the Amateur Service. As an example of the capabilities of this technique, consider Figs 3.26 and 3.27, which were included in an IEE Conference paper referred of signal strengths and ranges attainable using tropospheric propagation. The two sets of maps resulted from an analysis of many hundreds of individual reports, most of them collected in Germany by the DUBUS [3] organisation. It is

It should be clear that these techniques, which require no more from operators than the reporting of contacts that may well have had nothing to do with propagation research in themselves, have enormous potential, not only in tropospheric propagation studies, but in VHF Sporadic E and auroral E studies as well. It should be noted, however, that reports of bearings from both ends of the path are an important requisite of the latter.

It is only because of the truly international nature of

amateur radio and the seemingly tireless enthusiasm of so many people, not the least those who collect the observations and make them available for studies such as the one described, that this technique can be employed to the full. Your reports may be the ones needed to complete the task.

Bibliography

Radio Communication Handbook, Ed D Biddulph, G8DPS, 6th edn, RSGB, 1994, Chapter 11 – Propagation. ISBN 1 872309 24 0.

'Effects of the troposphere on radiocommunication', M P M Hall, IEE Electromagnetic Waves, Series 8, London 1980.

Understanding the Earth: a Reader in the Earth Sciences, Ed I G Gass and others, Open University Press, 1972. SBN 85141 308 0.

Auroral Physics, C-I Meng and others. ISBN 0 521 380499.

Radio Auroras, C Newton, G2FKZ, RSGB, 1991. ISBN 1 872309 03 8.

Meteorology Today: An Introduction to Weather, Climate and Environment, C Donald Ahrem, 5th edn, 1994. ISBN 0 314 02779 3.

Meteorology – The Atmosphere in Action, Joe H Eagleman, 2nd edn, 1980. ISBN 1 877696 05 6.

References

[1] European Meteorological Bulletin, http://www.dwd-shop.de/index.html?http://www.dwd-shop.de/gb/0095.en.html

[2] Met Office, FitzRoy Road, Exeter, Devon, EX1 3PB, Tel: +44 (0)1392 884841, email: metlib@metoffice.gov.uk, web: http://www.metoffice.gov.uk/

[3] DUBUS magazine, Roger Blackwell GM4PMK, Willowbank, Pennyghael, Isle of Mull, PA70 6HB, UK, Tel: 01681 704 245, email: dubus@marsport.org.uk, web www.dubus.org

[4] Met O 920b: Handbook of Weather Messages, Part II, Codes and Specifications, published by HMSO, London

[5] Manual on Codes, WMO No 306, in the section dealing with code FM35.

[6] The use of a dense network of amateur radio stations to determine the limits of long range tropospheric propagation within an anticyclone, by R G Flavell, IEE Conference Publication 195, Part 2, pp163–167

[7] The Dxrobot, Gouda based in The Netherlands - http://www.gooddx.net/

[8] Twenty-one years of TE, by ZE2JV and 5B4WR entitled, RadCom June/July, August 1980, pp626–634 and 785–788

[9] The British Astronomical Association, meteor section web site - http://www.britastro.org/meteor

[10] Sun Mag, Neil Clarke G0CAS, 39 Acacia Road, Cantley, Doncaster, DN4 6UR, Tel: 01302 531925, email: neil@g0cas.demon.co.uk, web: http://www.g0cas.demon.co.uk/sunmag.htm

[11] RSGB news, http://www.rsgb.org/news/

[12] Preliminary Report and Forecast of Solar Geophysical Data "The Weekly", National Oceanic and Atmospheric Administration (NOAA), http://sec.noaa.gov/weekly/index.html

[13] The Propagation Studies Committee of The RSGB, The radio propagation page, web site: http://www.keele.ac.uk/depts/por/psc.htm

[14] Space Weather Information Monitor (SWIM), web: http://solar.uleth.ca/swim/index.html

[15] Troposcatter at 50 MHz - 700 km QSOs any time, Palle Preben-Hansen, OZ1RH, Issue 49 & 50, May & August 1996 of The UK Six Metre Group (UKSMG) magazine. The article can be found on the UKSG web site, http://www.uksmg.org/tropo.htm

[16] DF5AI Net, Amateur Radio Propagation Studies, Dr Volker Grassmann, DF5A!, web: http://www.df5ai.net/

Chapter 4

Receivers, transmitters and transceivers

In this chapter :

- Receivers
- Preamplifiers
- Transmitters

- Transceivers
- Transverters
- Power amplifiers
- Sequencer

his chapter is designed to give the reader a good understanding of receivers, transmitters and transceivers and associated equipment for the VHF and UHF bands. Because the most common way that people start operating on the VHF and UHF bands is to buy a piece of commercial equipment, Table 4.1 shows a list of the current offerings. It is not an exhaustive list nor is it a list of recommended equipment. It should give newcomers to the VHF and UHF bands a good starting point.

The real reason for this chapter is to show a selection of modern designs for the reader to pick and choose the parts that suit their requirements. These cover a wide range of complexity from simple projects that can be built by inexperienced constructors to projects that require a high level of skill and experience. This should give something to appeal to all readers and encourage everyone to enjoy constructing some useful equipment that works and improves their enjoyment of the hobby.

I have decided not to reproduce the receiver and transmitter theory sections from previous handbooks, the basic theory has not changed and it has all been covered before, this leaves more space for new designs in this chapter. Useful design charts for tuned circuits, filters, matching circuits, splitters and combiners are shown in the appendix.

The chapter has a section for each major component and I have tried to include designs for all of the VHF and UHF bands:

- Receivers, there are two designs included, one for 4m and one for 2m. For readers interested in other recently published receiver designs, there is a 2m direct conversion receiver in the 8th edition of The RSGB Handbook [1].
- Preamplifiers, there are designs included for 2m, 70cm and 23cm. There more preamplifier designs in the 8th edition of The RSGB Handbook [1] plus 13cm preamplifiers in The International Microwave Handbook [2] and Microwave Projects 2 [3].
- Transmitters, there is a design for a 4m transmitter and a 70cm ATV transmitter.
- Transceivers, there is a design for a 2m transceiver

and an 23cm ATV transceiver. For readers interested in other recently published transceiver designs, there are 23cm and 13cm transceivers in The International Microwave Handbook [2].

- Transverters, there are designs for 6m, 4m and 70cm. For readers interested in other recently published transverter designs, there are 23cm and 13cm transceivers in The International Microwave Handbook [2].
- Power amplifiers, there are designs for all bands except 4m, 70cm and 13cm. For readers interested in other recently published power amplifier designs, there are other designs in The International Microwave Handbook [2] Microwave Projects [4] Microwave Projects 2 [3] and the 8th edition of The RSGB Handbook [1]
- Ancillaries, there is a design for a sequencer to control power amplifier and aerial changeover relays.

Receivers

The two receivers in this section are aimed at newcomers to the VHF bands, they are easy to construct and will give a good start on the bands.

The PW Mellstock 70MHz receiver

For many years Firemen have wanted a crystal controlled receiver suitable for monitoring Fire Station transmissions in their homes for themselves and their wives/partners. They operate around 77MHz in the area of Dorset. Tony Nailer, G4CFY had a design for such a receiver on his drawing board for 10 years or more. So when the need for the PW Mellstock [5] receiver occurred it was resurrected.

The PCB for the receiver was laid out using a conventional discrete front-end. The board was produced, populated and cleaned and was expected to work first time but there was some trouble with the impedance inverting Colpitts oscillator! This was traced to the use of a 63.6MHz crystal from the junk box that was marked 30pF loading. Overtone crystals are usually specified for infinite capacitance in series, so this was an oddball. A different crystal on 66.4875MHz worked fine, but with the usual 560Ω across it fired up on its third overtone of 39.8925MHz. However, with 220Ω of shunt resistance it fires reliably on the correct frequency.

Table 4.1: List of current (June 2007) commercial amateur radio equipment for VHF/UHF.

Make/model	Band	Comment	Make/model	Band	Comment
AKD 6001	6m	FM Mobile	Kuhne Electronics	4m	Transverter with
AKD 4001	4m	FM mobile	TR 70H	Transverter	28 – 30MHz IF
Alinco DJ-193E	2m	FM hand held	Yaesu FT60R	2m/70cm	FM dual band hand held
Alinco DJ-195E	2m	FM hand held	Yaesu FT2800R	2m	FM mobile
Alinco DJ-496	70cm	FM hand held	Yaesu FT7800E	2m/70cm	FM dual band mobile
Alinco DJ-596	2m/70cm	FM dual band hand held	Yaesu FT817	HF/6m/2m/	All mode mobile/base
Alinco DJ-C6	2m/70cm	FM dual band hand held		70cm	station
Alinco DJ-C7	2m/70cm	FM dual band hand held	Yaesu FT847	HF/6m/2m/	All mode mobile/base
Alinco DJ-V17E	2m	FM hand held		70cm	station. Some of these
Alinco DJV-5	2m/70cm	FM dual band hand held			were modified by Martin
Alinco DR-635	2m/70cm	FM dual band mobile			Lynch to operate on 4m
Alinco DX77	HF/6m	All mode base station	Yaesu FT857	HF/6m/2m/	All mode mobile/base
				70cm	station
Down East Micr-	23cm	Transverter with	Yaesu FT8800E	2m/70cm	FM dual band mobile
wave1296-144	Transverter	28 – 144MHz IF	Yaesu FT8900R	10m/6m/2m/	FM quad band mobile
Down East Micr-	2m	Transverter with		70cm	
wave 144-28	Transverter	28 – 30MHz IF	Yaesu FT897	HF/6m/2m/	All mode mobile/base
Down East Micr-	70cm	Transverter with		70cm	station
wave 432-28	Transverter	28 – 30MHz IF	Yaesu VX-2E	2m/70cm	FM dual band hand held
Down East Micr-	6m	Transverter with	Yaesu VX-5R	6m/2m/70cm	FM tri band hand held
wave 50-28	Transverter	28 – 30MHz IF	Yaesu VX-7R	6m/2m/70cm	FM tri band hand held
Icom IC-2200H	2m	FM mobile			
Icom IC-2725	2m/70cm	FM dual band mobile	**AKD**		
Icom IC-7000	HF/6m/2m/	All mode mobile/base	http://www.garex.co.uk		
	70cm	station	Garex, PO Box 52, Exeter, EX4 8WX		
Icom IC-703	HF/6m	All mode mobile/base	Tel: +44 (0) 7714 198374		
		station with 6m			
Icom IC-706	HF/6m/2m/	All mode mobile/base	**Alinco**		
	70cm	station	http://www.alinco.co.uk/		
Icom IC-7400	HF/6m/2m	All mode mobile/base	Nevada Radio, Unit 1, Fitzherbert Spur, Farlington,		
		station with 6m and 2m	Portsmouth, Hampshire, PO6 1TT		
Icom IC-756	HF/6m	All mode mobile/base	Tel: +44 (0) 23 9231 3090		
		station with 6m			
Icom IC-7800	HF/6m	All mode mobile/base	**Down East Microwave**		
		station with 6m	http://www.downeastmicrowave.com/		
Icom IC-910	2m/70cm/	Dual band all mode	Down East Microwave Inc., 954 Route519, Frenchtown, NJ		
	(23cm opt)	base station with	08825, USA		
		optional 23cm module	Tel: +00 908 996 3584		
Icom IC-E208	2m/70cm	FM dual band mobile			
Icom IC-E7	2m/70cm	FM dual band hand held	**Icom**		
Icom IC-E90	6m/2m/70cm	FM tri band hand held.	http://www.icom.co.jp/world/http://www.icom.co.jp/world		
		Some of these were			
		modified by Martin	**Kenwood**		
		Lynch to operate on 4m	http://www.kenwood.com		
Icom IC-T3	2m	FM hand held			
Icom IC-U82	70cm	High power FM hand	**Yaesu**		
		held with digital modes	http://www.yaesu.com		
Icom IC-V82	2m	High power FM hand			
		held with digital modes			
Kenwood TH-F7	2m/70cm	FM dual band hand held			
Kenwood TH-K2	2m	FM hand held			
Kenwood TH-K4	70cm	FM hand held			
Kenwood TM-271	2m	FM mobile			
Kenwood TS-2000	HF/6m/2m/	All mode base station			
	70cm/23cm				
Kenwood TS-480	HF/6m	All mode mobile/base			
		station with 6m			
Kuhne Electronics	23cm	Transverter with			
TR 1296H-28	Transverter	28 – 30MHz IF			
Kuhne Electronics	2m	Transverter with			
TR 144H	Transverter	28 – 30MHz IF			
Kuhne Electronics	70cm	Transverter with			
TR 432H	Transverter	28 – 30MHz IF			

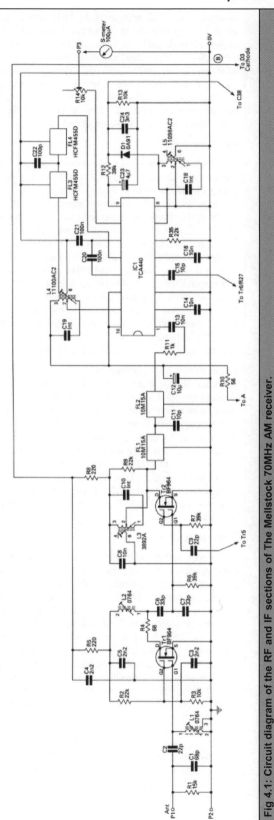

Fig 4.1: Circuit diagram of the RF and IF sections of The Mellstock 70MHz AM receiver.

Circuit description

The receiver circuit is shown in Fig 4.1 and 4.2. It is a crystal controlled double superhet with 10.7MHz first IF and 455kHz second IF. The RF stage is Tr1, a BF964 dual-gate MOSFET as a tuned input, tuned output, conventional amplifier. It has a drain stopping resistor R4 to prevent the device oscillating at UHF due to internal feedback between drain and gate 1. A resistor R1, of 15kΩ is employed to discharge static build up on the antenna and down lead.

The transistor, Tr2 is also a BF964 dual-gate MOS-FET. In this case used as a mixer with signal fed to gate 1 and the oscillator signal to gate 2. Both devices are third generation MOSFETs operating in directly grounded source mode, with no source resistor or decoupling capacitor. Notes: Both gates are biased to ground, which makes the device act like a switching mixer with good signal handling and low noise. An impedance inverting Colpitts oscillator, Tr5, provides the oscillator signal with two crystals switched by Tr3 and Tr4. It is also possible that when the correct crystals have been cut, that it may be necessary to increase the shunt resistance from 220Ω up to 560Ω. This will depend on whether the crystals are the fifth overtone of 11.9MHz or the third overtone of 19.85MHz. Output from the oscillator is taken from the collector where there is a bit of gain compared with emitter take off, also the collector output exhibits lower levels of second harmonic output.

Following the mixer are two 2 pole 10.7MHz centre frequency 15kHz bandwidth crystal filters in cascade. Together they achieve nearly 40dB of attenuation at 25kHz above and below the wanted channel. Output from the mixer is matched to the 3kΩ input impedance of FL1 by tapping down the winding of L3. The match is not exactly right, but it is corrected by the addition of R9 (22kΩ).

Filter FL2 feeds into IC1, a TCA440, which is the heart of the receiver. The input impedance is 2kΩ and 5pF. Resistor R11 brings the impedance up to 3kΩ to correctly load the filter.

Complex integrated circuit

The integrated circuit, IC1 is a complex device and comprises an RF stage, mixer, Hartley oscillator, 4 stage IF amplifier, AGC amplifier, and meter drive circuit. Not surprisingly it was originally designed for use in domestic AM receivers.

The input frequency range of the RF amplifier in the device is 0-50MHz. The input frequency of the 4 stage IF is 0-2MHz. The RF stage has an AGC input whilst the first three IF stages are connected to the AGC amplifier. When run at 455kHz, the IF stages have a control range of 62dB. This is quite adequate for use in this receiver without needing to apply AGC to the RF stage as well.

Having not worked out how to use the internal oscillator as a parallel mode crystal Colpitts circuit, an

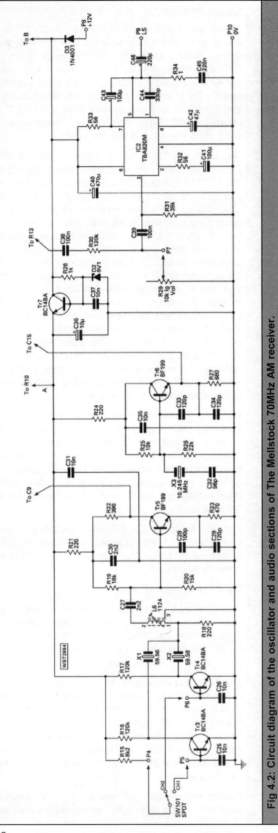

Fig 4.2: Circuit diagram of the oscillator and audio sections of The Mellstock 70MHz AM receiver.

external stage Tr6 with a 10.245MHz crystal was used. This signal is fed to one of the differential inputs of the TCA440 oscillator (which is pin 4) whilst the other (pin 5) is decoupled to ground. In this design the oscillator signal mixes with 10.7MHz to produce 455kHz and of course also 20.945MHz. The mixer is a four quadrant multiplier and has two open collector outputs, pins 15 and 16. (One is taken to an IF transformer, the other to the regulated rail).

Mechanical filters

A 4 element 455kHz mechanical filters designed for AM receiver is used. The HCFN1455D filters have 10kHz bandwidth, with a rejection of 9dB at plus and minus 9kHz and with an ultimate attenuation of 30dB. A pair of the filters cascaded will give 18dB attenuation of the adjacent channels. They will further add to the adjacent channel attenuation provided by the first IF filters, to allow comfortable working on 70.28MHz without problems from the 70.26MHz calling channel. The output impedance of the mixer is 250kΩ and 4pF. However, no off-the-shelf parts are really close to providing a match from the mixer to the input of the first of these filters. The nearest usable part is the Toko YHCS11100AC2 which provides about 3kΩ at the secondary when driven at its tap by the mixer.

Output from the second filter feeds into the input of the four stage IF that also has an input impedance of 3kΩ. Output from the 455kHz amplifier on pin 8 is an open collector of a PNP transistor, which allows the final IF transformer to be earth referenced. The signal is demodulated by diode D1, and is then split into two paths. One is fed back via R12 and C23 forming a low-pass filter for AGC control, and the other is the demodulated audio. The AGC signal is internally connected to an emitter follower which outputs on pin 10 and via a 10kΩ trimpot to drive a standard 100µA S-meter.

Demodulated audio

The demodulated audio amplitude is too large for the audio amplifier, IC2, and needs to be attenuated. An attenuator of 12:1 is formed by R30, 120kΩ, and the volume control R29 of 10kΩ. Note: Since producing the receiver more data on the TBA820M audio amplifier was available, which shows that if R32 is increased to 120Ω the gain is reduced by 6dB. Resistor R30 could then be changed to 56kΩ, giving the attenuator a 5.6:1 step down together with lower audio amplifier gain would result in an even quieter background noise level at the speaker. The TBA820M is rated at 1W output into an 8 ohm speaker on a 12/13.5V DC supply. Quiescent current of the device is typically only 4mA. The whole receiver only draws 40mA quiescent current that makes it ideal for portable battery operation. The supply rail for the two crystal oscillators and the TCA440 at 8.5V is supplied from a series regulator TR7 referenced to a 9V1 Zenner D2.

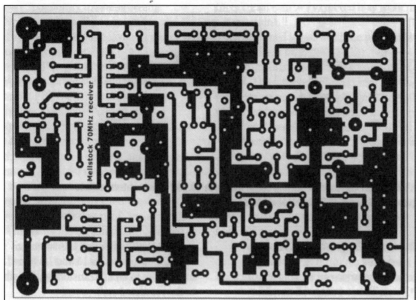

Fig 4.3: PCB layout for The Mellstock 70MHz AM receiver.

Construction and assembly

The main PCB design and component layout are shown in Fig 4.3 and 4.4. Start with the resistors and the diodes, which are the lowest profile components. Fit them into position and bend the leads over enough to hold them in position. Solder them all and then crop the leads off. Next fit the pins from the underside and force them into position with pliers, until the head is flush with the track. Solder them as a group. Next fit IC1 and IC2 holding them in place while dabbing solder at opposite diagonal pins. Then lay the board down and carefully solder the other plus and redo the pins originally dabbed. Fit and solder transistors Tr3 - 7. (Leave T1 and 2 until later).

Then fit the trimpot into place, holding it while soldering.

Warning: Keep your fingers away from the two exposed metal end tabs while doing this. They get hot!

Next, fit the ceramic capacitors and bend their leads to hold them in place. Again, do all the fitting of these parts and solder them as a group before cropping them off.

Note: The poly block capacitors, and electrolytic capacitors should be fitted individually. They should be held in place during soldering to keep them upright and close to the board.

The Toko coils should be fitted as a group, and soldered. The crystals and filters can then be done, one at a time, soldered as they're held in place. Finally, carefully tin the board where Tr1 and 2 are to be fitted. The long lead, which is the drain for Tr1, has to be towards L2 and the

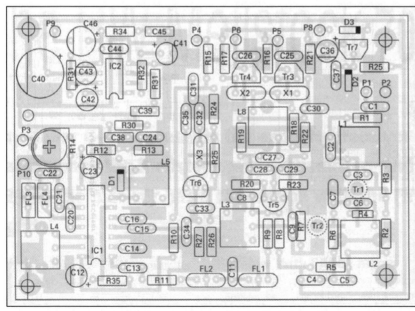

Fig 4.4: Component layout for The Mellstock 70MHz AM receiver.

Fig 4.5: Picture of the completed Mellstock 70MHz AM receiver PCB.

identification of the device should be readable from the top side of the board. Place Tr1 into position and solder the drain first, then the lead with the small protrusion, which is the source, then the other two leads. Similarly place Tr2 into position with the long lead (drain) towards L3 and identification readable from topside. Solder the leads in the same sequence as Tr1.

Check all components are in the correct positions. You may clean the board if you have suitable solvents. Then carefully examine the track side of the board for any imperfections in the soldering, solder splashes or shorts. When you are happy with the construction proceed to commissioning.

Mellstock signal source

Many of you will have the Mellstock transmitter. This can form a most useful signal source if you don't have a signal generator! Connect a link or a switch to activate either of the channel crystals. Connect a 10kΩ log potentiometer between pin P7 and ground. Next, connect a 100µA S meter between P3 and ground. Then connect a small 8Ω speaker between P9 and ground. Connect a coaxial lead to pins P1 and P2 to connect to a signal generator or connect a length of wire say 300mm long to J1 to 'sense' the Mellstock transmitter. Connect a 12 or 13.5V DC supply to the receiver. Provided any faults had been detected previously, a hiss should be heard from the speaker. If You are using the Mellstock transmitter, first connect it to a dummy load and select the right channel. If using a signal generator, tune it to 70.26MHz or 70.28MHz as appropriate. You may now discern a signal and audio if the signal generator is modulated, or if you talk into the transmitter microphone. If a signal is indicated on the signal meter you can then proceed to tune the coils for maximum deflection. Note: Do this in reverse order, L5 back to L1 and then repeat the process. If all appears in order the final adjustment is to tune L3 and L4 while listening for audio quality. (This is affected because

adjustment of these coils affects the matching to the filters). Note: The best audio quality may not necessarily coincide exactly with absolute maximum reading on the S-meter but it should be near.

Correct functioning of the first local oscillator can be checked by connecting the probe of a frequency counter across the gate 2 bias resistor, R7, of the mixer Tr2. The frequency should be 59.56 or 59.58MHz if the crystal is firing on its correct overtone. There may be a slight error of a few hundred Hertz only, which may be corrected by tuning L6. No two crystals of slightly different frequencies are going to have exactly the same loading, so it may be necessary to adjust the coil L6 for an equal small offset. (This is likely to be less than 100Hz). If either crystal is not firing then increase the value of R17, which can be as high as 680Ω. Note: any higher resistance is likely to allow the crystal to switch into parallel mode.

The frequency of the second local oscillator can be checked by testing pin 4 of the TCA440. The capacitor, C32 of 56pF together with C33 and C34 (each 120pF) gives a total series value of 29pF that should be just right for 30pF loading 10.245MHz crystals. If the crystal frequency is high then increase C32 to 68pF. If the frequency is low reduce C32 to 47pF.

To check if Tr1 is functioning correctly test across R5 with a voltmeter, the result should he 1.0-1.5V. Likewise with Tr2 test across R8 where the result is likely to be 0.5V. The chip, IC1, should draw about 10mA that will drop about 0.6V across R10. The supply rail to the oscillators should be checked from the top of R21 or R24 to ground as being 8.3-8.6V.

Calibration of the S-meter using a signal

Calibration of the S-meter using a signal generator is simple, just set R14 to give S9 for an input of 50µV. Without the aid of a signal generator the setting of this will be arbitrary.

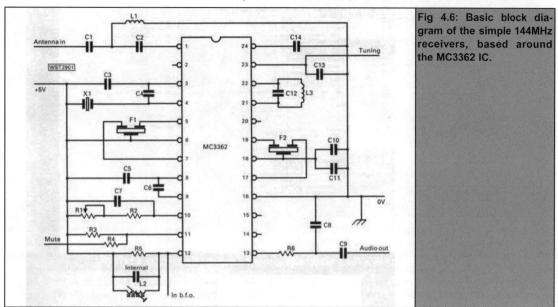

Fig 4.6: Basic block diagram of the simple 144MHz receivers, based around the MC3362 IC.

A simple 144MHz receiver

The receiver was published in PW [6] and is based on a Motorola MC3362. This integrated circuit is a dual conversion frequency modulation receiver that will work up to 200MHz. The audio output is quite low, so a TDA820 audio amplifier has been added (Fig 4.5). A BFO and muting arrangements are also included. Facilities are in place for the later addition of automatic scan and dwell tuning.

Basic Block Diagram

The basic block diagram is shown in Fig 4.6. Using the diagram we can see that the RF signals enter Pin 1 via an impedance matching circuit. The first mixer amplifies the signal and converts the RF to 10.7MHz. The IF signal is filtered externally (between Pins 19 and 17) and then fed

into the second mixer. Mixed with 10.245MHz from crystal X1 (at in 4) this is converted to a 455kHz IF signal, and again amplified.

After external band-pass filtering (between pins 5 and7), the low IF is fed into the limiting amplifier and detection circuitry. The coil L2 is the quadrature detector resulting in an audio output at Pin 13.

The RF signal levels are monitored and result in a variation of current at Pin 10. By adjusting the value of potentiometer R1, a suitable 'carrier detect' threshold voltage can be created at Pin 11, this voltage is used for muting purposes. The parts list is shown in Table 4.2.

Frequency Alignment

When it comes to frequency alignment and setting-up,

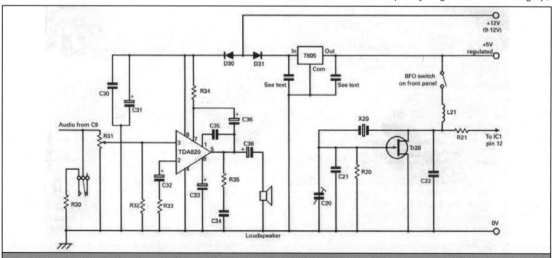

Fig 4.7: Circuit diagram of the audio amplifier and BFO of the simple 144MHz receiver.

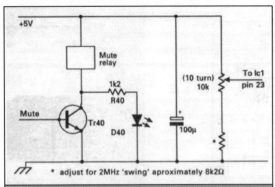

Fig 4.8: The muting circuit for the simple 144MHz receiver.

Fig 4.9: Picture or the completed simple 144MHz receiver

there are just three coils to worry about. The antenna input coil (L1) consists of just a few turns of wire. While not critical this can be tweaked for best reception once stations are being received. With the tuning control at mid-position the oscillator coil (L3) must be adjusted to give a local oscillator signal of 134.3MHz, which is the only really fiddly bit. During this procedure it would be handy to have a signal generator or beacon signal available. Note: There is a buffered local oscillator output on Pin 20 if a frequency meter or receiver are to hand. This LO frequency when mixed with an incoming RF signal of 145MHz, will provide a first IF of 10.7MHz (RF minus LO = 10.7). Note: If the coil is adjusted (by mistake) to 155.7MHz a 10.7MHz output will still be obtained (LO minus RF = 10.7). This higher LO frequency however, has the disadvantage of being more unstable and inverts sideband signals. The 10-turn tuning potentiometer may need a resistor in series with it in order that the tuning span is reduced to just the 2MHz range needed for 144MHz.

Other Adjustments

Other adjustments include muting: With no RF signal present Pin 11 should be `high' (approx 4.4V). This voltage (via R4) turns on the muting transistor Tr40, its associated relay thus operates (Fig 4.8). The relay contact drastically reduces the audio signal entering the audio amplifier, the audio being by-passed to earth via R30. While Tr40 is conducting the front panel LED will not glow. Once a signal is received the voltage on Pin 11 reduces causing Tr40 to switch off, muting is thereby removed and the LED illuminates. The switching threshold needs to be set by R1. The quadrature detector coil (L2) is easily adjusted for best audio quality and level. The associated capacitor shown in the drawing is included in the base of the purchased coil.

Beat Frequency Oscillator

With a carrier detected the BFO needs adjusting to create a suitable heterodyne. To adjust it, tune to the centre of a carrier, switch the BFO on and trim C20 for a suitable tone. Note: The capacitor, C21, may need to be changed between 27 and 56pF.

Practicalities and Stability

Due to the high frequency of the first LO (134MHz)

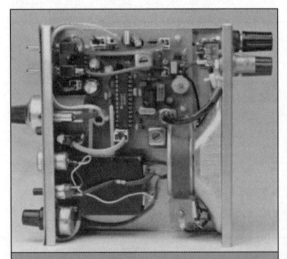

Fig 4.10: Top view of the completed simple 144MHz receiver

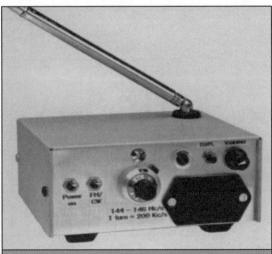

Fig 4.11: Front view of the completed simple 144MHz receiver.

Table 4.2: Parts list for a simple 144MHz receiver. A PCB layout is available [7]

Resistors (0.25W)

1Ω	1	R35
47Ω	1	R30
56Ω	1	R34
100kΩ	1	R33
1.2kΩ	1	R40
8.2kΩ	1	R6
10kΩ	2	R3, R32
39kΩ	1	R5
51 kΩ	1	R2
100kΩ	1	R4
1MΩ	1	R20
3.9MΩ	1	R21

Resistoprs (Variables)

10kΩ	1	R31
100kΩ	1	R1

Capacitors (Disc ceramic)

2.2pF	1	C12
6.8pF	1	C1
33pF	2	C21
50pF	1	C4
120pF	1	C3
220pF	1	C35
1nF	1	C2

Capacitors (Polyester)

10nF	1	C8
0.1µF	6	C5, C6, C7, C11, C13, C14, C22, C31
0.22µF	1	C34

Capacitors (Electrolytic 16V working)

10µF	1	C9
47µF	2	C10,C33
100µF	3	C30,C32,C36
220µF	1	C37

Capacitors (Variable)

90pF	1	C20

Semiconductors

IN4001	2	D30, D31
IN4148	1	D20
7805	1	IC3
BC547	1	Tr40
MPF102	1	Tr20
MC3362P	1	IC1
TDA820M	1	IC2

Ceramic filters

CS8455E	X20 (455kHz resonator)
CFW455F	F1
CFSH10.71M	F2
	(may be marked SKM1 orTaiyo10912C)

Crystal

10.245MHz	X1 (fundamental, 30pF)

Inductors

3 or 4 turns, 3 or 4mm former or self supporting	L1
Toko YHCS 17104 G02 (or Toko YMCS2A740AAE)	L2
Toko SI 18 series	L3 (red 2.5 turns)
1mH	L21

Relay = Dry reed i.e. Meder SIL12K 100-71 D or Hamlin HE3621A0510 or similar with quench diode included, the higher the resistance the better.

Molinex PCB connectors were used throughout with a sub-miniature Gelling Lee coaxial PCB connector leading to a rear panel BNC connector.

mechanical rigidity is important. A wobbly front panel of metal (close to L3) could vary the oscillator frequency every time you touch it! Even then the frequency stability is not perfect, while listening to an FM station tuning adjustment may be needed after a minute or so. After all, it is a simple receiver!

Loudspeaker Choice

Care needs to be taken over the choice of loudspeaker. Before choosing a speaker feed several with audio and compare them in the preferred case. The TDA820 will use less current when driving a higher impedance speaker and 8Ω upwards is to be preferred. The physical location of the speaker is important. The magnet in the speaker is also important this is because the magnetic field from the speaker can cause the reed relay to stick in either it's on or off position. It is recommended on any equipment that the operation of reed relays will not be effected before drilling the speaker holes!

Break through

The receiver was built as an introduction to the 144MHz band and was only used with a short whip antenna. If a large antenna is used, break-through from strong signals outside the Amateur Radio band may occur. This would be due to the lack of a tuned circuit in front of the first mixer. (An external band-pass filter could be added if this was to become a problem).

Preamplifiers

A preamplifier can improve the performance of a receiver. The natural assumption is to choose a preamplifier with as much gain as possible, this is not a good idea. The gain should be chosen with regard to the noise figure of the receiver and the preamplifier so that it is improved without overloading the receiver. A good description of this choice is given in [8].

2m MOSFET preamplifier

This amplifier uses a low cost silicon MOSFET (BF981 from Philips) to give more than 20dB gain with around 1dB noise figure on 2m. It was designed by Ole Nykjaer, OZ2OE [9]. You can build more advanced low noise amplifiers using GaAs FET's, but the dual gate MOSFET

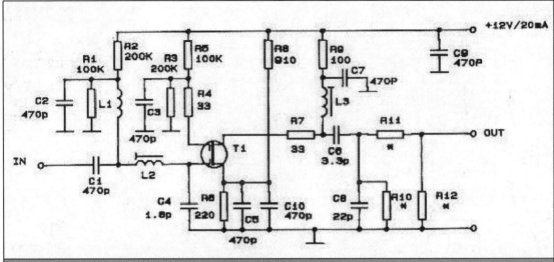

Fig 4.12: Circuit diagram for the 2m MOSFET preamplifier.

is not a bad performer. The difference in noise figure may not even show up on a terrestrial path. Besides it is a lot more forgiving in terms of accidental destruction and it is cheaper!

Mechanical design

The amplifier is built on a double sided board measuring 25 x 50mm shown in Fig 4.13 and 4.14. The upper side functions as a ground plane and the tracks are on the lower side. The board can either be build into the radio or mounted in a small metal box with BNC connectors.

Electrical design

The circuit diagram is shown in Fig 4.12. The input circuit is a series transformation, the output circuit a "normal" parallel circuit with a capacitive output tap. Because this amplifier has high gain, there is provision for a pi-attenuator on the output. Biasing of the transistor uses a source resistor/voltage divider and with voltage dividers on both gate1 and gate2. This circuit tightly controls the DC parameters of the transistor.

Circuit details

The input circuit is a bit unusual as it uses a series inductor L2 to step the 50Ω input impedance up to 1600Ω, which is the optimum gate impedance for noise matching. L2 resonates with C4 and gate1 input capacitance in parallel. This minimises the loaded Q of the input circuit - important to keep insertion loss down - and the correct impedance (noise) match is fixed by design.

The output circuit is a parallel circuit with L3, C6 and C8. The capacitive tap C6/C8 sets the drain impedance to 2kΩ. This also determines the gain.

Tune up

When powering up for the first time, start by checking the DC current consumption of about 20mA. Then adjust L2 and L3 for maximum signal. For best noise match use a weak unmodulated signal and a receiver in FM mode. Then tune only L2 for best noise suppression. By using a signal at the noise threshold, the FM (or PM) detector in the receiver will "amplify" any improvement of the S/N, so you can tune for optimum noise figure by ear! The limiter

Fig 4.13: Picture of the completed 2m MOSFET preamplifier.

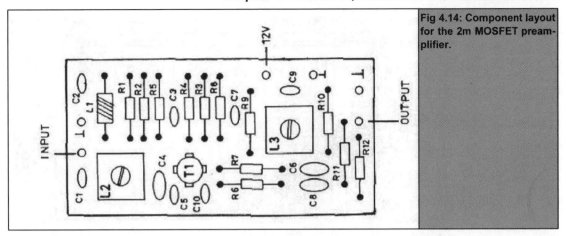

Fig 4.14: Component layout for the 2m MOSFET preamplifier.

in the FM receiver will nullify any resulting variation of the preamplifier gain.

Attenuator

The gain can be tailored to your specific needs - which should be "not more than enough" - by having an attenuator at the output of the amplifier. Table 4.3 shows resistor values for different attenuation.

Performance

Many of these amplifiers have build and measured, and they have almost identical performance. The typical result with a 3dB output attenuator is shown in Fig 4.15.

A low noise preamplifier for 70cm and 23cm

The ATF54143 is an excellent choice for a LNA but for the home constructor without access to a noise figure meter, optimising a narrowband circuit for best performance can be a difficult process. This design is by David Bowman, G0MRF and was published in Dubus [10].

The circuit shown in Fig 4.16 uses broadband input and output matching networks which are optimised for 432MHz, but provide good performance to beyond 1500MHz. The parts list is shown in Table 4.4.

At 432MHz the LNA has a gain of 20dB and a noise figure of 0.48dB. Graphs showing the gain and noise figure across the spectrum are shown in Figs 4.17 and 4.18. The design uses fixed value components and avoids trimmers. You just solder the components in and switch on.

An experimenter's PCB

The ATF54143 is a versatile device and can be used from

144MHz to beyond 2.4GHz. Across this range, there are a number of possible matching solutions for optimum noise figure and gain. The PCB designed for this preamplifier can be adapted for use with a number of different networks and represents a good general purpose board for projects using the ATF54143 or its variants. The choice of 0.8mm FR4 material provides an acceptable medium for 2.4GHz, while the inclusion of printed source inductors, which although not used in this design for 70 and 23cm, would be necessary for operation on the 2m band. Following general good practice, the PCB has 80 plated through holes for good RF grounding. It is 33 x 57mm, includes an on board 5V regulator, a PNP transistor providing active bias to the PHEMT and the ability to power the amplifier via the coax.

Circuit description

The ATF54143 is an enhancement mode PHEMT and requires a small positive voltage on the gate to bias it for correct operation. The active biasing compensates for any slight variations in the FET characteristics and for changes with temperature. For this amplifier, the drain voltage is set to 3V and the drain current 30mA. The active biasing functions as follows: The drain voltage is

Table 4.3: Attenuator and coil details for 2m MOSFET preamplifier.				
Attenuator	3dB	6dB	10dB	16dB
R10, R12	270Ω	150Ω	100Ω	68Ω
R11	16Ω	39Ω	68Ω	150Ω
L1	1 - 3µH			
L2, L3	6.25 turns 0.25mm wire on Neosid K3312, F100			

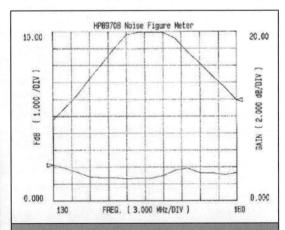

Fig 4.15: Noise figure and gain from 130 to 160MHz for the 2m MOSFET preamplifier. NF is 1.3dB and gain 20dB at 145MHz.

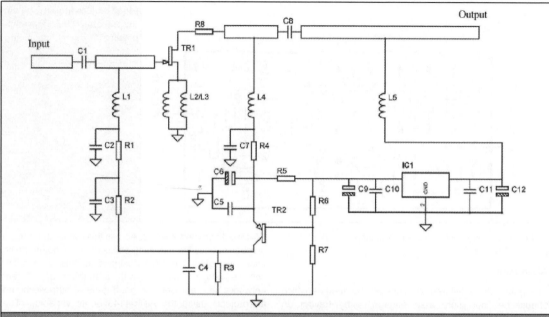

Fig 4.16: Circuit diagram of the low noise preamplifier for 70cm and 23cm.

set by resistors R6 and R7. This potential divider across the 5V supply sets the base voltage of TR2. Being a PNP device, the emitter voltage is 0.7V higher than the base. The emitter voltage feeds the drain via two 10Ω resistors, R4 and the damping resistor R8. At 30mA Id there will be 300mV drop across each of these resistors and so the emitter voltage required is 3.60V.

The drain current is set by the value of R5. The voltage across R5 is 5V, less the emitter voltage of 3.60V. Impedance matching the FET is achieved by C1 and L1 on the input and by L4 and C8 on the output. To ensure stability, the impedance matching networks also act as high pass filters giving a broad match from 350MHz to beyond 1500MHz. At lower frequencies, where the natural gain of the device is very high, the matching networks reduce the gain significantly and enhance stability. This

roll off in low frequency response also prevents overload from strong broadcast band radio signals. In this application the printed source inductors are not used and the two source connections are shorted directly to ground with small pieces of copper or brass foil. At 145MHz the amplifier has a loss of 16dB and testing several prototypes has revealed them to be unconditionally stable.

Transmitters

There are not many designs for VHF/UHF transmitters, it is more usual to use a transverter or transceiver. This section has one simple design for 4m to complement the 4m receiver design and an ATV transmitter.

The PW 70MHz 1W AM transmitter

This design was the brain child of Rob Mannion, G3XFD, editor PW Magazine, he published an old design from

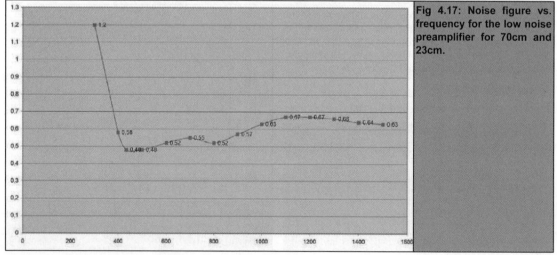

Fig 4.17: Noise figure vs. frequency for the low noise preamplifier for 70cm and 23cm.

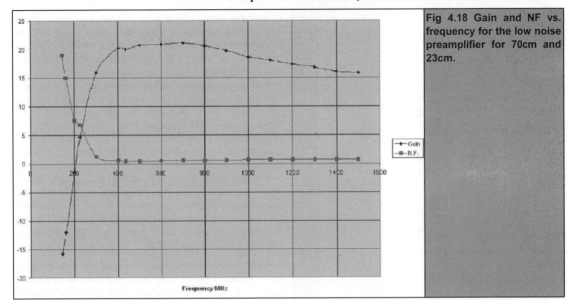

Fig 4.18 Gain and NF vs. frequency for the low noise preamplifier for 70cm and 23cm.

1968 in PW and presented a challenge to Tony Nailer, G4CFY to design the modern equivalent [11]. There were many problems but the modulation transformer was the biggest problem.

In his workshop Tony set about addressing the issues. Knowing that the problem would be the modulator and modulation transformer an audio amplifier IC was assembled onto a blank printed circuit board 'dead bug' style and checked that it worked well. Then the radio frequency section was assembled with a VHF oscillators, multiplier and amplifier which was fairly straightforward. The circuit, uses a 23MHz overtone crystal oscillator, a tripler, a driver

and power amplifier stage was quickly assembled dead bug style. On test it produced just under 1W output.

Transformer problem

Now came the difficult part, to modulate the transmitter! What was needed was a 1:2 ratio transformer. An LT700 audio transformer was tried, but it was no good at all. Then, on the suggestion of Tex Swann, G1TEX from PW, several small mains transformers with dual secondary windings were tried but they were horribly inefficient.

The answer, of course, was to find a suitable modern core and wind the transformer, just as John Hey G3TDZ had done in the 1968 design. Looking through the component suppliers catalogues the RM ferrite cores were found with a variety of bobbins. These looked ideal as they quoted operation up to 300kHz and it was presumed from this that they would work from low frequency to 300KHz. It was time to read through the pages and pages of literature accumulated over the years about transformer design. A 1:2 ratio transformer was designed using an RM10 core and tested it with the modulator and transmitter. Unfortu-

Table 4.4: Parts list for the low noise preamplifier for 70cm and 23cm.

Resistors 0805 unless stated

R1	47Ω	R2	5k6Ω
R3	1KΩ	R4	10Ω
R5	47Ω (1206)	R6	3k9Ω
R7	5k6Ω	R8	10Ω

Capacitors

C1	10pF	C2	68pF
C3	1nF	C4	10nF
C5	1nF	C6	10µF 6.3v tant
C7	27pF	C8	10pF
C9	10µF 6.3v tant	C10	10nF
C11	10nF	C12	4.7µF 20v tant

Semiconductors

TR1	ATF54143	TR2	2N3906SMD
IC1	78L05ACM		

Inductors

L1	3 turns 0.56mm enamelled coper, 2.7mm ID close spaced
L2, L3	Printed on PCB. Short to ground at source lead for 70cm
L4	2 turns 0.56mm enamelled coper, 2.7mm ID close spaced
L5	270nH SMD inductor. Only required if powered via coax

Fig 4.19: Picture of the low noise preamplifier for 70cm and 23cm.

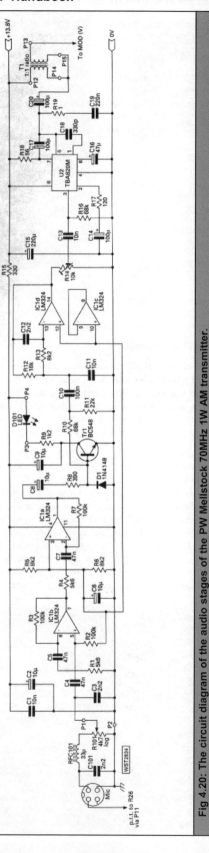

Fig 4.20: The circuit diagram of the audio stages of the PW Mellstock 70MHz 1W AM transmitter.

nately, the whole circuit went into LF oscillation. Many attempts to stabilise it finally tamed the beast but the modulation efficiency was low and the envelope pattern was distorted. Whilst sweeping the frequency of the audio generator the modulation depth increased with increasing frequency and the distortion steadily reduced. Sweeping it well above the audio range it was found that the efficiency approached 100% and with little distortion at 100kHz! However, the amplitude of the positive peaks was considerably smaller than the amplitude of the negative peaks. Clearly this would produce negative going modulation. Eventually, it was determined that the percentage positive modulation was about 60% of the theoretically value. Assuming that the low frequency lack of efficiency was due to insufficient turns, a new transformer was designed and wound on a new bobbin using hundreds of turns. When tried, the performance was worse but the maximum efficiency was still at 100kHz.

The conclusion was that the ferrite core was just no use at audio frequencies Unfortunately, suppliers of laminated core kits could not be found and there was no intention to wind and build transformers using them.

A different approach

It was time for a different approach, maybe there was a better way to produce 70MHz AM by generating the signal at a low RF level in a balanced modulator and then using wideband linear amplifiers to raise the level to 1W. So a whole new prototype transmitter was built. As before, the 23MHz overtone oscillator was used, then a tripler, and then into the two transistor balanced modulator described in [12]. This produced a perfect signal and according to all measurements was close to 100% positive modulation. A field effect transistor amplifier was added which gave about 10mW carrier and about 35mW peak power, with the positive modulation achieving 87%. A further stage comprising of two BSX20 transistors in transformer push-pull using ferrite bead transformers achieved 125mW carrier and 400mW peak with positive modulation achieving about 80%. That was unfortunately as far as this route progressed. Attempts to use a pair of 2N4427s in a push pull wideband amplifier failed to produce worthwhile results. Samples of toroid cores were obtained and a transformer was designed but nothing worked. In the end that was shelved and the modulation transformer problem re-visited.

Back to the drawing board

It was time to go back to the drawing board! The catalogues were searched again as well as the web, and even companies phoned to see if they had any suitable transformers. Most were willing to make a special but the minimum order value had to be £500. Then a transformer rated at 2W for audio use with a 1:1 turns ratio was found that might work configured as an auto transformer. A sample was ordered, when it arrived the original prototype modulator and RF strip was rebuilt and the circuit worked! Maximum efficiency was at 200Hz with a falling efficiency with increasing frequency. The coupling capacitor was recalculated to resonate with the inductance of the transformer at 600Hz and re-tested. Wonderful, a gently rising

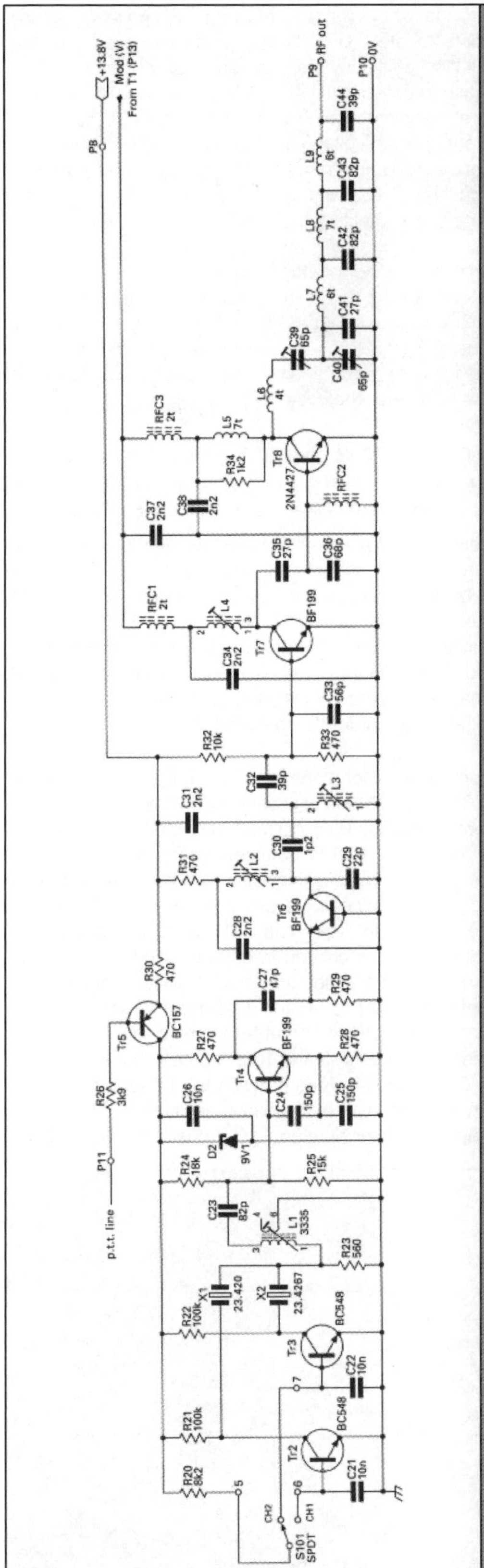

Fig 4.21: The circuit diagram of the RF stages of the PW Mellstock 70MHz 1W AM transmitter.

response from 200Hz to 600Hz and then a gentle fall with increasing frequency.

Speech Processor

In order to maximise the sideband power due to the higher voice tones, and to reduce the modulation depth due to low voice tones, a speech processor was incorporated, this had been designed for another transmitter project. In conjunction with the modulator a response was then achieved with a sharply rising characteristic from 200Hz to 600Hz and then a falling characteristic up to 2.5kHz. Quite high levels of amplification are used, and then the audio is clipped and filtered. The result is that full 100% modulation depth is achieved for a large part of the voice syllables but over modulation is severely restricted.

Modulator Described

The signal from a microphone is amplified in a non-inverting op-amp, IC1b. This stage has a high pass characteristic with -3dB point at 600Hz created by the components R1 and C5. The gain of the stage is x18 (25dB). The signal is then further amplified in IC1a which is an inverting amplifier with a of gain x18. This also has the same high pass characteristic due to R4 and C7. The output from IC1a is fed to D1 in parallel with the base emitter diode in Tr1. This is effectively a pair of back-to-back diodes to symmetrically clip the audio. Incidentally, use is made of the collector of this transistor to illuminate a light emitting diode when the base emitter junction is conducting. The LED feature allows the adjustment of the microphone gain control. It is an aid to setting the gain so the LED is fairly bright when speaking with a regular voice level. Following the clipper IC1d is configured as a multiple feedback low pass filter with a corner frequency around 2.4kHz.

Output from the processor section is then fed to the modulator IC via a trimpot used to preset the modulation depth. The IC has a low value input capacitor to couple voice frequencies well into its high impedance input but prevents low frequency instability.

The RF Section

The third overtone crystals operates in conjunction with Tr4 and the reactive components L1, C23, C24, & C25 to produce an impedance inverting Colpitts oscillator. (Details of the design of this stage are covered in detail in [13]). Transistors Tr2 and Tr3 provide switching of the crystals and prevent effects from switch wiring. When one of these devices is off, the collector will be a very high impedance and effectively the crystal is in series with the 100kΩ resistor to the positive rail. When the transistor is switched on, it grounds that end of the crystal thereby completing the circuit. Resistor R2 (560Ω) is across the active crystal and prevents operation in the high impedance parallel mode.

The output from the oscillator is taken from the collector where the signal is less rich in second harmonics than it would have been taken from the emitter. The following stage is a tripler, "hitting" it with high levels of fundamental and second harmonic would produce lots of unwanted

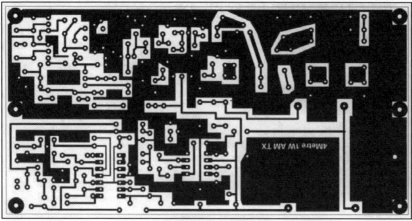

Fig 4.22: PCB for the PW Mellstock 70MHz 1W AM transmitter.

products. Transistor Tr5 is in series with the oscillator supply rail to act as a push-to-talk circuit. Unless the terminal P11 is grounded the oscillator will not run. Observing the envelope of the carrier on an oscilloscope when triggering the PTT pin P11, the leading edge of the envelope exhibits a cycle and a half of low frequency bounce. If this causes a 'burp' when the transmitter is keyed then a capacitor from the base of Tr5 to the junction of R30 and R31 may be needed. (values in the range 100nF to 10μF could be tried).

Transistor Tr6 is operated in grounded base mode, which produces higher levels of third harmonic than common emitter mode. The values of C27 and R29 are adjusted to reduce the portion of the driving wave during which TR6 will conduct.

When Tr6 conducts for just one third of the period of the negative swing of the fundamental wave the collector will produce an amplified copy of the same. This half cycle at one third the period is now a half cycle of the third harmonic. The coil L2 has its top end decoupled to ground by C28, which has a reactance of about 1Ω so the top of the coil is grounded at 70MHz. This puts the coil effectively in parallel with C29 and together they resonate at 70MHz. The output pulse from Tr6 triggers this resonant circuit, thereby enhancing 70MHz and rejecting other frequencies. The signal is coupled from L2 and C29 resonant circuit by C30 and into another resonant circuit

comprising L3, C32, and C33. This is another parallel tuned circuit where the series arrangement of C32 and C33 provides a low impedance output for the next stage.

Transistor Tr7 is a straightforward amplifier, biased so that it is just below conduction. The positive swing of the 70MHz signal applied to its base drives it hard into conduction during that half cycle. The collector produces a massively amplified negative half cycle for the same period. The collector circuit of Tr7 is another parallel tuned resonant circuit comprising L4, C35, and C36 with low impedance output for the following stage.

The power amplifier stage is biased through the RF choke (RFC2) so that it does not conduct until the driving positive half wave reaches 0.65V. The drive signal swing is of the order of 6V, so TR8 is switched on for 90% of the half cycle. This produces a corresponding negative half cycle swing of the collector circuit. Coil L5 is an RF supply choke and is not really part of the tuned circuit. The reactance of L5 is chosen to be about 10 times the load resistance of the collector circuit. Coil L6 together with variable capacitor C39 and C40 form a series driven parallel tuned circuit capable of matching a collector resistance between 35 and 100Ω to 50Ω. Capacitors C41, C42, C43, and C44 together with L7, L8, and L9 form a seven element Chebyshev low pass filter. This is as complex as a filter needs to get if it is to be built without

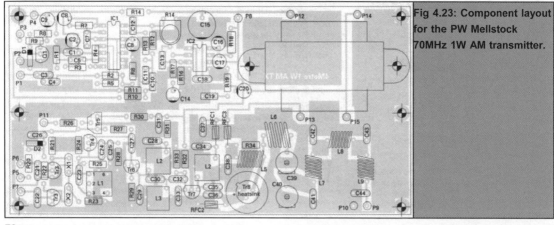

Fig 4.23: Component layout for the PW Mellstock 70MHz 1W AM transmitter.

Table 4.4: Parts list for the PW Mellstock 70MHz 1W AM transmitter.

Resistors (Fixed Film 0.25W)		
1Ω	1	R19
56Ω	1	R18
120Ω	1	R17
330Ω	1	R15
390Ω	1	R8
470Ω	6	R27, R28, R29, R30, R31,R33
560Ω	1	R23
1.2kΩ	2	R9, R34
3.9kΩ	1	R26
5.6kΩ	2	R1,R4
8.2kΩ	4	R5, R6, R13, R20
10kΩ	1	R32
15kΩ	1	R25
18kΩ	2	R12, R24
22kΩ	1	R11
68kΩ	2	RIO, RJ6
100kΩ	5	R2, R3, R7, R21, R22

Resistors (Variable)		
47kΩ	1	RL01

Resistors (Preset)		
10kΩ	1	R14

Capacitors (Polyester)		
2.2nF	1	C12
10nF	2	C11, C13
47nF	3	C4, C5, C7
100nF	1	C102
20nF	1	C19

Capacitors (Disc Ceramic)		
1.2pF	1	C30
22pF	1	C29
39pF	2	C32, C44
47pF	3	C27, C35, C41
56pF	1	C33
68pF	1	C36
82pF	3	C23, C42, C43
150pF	2	C24, C25
330pF	1	C18
2.2nF	7	C3, C28, C31, C34, C37 C38, C101
10nF	4	CI, C21, C22, C26

Capacitors (Electrolytic 25V)		
10µF	4	C2, C6, C8, C9
47µF	1	C16
100µF	3	C14, C17, C20
220µF	1	C15

Capacitors (Foil Trimmer)		
65pF	2	C39, C40

Semiconductors		
IN4148	1	D1
2N4427	1	Tr8
BC157	1	Tr5
BC548	3	Trl, Tr2, Tr3
BF199	3	Tr4, Tr6, Tr7
LM324	1	IC1
TBA820M	1	IC2 (wrongly labelled U2 in the circuit diagram)

Zener Diodes		
9V1	1	D2

Inductors		
33µH	1	L101
Toko 3335R	1	L1
Toko 0764	3	L2, L3, L4

Other

RFC 1, 2 and 3 are two or three turns on a ferrite bead

L7, L9 are 6t (spaced) of 0.92mm (20s.w.g.) copper wire on a 6mm mandrel

L5, L8 are 7t (spaced) of 0.92mm (20s.w.g.) copper wire on a 6mm mandrel

L6 is 4t (spaced) of 1.2mm (18s.w.g.) copper wire on a 10mm mandrel.

Miscellaneous

A suitable box, and interconnecting wire.

1 pole 2 way switch

A suitable 1:1 audio transformer

Two crystals (see text)

One or more LEDs colour to suit

Sockets and plugs. and another hardware are required

screens on the PCB.

Transmitter and filter performance

Performance of the transmitter and filter combination gives an unmodulated carrier of 1W output with the second harmonic -52dB, 3rd harmonic -55dB and no others except 700MHz at -60dB. These could possibly be further reduced if the output filter coils were screened from each other. The circuit diagram is shown in Fig 4.20 and 4.21. The PCB layout is shown in Fig 4.22 and the component layout in Fig 4.23. The parts list is shown in Table 4.4.

Construction

Fit the components in order of profile height starting with the resistors and diodes, these can be fitted and have their leads bent over to hold the parts in place. Do all the fitting of these parts and solder them as a group and crop them off. Next, fit the pins by pushing them into the board from the underside. Use pliers to force them into position until the head is flush against the board. The two pins for the transformer connections (along the centre line of the board) can be forced into final position using your hot soldering iron. Then solder all the pins as a group.

You should then find the three ferrite bead chokes, cut the leads to about 15mm long. Use the soldering iron and solder to pre-tin these before fitting. The enamel is a type, which dissolves at soldering temperatures so it is not necessary to scrape them first. While soldering hold them individually in position to keep them tight to the board.

Next, select the LM324 (IC1) and carefully align the rows of legs so they are parallel by pressing them gently

Fig 4.24: Picture of the completed PW Mellstock 70MHz 1W AM transmitter PCB.

against the workbench. Fit the device into the board and hold in place while soldering a pin at opposite corners. Then proceed to solder all the other pins, and if necessary re-do the corner pin connections. Then do the same with the TBA820M (IC2).

Fit the trimpot, R14, into place and hold while soldering. Be careful to keep your fingers off the exposed metal of the rear tabs, which will, of course, get very hot. Then fit the ceramic capacitors and bend their leads to hold them in place. Again, do all the fitting of these parts and solder them as a group and crop them off. The poly block capacitors, and electrolytic capacitors should be fitted individually and held in place during soldering to keep them upright and close to the board.

Next, you should fit the transistors by gently pushing the BF and BC types into the board so their legs gently splay until they are tightly held and reasonably close to the board. Solder them as a group and crop off but don't fit the 2N4427 yet.

The four TOKO coils are quite a tight fit and can be fitted and soldered as a group. The open wound coils have to be fitted and held in place while soldering. This is a tricky job as the turns of the coil should be 1.5 to 2mm above the PCB. Note: A scrap piece of PCB material can be used as a spacer between the turns and the board while soldering.

The next job is to fit the 2N4427, the crystals, and the trimmer capacitors, C39, and C40 to the board. Don't forget to hold each in place, tight to the board while you are soldering.

Then you should fit the transformer to the board using the screws fitted from the underside of the board, securing them with a crinkle washer and nut. Wire the terminals of the transformer to the corresponding pins using straight pieces of tinned copper or PVC covered equipment wire. Finally, fit the TO5 heat sink to the 2N4427 with the aid of a screwdriver to hold it open.

Checks and alignment

After checking for solder bridges and less-than-perfect solder joints you are ready for checking and alignment.

Before applying power to the board, carefully examine all the joints using an eyeglass to ensure good connections have been made and there are no solder bridges between adjacent pads or tracks.

Solder a patch lead to the RF output pins and connect the other end to a power meter with a dummy load. If possible have a low power RF sniffer in line as a take-off from the meter to an oscilloscope. Connect a piece of equipment wire between the PTT pin and the ground pin of the microphone input, P1. Then connect three pieces of equipment wire between P6, P5, and P7 and corresponding pins of the single pole double throw (SPDT) toggle switch. Temporarily solder the LED to pins P3 and P4 with the large metal section in the LED to J3.

Using a flat blade trim tool, you should then set trimmer capacitors C39 and C40 to half mesh. Next, connect your bench 13.5V supply to P8 and P2 and observe the power meter. If you see no power reading at all you have probably done something wrong. This needs to be solved before proceeding. If you observe some output from the transmitter, adjust C39 and C40 for maximum output. Using suitable trim tools adjust L2, L3, and L4 for maximum output, then re-adjust C39 and C40. Note: It is worth repeating the tuning of these coils and trimmer capacitors to ensure maximum output is obtained.

Frequency Counter

With the aid of a frequency counter attached to the RF sniffer you can then adjust L1 to put the frequency exactly 70.26 and 70.28MHz. Because only one coil is used to tune two crystals there may be a small error (of no more than 100Hz), which should be equalised between the two channels.

If you have an audio signal generator it is worth applying a signal at 600Hz to pins P1 and P2 and observing the envelope via the sniffer on the oscilloscope. Increase the audio level from zero until the LED just glows about two thirds full brightness. You should then adjust the modulation level with trimpot R14 until the envelope is just above 'pinch-off'. Re-adjust trimmer capacitors C39 and C40 for maximum peak excursion and then re-adjust the trimpot

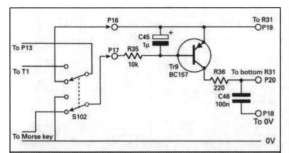

Fig 4.25: A small keying circuit for the PW Mellstock 70MHz 1W AM transmitter.

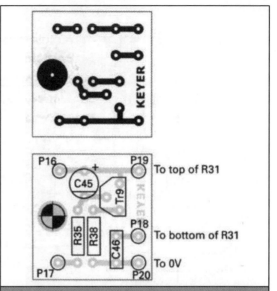

Fig 4.26: PCB and component layout of the keying circuit for the PW Mellstock 70MHz 1W AM transmitter.

R14 until pinch-off occurs. This will then correspond to 100% modulation and measurements can be taken of both carrier power and peak power.

Prototype testing

To help constructors these are the results of tests on the prototype transmitter. Using a Telewave power meter with dummy load the power read 1W unmodulated and 1.25W modulated. The output observed on a Tektronix 465B oscilloscope from the sniffer on the meter was an unmodulated envelope of 30mm and a modulated one of 45mm. The observed measurements means the voltage peak due to modulation was 1.5 times the unmodulated output level. On the proviso that the modulation envelope was close to a perfect sine wave, this would mean the peak power would be 1.5 x 1.5 x carrier, which is 2.25W. Power measured on a Bird Thruline power meter with a 060-2 60-80MHz 2.5W full scale deflection plug-in was 1.08W unmodulated and 1.01W modulated. Technical books on amplitude modulation power clearly show that a fully upward modulated a.m. transmitter at 100% modulation has an average power 1.5 x carrier. In such a case the peak voltage envelope will be twice the unmodulated level, then peak power will be 2 x 2 x carrier, which would be 4W.

On a 13.5V supply the transmitter draws exactly 200mA unmodulated and 330mA modulated. The DC input power to the whole transmitter is then 2.7W unmodulated, 4.6W modulated. In terms of overall transmitter efficiency the results are exceedingly good for a circuit so complex. It represents an efficiency of 37%.

The Morse option

Earlier in the project it was mentioned that the switch-on carrier envelope showed a cycle and a half of low frequency 'bounce'. This was originally thought to be the oscillator. However, since producing the transmitter it has been evaluated for keying. When keying the tripler stage this bounce was at the leading edge of each RF envelope.

It was then suspected that the bounce was due to the inductance of the modulation transformer limiting the current flow to the driver and output stage. To investigate, a link was connected from the positive supply pin P8 to P13, shorting out the transformer. The leading edge bounce then disappeared leaving sharp rise and fall edges. A simple circuit was developed to replace R31 on

the transmit strip to key the supply to the tripler stage. The keying circuit is shown in Fig 4.25. A small printed circuit board has also been created for the keying unit with the track artwork and overlay shown in Fig 4.26. To interface the keyer option with the main board, remove R31 and also the link from P13 to the transformer. Ideally fit pins to the holes left by R31. Note: The keyer board can be located at the crystal end of the main board and wires run along the centre of the main board. A double pole switch is wired as shown on the keyer diagram. One pole and two ways will connect P13 either to the transformer for AM transmission or directly to the positive supply when in the Morse mode. The other pole and two ways will either ground the keyer input when in AM mode or take it to the key for Morse mode. The output from the oscillator is taken from the collector of Tr4 and is therefore already partly isolated from the base emitter oscillatory circuit. The tripler stage is grounded base and hopefully will provide some further isolation from the oscillator.

70cm ATV transmitter

This design is a updated version of the original "pocket transmitter" by Marc Chamley, F3YX published in 1984. The new design is by Amand Cauquelin, F1GFF and Christian Denolle, F1FAU and published in CQTV [14]. The diode modulator and video amplifier have been retained. The VCO and the RF amplifier chain are new, taking shape after two years of experimentation. The transmitter is characterised by PLL frequency locking, extremely linear amplification and the use of surface mount power transistors. The design also eliminates canned inductors, it has reduced audio subcarrier harmonics and a 4053 solid state switch instead of a DIL relay.

The unit consumes about 350mA at 12V. For use in

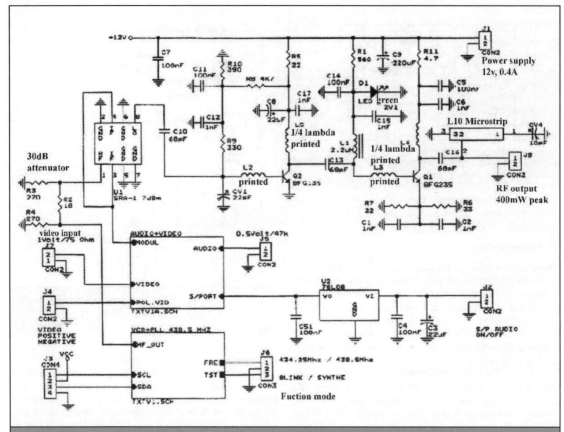

Fig 4.27: 300mW amplifiers section of the 70cm ATV transmitter.

vehicles four regulators protect the voltage sensitive elements from voltage variation. Finally the widespread use of surface mount (SMD) components allows the PCB to be placed inside a commercial metal case.

The PLL, VCO and buffer stages

The VCO covers just 50MHz (420 - 470MHz), the circuit diagram is shown in Fig 4.29 and 4.30. The frequency range is reduced by the use of a variable capacitor (CV3) to centre the operating range to suite the frequency of ATV operation. The output of the VCO is 8 – 12mW after the BFR93 amplifier. The operating properties of a green LED are used to stabilise Q12 using its zener voltage of 2.1V. This LED sets the collector base voltage to around 3V (2.1 + 0.7 + V of R45) and consequently the quiescent current of the transistor (8V - 3V = 5V divided by the 180Ω of R56).

Communication between the PIC, 12C508A-04P and the PLL IC, TSA5511, is via the I²C bus. The TSA5511 is referenced to a 4MHz crystal. The PIC is programmed for the two ATV frequencies in use. Connector J6 is provided for selecting frequency 438.5MHz with pin 1 open and 434.25MHz with a jumper between pins 1 and 2 (pin 2 is chassis/ground). To test that the PIC is functioning place a jumper between pins 2 and 3 of J6; the red LED will flash while it is in place.

Amplification following the mixer

F1FAU had the idea of experimenting with transistors from the Farnell catalogue [15], in particular BFG135, BFG235, BLU86 and BFG591 (all types used in mobile phones, detailed on the Philips website [16]). Supplied in surface-mount form, they offer remarkable gain and power at a competitive price. The last three are in the 2W at 12V category.

Regulating the transmitter for 250mW output achieves extremely high linearity and stability at the same time. The BFG235 does not need a heatsink, the heat being dissipated partly through the copper tracks. With this level of amplification, a 17dBm mixer such as SRAI-H is not justified. For Class A operation the quiescent current of the transistors is adjusted as high as possible; 40mA for the BFG135 and 100mA for the BFG235.

The bias circuit for the BFG235 is the classic design, the circuit is shown in Fig 4.27. It uses the zener function of a green LED being 2.1V. The voltage drop between base and emitter being 0.7V, the emitter voltage is stabilised at 2.1 - 0.7 = 1.4V. The two emitter connections of the BFG235 are used, one has a 22Ω resistor and the other a 33Ω resistors to make an equivalent resistance of 13Ω. The voltage at the emitter is 1.4V, which determines the current (I = V/R) at around 105mA, which is the collector current of the transistor.

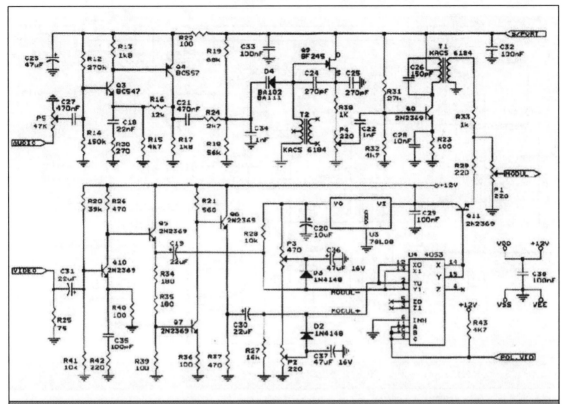

Fig 4.28: Audio and video modulator section of the 70cm ATV transmitter.

Audio modulator

Two Toko KACS6184 inductors replace the two 7F10 inductors of the original design. The circuit diagram is shown in Fig 4.28. The KACS6184 filters the harmonics perfectly and imparts a neat sinusoidal shape with straightforward tuning. The secondary of the KACS6184 coil has too many turns to pass the video signal. The components have the same values as in the TX ATV 1200 design by F3YX.

Video modulator

This section of the circuit conforms closely to the original "Pocket Transmitter". The DIL relay has been changed for

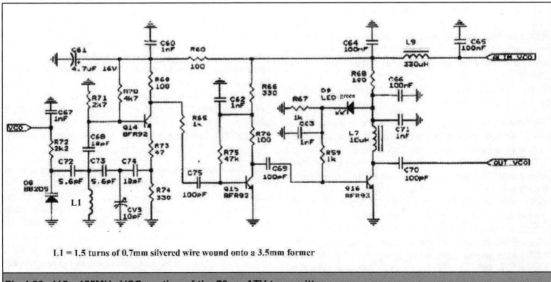

Fig 4.29: 415 - 455MHz VCO section of the 70cm ATV transmitter.

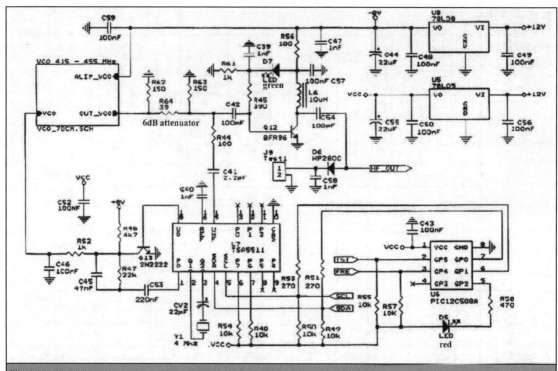

Fig 4.30: Synthesiser section of the 70cm ATV transmitter.

an analogue switch (4053). A resistor and a capacitor have been added on the emitter of transistor Q10 to improve the crispness of the picture.

Construction

Using surface mount (SMD) components means there are fewer holes to drill. Their wide availability and frequently lower price make them ideal. Their use becomes easy with a little practice it is also rapid and quite agreeable.

This is a double sided PCB (Figs 4.31 and 4.32), the SMD components that need grounding are connected by tinned rivets through the board. The unit is built into a 146 x 72 x 30mm tinplate housing which would have been unthinkable without the use of SMD components. The metal housing is an effective shield against RF from the PA affecting the VCO and against interference from the microprocessor. Leaving the lid off may affect the picture on the check monitor.

The housing is in two L shaped parts and two lids. Fit the two L shaped parts into one of the lids and solder the assembly to form an open box. The holes to be drilled are 3.5mm for the bypass capacitors and 3mm for the BNC connectors. The square flange of the BNC connectors should not hinder the fit of the lid. The spigot of the BNC connectors should be a maximum of 2mm above the ground plane, reduce the diameter of the sleeve so that it is possible to connect the spigot to the PCB. When fitting the PCB into the housing the distance between the floor of the housing and the component side of the PCB should be 18mm. The PCB can be soldered in with wedges under the PCB to hold it in place, it should be fitted into the

housing after testing.

If the bypass capacitors are fitted on the long side of the enclosure it will be possible to mount the TX module either on the front or rear panel of a large cabinet with the BNC connectors passing through the panel. The video input should be made either by a ceramic feedthrough having very little capacitance or by means of a sub miniature coaxial connector (SMA / SMB / SMC series).

Before assembling the PCB, it should be offered up and trimmed to the exact size of the inner dimensions of the housing, using a file or glass paper. Positioning the components is done using the component layout (Fig 4.33). The normal components are fitted to the ground plane side of the board and the SMD components are fitted to the track side. Solder the conventional components first to give a reference point for placing the SMD parts. Construction of the VCO section is described separately below. The PIC, PLL and mixer ICs are fitted after the first test and adjustment of the VCO. The BFG235 output transistor is fitted as part of the PA testing.

The SMD components can be grounded by means of pieces of wire passing through the board, linked to the ground plane but tinned rivets give a lower inductance connection. To solder the SMD components flat and close to the PCB, the through wires are soldered first only on the copper side. Off-cuts of resistor leads are not recommended for this task. Pay attention to the pin connections of SMD transistors in SOT23 style; it is easy to reverse the base and emitter. Pay attention that on tantalum capacitors (normal or SMD) the dash indicates `+'.

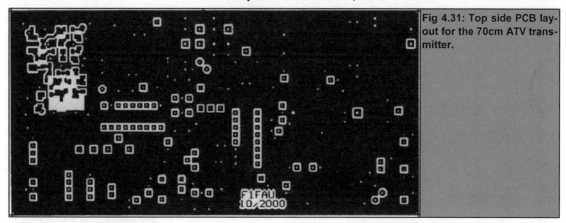

Fig 4.31: Top side PCB layout for the 70cm ATV transmitter.

Assembling the VCO section

All parts are surface mount except the inductor L1 and the variable capacitor CV3. A ground plane (tracks side) contributes to shielding as well as protection. The high density of components in the VCO means using a 20W or 30W soldering iron with a very narrow tip. Don't forget to provide a wire for the +8V supply. The variable capacitor CV3 (Murata or Philips CO50) should be fitted so that the connection in contact with the adjustment screw is grounded.

This section of the PCB is shielded with a protective cover. It is made from a piece of 0.4mm brass 57 x 47mm folded to make a 35 x 25 x 11mm cover for the components. This cover is fitted after preliminary tests and adjustment of the VCO.

Test and adjustments

Once the PCB is assembled it should be checked to make sure it is free from errors. All adjustments are simple and setting up should take no more than a quarter of an hour. To avoid unpleasant surprises when you are ready to fire it up for the first time, use a voltmeter and a capacitance meter to check the position and polarity of components.

The instruments needed are an oscilloscope, a frequency counter, a triangular wave signal generator and a high quality video signal. Two probes are needed; these can be home made and a design is available from F1GFF [17].

One probe coupled to the oscilloscope measures the peak voltage to represent power. The second "video" probe, designed specially, demodulates the RF and permits the picture to be viewed on a colour monitor and oscilloscope. A 12V power supply limited to 0.5A avoids cremating components in case any mistakes occur. Power levels are expressed in peak power and are independent of picture content. This allows realistic comparisons of power level (mWc = peak milliwatts).

Preliminary tests

The first checks should be made before the mixer, PIC, PLL and the BFG235 PA transistor are fitted. Connect a small Teflon covered cable with a female BNC at the output of the 3dB attenuator, between pin 1 of the mixer and ground, so that you can connect the frequency counter or a 50Ω load.

To check the free running operation of the VCO, remove the 1kΩ resistor R52 to connect the centre tap of a 47kΩ potentiometer to the input of the VCO control. The two outer connections of the potentiometer go to +8V and ground. Connect the supply; the green LED D1 should light up. Check the output voltage of all the regulators. Adjust the control voltage of the VCO to give 3V on the centre tap of the 47kΩ potentiometer. Connect a 50Ω load to the end of the cable. Check the VCO is working by measuring at test point J9 for a voltage between 1.2 and 1.5V. Remove the load and replace it with the frequency counter, using an attenuator if necessary (say 10dB or

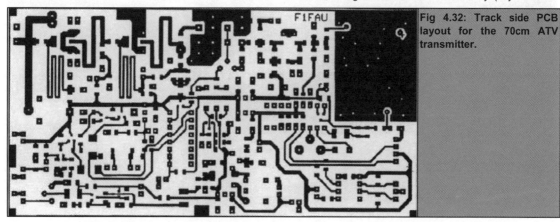

Fig 4.32: Track side PCB layout for the 70cm ATV transmitter.

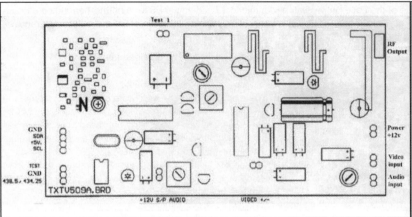

Fig 4.33: Component layout for the 70cm ATV transmitter.

according to the sensitivity of the counter). Set the VCO frequency to 438.5MHz by adjusting CV3.

Remove the 47kΩ pot and replace resistor R52 (1kΩ). Fit the PIC, 12C508A, and PLL, TSA5511, in their sockets. Connect the supply and check that the microcontroller is working. With pin 3 of J6 grounded, the red LED D5 flashes at 1Hz, indicating the PIC is working properly.

Select 438.5MHz (no strap on J6), measure and adjust with CV2. Once these checks have been made the VCO cover can be soldered in place. This itself will have an influence on the frequency so it will be necessary to adjust the VCO control voltage to around 3V with the aid of CV3. Remove the coaxial cable and fit the mixer, SRA-1 in place, ensure that the case is soldered to the ground

Table 4.5: Parts list for the 70cm ATV transmitter.

R11	4.7Ω	P2,P4	adjustable	220Ω	L1		2.2μH	
R2	18Ω	P3	adjustable	470Ω	L6, L7		10μH	
R5, R7	22Ω	P1	vert. adjustable	220Ω	L9		330μH	
R6	33Ω	P5	vet. adjustable	47kΩ				
R64	39Ω				D1	3mm or 5mm	Green LED	
R73	47Ω				D7, D9		Green LED	
R25	75Ω	CV3	Murata white	10pF	D5	3mm	Red LED	
R9, R22, R23,	100Ω		or CO50 white		D2, D3		1N4148	
R36, R39, R40,		CV4	3 vane yellow adj.	10pF	D8	UHF varicap	BB105	
R44, R60, R69,		CV1, CV2	3 vane green adj.	22pF			or BB205	
R76, R78		C41		2.2pF	D4	HF varicap	BA102	
R62, R63	150Ω	C72, C73		5.6pF			or BA111	
R34, R35, R56	180Ω	C68, c74		18pF	D6	schotky	BAR28	
R68		C10, C13, C16		68pF			or BAT41	
R29, R42	220Ω	C35, C42, C54, C69, C70, C75		100pF			or HP2800	
R3, R4, R30, R51	270Ω	C26		150pF	Q9		BF245	
R53		C24, C25		270pF	Q3		BC547	
R66, R74	330Ω	C1, C2, C6, C12, C15, C17, C22,		1nF	Q4		BC557	
R10, R45	390Ω	C34, C39, C40, C47, C58, C60,			Q13		2N2222	
R26, R37, R58	470Ω	C62, C63, C67, C71			Q5, Q6, Q7, Q8, Q10,	2N2369		
R1, R21	560Ω	C28		10nF	Q11			
R33, R38, R52,	1kΩ	C18		22nF	Q14, Q15		BFR92	
R59, R61, R65,		C45		47nF	Q16		BFR93	
R67, R77		C4, C5, C7, C11, C14, C29, C32,		100nF	Q12	SOT23	BFR96	
R13, R17	1k8Ω	C33, C38, C43, C46, C48, C49,			Q2		BFG135	
R72	2k2Ω	C50, C51, C52, C56, C57, C59,			Q1		BFG235	
R24, R71	2k7Ω	C64, C65, C66						
R8, R15, R32,	4k7Ω	C53	1812	220nF	T1, T2 Toko		KACS6148	
R43, R46, R70		C21, C27	1812	470nF	U1		SRA-1	
R28, R41, R48,	10kΩ	C61	1812	4.7μF 16V	U2, U3, U8		78L08	
R49, R50, R54,		C20	Radial	10μF 16V	U4		4053	
R55, R57		C3, C8, C31,	Radial	22μF 16V	U5		78L05	
R16	12kΩ	C44, C55			U6	PIC	12C508A	
R27	18kΩ	C19, C30	1812	22μF 16V	U7	PLL	TSA5511	
R47	22kΩ	C23	Radial	47μF 16V	Y1	HC18	4MHz	
R31	27kΩ	C36, C37	Radial	47μF 10V				
R20	39kΩ	C9	Radial	220μF 25V				
R75	47kΩ				6 x 1nF Feedthrough capacitors			
R18	56kΩ				146 x 72 x 30mm Tinplate box			
R19	68kΩ				PCB contact F1GFF [17]			
R14	150kΩ							
R12	270kΩ							

plane at two points on each side of the case. Verify with a digital multimeter that there is a good 1.5V on J9 (RF test). The RF level can be readjusted by modifying the value of R56, the limits being 150 to 270Ω.

Adjustment of video amplifier

With no video signal at J7 adjust P3 to give 5.0V at the cathode of D3. Adjust P2 to give 2.0V at the anode of D2. For positive modulation ground pin 1 of J4. For negative modulation pin 1 of J1 is floating. With no signal at the video input, verify that there is 0.93V on the emitter of Q11.

With a triangular waveform on the video input (1kHz, 1V peak to peak), a signal of 4.5Vp-p should be present at the emitter of Q11. Switching from positive to negative video, the two traces should superimpose on one another and if this is not the case, go into negative and bring the two curves closer using P3.

Insert the BFG235 but before soldering this transistor in place check that there is a good 2.1V between ground and the base of Q1, also that the LED D1 is lit. Solder the BFG235 in place and measure 0.47V on R11 (4.7Ω). The BFG235 gets hot to the point that fingertip contact is painful; this is normal. An oscilloscope is essential to measure peak power when adjusting the amplifier. Connect the RF power probe to transmitter output and the oscilloscope to the output of the probe. Inject a 1kHz 1Vp-p triangular signal. Position the trace at foot of the scope screen; this will be the 0V reference. On the screen you will see a deformed triangle (normal without the 10kΩ). Measure the voltage V at the upper summit of the peak and apply the formula peak power $= (V - 0.3)^2 / 100$. Turn P1 to a quarter of its travel from the ground side, then CV1 to minimum and CV4 to the centre of it's travel. The oscilloscope should display a deformed triangle, adjust CV1 and CV4 for maximum power (maximum amplitude on oscilloscope screen). Adjust P1 to give peaks of 4.5V on the oscilloscope corresponding to 250mW peak. P1 can be used to reduce or increase power but linearity is degraded beyond 5V (corresponding to 300mW peak).

With the audio subcarrier off, inject a normalised 1Vp-p triangular signal. Set modulation to positive. Adjust P2 to place the bottom "peak" a little above the peaking threshold so that the audio subcarrier is not pulled down by the bottom peak. Set modulation to negative, with pin 1 of J4 floating. Adjust P3 to superimpose the new trace with that of positive modulation. Check the traces overlay by flipping the video switch rapidly.

Apply power and put P4 at centre of its travel. Check the presence of RF with audio subcarrier active. Carefully adjust the core of T2 to bring the frequency to 5.5MHz. There should be an RF signal of around 0.2Vp-p at the centre terminal of P4. Connect the oscilloscope to the secondary of TI and adjust its core for maximum signal. You should have 3.5Vp-p with P4 at centre travel. Connect the oscilloscope to the junction of R29, R33 and P1. Adjust subcarrier amplitude with P4 in conjunction with the circuit diagram. To check audio operation apply

audio to J5 and adjust P5 for a normal hearing on a check receiver. Correct regulation of the audio deviation requires a spectrum analyser.

Further details can be obtained from F1GFF [17].

Transceivers

There is a trend towards software controlled radio and the use of Digital Signal Processing (DSP), so a project by Bob Larkin, W7PUA originally published in QST [18] has been included in this section. This is a complex project with endless opportunities for experimentation. The other transceiver in this section is an ATV project made from ready built modules which provides an easy way to start with this branch of the hobby.

The DSP-10 Transceiver

This project has been around for a few years now and has generated quite a following, there is a comprehensive web site [19] giving all of the latest updates and software enhancements. It is an ideal project for the more experienced constructor; it is a fully functioning software controlled 2m QRP transceiver. It is ideal for those who are interested in weak signal modes, many of the enhancements are for these modes. The current list of features is:

- Coverage from 144 to 148MHz
- Complete transceiver for USB, LSB, CW, and FM operation
- Four additional weak signal modes; EME-2, LHL-7, PUA-43, LTI.
- 1Hz frequency control (except FM)
- Full integration of UHF/Microwave transverters
- IF and audio is defined in software (SDR) to allow additions and improvements
- Low power 20mW with an add on 8W amplifier
- Eight audio filters
- One audio filter that can be custom tailored from the screen
- 13 point receive audio equalizer
- LMS noise reduction and auto notch
- Two selectable IF bandwidths
- Binaural audio with delay de-coherence for amazing sound and signal copy
- Fully definable spectral analysis
- FM Tones, DTMF, CTCSS and bursts
- SSB End tone burst
- 9999 definable memories.
- 20 definable VFO's
- 20 definable transverters
- Spectral Waterfall display
- Data record to disk
- GIF Screen saves built in
- User changeable help screens.
- Timed (Beacon) transmit and receive control, with data collection
- Precise EME (Moon bounce) Doppler correction of frequency for all modes
- Real time Moon and Sun tracking in Az, El & distance

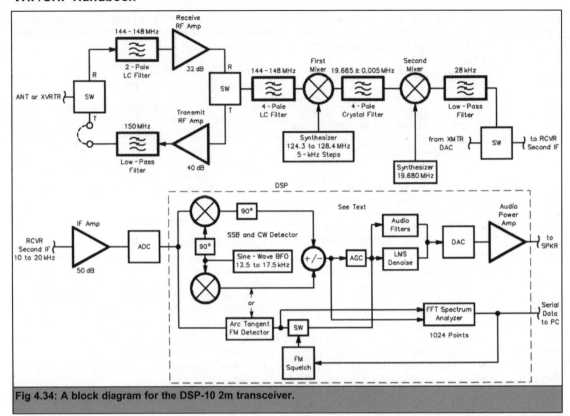

Fig 4.34: A block diagram for the DSP-10 2m transceiver.

- Complete CW sending from the PC keyboard.
- Pre-recorded CW messages with looping and transmit/receive control.
- Audio frequency equaliser for transmit, makes any mike DX capable.
- S meter that is accurate from -140 to 25dBm
- Provision for frequency control to a fraction of a Hertz
- Highly accurate Sun (and Moon) noise measurements with Power to Tone peaking.
- Automatic Time setting from GPS to support the weak signal modes and the EME Doppler corrections.
- Calculation of Distance and Bearing for a full QTH list.

The original article by Bob Larkin follows but anyone who wants to construct the DSP-10 should also read the details on Bob's web site [19].

The original DSP-10 article

The DSP-10 is a low power, all mode 2m transceiver using DSP at the last IF and audio stages. You control the radio via a PC acting as the virtual front panel. A built in audio spectrum analyser allows you to see what is happening at the audio level. A number of features make this rig particularly well suited for use as an IF radio for UHF and microwave transverters.

Three basic components are involved. A minimal amount of RF hardware (on a single PCB) translates the signal frequency up and down with the IF and audio processing done using a DSP. The original design of DSP-10 in 1999

used the Analog Devices EZ-Kit for the DSP processor, this is no longer available but a replacement kit KDSP10 [20] has been designed by Lyle Johnson, KK7P, this has also been used in the Pic-A-Star project. A DSP program processes the IF and audio portions of the radio signals. Finally, software running in the PC controls the DSP and presents a front panel interface to you, the user.

PC requirements are minimal, almost any PC running DOS equipped with a 640 x 480 VGA display can be used. No extended or expanded memory is needed, nor is a maths co-processor required but it is useful for the latest versions of software. The program can operate with very slow processors. Most of this transceiver's testing was done using a 20MHz 386 laptop computer. Communication between the DSP and the PC is at 9600 baud.

Constructing a piece of electronic hardware requires a description through schematics, PC layouts and the like. To help you understand the inner workings of this radio and as a starting point for customising your radio, or for building a new project altogether, this project's source code is available [21].

Figure 4.34 shows a block diagram of the transceiver. This is a conventional double conversion design. An RF amplifier increases the signal sufficiently to overcome the first mixer noise. Two RF filters ensure that the image frequency, which is in the FM broadcast band, is adequately rejected. The first conversion synthesiser in the 125MHz region is programmable in 5kHz steps. The first mixer produces a first IF at 19.665MHz, which is equipped

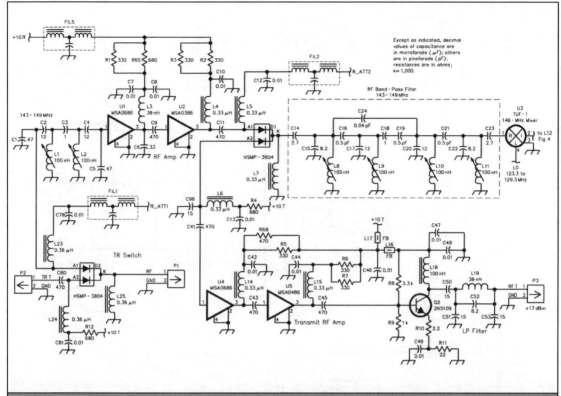

Fig 4.35: Transmit and receive signal paths for the DSP-10 2m transceiver.

with a crystal filter. This filter's bandwidth is about 12kHz and provides image rejection for a second IF at only 15kHz This low frequency second IF allows use of a low cost audio analog to digital converter (ADC) to prepare the signal for the DSP.

All 15kHz IF and audio signal processing is done in DSP. The software BFO for SSB and CW can be programmed in steps smaller than 1Hz; this is image reject mixed with the IF signal to produce audio. At audio, you can select bandpass filtering or a least mean square (LMS) de-noise algorithm [22]. Following the audio processing, a DAC readies the signal for the audio power amplifier. At audio, a fast Fourier transform (FFT) spectrum analyser is always operating, sending the resulting data to the PC through a serial port.

The FM detector also operates at the 15kHz IF. No fine tuning control is available for this mode, so it is tunable in 5kHz steps, adequate for most applications. The spectrum analyser continues to operate on the detected audio for FM. The FM squelch is derived from the spectrum analyser output by examining the level of the high frequency noise.

The transmit path is essentially the receive path in reverse. The CW, SSB or FM signal is generated by the DSP at about 15kHz. This signal is then double converted to 2m using the same mixers and filters that are used in the receive path. A three stage amplifier raises the power output to more than 20mW. Provision is made to use external amplifiers to raise the power level further.

Transceiver Hardware

Fig 4.35 shows the received signal path. Signals from an antenna (or a transverter) go to P1 on the main circuit board. A dual PIN diode (D2) is used for TR switching. The current through this diode is under PC control (through the DSP) and is used as an adjustable RF attenuator. This is a very simple way to achieve an attenuation range of about 18dB. It is, however, a compromise method because the impedance seen by the following filter varies with the attenuation level. This, in turn, causes some distortion in the RF passband response. However, because the attenuation is set for minimum except when handling a strong local signal, this approach does not cause problems.

The signal passes through a two pole filter consisting of L1, L2 and associated capacitors. This filter derives from a design by Rick Campbell, KK7B [23] and has a 20dB rejection 25MHz out of band. The filter's insertion loss is about 2dB. Two RF amplifier stages, U1 and U2, provide a gain of about 32dB. This high gain level is needed to overcome the first mixer noise. It does, however, make the front end more prone to overload.

Following the RF amplifier is a second dual PIN diode switch, D1. This, too, serves dual roles as a TR switch and as a variable attenuator for the receive path. Here is another 19dB of RF gain control, again under control of the PC.

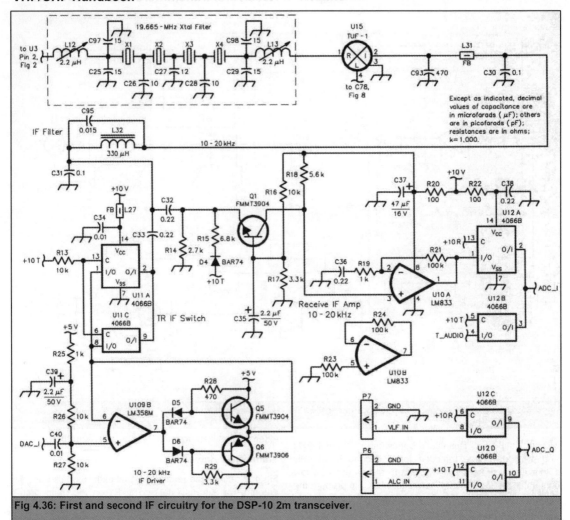

Fig 4.36: First and second IF circuitry for the DSP-10 2m transceiver.

The four pole bandpass filter built around L8, L9, L10 and LI I provides most RF signal filtering. A conventional top coupled, or Cohn, filter, it has its greatest rejection on the low frequency side. C24 is added to produce a notch at about 126MHz. A "gimmick" capacitor, C24's value is very small (about 0.04pF) and consists simply of a piece of tinned wire placed near a PCB pad. The filter response, shown in Fig 4.37, shows this notch with an attenuation of about 97dB. Rejection exceeds 95dB for all frequencies below 128MHz, which includes the conversion oscillator and image frequencies. Filter insertion loss is about 10dB and is compensated for by the RF amplifier gain.

A Mini Circuits TUF-1 double balanced mixer (U3) converts the 2m input signal to a 19.665MHz IF. When transmitting, U3's signal passes through the RF filter, goes through TR switch D1 and arrives at the first transmit amplifier (U4) at a level of about -27dBm. Two MSA amplifiers (U4 and U5) and Q2, a 2N5109 operating class A, provide a gain of about 40dB to raise this level to +13dBm (20mW). The measured 1dB compression point of this amplifier is +19dBm, making it very linear at the operating point. A Low pass filter consisting of L19 and

three capacitors (C51 through C53) reduces the transmitter harmonic levels. The transmitter output does not go directly to the PIN diode TR switch D2. Instead, the lines go to a pair of connectors identified as P2 and P3 that attach to rear panel jacks. Such routing allows the transceiver to be connected to a transverter or a power amplifier without the need for another TR switch. P2 and P3 can be connected together for stand alone QRP operation.

First and Second IF

As shown in Fig 4.36, the receive path accepts a 19.665kHz signal from the first mixer, U3. A four pole crystal filter using low cost standard crystals (X1 to X4) provides selectivity. The series crystal configuration used has a rejection notch at a frequency above the passband [24]. This rejects the image before the second mixer. L12 and L13 along with C25 and C29 form L networks that step up the 50Ω impedance to the 1.5kΩ required by the filter. The rejection for the out of band response at the image frequencies above 19.690MHz is greater than 70dB; passband insertion loss is just over 1dB.

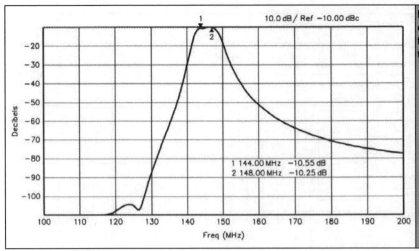

Fig 4.37: Measured frequency response of the four pole interstage filter of the DSP-10 2m transceiver.

A second TUF-1 double balanced mixer, U15, converts the received signal to the next IF at 15kHz. A three pole, elliptical, lowpass filter, built around L3, restricts the band of signals passed on to the IF amplifier. The cutoff frequency of this filter is about 28kHz.

Next, the received signal is amplified by a 50dB low noise amplifier using Q1 and U10A. This circuit is essentially the same as that used by KK7B in his R2 receiver [25], but the roots of the grounded base IF appear to go back to Roy Lewallen, W7EL [26]. No active power supply decoupling is needed because the lowest frequency amplified (set by C32) is a few kilohertz. D4 and R15 disable Q1 during transmit. This circuit provides flat response to frequencies well beyond 20kHz and provides the gain needed to drive the DSP board ADC. CMOS switches U12A and U12B determine whether the ADC is connected to the IF amplifier for receive or to the microphone for transmit.

Received signals are converted to digital data by the ADC operating at a 48kHz rate. It is important that the alias frequencies above this be removed. This function is handled by filtering that is part of the DSP board ADC. (All remaining processes for detection and signal filtering are performed in the DSP and are discussed later.)

Following the DSP is a DAC on the DSP board that includes low pass filtering of the analogue signals. Next (see Fig 4.38) is a dual audio amplifier (U14) that raises the audio signal amplitude to speaker level.

The transmitted signal in the 15kHz range is produced by the DAC on the DSP board. In order to drive the 50Ω port of mixer U15 (Fig 4.36), there is an amplifier consisting of a U109B op amp and a pair of current boosting transistors, Q5 and Q6. Here we have a case where the 50Ω IF impedance of the mixer is not very convenient. Adding to the IF drive requires a reduction of the CMOS TR switch

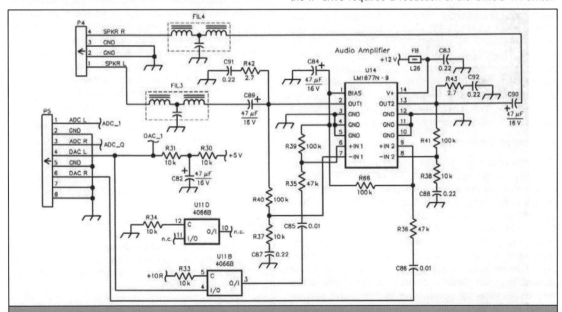

Fig 4.38: Dual integrated audio amplifier for the DSP-10 2m transceiver.

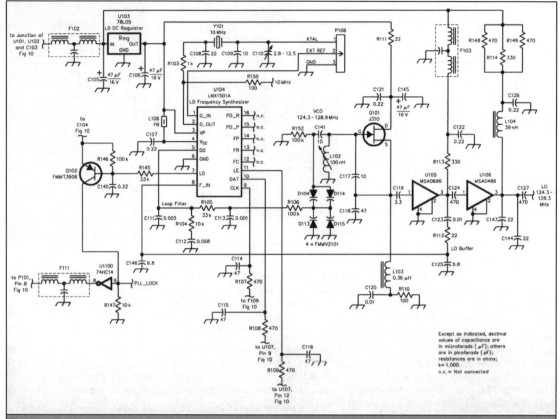

Fig 4.39: Frequency synthesiser for the first conversion oscillator of the DSP-10 2m transceiver.

"on" resistance. To reduce the resistance, two sections of 4066 switch U11 are connected in parallel. All of this gets a 10dBm signal to the mixer.

From here, the transmit signal goes through the crystal filter to mixer U3 (Fig 4.35), ready to be converted to the output frequency. As pointed out previously, the crystal filter has particularly high attenuation on the high frequency side of the passband. This provides good attenuation of the 19.68MHz conversion oscillator signal that gets transmitted 15kHz away from the desired output signal. In addition, the TUF-I mixer has good balance to further reduce the level of this signal.

Conversion Oscillators

The first conversion oscillator, shown in Fig 4.39, ranges in frequency from about 124.3 to 128.4MHz in 5kHz steps. This is a simple single loop synthesiser using U104, which contains the programmable frequency dividers and a phase detector. The VCO, Q101, is tuned by four varactors (D104 and D113 - D115) in the standard parallel, reverse connected configuration that improves the resonator Q at low tuning voltages. A separate 5V regulator, U103, prevents interaction with other parts of the circuit through the power source. A pair of IC amplifiers, U105 and U106, raise the power level to 7dBm and prevent strong signals from getting back to the VCO. At a 10kHz offset, the phase noise is about -105dBc.

A similar circuit is used for the 19.68MHz fixed frequency second conversion oscillator (Fig 4.40). This synthesiser uses an active loop filter built around op amp U6. The reference frequency of 20kHz along with the relatively low operating frequency results in a clean spectrum. Buffers U8 and U9 produce a +7dBm output level. At first, an LMX1501A synthesiser IC was tried as the first conversion oscillator. It would appear to lock, but the output spectrum was very poor. After much experimentation, it was found that the LMX1501A cannot be used below about 100MHz because of the counter circuitry employed, although that restriction is not mentioned in the data sheets.

Both synthesisers used in the transceiver are referenced to a common 10MHz signal. An internal crystal oscillator is used and provides good frequency stability. For more stringent applications, provision is also made for an external frequency reference. The availability of GPS frequency standards allows stability of a fraction of a hertz at 144MHz.

Control Functions

Other transmit functions on the board (Fig 4.41) include a microphone amplifier (U109A), logic level converters for the CW key (U110E and U110F) and the PTT line from the microphone (U110C).

Except for the voltage tolerant audio amplifier, U14, the main circuit board is powered through a 10V regulator,

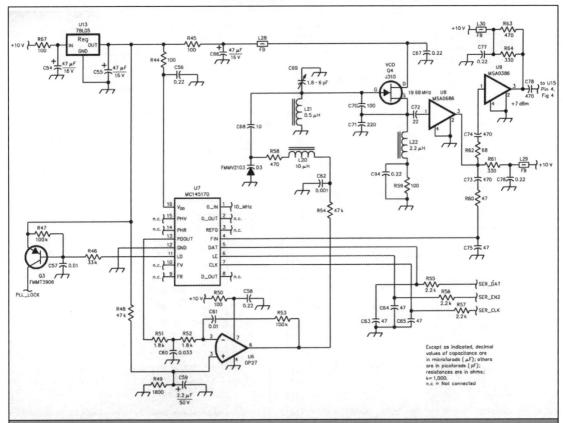

Fig 4.40: Frequency synthesiser for the second conversion oscillator of the DSP-10 2m transceiver.

U101, as shown in Fig 4.41. This low dropout regulator makes operation independent of input supply voltages ranging from 11 to 16V. A noise filter consisting of C101, L101 and C102, along with reverse voltage protection from a 1A fuse (F1) and diode (D101) provide power conditioning.

MOSFETs Q105 and Q106 are used to switch the +10V line between transmit and receive. Typically, there is a drop of about 0.25V in these switches.

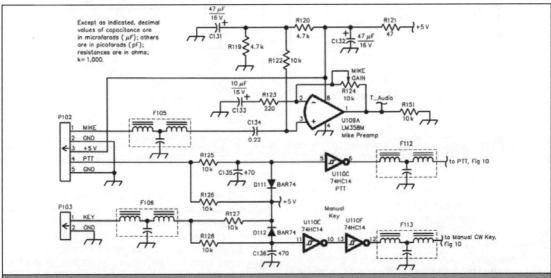

Fig 4.41: Microphone preamplifier, PTT and keying logic for the DSP-10 2m transceiver.

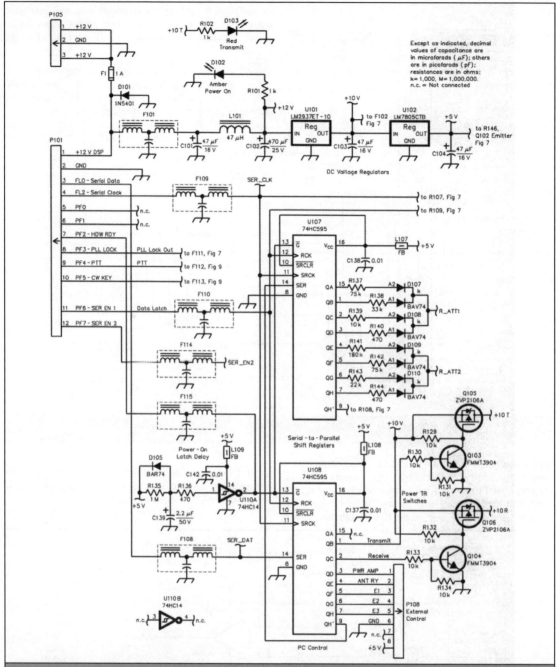

Fig 4.42: Power regulator and control circuitry for the DSP-10 2m transceiver.

Two serial data streams coming from the DSP control the various functions on the main board. These DSP interconnects are three wire system having one common line for data, one common line for clocking the data and two separate enable lines that indicate when all data has been clocked to the board. One of these serial streams goes to the second conversion synthesiser, U7 (Fig 4.40). The other goes first to a pair of eight bit serial to parallel shift registers, U108 and U107 (Fig 4.42), and then to the first

conversion synthesiser, U104.

Shift registers U107 and U108 have 16 outputs for control functions such as transmit, receive, external amplifier relay and external antenna relay. The latter two functions are for relay sequencing that is controlled by the PC, eliminating the need for an external sequencer. There are three spare external control leads, EI, E2 and E3 at P108. The shift register also controls the receiver RF stage gain by changing the current through the PIN diodes used for

TR control.

Once full voltage has been applied to all circuits, U110A and its associated components reset the shift registers to a known condition. This reset status is also an input to the DSP so that hardware programming does not occur when the shift registers are not ready.

DSP Software

The original DSP program was roughly 2,000 words long and written in assembly language. Since 1999 there have been many additional facilities added, in July 2006 version 3.80 of the software was released [27]. No attempt will be made here to show program details. A number of articles and books are available that provide details on the algorithms used for signal processing. The source code for the transceiver programs is quite well commented and is available for study and change [28].

The DSP program is synchronised by an AD1847 codec that performs the analog to digital conversion. To accomplish this, interrupts are generated by the codec 48,000 times each second. All internal timing is derived from these interrupts for functions such as frequency conversion, IF and AF filtering, SSB generation and serial communications with the PC. Some of these functions operate directly at the 48kHz rate, while others run every fifth cycle at a rate of 9.6kHz.

The input signal is an IF centred at 15kHz. SSB and CW reception require mixing down to audio frequencies. The conversion oscillator (BFO) is a DSP calculated sine wave in the 12.5 to 17.5kHz range, with a resolution better than 1Hz. This provides the fine tuning needed because the first conversion synthesiser changes in 5kHz steps. To discriminate between LSB and USB, there are two software mixers, one driven by a sine wave and the other driven 90° out of phase by a cosine wave. The two audio signals, called in phase (I) and quadrature (Q), are low pass filtered at 2.8kHz to remove the high frequency conversion products and other possible interfering signals. Up to this point, all processing is at a 48kHz rate.

Because the audio bandwidth has been limited at this point, it is possible to drop to a 9.6kHz rate. The two audio signals must have a 90° phase difference to allow sideband selection. A DSP routine called a Hilbert transform [29] accomplishes this. The desired sideband, upper or lower, is selected by respectively adding or subtracting the two audio signals.

Following the sideband selection are optional narrowband audio finite duration Impulse response (FIR) filters and an LMS adaptive noise reduction routine. Two CW filters having bandwidths of 200 and 450Hz centred at 600Hz are available. These filters can be changed easily by reassembling the DSP program with new files for the FIR filter coefficient.

NBFM Reception

Narrowband FM is received in a manner that starts much like SSB reception. The I and Q audio signals generated by mixing are used to calculate a phase angle relative to a centre frequency, using an arctangent function. The phase angle is subtracted from the previous measurement taken 1/48000 second earlier. This phase angle difference, after low pass filtering, is the desired detected FM signal.

During reception, spectral analysis is being done with a 1024 point FFT using the audio data sampled at a 9.6kHz rate. The spectral data from 12 overlapping data sets are averaged and converted to decibels. These are transmitted serially to the PC at 9600 baud. The decibel conversion allows the spectral data to he transmitted using only eight bits per frequency point.

SSB Transmit

The SSB transmit process is essentially the same as that used for reception, but in reverse order. The microphone's audio signal is converted to a 16bit word by the ADC. Next, a low pass FIR filter limits the bandwidth of the audio signal. A Hilbert transform [29] then generates a pair of signals with a 90° phase difference. These two signals are run through a pair of mixers having 90° out of phase conversion oscillators. Finally, the resulting signals in the 15kHz region are either added or subtracted to form an USB or LSB signal, respectively, which is sent to the same DAC used for audio output during reception.

CW Transmit

For CW, the process is simpler. The keying signal comes from the PC or a key connected to the RF board. This signal is fed through a 500Hz low pass filter to limit key clicks, producing a signal that amplitude modulates a sine wave in the 15kHz region. In the DSP, this modulation is simply a multiplication routine. The resulting modulated output is ready for the DAC.

FM Transmit

FM transmission starts by limiting and filtering the microphone input as is done for SSB. This signal is then used to determine the frequency of a software oscillator in the 10 to 30kHz range, which is sent to the DAC.

Serial communication with the DSP is at 9600 baud, and all UART functions are in software. All commands from the PC to the DSP consist of six bytes. This allows us to send commands for controls such as audio gain. About 15 different commands are available. These commands are kept as simple as possible and decision making is concentrated in the PC.

PC Software

To keep things simple, the original PC software runs under DOS. It is written in C (not C++) and uses the Borland DOS Graphics Interface routines. The programs were compiled using Borland C++ version 4.0.

All transceiver control is done via the PC keyboard. Alphanumeric keys and standard punctuation marks are reserved for sending CW; thus, most control operations involve the use of function keys, the ALT key and the CTRL key. A mouse is not used.

Basic display updating is controlled by the reception of the spectrum and status data from the DSP. This is about 535

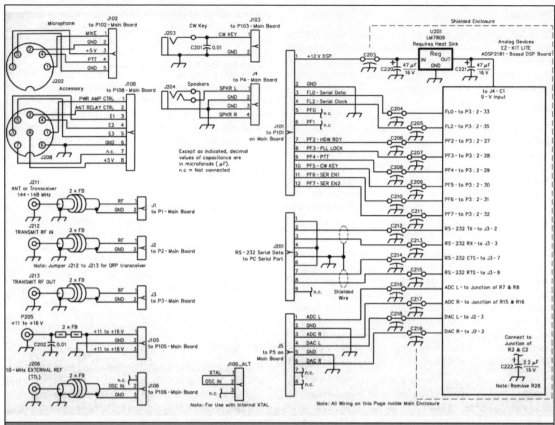

Fig 4.43: Interconnection diagram for the DSP-10 2m transceiver.

bytes of data and takes approximately 0.6 seconds to receive. Once a full data set is received, and after the desired averaging, the display is updated. The received data is buffered up to 8KB by the interrupt routine, so the display data updates can be delayed for up to eight seconds before data is lost. This provides some program operation flexibility.

Parameters that define the transceiver operation such as audio gain can be derived from an ASCII configuration file that is read when the PC program starts. These parameters override the default parameters, and in many cases serve to customise the transceiver. When a shutdown command is given, a new file is written that allows the transceiver to start up with the configuration last used.

Building the Transceiver

Circuit immunity to noise and spurious response benefits greatly from use of a solid ground plane on the PC board. For this reason, a double sided board is employed. The main drawback to this approach is the need for jumper wires on the backside, but the advantages far outweigh this minor inconvenience.

Surface mount components are used for several reasons. The board ends up being smaller and costs less, the RF and ground paths are often shorter and troubleshooting is easier. That is because tracks are not hidden on the back

of the board and are easier to follow. After building many boards with both through hole and surface mount approaches it is concluded that surface mount boards are easier to assemble, the main reason being that all work can be done on one side of the board.

A diecast box holds the main board and the DSP board. The latter is mounted in a separate box, made from PC board or brass sheet, to provide shielding. The mounting holes for the main board line up with the holes for the DSP, so it is easy to stack the entire sandwich of boards, boxes and standoffs. The two voltage regulators, U101 and U103, are mounted on the bottom side of the PCB. The ICs are fastened directly to the box for heat sinking. The main board is secured to the diecast box using four ½ inch long spacers. Above the board are 1 inch long threaded spacers that hold the DSP box.

All leads from the DSP pass through feed through LC filters as they leave the inner box. This greatly reduces "birdies" and noise caused by coupling between the DSP and RF circuit. A cover on the DSP box completes the shielding. Good shielding requires a connection between the cover and the box every two inches or so. Small pieces of finger stock can be used for this. Alternatively, brass screws and nuts soldered to the box can be used.

All external transceiver connectors are fastened to the diecast box. In some cases, there are bypasses right

Table 4.6: Nominal voltages in the DSP-10 2m transceiver.

U101 pin1	10V regulator input	11.0V
U101 pin3	10V regulator output	10.0V
U102 pin3	Main 5V regulator	5.0V
U103 pin3	First synthesiser regulator	5.0V
U14 pins 2 & 13	Audio outputs	5.5V
U1 pin3	First RF amplifier	3.5V
U2 pin3	Second RF amplifier	4.7V
R110	Source of Q101 VCO	0.23V
U105 pin3	VCO buffer	3.5V
U106 pin3	VCO buffer	4.6V
R59	Source of Q4 VCO	0.91V
U8 pin3	VCO buffer	2.8V
U9 pin3	VCO buffer	3.6V

where a connector is mounted and ferrite beads are placed over the connecting wires. These beads are shown in interconnection diagram Fig 4.43. It is best to err on the side of extra shielding and filtering than having to add parts later on.

After testing the DSP processor, mount it in its enclosure and wire the feed through capacitors according to Fig 4.43. When making the connections to the main board and the RS-232 connector on the main enclosure, solder the wires of the three interconnecting cables to the feed through capacitors. Leave an inch or two of slack in the cables so that the DSP box can be lifted above the main board with everything operating.

Main board assembly requires some care, but there is a reasonable amount of room between components. There are no components on the back of the board, so it can be placed in the enclosure for testing.

Testing

For transceiver main board alignment and basic troubleshooting, you need a voltmeter. A signal generator covering 144 -148MHz is helpful, but on the air signals are an adequate substitute and their use is assumed in the following steps. First, apply +11V to the main board without using the DSP board. At 11V, it is not necessary to heat sink the voltage regulators, so the board can be tested outside the box. At this point, current consumption should be around 350mA. If everything is operating properly, your checks should show the nominal voltages given in Table 4.6.

All DC voltages must be correct before further testing is possible. If they are not right, find out why. Next, mount the main board in the diecast box and fasten the two regulator heat sinks to the box. Connect the DSP box wiring, but leave the box separate from the main box so that it can be moved out of the way of the main board. Connect the transceiver serial connection to the PC's serial port using the 9 pin cable. Now both the main board and the DSP can be powered via the power connector. With power applied, load and run the DSP program UHF3.EXE. Next, execute the PC program UHFA.EXE that initialises all the parameters for the DSP program, including programming the synthesiser.

The amber Power LED, D102, should be lit, but the red Transmit LED, D103, should be off. Confirm the voltage readings at the following points:

Q106 pin 1	10V receive	9.7V
U10A pin 3	IF amplifier	6.0V
U109B pin 6	Transmit IF driver	2.4V

Be sure that the RF gain is at 100 (press Ctrl-F8 on the PC keyboard) and confirm the following voltages:

D2-A1	Antenna TR diode	0.73V
D1-A1	RF Filter TR diode	0.73V

Measure the 19.68MHz synthesiser tuning voltage at the U6 pin 6 side of R54 (Fig 4.40). Set this to about 4V using C69. If it is not possible to set the voltage to that level, adjust the turns on the VCO coil, L21. Pushing the turns together raises the tuning voltage. After you are sure that L21 is at its proper setting, use a small dab of RTV sealant to hold the windings in place and secure the coil to the board.

Set the MODE to CW and set the Operating Frequency to 147.000MHz. Adjust the 126 to 128MHz VCO coil, L102, until the tuning voltage measured at the junction of R104 and R105 is about 3.5V.

Ensure that a jumper is in place between pins 1 and 2 of P106, or that an external reference signal is being fed to P106 pins 2 and 3. Attach an antenna and see if you can receive a local repeater signal, with the transceiver in CW mode. If so, adjust the reference oscillator frequency with C110 until the carrier pitch is about 600Hz with the repeater frequency on the display. If it is not possible to get on frequency adjusting C110, change the value of C109. As you obtain more accurate frequency references than a local repeater, it will be necessary to repeat this adjustment.

Next, peak crystal filter coils L12 and L13 for maximum signal. The signal level indication can be helpful for these adjustments. Select a repeater frequency as close as possible to 147MHz and peak the RF filter coils L1, L2, L8, L9, L10 and L11 at that frequency. Now, centre the MIKE GAIN. That completes all adjustments.

Connect a dummy load to the antenna connector (51Ω, 1/4W resistor is adequate) and press the Home key to put the transceiver into transmit. With the key up, you should measure the following voltages:

D1-A2	RF Filter TR diode	0.73V
U4 pin 3	1st transmit amplifier	3.6V
U5 pin 3	2nd transmit amplifier	4.6V
Q2 emitter	Power amplifier emitter	1.2V
Q2 base	Power amplifier base	1.9V

While holding down the CW key (right hand ALT key), measure the transceiver's output power. It should be at least 20mW at full power setting. Fig 4.44 shows a circuit that can be used to measure the power output if a power meter is not available.

Operation

By simply attaching an antenna, speaker and microphone

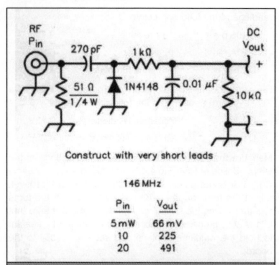

146 MHz

P_{in}	V_{out}
5 mW	66 mV
10	225
20	491

Fig 4.44: A simple power meter suitable for testing and alignment of the DSP-10 2m transceiver.

to the transceiver, you can operate 2m QRP. First, connect the transceiver's DB9 connector to a PC serial port you've chosen, then apply power to the transceiver and PC. Programs load first into the DSP, then into the PC. The default PC configuration screen (Fig 4.45) is that of a 2m transceiver with a large frequency display and a help summary. For weak signal work, an alternate display (Fig 4.46) is available.

The frequency to which the transceiver is tuned is displayed on the PC's screen and changed by using the F9 (down) and F10 (up) keys. Used alone, these two keys tune the transceiver in 10Hz steps. For faster tuning, press and hold the keyboard's SHIFT key in combination with the F9 or F10 key to tune in 100Hz steps. Other modifier keys allow tuning in steps ranging from 1Hz to

1MHz. You'll likely find that using a PC keyboard to tune a radio takes some getting used to. That's because most of us are accustomed to turning a knob. But the simplicity of being able to go "up 20kHz" in two keystrokes is great!

Function keys F7 and F8, respectively, increase and decrease the audio gain in 2dB steps. Pressing the SHIFT key modifies this function to adjust RF gain in 6dB steps. Mode selection USB, LSB, CW, or FM is controlled by the Alt-M or Alt-m keypresses. Various other keys are used to control receiver functions such as RIT, CW filters and LMS de-noise gain.

Signal strength is displayed in dBm. When a transverter is used ahead of this transceiver, this readout is corrected to allow for the transverter's gain. A bar graph above the signal level display acts as an S meter with 6dB steps.

The maximum available transmitter output power is 20mW. This is sufficient to drive any mixer used in a transverter. If your transverter is equipped with an attenuator for use with drive levels greater than 20mW, you'll need to alter the attenuator pad values to decrease the attenuation level. Unless you're a dedicated QRP operator, you'll want to add an external amplifier when operating this transceiver on 2m.

To transmit, push the mike button or press the PC's Home key. If there's a backlog of data coming from the DSP to the PC, there can be a delay (a fraction of a second) between pressing the PTT switch and transmitting. Pressing the Home key, however, makes the changeover immediately. A relay sequencer, controlled by the PC's software, produces logic level outputs for antenna relay and power amplifier control. For our simple example, we do not need this feature because we are not using an external amplifier. An on screen display shows output power when operating SSB and deviation when using FM. You'll find that operating SSB or FM with this transceiver

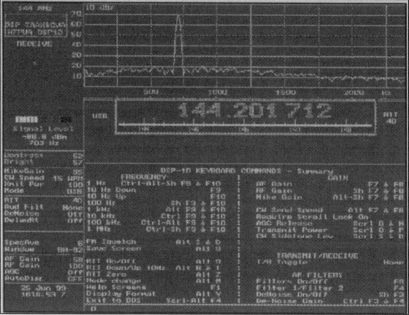

Fig 4.45: The default PC configuration screen for the DSP-10 2m transceiver.

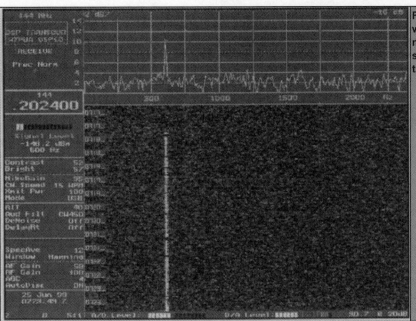

Fig 4.46: For weak signal work you can use the alternative PC configuration screen for the DSP-10 2m transceiver.

is quite similar to using a conventional multimode transceiver.

For CW operation, you have several keying options. A key jack mounted on the enclosure accepts a hand key. Alternatively, the PC keyboard's right hand Alt key can function as a hand key. Finally, you can use the computer keyboard as a CW generator. Alphanumeric keys enter information into a buffer that is sent when in the transmit mode. During receive or transmit, data can be entered into the buffer. The buffer data is shown in a three line display at the top of the screen. By enclosing a sequence of characters between hash signs (#), that character sequence can be sent repeatedly. As soon as the hash sign is encountered, the character sequence is repeated continuously until cancelled by pressing the @ key. Pressing the Home key switches the DSP-10 to transmit and starts the CW transmission. The next Home keypress toggles back to receive. CW speed is changed by using the Alt-F7 (increase speed) and Alt-F8 (decrease speed) keys.

When operating CW, the spectral display offers tuning information that is not otherwise available. One display line shows the current CW offset. A marker on the display identifies the frequency of the strongest signal in the passband; this can be used to set the operating frequency. The spectral display shows the entire audio spectrum, unrestricted by any narrowband filter that might be in use. In the voice modes (FM and SSB), the spectral display offers little new information except, perhaps, when on FM where repeater tone signals are easy to observe and identify.

One design goal of this transceiver was to remove operating frequency ambiguities as much as possible. The CW mode is one area where this often can present problems. During transmit, the displayed frequency is the actual transmitted frequency. In receive, the displayed frequency is that required to produce an audio pitch equal

to the CW offset. The CW offset is normally set to the centre frequency of the audio filter, if one is used, but it can be set to any value. If RIT is in use, the transmit and receive frequencies can be separate, but the receive frequency display will reflect this change. The sidetone sent to the speaker when the key is down is the same frequency as that of the CW offset.

If you want to use a transverter for, say, 1296MHz, with the transceiver, there is provision to correct the display to show the actual transmitted frequency. The conversion frequency and other transverter information are obtained from a configuration file.

Band changing is accomplished from the keyboard using the Ctrl-Alt modifier. The key used is then the same as the letter or number used in the ARRL VHF Contest band designators. For instance, 1296MHz would be displayed if Ctrl-Alt E is pressed. This band changing is treated in the way usually referred to as a "VFO", meaning that if you switch to another band and then return to 1296MHz, the transceiver is returned to the last 1296MHz frequency used. If the transceiver is turned off, it is returned to the last frequency used when turned on again.

A number of seldom used controls, such as the CW Offset discussed earlier, require use of the Scroll Lock key. This serves as an element of protection against inadvertent control changes. Another example is program termination: That requires simultaneous keypresses of Scrl Lock-Alt-F4.

To store the state of the transceiver at shutdown, the PC uses a configuration file (UHFA.CFG). This same file can be used to alter the transceiver's operational parameters. For instance, the calibration constant for the Signal Level display come, from this file. In order to have a known starting point, it is best to start with no configuration file. At shutdown, the program will write a file that contains the

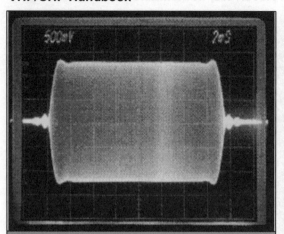

Fig 4.47: Keyed waveform of the DSP-10 2m transceiver.

Table 4.7: Measured performance for the DSP-10 2m transceiver.

General

Power requirements	13.6V 0.72A max on receive 0.75A max on transmit
Operating voltage range	10.6V - 16.0V
Frequency coverage	144 - 148MHz

Receiver

Receiver noise floor	-136.8dBm (450Hz filter)
FM 20dB quieting	0.31µV
2nd order intercept point	+69dBm (66 and 78MHz I/P)
3rd order intercept point	-21dBm
IF rejection	127dB (19.665MHz)
Image rejection	125dB (104 to 108MHz)
Audio power each channel	0.77W into 4Ω, 0.85W into 8Ω @ 13.6V
Audio power each channel	0.54W into 4Ω, 0.48W into 8Ω @ 11V
Audio response	-6dB, 190 to 3020Hz (SSB filter)
Audio response	310 to 750Hz (450Hz CW filter)

Transmitter

Max output power	CW or FM, 40Mw (rated output 20mW)
Harmonic suppression	Greater than 63dB (at full output)
Conversion oscillator feed through	-69dB (f_o=19.665MHz)
3rd order intermodulation	-33dB (700 and 1900Hz tones, 20mW peak power)
5th order intermodulation	-42dB (700 and 1900Hz tones, 20mW peak power)
Carrier suppression	Greater than 50dB
Opposite sideband suppression	Greater than 60dB

default parameters. Eventually you'll find it necessary to add more parameters such as transverter gains and conversion oscillator frequencies, but not initially.

Performance

The obvious question regarding this transceiver is "How well does it work?" For use as an IF for a UHF/microwave transverter, it is quite satisfactory. The transceiver works well as a 2m radio if not subject to many strong local signals. As we'll see, the dynamic range of the receiver is probably the weakest point of this design. Early on it was realised that providing state of the art dynamic range would add considerably to hardware complexity. This radio's design is intended to minimise hardware complexity wherever possible.

Now to the numbers. Table 4.7 shows the transceiver's measured performance. The receiver sensitivity is adequate for most general work; any transverter used ahead of the DSP-10 will dominate the overall noise figure. Gain added ahead of the transceiver is detrimental to dynamic range. If the transverter gain is more than 10 to 15dB, reduce the RF gain of the DSP-10.

The input third order intercept point is an issue when more than one strong signal is present in the passband. Two 500µV signals will produce an intermodulation product of about 0.3µV. This level of interference would certainly be a problem. However, most 2m operators do not encounter such signal levels. The image and IF rejections are very high, eliminating "birdie" problems.

Transmitter spurious outputs are better than current FCC requirements for a transceiver of this power level. If an amplifier is used with the transceiver, the LO signal at 19.665MHz below the transmitter frequency is probably the one that you should watch for spectral compliance problems, that signal level is -69dB.

Using DSP to generate SSB produces results that are somewhat different from their analogue counterparts. It is very easy to suppress the carrier and the opposite sideband. During transmit, however, there is a flat level of

noise across the 3kHz transmit band that is caused by A/D conversion. The total noise power is about 65dB below peak output, so it should not be a problem on the air.

On CW, the noise level is lower than on SSB and comes from the DAC. This noise occupies roughly 5 to 8kHz on either side of the transmitted carrier and is limited by the crystal filter.

Fig 4.47 shows the transceiver's CW keying waveform. In spite of the rapid rise time of about one millisecond, key clicks are still concentrated within 500Hz of the carrier frequency. Ripple can be seen on the waveform at both turn on and turn off. This rather ideal keying characteristic results from the band limited keying waveform that amplitude modulates the carrier to produce CW. As you might expect, the on the air sound is crisp without audible key clicks.

At a peak output of 20mW, the transmitted SSB signal third order intermodulation products are down at least 33dB. More importantly, the fifth and higher order product levels drop off rapidly. Keep in mind that as this signal is amplified, it tends to degrade the intermodulation levels relative to the peak output.

Fig 4.48: ATV Modules 1 - 3; transmitter, receiver and transceiver controller.

Fig 4.49: ATV module 4; power amplifier.

A modular approach to ATV

A good start to build a new ATV station is to use some of the modern components available. Giles Read, G1MFG [30] runs a small, but busy, Internet and magazine mailorder business specialising in amateur television products. He can supply a range of modules to construct a full ATV station, these are shown in Fig 4.48 and 4.49.

The ATV transceiver

Fig 4.50 shows a block diagram of the basic transceiver. It is configured around four modules; a receiver, transmitter, controller, and a solid state power amplifier. The only module not supplied by Giles is the DC power supply, which is an external 13.8VDC supply. The modules can be built into a small desktop case so that it can live on a shelf, of course the modules can be housed in any suitable enclosure that meets your needs. It really does not need to be anything spectacular, but using a metal enclosure is advisable as it is an RF kit and should be screened.

Before describing how the whole unit fits together, it's worth looking at some of the features of each of the modules, as they will work as standalone units if required.

Module 1 - the synthesised transmitter

This module comes built and working and the size of it is just amazing! It is simply a case of mounting the unit into the chosen enclosure. The board measures 125 x 60 x 18mm with a very low component count. The biggest component is a screened tinplate unit that houses all the RF components. Other than input sockets for audio/video and DC power, there is not a great deal else on the board to talk about. RF output is fed via an SMA socket. Frequency selection is made via an 8 way miniature PCB mounting, DIL style switch which, in a stand alone unit, selects the operating frequency from a PIC microprocessor. Frequency steps are selectable in 500kHz steps and will cover the whole of the 24cm amateur band. The board requires 12 - 18VDC and produces between 50 and 100mW RF output.

Module 2 - the receiver

The receiver module looks similar in style to the transmitter module, but is slightly larger measuring 150 x 60 x 18mm. Again, the board looks sparsely populated, although it has a few more components than the transmitter; it is also dominated by the metal screened RF module at one end of the PCB. RF input is again via an SMA socket. Audio and video outputs are via phono sockets, with sockets for 6 and 6.5MHz sound output, and the DC connector is also a 2.1mm socket (tip positive). As with the transmitter, this unit also requires 12 - 18VDC. Frequency control is also in 500kHz steps, using an 8 way DIL PCB switch and a PIC microprocessor. A small on board LED shows when the PLL is locked. This version of the receiver range is the "Platinum" model, which includes a video de-emphasis filter on the PCB.

Module 3 - the lcd transceiver controller

Although both transmitter and receiver units can act autonomously, it would be rather unwieldy, in a transceiver, to keep adjusting the internal DIL switches every time a frequency change was necessary. To overcome this problem, a companion controller PCB has been introduced. This module contains a PIC microprocessor, which provides the frequency control signals directly to the transmitter and receiver synthesisers, instead of the on board PIC processors (which are removed) and DIL

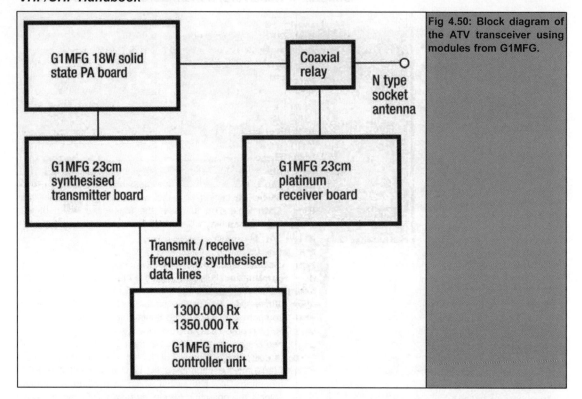

Fig 4.50: Block diagram of the ATV transceiver using modules from G1MFG.

G1MFG 18W solid state PA board

Coaxial relay

N type socket antenna

G1MFG 23cm synthesised transmitter board

G1MFG 23cm platinum receiver board

Transmit / receive frequency synthesiser data lines

1300.000 Rx
1350.000 Tx

G1MFG micro controller unit

switches. There are several benefits of using the controller module other than simply allowing easy control of both transmit and receiver modules. Because frequency control is no longer limited by an 8 digit binary number programmed by the DIL switches, the frequency control step resolution can be increased to 125kHz steps. This can also be used to extend the receiver range, although the transmitter has been intentionally limited to the 24cm amateur band range. Frequency selection is achieved via a set of up/down tuning buttons and the transmit/receive frequency control is displayed on a two line LCD display; a back lit version is also now available for that added look and feel. Transmitter and receiver frequencies are controlled independently. Three VFOs are provided for both receiver and transmitter; these act independently also. One very useful function is an "autonet" switch. This feature automatically retunes the receiver to the selected transmit frequency when the transmitter is enabled, allowing off air monitoring of the transmitted signal. This is a particularly useful function when using ATV repeaters, for example.

To use the frequency controller module with the G1MFG receiver and transmitters, there are several small modifications that need to be made. These are detailed later.

The controller module is designed to be mounted close to both the receiver and transmitter modules. The modules can be remotely mounted by up to 3ft if required, and longer distances are possible by utilising Philips I²C bus driver ICs; again, details are included in the paperwork, and use of these ICs could allow the modules to be used in a masthead mounted configuration.

Module 4 - the transmitter power amplifier

Although the transmitter modules are usable as supplied, their low power output does tend to limit their capabilities to cover any significant distance. Some additional power amplification can be built into the transceiver in the form of the matching G1MFG 24cm solid state PA. This module is designed around a Mitsubishi "black brick" PA module. Unusually, the G1MFG PA does not use the M57762 that is normally selected for amateur 24cm use, but uses an M68719 instead. There a few minor electrical differences, but physically they are the same. The most important difference is their ability to provide around 18 - 20W of RF at around 1250 - 1300MHz when driven by the G1MFG transmitter module. The module should be mounted on a hefty 0.5°C/W heat sink on the rear panel of the case. Make sure the module is well ventilated, as it does not like being run hot or supplied with more than 15VDC. If you treat them badly they tend to give up on life very quickly and in a most expensive fashion! You will need to feed the board with 13.8VDC at around 5A. The kit includes all the PCB mounted components and the PA module, but not the heat sink.

Building the transceiver

The modules are mounted into the chosen enclosure using small stand off pillars; these should be high enough so that the metal case does not interfere with the base of the PCB. Connectors and switches, both RF and DC, are mounted on the case and wired using small gauge wire and miniature RF coax. Audio and video lines should also be wired using coax, to minimise the potential for interference on these signal lines. The PA DC lines are wired

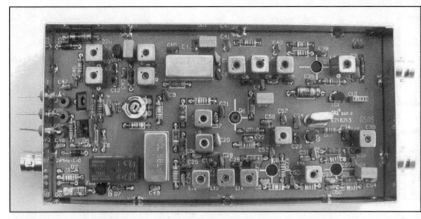

Fig 4.51: Picture of the completed 70MHz transverter.

directly to the DC input connector using an in line fuseholder, but using heavier gauge wiring as this module requires a much higher current supply.

Both transmitter and receiver modules are capable of operating independently but, in our case, we want the units to operate together as a unit using the controller as the central transceiver control module. To achieve this, the microprocessors of both transmitter and receiver need to be removed, and the controller's transmit and receive data lines are directly wired to the respective PCB pins of the RF modules. This is a relatively simple task and the PICs are easily removed from their sockets using a small screwdriver. The documentation supplied with the modules identifies the necessary pins that need connecting on the respective modules.

Power is connected via small gauge wiring except for the PA module, which uses much thicker wiring due to the higher currents involved. Switches for power, transmit/receive changeover and autonet functions are all panel mounted. A fuseholder, DC power connector and N type antenna connector are mounted on the rear panel, as is the large heat sink for the PA module.

A small 12V RF relay is mounted internally to allow the single N type connector on the rear panel to be switched between the transmit and receiver modules. This is switched using the transmit/receive control line. Make sure the relay you choose is capable of carrying the power you are running, and that it is also rated at 23cm, or you will find it becomes lossy and simulates an unwitting dummy load!

RF interconnections between the modules are made using miniature PTFE coax and small SMA connectors. These connectors are an excellent choice at these frequencies and allow good, reliable, low loss connections to be made between the modules.

Testing

Once the unit is wired, you can carry out the basic DC tests, and once the unit has passed the initial "smoke" test, you can test the frequency controller. The two line display should follow the up/down keys on the controller. With a suitable dummy load and power meter connected, you can test the output of the unit which should be

approximately 15 - 18W.

The VFO buttons and autonet functions can be checked, and that just about completes the testing. As all the modules are ready built, there is no alignment to carry out.

70MHz Transverter

This design was published in the Danish amateur radio magazine, "OZ", in order to boost the interest and activity on the 4m band in Denmark, more details can be found at [31]. The 70MHz band was introduced in Denmark during 2003 at that time the only equipment available was 4m PMR radios, the Yaesu FT847 or ready made transverters brought in from the UK. The FT847 was the only available commercial radio but did not perform particularly well, so a suitable transverter design was sought.

The late OE9PMJ, Peter Riml's 50MHz transverter design, originally published in 1990 was chosen as a basis for the new transverter The advantages of this were that it is a modern design, reproducible by most amateurs and only uses conventional components with no microscopic SMD components although the layout is relatively compact. Another advantage is that all inductors are available as ready made components.

The first unit was built without too many calculations by OZ7IS using plain common sense! A few experiments later and it was working quite satisfactorily. Unit two was copied from the first one and tested thoroughly by OZ2M in the following months while simulating and testing all circuits, section by section on unit three. Several details were optimised and a few improvements relating to the original design were made. Among other things the changeover relay was changed for a cheaper type, no need for expensive relays on 28MHz! Erik, OZ1TF, designed a new PCB layout for 70MHz but it is still also usable for 50MHz. All in all it is a proven and well-documented design presented below.

Circuit

The circuit is shown in Fig 4.52. The 70MHz input signal passes through the input filter (L1, C1, C2) to the input amplifier (BF988) where the gain is approximately 25dB. Then through the band pass filter (L2 - 4, C3 - 8) providing a suitable selectivity.

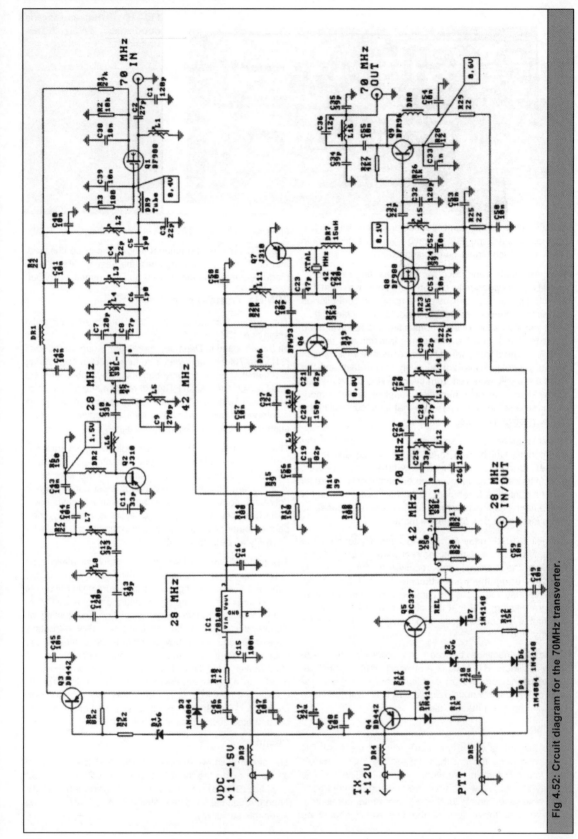

Fig 4.52: Crcuit diagram for the 70MHz transverter.

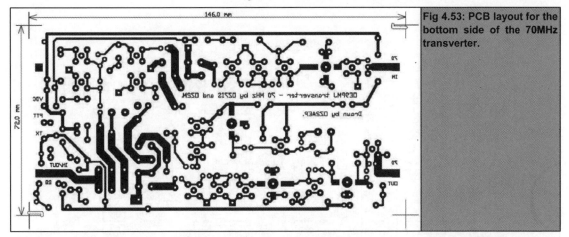

Fig 4.53: PCB layout for the bottom side of the 70MHz transverter.

The balanced mixer MX1 mixes the 70MHz signal down to 28MHz losing approximately 6dB in the process. Next the signal is amplified by approximately 10dB in a low noise J-FET (J310). The bandpass filter (L7/8 and C11 - 14) increases the selectivity considerably. Undesired products are decoupled via R5 in the L5/C9 diplexing filter.

For better stability the oscillator chain is supplied with 8V from a 78L08 voltage regulator. The oscillator, another J310, oscillates on 42MHz using a 3rd overtone series resonant crystal. The 42MHz signal is amplified by Q6 to approximately 17dBm/50mW. The harmonics are attenuated in the lowpass filter. Then the signal is attenuated to approximately 7dBm/5mW through R14 - 18 that also provides impedance matching for the TX and RX mixers.

The transmit mixer, MX2, only needs approximately -15dBm/30µW 28MHz IF signal from the transceiver. A suitable level can be achieved by adjusting VR in the attenuator (R30, R31 and VR). The resulting 70MHz TX signal is then filtered through a three-stage bandpass filter (L12 - 14/C 25 - 30) before being amplified in a BF988, and finally a BFR96 to a level exceeding 100mW. The TX signal reaches the output terminal through the final pi-filter (L16/C34 - C36)

The PTT circuit uses two BD442 transistors for the RX/TX switching, TX when PTT is grounded. +12V/1A is available at the "DR4" terminal during TX that is intended to

switch the antenna relay and/or a PA. The circuit around the BC337 delays the TX key but activates the antenna relay immediately. This means that the TX output (70 OUT) is delayed by approximately 100ms after the antenna relay is activated. Consequently the antenna relay switches without any TX signal present.

Construction

The complete transverter is built on a 1.5mm double-sided glass-fibre epoxy PCB, shown in Figs 4.53 and 4.54, fitted into a standard metal sheet box measuring 148 x 74 x 30(50)mm. The component (upper) side of the PCB is mainly a "ground plane". When drilling the PCB please remember to drill the "centre-hole" for the coils approximately 3.2mm. Then it is possible to change the coil core without de-soldering the coil, in case of a broken core! The component layout is shown in Fig 4.55, the = indicates where the components are soldered directly onto the "ground-plane". The parts list is shown in Table 4.8.

Initially all resistors and "vias" are fitted and soldered if you are not using a ready made plated through PCB. One end of R3 and R6 are soldered directly to the "ground-plane". Then the four stripline transistors; 2 x BF988, BFW93 and BFR96 are soldered into place. Then the diodes, capacitors (short wires please!) and the rest of the components are fitted according to their height. All components connected to ground are soldered to the upper side

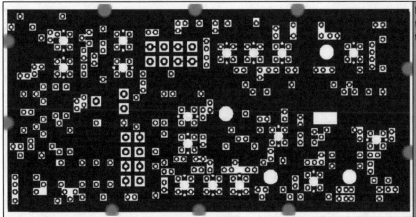

Fig 4.54: PCB layout for the top side of the 70MHz transverter.

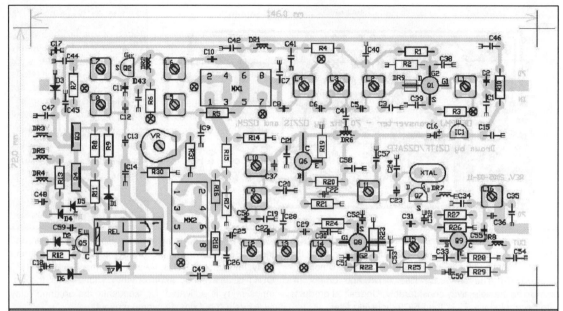

Fig 4.55: Component layout for the 70MHz transverter.

(ground-plane) of the PCB. If you are mounting the Neosid coils on a PCB without holes for the ground flanges they should be cut off before mounting. The copper housing of the coils are soldered directly to the "ground-plane" where indicated. If the coils have a fifth leg - NOT in a corner - it should be cut off. On L6 to L11 and L16 it is clearly visible to which legs are for the coil, be sure to mount them correctly!

The RX/TX changeover is arranged for transceivers that only have a single transverter RF connector, common for the RX input and the TX output. If you have separate connectors for RX and TX, the 28MHz relay is not needed! Just attach a short piece of coax from the point of the incoming 28MHz point of the (now missing) relay, to the unused pad below D3.

Finally mount the screen over the oscillator and fit the

Table 4.8: Parts list for the 70MHz transverter.

Resistors, 0.25/0.4W metal film		C10, C11, C25	33pF	Q6	BFW93 or BFW92
		C12	3.3pF	Q9	BFR96
R1, R22	27kΩ	C13, C34, c35	39pF		
R2	10kΩ	C15	100nF polyester.	**Inductors**	
R3, R14, R18	180Ω	C16	1µF 16V axial		
R4, R7, R25, R29	22Ω	C17, C18	22µF 16V axial	DR1, DR2, DR3,	VK200, 10µH choke
R5, R19	47Ω	C19, C21	82pF	DR4, DR5, DR6,	
R6, R17	150Ω	C20	150pF	DR8	
R8	8.2kΩ	C22	10pF	DR7	15µH choke
R9	2.2kΩ	C23	47pF	L1, L2, L3, L4, L12	Neosid 00 5231 03
R10	1.2kΩ	C33	1nF	L13, L14, L15	
R11	5.6kΩ	C36, C37	12pF	L6, L7, L8	Neosid 00 5048 00
R12	15kΩ	C38 - C59	10nF	L9, L10, L11	Neosid 00 5049 00
R13, R26	1kΩ			L5, L16	Neosid 00 5061 00
R15, R16, R24	39Ω	**Semiconductors**			
R20	22kΩ			Ferrite Beads	Mount on Q1 and Q8
R21	3.3kΩ	D1, D2	5.6V zener 0.5W		drain
R23	1.5kΩ	D3,D4	1N4004 or equiv.	Crystal	42MHz 3rd overtone
R27	4.7kΩ	D5, D6, D7	1N4148 or equiv.		HC49/U
R28	12Ω	IC1	78L08	Metal box	148 x 74 x 30mm
R30, R31	82Ω	MX1, MX2	SBL-1 or IE500,	BNC sockets	
			IE800, HPF505,	Feedthrough caps.	1nF
Capacitors, ceramic unless stated			MS85, MS83D	Metal sheet	For screen
		Q1, Q8	BF988 or BF981,	Relay	Omron G5V-2, 12V
			BF900, BF960		
C1, C7, C14, C24,	120pF	Q2, Q7	J310 or U310		
C26, C32		Q3, Q4	BD442 or BD434,		
C2, C8, C28	27pF		BD438, BD316,		
C3, C4, C30, C31	22pF		BD140		
C5, C6, C27, C29	1pF	Q5	BC337		
C9	270pF				

Table 4.9: Performance of the 70MHz transverter,

General

Operating frequency	70.0MHz - 70.65MHz
IF	28.0MHz - 28.65MHz

TX

Output power	>100mW
Drive power	-15dBm - 0dBm/30μW - 1mW
Gain	25dB - 40dB
Spurious suppression	>60dB

RX

Gain	approximately 23dB
Noise figure	<2.5dB
1dB compression point	0dBm/1mW
Intercept point	7dBm/5mW
Attenuation of 56MHz	98dB
Attenuation of 126MHz	95dB

small screen on the bottom side. Once tested the PCB is soldered into the box, AFTER drilling the holes for connectors, feed through capacitors, etc.! A picture of the completed transverter is shown in Fig 4.51.

If you have access to a range of suitable test equipment you should wait before mounting the mixers, Q2 and the relay. It will be an advantage to sweep the front end with its filters (70MHz), the diplexer (28MHz), the IF amplifier (28MHz), the lowpass filter in the oscillator (42MHz) and the transmitter (70MHz).

Please note the components locations on home made PCBs: (×) denotes a "via" from top to bottom layer. = denotes that the component must be soldered to ground on the top layer. Square pads, on the bottom layer denotes that the component must be soldered on both sides.

An option for adjustable TX gain; If the TX IF signal source is not adjustable and the TX mixer is fed with the proper levels, it is possible to introduce an adjustable TX output by changing the gate 2 voltage on Q8 (BF988). This can be done fixed or adjustable by connecting gate 2 to an external potentiometer instead of R23. Do remember to make a decoupling similar to the one on DR3 - DR5.

Alignment

First of all the oscillator is started. If it is not oscillating, turn the core of L11 until the voltage across R19 suddenly changes from approximately 0.1V to 0.8V. The core is left between the upper and lower position where it stops oscillating, i.e. 0.1V across R19. Do check that the oscillator starts again after the voltage has been removed for a while before you continue the adjustment procedure!

The coils L9 and L10 are adjusted for maximum 42MHz RF signal on pin 8 of the mixers. At the same point the frequency is verified with a counter. Because the 70MHz band only covers 500kHz the simplest way possible is to adjust the transverter on a frequency near the centre of the band while making some simple measurements. The best way would be to sweep it, but the simpler method is acceptable. With a suitable signal around 70.200MHz, the coils L1 - 8 are adjusted for maximum reading on the S meter of the 28MHz receiver. Verify at the band edges as well.

The same principle is used when adjusting the transmitter chain. Inject a 28.2MHz signal, connect the PTT terminal to grounded and with an RF millivoltmeter, adjust L12 to L16 is for maximum reading at 70.2MHz. Here too, verify the readings at the band edges. The 28.2MHz carrier, maximum of 500mW, is adjusted by turning VR counter clockwise until the signal on MX2 pin 3 or 4 is approximately one third of the oscillator signal. In case of difficulties in measuring this, the 28MHz drive signal is reduced to the point where the 70MHz output first starts to drop.

For those with access to all the right instruments; after sweeping the filters mount the remaining components (mixers, Q2 and the relay). Connect a spectrum analyser to pin 8 on one of the mixers. Adjust L10 until the 84MHz, the second harmonic, is attenuated most. It may cost you up to 0.5dB on the 42MHz signal, but the 84MHz will be approximately 75dB below the level of the 42MHz signal. If you do it "by ear" it may only be 50dB below. Now connect the spectrum analyser to the 70MHz TX output (70 OUT) and adjust L16 for max attenuation of the

Fig 4.56: Picture of the 50MHz 500W linear amplifier.

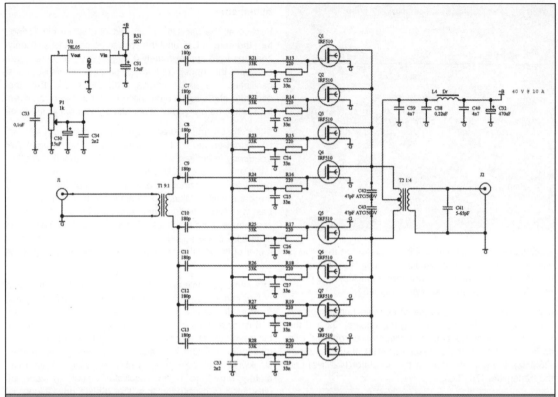

Fig 4.57: Circuit diagram for one 250W module of the 50MHz 500W linear amplifier.

second harmonic on 140MHz. It will affect the desired signal, but only a few tenths of a dB! On the other hand, the second harmonic should be at least 60dB below the desired 70MHz signal. The performance of the transverter is shown in Table 4.9.

50MHz 500W IRF510 based amplifier

This amplifier project was based on a prototype circuit developed for the HF bands by Steen Møller, OZ3SW. The HF project was eventually scrapped because of widely varying gain from 160m to 10m but Peter Frenning, OZ1PIF matured the basic circuit design into a single band 50MHz amplifier and it was published in Dubus Magazine [32] issue 2/2005.

The basic building block is a 4+4 push-pull configuration, biased at 500mA, delivering 250W out for 10W in at

Fig 4.58: The input transformer, T1, for the 50MHz 250W linear amplifier.

40V/10A, the circuit is shown in Fig 4.57. To make life easy on yourself, use devices from a single batch, as these are most likely to be closely matched. Devices from Intersil (Fairchild) have been used, these are no longer being produced, but there should be an ample supply in the distribution channel. The FQP7N10 device looks to be a very suitable (and somewhat better) alternative, but these have not been tested, one interesting comparison would be IMD3 figures!

The individual IRF510s are mounted on the heatsink using Aluminium Oxide heat transfer isolation bricks and silicone grease, for sufficiently low coupling between the MOSFETs and the heatsink to insure stability.

L4 is just a choke, and thus fairly uncritical, a couple of turns of the supply wire on any available piece of ferrite, see the photograph in Fig 4.59, it is just below the electrolytic capacitor.

The input transformer, T1, uses 4C65 cores. It is made by threading a piece of wire three times (the primary) through a piece of coax outer conductor (the secondary) around four 4C65 (4 x Ferroxcube core material TN14/9/5 (4C65); Part No: 4322 020 9718 an equivalent Amidon would be material type 61 part No: FT50-61) cores glued together using cyanoacrylate (superglue), thus creating a 9:1 impedance transformation and a very reasonable input match, see Fig 4.58. Also fig. 4 & 5 in AN749-PDF, a classic work by Helge Granberg [33].

The output transformer, T2, is made from two pieces of

Fig 4.59: Picture of a completed 250W module of the 50MHz 500W linear amplifier.

teflon coax (RG316) 14.5cm in length, see Fig 4.60, the outer conductors joined at the middle and the ends, for the primary, and the inner conductors in series as two windings (the secondary) giving a 1:4 ratio and a close match to 50Ω (fine tune with C41), the B+ supply must be as near the midpoint of the primary as possible. A very thorough description of the construction of HF transformers can be found in: Motorola application note AN749 [33].

Two of these amplifiers are combined using a simple ¼ lambda combiner made from 75Ω coax, the input splitter is made in the same way. This works fine if the two modules are closely matched, and if you can accept the loss of both halves, in the event of a failure in either one. Here it is no problem because of the very cheap semiconductors (less than 4€/module). If this compromise is unacceptable for some reason there are many other, and more failure tolerant, solutions available.

The end result is then passed through a low loss elliptical lowpass filter with a 70dB notch at the 2nd harmonic and 80dB at the 3rd, this is described below.

Bias is 500mA per module; IMD3 has not been measured, but reports on the band have been uniformly good. More than 2000 QSOs have been made so far with this amplifier. The only mishap was during an F2 opening to NA in 2001, when the transverter output was not reduced to 20W, 4½ QSOs were made before things went wrong (12 of 16 IRF510 blew loudly and smelly) These were quickly replaced (at less than 30c a piece) and no one ever commented on the output, despite the vast overdrive.

This event was the lesson never to rely on manual throttling of drive to an amplifier; things will go wrong, and Murphy taught us that it will happen when most inopportune, e.g. when in the middle of a humongous pile up for the rarest of DXs! This amplifier now has a power attenuator built in, to reduce the 100W from my FT847 to the 20W required for full output. An added benefit is the reduction of splatter produced by the overshoot from the transceiver's output regulator, the more you throttle back the worse it gets, some modern transceivers produce spikes of more than 150W on VHF, the FT847 is far from the worst of the bunch!

An arbitrary number of the 250W modules can be combined to obtain the desired output level, the reason for deciding on 500W was the availability of a suitable power supply.

PCB layout

The size of PCB is 118mm x 85mm split along the horizontal line, shown in Fig 4.61. It is etched on double-sided material. All holes for component mounting should be countersunk on the back side, the rest are being used for "through plating" to connect the ground areas on both sides of the PCB.

Since the PCB design the bias circuit has been added in

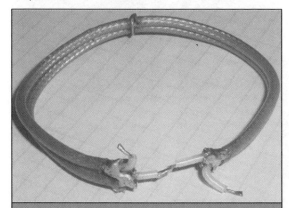

Fig 4.60: The output transformer, T2, for the 50MHz 250W linear amplifier.

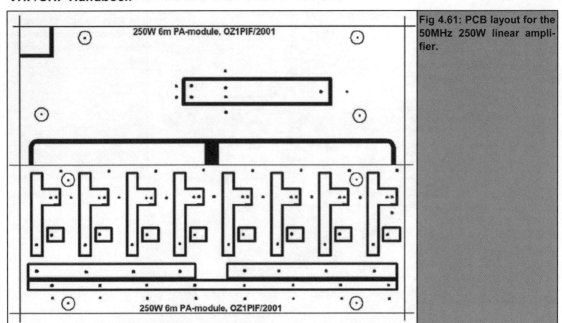

Fig 4.61: PCB layout for the 50MHz 250W linear amplifier.

the upper right corner, dead bug fashion; see Fig 4.59. The coils of coax cable are the splitters and combiners. The small circuit added to the heat sink, next to the bias circuit, is a fan speed controller [34]. The large finned object is a surplus commercial 800W switch mode power supply. On top of that is the elliptical lowpass filter. The small PCB over the power supply, contains 12V and 24V regulators and changeover relays. These were originally cheap 20A washing machine type, but still better than -20dB return loss at this frequency! The grey RS232 cable connects control LEDs on the front to the power supply.

There was a small but sometimes very annoying problem right from the start. In receive mode there was a small but just audible broadband noise on a very quiet band, no problem when working a contest, ES opening or F2, but bad enough to be a problem when working very small signals in JT6M or JT65 modes. A very rare Norwegian square was being sought, and the amplifier had to be turned off during receive periods in order to be able to decode him at all! Finally something had to be done about it! It turned out to be RF hash coming from the switch mode power supply and the fan. Various attempts to get rid of it proved fruitless, so instead of curing the disease, something had to be done about the symptoms. The noise entered the signal path at several points internal to the amplifier (demonstrated by taking the two coax cables connected by a female-to-female adapter and routing this

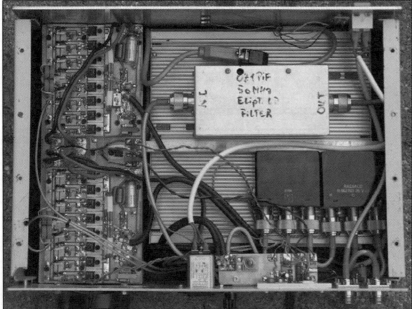

Fig 4.62: Picture of the completed 50MHz 500W linear amplifier after the rebuild to improve the low level noise problem on receive.

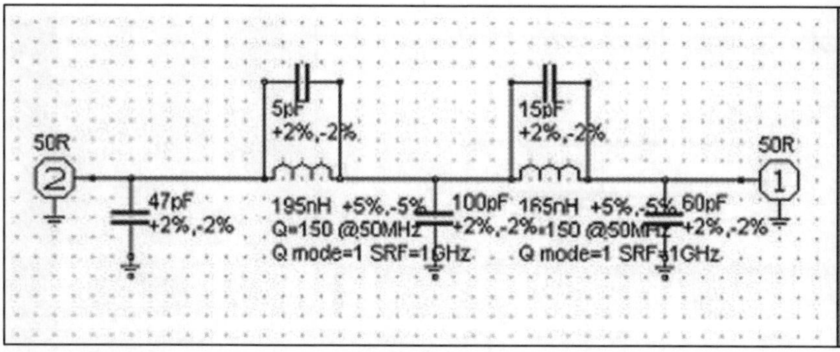

Fig 4.63: Circuit diagram of the lowpass filter for the 50MHz 500W linear amplifier.

through the amplifier, with no detectable noise when the amplifier was turned on. The main culprit was determined to be the open RF relays and coax joints done on the cheap at various points.

It was decided to completely redo the internal RF cabling, using high quality coax relays, RG400 cable and crimped N connectors throughout. The 25V and 12V power supplies were changed and a transistorised PTT circuit was also added. The rebuild has been a complete success, nothing can be heard or measured in receive mode, it is at least below -100dBm. Fig 4.62 shows the rebuilt amplifier.

Last, but not least, the whole thing, ready to plug in, weighs just under 12.5kg, ideal for /P use or DXpedition travel. That is with the present heavy duty steel cabinet, 3 to 4Kg could probably be shaved off with an aluminium enclosure. The total costs for all parts (without PSU) were around €250.

Lowpass filter

The circuit for the lowpass output filter is shown in Fig 4.63. It was simulated with RFsim99 as shown in Fig 4.64. The trace in the left upper corner is RL = 27dB at 50MHz, the 2nd harmonic is -70dB and the 3rd harmonic is -80dB. The insertion loss < 0.15dB. Real life measurement is almost identical to the simulation. The components used were:

- L1 = 165 nH (3mm silvered copper wire)
- L2 = 195 nH (3mm silvered copper wire)
- C1 = 60pF (1000V NP0)

- C2 = 15pF (8pF Johnson trimmer par. 10pF ceramic 500V)
- C3 = 100pF (4 x 100pF/1000V NP0, in series/parallel)
- C4 = 5pF (piece of copper foil on a lead "flapper")
- C5 = 47pF (1000V NP0)

A picture of the filter is shown in Fig 4.65.

VMOS Solid State 2m Power Amplifier

The circuit diagram for the VMOS power amplifier designed by Dragoslav Dobricic, YU1AW [35], is shown in Fig 4.66. There are two identical amplifiers connected by wideband baluns operating in a symmetrical anti-phase or push-pull. The input of each amplifier is fed via a wideband balun made from 95mm of 50Ω Teflon coax cable wound into a coil around three ferrite beads as shown in Fig 4.67. Each amplifier is matched using C1 and L1 and balance between the input circuits is achieved with C2. The gate bias for each amplifier is fed from a 5V regulated supply with bias adjustment by 2k2 potentiometer. The drains are fed from the 28V – 29V supply via an RF choke, which is open wound from 0.8mm copper wire, 8 turns, 6mm diameter and 12mm long. The output is matched with L2 and C3 and balance between the output circuits is achieved with C4. The outputs are combined with a wideband balun made from 95mm of 50Ω thick Teflon coax cable, such as RG142, wound into a coil around three ferrite beads as shown in Fig 4.67.

Using self-resonant baluns gives an improvement over the wideband balun made from 95mm of coax cable. A 144MHz resonant balun can be made from 620mm of 5mm diameter PTFE coax cable, RG142 or similar. Close wound into 6 turns with 30mm inner diameter and about 30mm long with no space between turns.

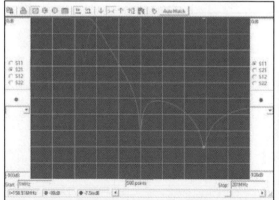

Fig 4.64: RFsim99 simulation of the lowpass filter for the 50MHz 500W linear amplifier.

Fig 4.65: Picture of the lowpass filter for the 50MHz 500W linear amplifier.

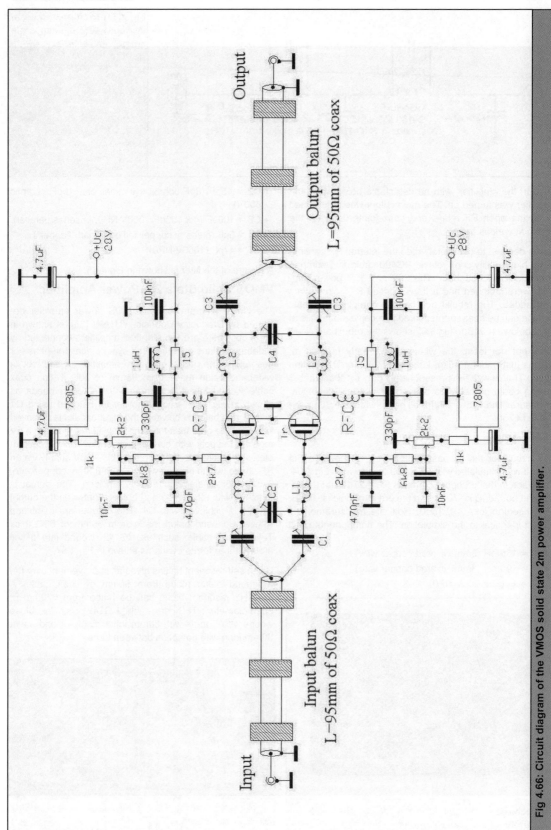

Fig 4.66: Circuit diagram of the VMOS solid state 2m power amplifier.

Fig 4.67: Picture of the assembled VMOS solid state 2m power amplifier.

It is very important that the entire amplifier has to be totally symmetrical with regards to the mechanical layout of components and electrical parameters (values of elements, currents and voltages, etc.), so that more power, amplification, efficiency and suppression of even harmon-

ics can be achieved. While adjusting, it is very important to maintain the same capacitances of C1 and C3 in both amplifiers.

Mechanical Construction

The whole amplifier has to be built on a relatively small piece of a single layer FR4 printed circuit board (Fig 4.67). Source leads are soldered as short as possible onto the ground of the board. The transistor should be mounted onto a large heatsink using thermal paste. The details of the main parts are shown in Table 4.10.

Once everything is connected, check once again to ensure that there are no mistakes and short circuits to the ground and adjust the potentiometers for maximum resistance. Connect the supply to one transistor and adjust the collector current to 600mA. The same procedure should be carried out with the second transistor. Even more important than the exact value of quiescent current is that

Table 4.10: Main parts for the VMOS solid state 2m power amplifier.

C1	22pF Arco trimmer
C2	65pF Arco trimmer
C3	19pF Arco trimmer
C4	27pF Arco trimmer
L1	8.5nH, 0.8 turn, 8mm dia of 1.2 - 1.5mm copper wire
L2	16nH, 1 turn, 10mm dia of 1.5 - 2mm silver plated copper wire
RFC	8 turns, 6mm dia, 12mm long of 0.8mm copper wire
Tr	DV28120T

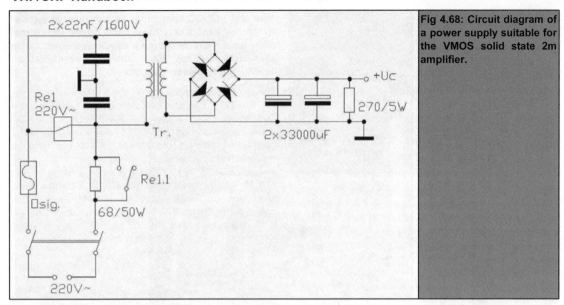

2×22nF/1600V

Re1
220V~

Tr.

Osig.

68/50W

Re1.1

220V~

+Uc

270/5W

2×33000uF

Fig 4.68: Circuit diagram of a power supply suitable for the VMOS solid state 2m amplifier.

they are identical in both transistors! Then connect both transistors to the supply and connect a 50Ω dummy load to the output via a wattmeter or SWR meter. If you do not have a dummy load, a good aerial with low SWR can be used. Supply minimal excitation and by measuring the output power alternately adjust trimmers until maximum output power is achieved. Repeat the adjustment several times, gradually increasing the excitation power. Finally, with full excitation, which should not exceed the permitted output power, adjust all trimmers to the highest output power. At the same time the transistor's current should be measured so as not to exceed the maximum allowed value. The typical parameters for the amplifier are shown in Table 4.11. If input trimmers, C1 or C2, need to be at maximum or minimum capacity during adjusting, it is necessary to change the length of the cable between the exciter and the amplifier itself. The optimal length of the cable should be determined experimentally to obtain adjustment with approximately the same values of C1 and C2. This experimentally determined cable should always be used when operating the amplifier. A change of exciter could occasionally require a new length of cable to be determined. In push-pull amplifiers it is extremely important to perform adjustment so that the corresponding trimmers on each transistor are adjusted simultaneously to ensure that they have approximately the same capacity during adjustment. By maintaining symmetry during adjustments, extremely dangerous situations are avoided which can cause the amplifier to self-oscillate.

A non-stabilised supply can be used, but it should be constructed so that it has very good voltage regulation. It should be well specified with good quality electrolytic

capacitors. The transformer should be slightly over specified. To avoid blown fuses caused by the charging current of electrolytic capacitors, it is necessary to build in a delayed switching device. It is performed simply by a 220V relay connected as shown in the circuit (Fig 4.68). At the moment when power is switched on, the transformer is connected to a power supply via a resistor that limits high charging currents. When the capacitors are charged and transients in the transformer settle down, the current through the resistor decreases, the voltage on the primary increases and the relay that bridges the resistor with its contacts is switched on. It is also possible to use relays that switch on via some electronic timer after a couple of dozen seconds. Although this appears to be a more elegant solution, it is a far worse solution, for two reasons: first, in the case of a very short interruption of supply voltage the timer has not been reset, voltage is switched on without delay; and second: in the case of a fault that causes high current consumption, when the relay would not be switched on, the entire system would protect itself, whereas the timer would switch on the relay and subsequently full power.

The Development of Power Amplifiers Utilising MOSFET Hybrid Modules

This article was written by Steve Kostro, N2CEI and published on the Down East Microwave web site [36]. Bipolar hybrids have been the standard in solid-state VHF/UHF transceivers and transverters ranging from 6m to 23cm. The chances are that if you have 3W or greater of solid-state power on 23cm, it is generated by a bipolar hybrid. To date, hybrids have been the easiest way to achieve gain and power output in a small amount of space. Recently with the advent of multi-band HF/VHF/UHF transceivers, it has been the only way manufacturers could get all of that stuff in one box! Now with the popularity of personal communications equipment such as commercial VHF/UHF radio services, hybrid manufactures are being asked to decrease the size and

Table 4.11: Operating parameter for the VMOS solid state 2m power amplifier.

Supply voltage	28 – 29V
Supply current	2 x 9A
Quiescent current	2 x 600mA
Output power	2 x 120W
Drive power	2 x 10W

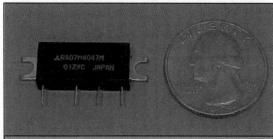

Fig 4.69: The 7W RA07M4047M compared with an American Quarter.

eliminate support circuit components while improving efficiencies. They have met the challenge; Fig 4.69 is one of the newest UHF versions available off the shelf. Yes, it is that small! The picture is proof that MOSFET hybrids are here to stay. Further proof is that manufacturers of hybrids are making Bipolar hybrids obsolete. The problem in the future will be that if you damage your bipolar, for whatever reason, it will need to be replaced with the newer, and more economical MOSFET type in its class. This is OK and considered an "Upgrade" in performance but the newer MOSFET hybrids are not completely drop-in replacements. The differences in operation are those discussed and the direction of either replacing the bipolar with a MOSFET or building a completely new amplifier using the newer MOSFET type hybrids are covered.

A popular bipolar hybrid, the Mitsubishi M57762 has been declared obsolete. This should be a concern if you own an amplifier that utilises two or more of these hybrids in a combined circuit. Amplifiers do exist with 2, 3, 4, 5, 8 or 16 hybrids in a circuit. If you have a "single brick" amplifier, you may decide not to use the obsolete part and elect for the new MOSFET. The specifications of the M57762 will vary depending on who you talk too, (like everything else in the Ham world!) but directly paraphrasing from Mitsubishi's data sheet it says 18W linear output with up to 1W of drive, 12VDC operation (13.8VDC preferred) at around 5A current drain. It requires a maximum of 9VDC at 0.5A on the control pin for maximum power output. The reality was 20 – 25W output with ½W drive, 5 – 6A current drain with a regulated +9VDC on the control pin. The hybrid would handle the occasional "oops" of up to 2W

drive and +17VDC from an un-regulated mobile installation. It has been a very rugged and reliable device that many have been considered a miracle in the mid 1980s after building a few 20 – 30W linear amplifiers on 1296MHz from discrete transistors.

The electrical specifications of its replacement, the RA18H1213G can be found on the Mitsubishi web site [37]. The part number says it all, RA18H1213G, The "RA" is the designator for the MOSFET line. The "18" is the established specified output power in watts. The "H" is the designator for the package size and pin out spacing, (H3 is the M57762) "1213G" is the frequency range, 1.2 to 1.3GHz. So far, this is good. Read the part number and it self identifies! Therefore, an RA20H8994M is a 20W unit operating between 890 – 940MHz. Further details on the data sheet reveal that the new MOSFET only has four pins. Input, Gate, Drain, and Output. The M57762 had five; Input, 1st DC supply, Base, 2nd DC supply and Output. The RA18H1213G is specified at the same output power but only requires 200mW drive and a gate voltage of +5VDC at only 1mA compared to the M57762 which was specified at 1W of drive and +9VDC at 500mA on the control line. So we now have a hybrid that has one less pin (less bypass components) requires less drive, (can be driven with a low cost MMIC directly) and does not require a regulator mounted on a heat sink for the control or gate pin. Sounds better so far? Well a quick check of Figs 4.70 and 4.71 shows that the pin alignment and mounting hole spacing are the same or close enough for direct physical replacement in a M57762 circuit.

Great! Lets just drop it into an M57762 circuit, change the regulator, and rewire the pins and get on the air! Well, if you do this, which is what Steve did, you will have limited success. You may see the current meter spike up to 10 – 12A and see some output flash on your power meter. It may be the fastest 50W you ever saw! The disappointing fact is there is no noticeable smoke from the blown hybrid! Yes, it will self destruct in a matter of seconds! So let us find out what is required to make this MOSFET work correctly.

Reviewing the data sheet from top to bottom reveals a bunch of information. First it says that if we use the hybrid in a beacon, we could key it by toggling the control line. It

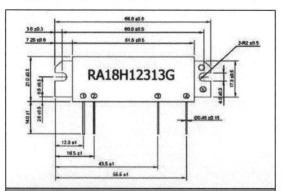

Fig 4.70 Dimensions for the RA18H12313G MOSFET amplifier.

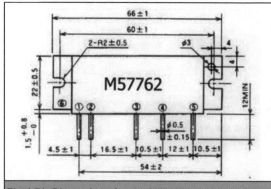

Fig 4.71: Dimensions for the M57762 bipolar amplifier.

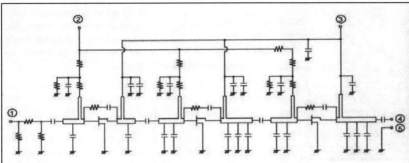

Fig 4.72: The equivalent circuit for the RA18H1213G MOSFET amplifier.

offers 60dB of isolation in the off state. Then it says that frequent on/off switching is bad! This will require further testing. It does state the hybrid may be used in a linear system and suggests how to use it which is very similar to the way hams use SSB. The section under Oscillation is what caught my eye. It states what values to use for bypassing the voltage leads and asks a question to ensure that you provide a low inductance path from the bypass capacitors to the ground of the power supply and hybrid. I thought I did that when I dropped the 1213G in the M57762 circuit. It broke into oscillation when I applied the control voltage. What could be wrong? We need to keep reading the data sheet. Meanwhile, lets look at the circuit equivalent of the RA18H1213G shown in Fig 4.72.

It looks plain and simple. Just a standard circuit with three MOSFET's in series sharing a common gate and drain supply lines separated only by the resistive divider networks on the control line. Nothing shown here should require anything special on the power supply circuits. Examining the modified M57762 circuit, Fig 4.73, and component list (show in Table 4.12) does not reveal anything that could be a problem. Therefore, the only question is how good is the grounding of the M57762 circuit and if it worked with the bipolar, how could it be a problem with the MOSFET? Well, we need to look at the physical design of this potential amplifier anyway, so let check out the heat sink requirements.

Reviewing the 2nd page of the data sheet shows the maximum specifications (The specs "Hams" use) and the electrical characteristics for normal operation (non-Ham types). In the maximums, there is lots of good stuff like

+17VDC. Most mobile charging systems connected to a battery will not reach that. The gate voltage is 6VDC so a 5V regulator is not a problem no matter how bad the tolerance is and it will tolerate 300mW of drive! Now the best part of this maximum rating data is the 30W of output power.

When reviewing the Electrical Characteristics, always check the conditions. The point to be made here is that 18W is listed as the minimum output power required at 12.5VDC, with 200mW of drive operating at 20% efficiency. What does this mean? It means that higher output power may be possible if the efficiency is better than 20%. If the DC power consumption remains the same and the RF output power increases, then no harm is done concerning total power dissipation of the hybrid. Reviewing what we know so far and developing an "Interpretation" of the specifications so far, we know that the hybrid is specified as 18W minimum and 30W maximum at 20% efficiency. All data provided is at 12.5VDC. The total current drain is established by the efficiency. The gate voltage controls the gain and the idling current drain. Interpreting the maximum specifications 30W power output maximum at 20% efficiency:

- If 30W = 20% then 150W = 100% total power dissipation
- 150W (total dissipation) minus 30W (RF output) equals 120W of heat dissipation!
- 150W total dissipation @ 12.5VDC = 12.0A of total current!

Questions now come up about the heat sink required for 120W of heat and how to keep the case temperature of the hybrid within specification. Also, the 12A of current drain is large but at 13.8VDC, 150W is lower at 10.9A. The physical mounting will be discussed later so for now, lets look at Mitsubishi's RF test data to verify that the interpretation of 150W of total power dissipation is real and is what we have to play with. Fig 4.74 shows that at

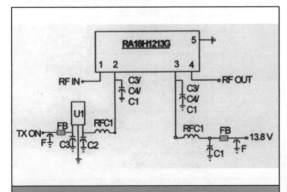

Fig 4.73: Circuit for RA18H1213G amplifier.

Table 4.12: Parts list for RA18H1213G amplifier.

C1	3	100µF electrolytic
C2	1	22µF electrolytic
C3	3	0.1µF chip
C4	2	100pF cip
RFC1	1	8 turns 1/8 inch dia 24swg enamel
RFC2	1	8 turns 1/8 inch dia 24swg enamel
U1	1	78L05 regulator
	1	RA18H1213G

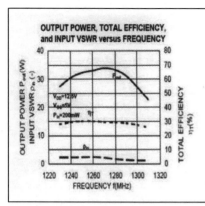

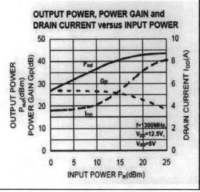

Fig 4.74: Graphs of output power in watts and dBm versus frequency and input power for the RA18H1213G.

1270MHz, the hybrid will produce 35W output at 12.5VDC, with 200mW of drive and +5VDC on the control pin. This example shows that it is just under 30% efficiency. Fig 4.74 shows that at 1300MHz, it only requires 100mW to saturate the output power at +44dBm, (or 25W) and 7A current drain at 12.5 VDC. That is a total dissipation of 88W. It also demonstrates that the hybrid is approaching compression.

A quick look at Figs 4.75 shows that if we increase the drain voltage the output power and current drain increases, but if calculated, the efficiency also increases. That is good! Now if we increase the control or gate voltage, it allows the hybrid to draw more current but doesn't make a large change in output power. One could deduce that the gain will increase so it would require less drive but for now that is not the issue. We are looking for total power and efficiency. If calculated, the increase in drain current will allow the output power to increase but will not increase the efficiency. That is not so good! So maybe we need a compromise or find the sweet spot for the control voltage. We are ahead of the game if we can do >30W with less drive than the M57762. The good thing to notice is that at 16VDC on the drain, 40W+ output is acceptable with 9A current drain. That is 28.4% efficiency with 144W total dissipation! Close enough to 150W! That proves that the hybrid can do it. What will it take to do it at 13.8VDC? Or worse case, at 12VDC in a mobile operation. Testing to find out is the only way.

The data sheet specifies the mounting of the hybrid and how to determine the type of heat sink that will be required. Mounting is simple. The flatter, the better. The thermal design of the heat sink isn't that simple. Without going into to many details, the formula given by Mitsubishi determines the required thermal resistance of the heat sink (the rating that heat sinks are designed too) that will ensure that the channel temperature of the hybrid (the internal working of the individual MOSFET within the hybrid) cannot be exceeded when operated under the given conditions. In this case, the conditions are 20% efficiency with 18W output power. This will require a heat sink with a 0.42°C/W of thermal resistance to maintain a channel temperature of 100°C worst case. The maximum is 175°C. Channel temperature cannot be measured accurately without an IR scanning device. We can only measure the case temperature and the maximum is 110°C as stated on the second page of the data sheet. From Mitsubishi's operating specification:

- 18W output with 200mW input drive at 12.5VDC, 7.2A = 20% Efficiency
  Thermal resistance = (90°C - 60°C) / (18W / 20% - 18W + 0.2W) = 0.42 °C/W

If we now substitute the maximum specifications into the formula, we see that it will take a bit more heat sink to maintain a 100°C channel temperature.

- 30W output with 200mW input drive at 12.5VDC, 12.0A = 20% Efficiency
- Thermal resistance = (90°C - 60°C) / (30W / 20% - 30W + 0.2W) = 0.25 °C/W

A heat sink with a thermal resistance rating of 0.25°C/W would need to be solid copper and is quite a demand to

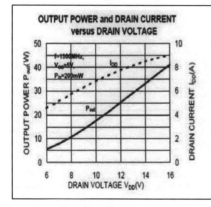

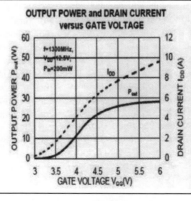

Fig 4.75: Graphs of output power and drain current versus drain voltage and gate voltage for the RA18H1213G.

Fig 4.76: Photograph comparing the flange on a bipolar amplifier and a production MOSFET amplifier.

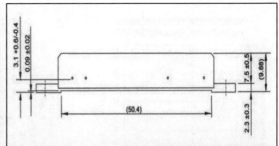

Fig 4.77: Dimensions of the flange on an RA18H1213G amplifier.

only generate 30W of RF at 1296MHz. It is more than what would be expected to be under an "H" size hybrid module. To reduce the thermal resistance requirement, the efficiency would need to be increased to keep this hybrid from self-destructing during operation. It is also understood that this is a worst-case condition.

Now, is this the reason for the first failure? The first failure was instantaneous. When the hybrid broke into oscillation, it exceeded the maximum channel temperature. In theory, if the heat sink were large enough, the hybrid would still be oscillating as long as it didn't exceed the channel temperature maximum. However, even in theory, I can't imagine how large the heat sink would need to be! The hybrid popped like a fuse instantly! Therefore, the heat sinks thermal characteristics were not actually the problem. They would have been a problem if the amplifier operated over a period of time with a poor efficiency resulting in over heating the hybrid and allowing the channel temperature to exceed the maximum limit. That would be a slow burn! We need to solve the oscillation problem and the amplifier will have a chance.

The five units received as prototypes for the 33cm band (RA20H8994M) looked identical to the M57762 hybrids. They worked great as drop-ins to the circuit and produced beyond specifications in performance. The 23cm samples did have a slightly different appearance and in fact looked identical to the production 33cm units received at a later date. From the topside, the flange is cropped a bit and the plastic cap is smaller. The pins line up to the detailed drawing. The new hybrid just has one less pin than the M57762 hybrid. A further examination reveals that the big difference is on the bottom, there is a flange as shown in Fig 4.76 and 4.77. The mounting precautions go into detail of how flat the heat sink should be for the best performance so I didn't expect to see the "Flange" and I overlooked it on the data sheet. This is new to the

industry. The measured gap under the flange will vary from 4 - 6mils. I went back to the only known set of data, that was for the 900MHz amplifier built out of the original RA20H8994M samples. As mentioned, the new production units had the new style flange. I replaced the old style hybrid (operating flawlessly) with the new type flange hybrid and had a marginal amplifier that wasn't stable and exhibited thermal problems until it just stopped working, (It self destructed). I tested the next 900MHz hybrid with brass shim stock between the flange and the heat sink. This unit appeared to be more stable but still had thermal problems when I pushed the drive up to produce more than 35W. A transceiver manufacturer then relayed a brief explanation about Mitsubishi's recommendations, which is to just fill the gap with thermal compound. This process was on lower frequency hybrids and they were not being used beyond the stated operating conditions. I tried it on both the 8994M and the 1213G with limited success at 900MHz and no success at 1.3GHz. Next a heat sink was machined to fit the 8994M hybrid. It worked, it was stable, and thermally under control while producing more than 60W output. That's it! Problem solved! The 8994M was replaced with the 1213G in the same circuit. As the last mounting screw was being tightened a "tick" sound was heard, the type that makes you sick to your stomach. The ceramic in the hybrid was broken. While tightening the flange, which is copper, the flange bent down and cracked the hybrid. Why? The tolerance of the depth of the flange is too great to machine a one size fits all heat sink. This 1213G was shallower than the 8994M. The heat sink was modified to fit the next 1213G. It worked and behaved correctly concerning thermal management but still exhibited some slight instabilities but nothing that would cause it to self-destruct.

For production reasons, we cannot machine every heat sink to match a particular hybrid nor would I expect a ham in his shack to be able to "tweak" their heat sinks if they needed to replace their hybrid with a new one. Various manufacturer's versions of heat transfer inserts and thermal pads were tested with bad results if you want to push the hybrid to their maximums. Nothing works better than metal-to-metal contact for heat and this applies to the RF circuit as well. In the section of the data sheet under "oscillation", it asked the question about providing a low inductance path from the bypass capacitors to the ground of the power supply and hybrid. The answer is "no" with a stock hybrid. How can it be low inductance if the flange is

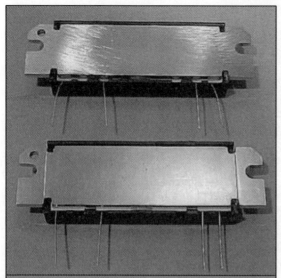

Fig 4.78: Picture showing the modified and un-modified flange of an RA18H1213G.

only making contact to the heat sink at the mounting screws and the gate and drain voltages are bypassed to the circuit board in the middle of the Hybrid. The inductance may only be in the nH range but would be a worse problem as the frequency is increased. This is also, what my data showed.

It became obvious that the hybrid manufacturer realised a few things during the development of this new MOSFET line. They realised that the RF design outperformed the thermal management design and took steps to ensure that OEM's would not attempt to abuse the product. If the hybrids are used at the recommended operation specifications, they will perform as specified. Another assumption is that the manufacturer made a million of these hybrids upside down and have tweaked the data sheet to solve the problem. If it wasn't a mistake why isn't there a recommendation that the mounting surface should be machined to match the hybrid instead of just a flatness specification?

Using what we now know, I started from scratch to build a 23cm amplifier with the RA18H1213G. If the machining process of the heat sink is not desirable for future M57762 replacements, the next best thing is to machine the hybrid. This is simply done on a belt sander. The surface is as smooth as the original M57762, see Fig 4.78. It is very simple to do but care must be taken not to over heat the hybrid. Copper conducts heat fast! To eliminate the amount of inductance from the bypass capacitors to the flange, a few further steps have been performed. The important things to notice are the shield and the extra mounting screw between the gate and drain voltage pins. In combination, the screw holds the bottom of the PCB down to the heat sink to ensure the shortest path of the by-pass capacitors to modified flange of the hybrid. The addition of the shield after it is soldered to the ground connections on the PC board is to now reduce the inductance even further. This design is now uncondition-

ally stable and ready for the RF test.

During the RF testing, it was then found out that the output load impedance of the hybrid changed above the 30W output level. (DAH!) Additional line width or capacitance added to the output 50Ω line produced higher output and increased efficiency. This could have been Mitsubishi's problem with the design. If the hybrid was allowed to be pushed up in power, it was no longer 50Ω and would require additional matching. This isn't a problem for Hams or a microwave armateur radio equipment manufacturer. The testing proved to be so encouraging, that two hybrids were combined with excellent results. 100W of output was achieved at saturation. With the additional tuning, the pair of hybrids achieved almost 40% efficiency. The unit had a total of 256W of power dissipation. That is only 156W of heat for 100W of RF. 78W of heat per hybrid and each hybrid is drawing 9.25A. If we break this down further and apply it to the formula to calculate the thermal resistance of the heat sink, it looks very favourable. The loss of the combiners should be included in this calculation because it is heat dissipated in the splitter/combiners and not the heat sink. Therefore, a single hybrid will look like this:

Power divider/combiner has a ½ dB loss

- 50W (55W) output with 200mW input drive,13.8VDC at 9.25A and 43% Efficiency
  Thermal resistance = (90°C - 60°C) / (55 W / 43% - 55 W + 0.2W) = 0.41°C/W

The recommendation by Mitsubishi for normal operating conditions was 0.42°C/W. A modest heat sink 6 inches square and greater than 1 inch tall with a rating of 0.4°C/W or better would keep the channel temperature within specification for a two hybrid amplifier. Adding a low CFM fan will increase the heat sink's performance. If the goal of replacing a M57762 with a RA18H1213G is desired, the modifications shown previously will produce a great amplifier. Amplifiers to this design are available from Down East Microwave [36].

A 500mW linear amplifier for 1249MHz

This amplifier shown in Fig 4.79 was designed by Geoffrey Pike, GI0GDP, to replace the Mitsubishi M67715 module that is often used in conjunction with the bigger module, M57762, to achieve 18W. Typically a G1MFG module produces 60mW and this will drive this amplifier to 500mW, which drives my M57762 to 16W.

This is a cost effective solution to buying the M67715 module as a driver, as the single device used here costs approximately £3.50 at the time of writing.

The single BFG235 device (Farnell [15] part number 300-6736) is built using transmission lines and the design simulated with Puff [38]. The component values and simultaneous conjugate impedances are calculated with Component layout Excel, using S parameter data from Infineon [39]. The circuit diagram is shown in Fig 4.80.

The bias conditions are approximately 150mA at a supply of 13.8V. The S2P file from Infineon was for V_{ce} 8V and I_c =150mA.

Fig 4.79: Photograph of the 500mW linear amplifier for 1249MHz.

This gives starting S parameters of

- S11 0.853 ∠144.3°
- S21 1.430 ∠38.1°
- S12 0.136 ∠ 48.0°
- S22 0.583 ∠147.4°

These reflection coefficients translate to an input imped-ance S11 of 4.38 + j 15.97Ω, with an associated output impedance S22 of 14.2 + j 13.5Ω.

However these are not used to design the amplifier; instead, the new conjugate values are used

- S11 new 4.32 + j 13.13Ω
- S22 new 25.5 - j 56.9Ω

These values are used to compute the transmission line geometry in Puff.

This results in an input line of 78Ω with a length of 86°, which equates to a line 1mm wide and 3.1 cm long on standard 1.6mm double sided FR4 PCB.

The output line is a 50Ω line 47° long which equates to a line 1.6cm long and 2.5mm wide.

The simulated plot in Puff shown in Fig 4.81 gives excellent predicted input and output matches of -33dB, which is an SWR of 1.05:1. The forward gain is estimated to be 9.66dB and the two prototypes measured 9.8 and 9.0dB. This was fed with 60mW from a G1MFG TX, which resulted in 580 and 480mW output respectively, meas-ured using a HP432A power meter with a Mini-Circuits 20dB attenuator.

The PCB, shown in Fig 4.82, is made from a normal double sided 1.6mm FR4 PCB measuring 6cm by 3cm. The board is not etched, but the lines cut with a sharp modelling knife. The gaps are then peeled away using a hot 25W soldering iron.

Adjacent to the input and output line there are 6 Vero pins to ground the top ground plane to the bottom plane. This is the bare minimum grounding and really the PCB edges should have their edges bonded using copper foil from H100 coax or similar.

The passive SMDs are all 1206, except for the input 100pF, which is 0603, and the two 2.2pF reactance cancelling capacitors mounted close to the base emitter

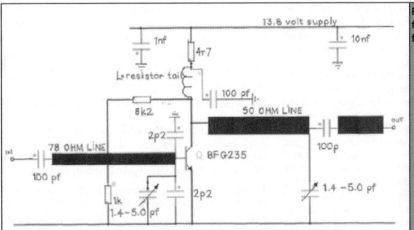

Fig 4.80: Circuit diagram for the 500mW linear ampli-fier for 1249MHz.

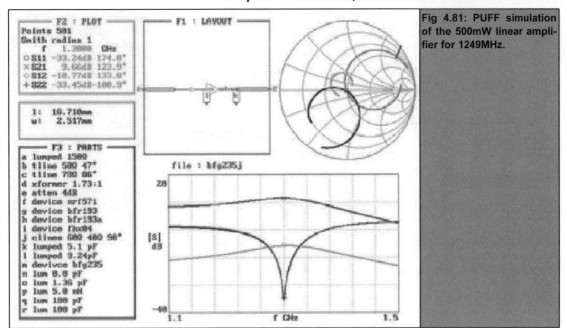

Fig 4.81: PUFF simulation of the 500mW linear amplifier for 1249MHz.

leads of the BFG235, which are 0804. Conventional ¼W leaded resistors are used for R bias and R collector. The 4.7Ω collector resistor also forms the inductor and is 2 turns over a 1/8 inch former.

Construction

After preparing the PCB it needs to be cleaned with methylated spirits or similar to make soldering on the upper ground plane easier.

After marking the holes for the through pins, they can be drilled with a 1mm drill and the pins soldered top and bottom; the two pins adjacent to the emitter leads can be left to the last and soldered at the same time as the 2.2pF capacitors.

Next fit the BFG235, the SMD parts and the two trimmers. Make sure that the earthy side of the trimmer is earthed to the upper ground plane. Use good SMA end connectors and thoroughly solder.

Preset the trimmers at 15% meshed (2 dots at 2 o'clock position). Use 12V initially and then when all is OK go to 13.8V. Typical current drain is 150mA approximately 0.7V across the 4.7Ω collector resistor.

Tune the trimmers for maximum output, bearing in mind that S12 is a major player here and the output effects the input and vice versa. This may take a few iterations. Most power meters are inaccurate at this power level, so don't be surprised if only 100mW is indicated. When connected to a M57762 module 16W can be achieved using a G1MFG as a drive source.

A 1watt 1240 -1300MHz utility linear amplifier

This amplifier was designed by Geoffrey Pike, GI0GDP, to be a utility amplifier up to 1W and up to 20dB gain and tunable over the range 1240 to 1300MHz. This would allow for the current range of ATV transmitters to produce sufficient power to drive either a 2C39 or a pair of

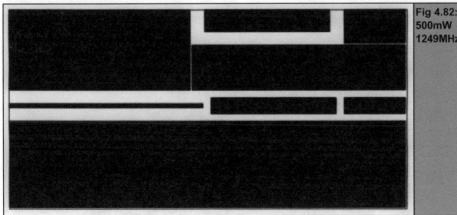

Fig 4.82: PCB layout for the 500mW linear amplifier for 1249MHz.

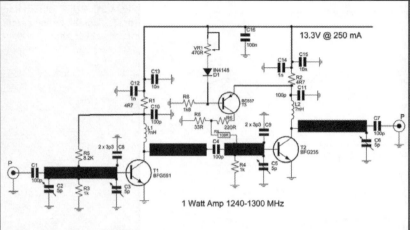

1 Watt Amp 1240-1300 MHz

Mitsubishi M57762 modules to 30 – 35W. This could equally be used with some of the low power 1296MHz linear transverter designs with only 5mW available. The choice is yours and the applications are limited by your own imagination. With the introduction of the new Mitsubishi MOSFET modules for example the RA18H1213G, it is just possible that this utility amplifier could be placed between a mixer in a transverter system and the module and drive it to say 20W.

The amplifier is a two stage affair and is actually is from two separate designs which have been joined together, the circuit diagram is shown in Fig 4.83 with a picture of the prototype in Fig 4.84. This is a BFG591 driving a BFG235 which from Puff [38] suggests a possible forward gain S21 of up to 21dB. Both individual stages will be described and the method of joining the two parts together by using a reactive intermediate impedance of almost equal opposite sign.

Driver stage

This uses a BFG591 and uses the S2P file from Infineon [39] and is biased at 12V and 100mA.

This gives the following S parameters;

- S11 0.43 ∠148.8°
- S21 3.169 ∠63.3°
- S12 0.153 ∠65.3°
- S22 0.119 ∠78.3°

These reflection coefficients give in a 50Ω system the following impedances;

- S11 = 21.2 +j11.5
- S22 = 51.0 - j12.1

These however aren't used to design the input and output matching networks but instead the simultaneous complex values are used and in a 50Ω system are

- S11 = 8.13 +j10.8
- S22 = 77.7 – j 89

There are as always many different ways to realise a match to these new input and output impedances. But all methods will use the conjugate of these values i.e. the sign in front of the "j" will change from + to – and vice versa.

It was decided to convert the series input impedance values to parallel format and then cancel the inductive part with capacitance. The parallel equivalent values for S11 become, 22.5Ω in parallel with 16.9Ω; which is cancelled with 7.25pF. It is then only necessary to transform this

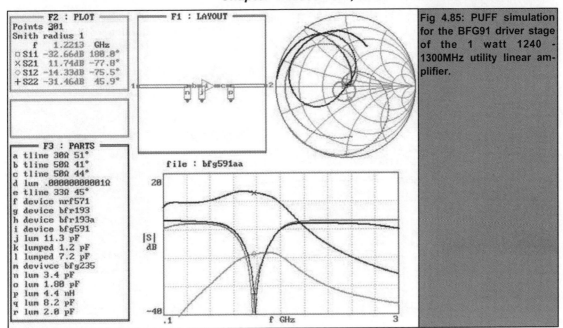

Fig 4.85: PUFF simulation for the BFG91 driver stage of the 1 watt 1240 - 1300MHz utility linear amplifier.

resistive part to 50Ω. This can be achieved with a ¼ λ low Z line and no end capacitance or with a 50Ω line which will permit some end capacitance to allow for some degree of tuning. This translates to a 50Ω line 34° long with about 2pF at the end for tuning purposes. It is also possible to make the line longer at 41° and use 11pF at the transistor base connection and this will exhibit a broader tuning.

The output impedance S22 = 77.7 - j89 is handled in a different manner from the input in that it is capacitive in nature and is not matched to 50Ω resistive but is left inductive so that the capacitive input to the next stage will almost cancel this. The line is 50Ω and 44° long that leaves the impedance at 50Ω resistive and about 4.4nH inductive.

This will then match into the next stage with an appropriate amount of capacitance.

Output stage

This uses a BFG235 device and uses the S2P file from Infineon at 8V and I_c=150mA. This gives the following S parameters:

- S11 0.853 ∠144.3°

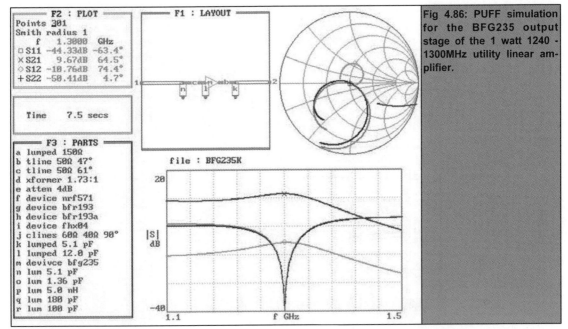

Fig 4.86: PUFF simulation for the BFG235 output stage of the 1 watt 1240 - 1300MHz utility linear amplifier.

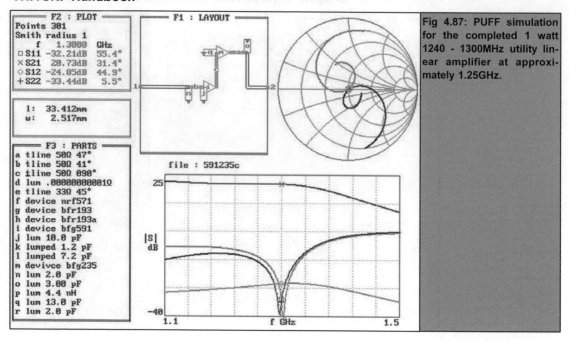

Fig 4.87: PUFF simulation for the completed 1 watt 1240 - 1300MHz utility linear amplifier at approximately 1.25GHz.

- S21 1.430 ∠38.1°
- S12 0.136 ∠48.0°
- S22 0.583 ∠147.4°

These reflection coefficients give in a 50Ω system the following impedances:

- S11 4.38 +j 15.97
- S22 14.2 +j 13.5

These however aren't used to design the input and output matching networks but instead the simultaneous complex values are used and in a 50Ω system are

- S11 1.42 + j 13.2
- S22 10 – j 22.6

Again the input impedance is converted into its parallel equivalent form and the inductive part is cancelled with capacitance and then the real part is transformed to 50Ω with a transmission line. In this case the capacitive reactive part at the end of the line is left uncorrected but is matched by the previous stage. The base inductive part is cancelled with 9.2pF. This is transformed to 50Ω with a line 61° long and 50Ω impedance. This leaves the end of the line capacitive about 5.1pF. This is overcompensated

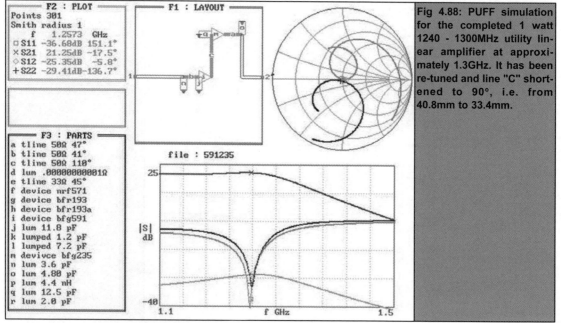

Fig 4.88: PUFF simulation for the completed 1 watt 1240 - 1300MHz utility linear amplifier at approximately 1.3GHz. It has been re-tuned and line "C" shortened to 90°, i.e. from 40.8mm to 33.4mm.

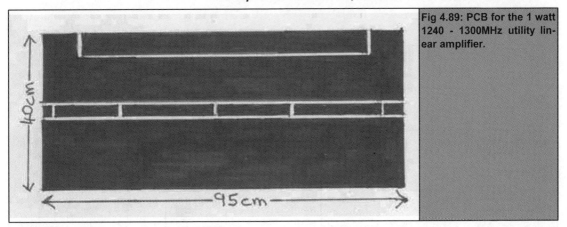

Fig 4.89: PCB for the 1 watt 1240 - 1300MHz utility linear amplifier.

by the end inductance of the previous stage, but is in practice tuneable and the overall response of the amplifier is quite acceptable.

S22 is matched conventionally with a 50Ω line 47° long and tuned with a trimmer at the end of the line of 5.1pF.

The two amplifiers are joined with a common transmission line for the output of the driver and the input of the output stage, the overall result returned from Puff are quite good with a forward gain of about 21dB available input and output matching will vary across the band but are in general return losses of -30dB are possible which is more than adequate.

Construction Notes

These are in a general form, ideally the SMD parts should be the smallest that you can handle and really the larger size 1206 should be avoided for best results. The PCB shown in Fig 4.89 should have its edges wrapped in copper foil and soldered top and bottom. Vero pins can be used as vias and these should at least be used as close as possible to the device's emitter connections and also beneath the earthy connection to the Murata trimmers.

The originals use Murata blue trimmers, these have a high value of minimum capacitance which is undesirable but workable. The SMD capacitors in the circuit diagram (Fig 4.83) marked "j" and "q" are equal values placed either

side of the PCB, see Fig 4.84. Use SMA connectors to ensure a repeatable connection.

Sequencer

If you add a power amplifier to your station it is important to make sure that the changeover from transmit to receive does not feed your powerful signal into the receiver input as the aerial is switched and the amplifier signal decays. This is the job of the sequencer, it makes sure that things happen in a controlled sequence. The timing diagram Fig 90 shows the sequence of events. The PTT signal is the input that you control to switch from receive to transmit, the sequencer then controls the timing of the aerial changeover relay, the power amplifier and the transmit/receive signal to the prime mover (transceiver). To ensure that the receiver input never receives any signal from the power amplifier the aerial changeover relay is switched first when going from receive to transmit and released last. Next the power amplifier is switched on and finally the transmit signal is applied.

Bo Hansen, OZ2M, designed the sequencer shown in Fig 4.91, it uses a PIC to produce the timing signals, the source code for the PIC can be downloaded from his web page [40]. It has the following facilities:

- Control three separate power amplifiers and aerial changeover relays for three different bands.
- Different delays for SSB with a "K" signal at the end of

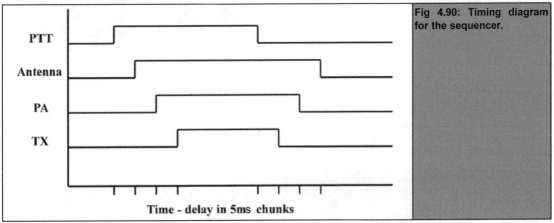

Fig 4.90: Timing diagram for the sequencer.

PTT

Antenna

PA

TX

Time - delay in 5ms chunks

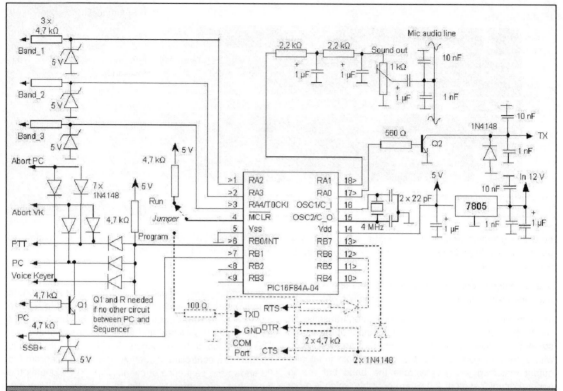

Fig 4.91: Circuit diagram for the sequencer. Q1 and Q2 are BC337 or 2N2222. The circuit shown dotted is optional for in circuit programming, if not used the switch should be replaced with a short as shown. For outputs, select a sink or source circuit to suit your application.

SSB transmission.

• All timing parameters changeable in software.

To use the sequencer, one of the three band inputs is set; the corresponding PA and ANT outputs will be activated when the timing starts. Table 4.13 shows the pin assignments on the PIC for the three sets of outputs. These pins are connected to either a source or sink circuit shown in Figs 4.92 and 4.93. The source circuit has a transistor that switches the output to +12V and the sink circuit has a

transistor that switches the output to ground. There are three inputs to start the timing sequence (PTT, PC or voice keyer) and two to abort the sequence (Abort PC or Abort VK). If the SSB input is set, the "K" output will be sent to the Mic audio when switching from transmit to receive.

Table 4.13: Pin assignments for the outputs of the sequencer. These are pins on the PIC.

Pin	Name	Function
8	RB2	PA band 1
9	RB3	Antenna band 1
10	RB4	PA band 2
11	RB5	Antenna band 2
12	RB6	PA band 3
13	RB7	Antenna band 3

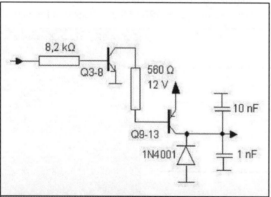

Fig 4.92: Output circuit for use as a source to switch a relay or similar to +12V. Q9 - Q13 are BC327 or MPS6533.

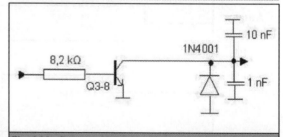

Fig 4.93: Output circuit for use as a sink to switch a relay or similar to 0V. Q3 - Q8 are BC337 or MPS6533.

References

[1] Radio Communications handbook 8th Edition, edited by Mike Dennison, G3XDV and Chris Lorek, G4HLC, Radio Society of Great Britain, www.rsgb.org/shop

[2] The International Microwave Habdbook, edited by Andy Barter, G8ATD, Radio Society of Great Britain, www.rsgb.org/shop

[3] Microwave Projects 2, edited by Andy Barter, G8ATD, Radio Society of Great Britain, www.rsgb.org/shop

[4] Microwave Projects 2, edited by Andy Barter, G8ATD, Radio Society of Great Britain, www.rsgb.org/shop

[5] The PW Mellstock 70MHz Receiver, PW Magazine November 2005 pp 36 – 39, PW Publishing Ltd, Arrowsmith Court, Station Approach, Broadstone, Dorset, BH18 8PW, www.pwpublishing.ltd.uk

[7] A 1.5 times oversize copy of the track layout for the Simple 144MHz Receiver is available by sending 3 second class stamps and your address to: Oliver Tillett, G3TPJ, 27 Cranbrook Drive, Gidea Park, Essex, RM2 6AP.

[8] Description of choosing preamplifier gain can be found in Radio Communications handbook 8th Edition [1] pp 9.18 – 9.22 or http://yu1aw.bakarlsruhe.de/Ultra%20Linear%20Low%20Noise%20VHF%20and%20.pdf

[9] Ole Nykjaer,OZ2OE web page http://hjem.get2net.dk/ole_nykjaer/oz2oe/bf981/981.html

[10] A Low Noise Preamp for 432 and 1296MHz, David Bowman, G0MRF, DUBUS Magazine 4/2005 pp 40 – 44, DUBUS, Grützmühlenweg 23, D-22339 Hamburg, Germany, www.dubus.org

[11] The PW Mellstock 70MHz 1W AM Transmitter, PW Magazine Part 1 September 2005 pp 24 - 27 and Part 2 October 2005 pp 30 – 33, PW Publishing Ltd, Arrowsmith Court, Station Approach, Broadstone, Dorset, BH18 8PW, www.pwpublishing.ltd.uk

[6] A Simple 144MHz Receiver, PW Magazine May 2006 pp 32 – 33, PW Publishing Ltd, Arrowsmith Court, Station Approach, Broadstone, Dorset, BH18 8PW, www.pwpublishing.ltd.uk

[12] Doing it by Design, PW Magazine July 2005, PW Publishing Ltd, Arrowsmith Court, Station Approach, Broadstone, Dorset, BH18 8PW, www.pwpublishing.ltd.uk

[13] Doing it by Design, PW Magazine September 2004, PW Publishing Ltd, Arrowsmith Court, Station Approach, Broadstone, Dorset, BH18 8PW, www.pwpublishing.ltd.uk

[14] 70cm ATV Transmitter – 300mW, new version, CQ-TV 198, May 2002 pp 28 – 34, CQ-TV is the magazine of the BATC, www.cq-tv.com.

[15] Farnell In One, www.farnell.co.uk

[16] Phillips Semiconductors, www.semiconductors.phillips.com/pip/BFG135

[17] Amand Cauquelin, F1GFF, cauquelin@worldonline.fr

[18] The DSP-10: An All Mode 2 Meter Transceiver Using a DSP IF and PC Controlled Front Panel, Bob Larkin, W7PUA, QST Magazine September 1999 pp 33 – 41, October 1999 pp 34 – 40, November 1999 pp 42 – 45

[19] DSP-10 Project web site http://www.proaxis.com/~boblark/dsp10.htm

[20] The KK7P KDSP10 DSP Development and Interface Board, http://www.kk7p.com/kdsp10.html

[21] The source code for current version of the DSP-10 program is available from http://www.proaxis.com/~boblark/uhf3sc32.zip

[22] The LMS de-noise algorithm is widely used to reduce the noise on signals by seeking out the coherent portions of the signal. The implementation in this transceiver is based on the article by Johan Forrer, KC7WW, "A DSP Based Audio Signal Processor," QEX, Sept 1996, pp 8 - 13. This project also uses the EZ-Kit Lite and has other useful information on programming this board.

[23] Rick Campbell KK7B, "A Single-Board No-Tune Transceiver for 1296", Microwave Up-date 1993, pp 17-38.

[24] The crystal filter is based on the principles set forth in the article by Wes Hayward, W7ZOI, "A Unified Approach to the Design of Crystal Ladder Filters," QST, May 1982, pp 21 - 27. Minor optimisation was done with the ARRL Radio Designer program (available from QST Publication Services).

[25] Rick Campbell, KK7B, "High Performance Direct Conversion Receivers," QST, Aug 1992, pp 19 - 28. The amplifier circuit is discussed in detail in the follow up note "Direct-Conversion Receiver Noise Figure," Technical Correspondence, QST, Feb 1996, pp 82-84.

[26] Roy Lewallen, W7EL, "An Optimised QRP Transceiver," QST, Aug 1980, pp 14-19.

[27] A list of the changes in version 3.80 of the DSP-10 software are available from http://www.proaxis.com/~boblark/chngs380.htm

[28] Bob Larkin, W7PUA, "A DSP Based Trans-ceiver for UHF and Microwaves," Proceedings of Microwave Update 1996, pp 15 - 31; available from ARRL. This paper covers an early version of the transceiver. The single-conversion transmitter approach shown was not able to achieve adequate spurious levels and was modified to the double-conversion approach used here; Rob Frohne, KL7NA, "A High Performance, Single Signal, Direct-Conversion Receiver with DSP Filtering," QST, Apr 1998, pp 40 - 45. Analog Devices, Digital Signal Processing Applications Using the ADSP-2100 Family, Vol 1 and 2. These are available at some book-stores and directly from Analog Devices, (One Technology Way. PO Box 9106, Norwood, MA 02062-9106; tel 781-329-4700, 800-262-5643; Vol 1 has most of the basic routines needed.

[29] A description of The Hilbert Transform used to generate SSB can be found at http://www.mathworks.com/products/signal/demos.html?file=/products/demos/shipping/signal/hilberttransformdemo.html

[30] Giles Read, L'Eglise, Durley Street, Durley, Southampton, United Kingdom, www.g1mfg.com

[31] Full details on the 70MHz transverter can be found on http://rudius.net/oz2m/70mhz/transverter.htm

[32] 50MHz 500W IRF510 based amplifier, Peter Frenning, OZ1PIF, DUBUS Magazine 2/2005 pp 54 – 57, DUBUS, Grützmühlenweg 23, D-22339 Hamburg, Germany, www.dubus.org

[33] Motorola application note AN749 http://home24.inet.tele.dk/oz1pif/AN749.pdf

[34] Fan speed controller details http://home24.inet.tele.dk/oz1pif/Fancontrol.htm

[35] Dragoslav Dobricic web site for power amplifiers http://www.yu1aw.ba-karlsruhe.de/VHFPower.htm

[36] Down East Microwave Inc., 954 Rt. 519 Frenchtown, NJ 08825 USA, Tel. 908-996-3584 (Voice) , 908-996-3702 (Fax) http://www.downeastmicrowave.com

[37] Data sheet for the Mitsubishi RA18H1213G, http://www.mitsubishichips.com/Global/content/product/hf/sirfpowermod/1.2g/1.2g/ra18h1213g.pdf

[38] PUFF CAD software is available from K M Publications, 63 Ringwood Road, Luton, Beds, LU2 7BG, UK, andy@vhfcomm.co.uk. There are two useful articles on the web site at www.vhfcomm.co.uk/puff2_1.htm and www.vhfcomm.co.uk/pdf/PUFF%20alphabetic%20index.pdf

[39] Infineon S parameter page http://www.infineon.com/cgibin/ifx/portal/ep/programView.do?channelId=77767&programId=43702&programPage=/ep/program/document.jsp&pageTypeId=17099

[40] Bo Hansen, OZ2M web site where sequencer source code is available http://rudius.net/oz2m/seqmulti.zip

Chapter 5

Antennas and transmission lines

In this chapter :

- Antenna fundamentals
- Antenna arrays
- Transmission lines
- Selecting and installing antennas
- Directional antennas
- Omnidirectional antennas
- Antennas for mobile use
- Antennas for satellite use
- Antenna CAD

T he antenna and its associated feeder or transmission line are arguably the most important elements of any VHF or UHF station, but are frequently considered least in its assembly. Without a good antenna system, and equally good feeder arrangements, much of the RF power generated by the transmitter will be dissipated as heat before it reaches the antenna. If the antenna is badly sited, or unsuitable for the location, the power reaching it may be radiated in the wrong direction, or scattered from other nearby antennas and structures, again wasting the RF generated by the transmitter. The problems of line loss increase with increasing frequency, and greater care is required to make the most of the power available and it is generally more difficult (or expensive) to generate more power as the frequency increases.

Similar arguments apply to reception; why throw away a large percentage of the signal captured by the antenna before it reaches the receiver? Solutions using mast-head preamplifiers can be used but they entail some complexity and expense if the antenna is to be used for both transmission and reception.

Of course, it is not always possible to find and erect an ideal antenna in an ideal location, particularly in an urban environment. This chapter describes the principles of antenna and transmission lines for the VHF and UHF amateur bands, such that the reader can make informed choices about installations that are both practical and effective for their environment. The designs for home construction are practical, and can be built with confidence that they will work if the details are followed closely. However, at VHF/UHF small deviations from detail can affect the performance of the antenna quite markedly, and if suitable measuring apparatus is not available, much frustration can ensue in trying to make the antenna work. This chapter includes some more complex antennas that require some measuring facilities to optimise performance after construction; these are for the enthusiast antenna experimenter.

However, before tackling the selection and installation of antennas, it is useful to understand some of the underlying theory of their operation and use.

Antenna fundamentals

All antennas have certain basic properties that can be well defined. These are:

- Radiation pattern
- Polarisation
- Gain
- Input impedance
- Impedance and radiation pattern bandwidths

Of these, the radiation pattern is generally the most basic parameter used for selecting an antenna for a particular purpose. Many amateurs use highly directional antennas that require rotation to point in the desired direction of communication. However, antennas providing all round (omni directional) coverage are usually required for repeater stations, and are of course essential for vehicle installations.

Radiation pattern

The radiation pattern describes the spatial distribution of the power radiated by the antenna, that is, the directions in which the signal is transmitted or from which it is received. The key characteristics of directional antennas are usually expressed as the beamwidth in two principal planes at right angles to each other, known as the E plane and the H plane, and described in the next section. The beamwidth in these principal planes is usually defined as the angle including the main beam at which the radiated energy falls to one-half the maximum level. This is called the half-power beamwidth, and the points on the radiation pattern are often called the 3dB or half power points of the radiation pattern, being 3dB below the main beam. See Fig 5.1.

Fig 5.1 shows the spatial distribution of power in one principal plane for a typical directional VHF antenna. This representation is called a polar diagram, where the power in a given direction is indicated by the distance of the curve from the centre of the diagram (in this case, where the lobes touch), and can be thought of as a plan view of

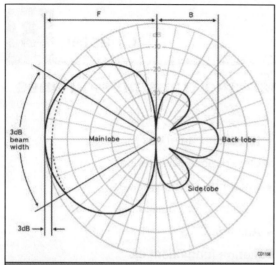

Fig 5.1: Typical polar diagram of a VHF Yagi antenna.

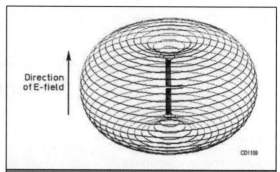

Direction of E-field

Fig 5.2: Radiation from, and polarisation of, a dipole antenna.

the variation in radiated power. The radiation pattern can be presented on a variety of polar diagram charts, the principal difference being the arrangement of the radial scale. The most usual forms are linear, where the radius of the pattern is directly proportional to the radiated power in a given direction, and logarithmic, where the radius represents the relative power in decibels.

Key features of the radiation patterns of the antenna shown in Fig 5.1 are the main lobe or main beam, and the presence of several minor lobes including one pointing in the opposite direction to the main lobe. The front-to-back (F/B) ratio is the ratio of the energy radiated by the peak of the main lobe to that in the opposite direction, and is often used as an estimate of the 'goodness' of a beam antenna. This ratio is usually expressed in decibels. As more power is radiated in minor lobes, less power is available in the main lobe, and the gain of the antenna is reduced (see below). Omni directional antennas ideally have a circular radiation pattern in one plane, but will still have a shaped radiation pattern in the other principal plane, at right-angles to the first.

The linearly scaled graph is useful for measuring the beamwidth of the main lobe accurately, whereas the logarithmically scaled chart more clearly shows the levels of the side lobes, which may be barely visible on the linear chart. The ARRL has promoted the use of a hybrid chart which combines features of both types of graph, by using a quasi-logarithmic radial scale marked in decibels [2].

Polarisation

Radio waves comprise both electric and magnetic fields mutually coupled at right angles to each other and at right angles to the direction of propagation. The two principal planes used in describing radiation patterns are derived from this; the E-plane lies parallel to the electric vector or E-field in the main lobe, and the H-plane lies parallel to the magnetic vector or H-field in the main lobe. Accordingly, these two principal planes will be at right angles to each other.

The polarisation of an antenna is defined in terms of the orientation of the electric field vector in the direction of maximum radiation. The maximum radiation from a dipole occurs in a plane bisecting its centre and at right angles to the dipole arms. The electric field vector, in this plane lies parallel to the arms of the dipole, see Fig 5.2.

Thus a dipole mounted horizontally above the ground is said to radiate horizontally polarised signals, and the same dipole mounted vertically would radiate vertically polarised signals.

Whilst many amateurs use vertical or horizontal linear polarisation for terrestrial communications, satellite users often use circular polarisation to reduce the effects of propagation, ground reflections or the spinning of the satellites on the signals. The effect of circular polarisation can be visualised as a signal emanating from a dipole rotating about its centre at the frequency of radiation. The tip of the electric vector traces out a corkscrew as it propagates away from the antenna, and like a corkscrew, the polarisation is described as right or left handed circular, dependent on the direction of rotation of the electric vector as seen from the transmitter.

A fixed linear dipole will receive an equal signal from a circularly polarised wave whether it is mounted vertically, horizontally or in an intermediate position. The signal strength will be 3dB less than if a circularly polarised antenna of the same sense is used; however, a circularly polarised antenna of the opposite sense will receive no signals. Both these effects are due to polarisation mis-match between the wave and the receive antenna.

In practice, an antenna may radiate unwanted polaristions in a variety of directions, including the main lobe. This is called cross-polarised radiation, and for linearly polarised antennas it will be perpendicular to the wanted radiation. In circularly polarised antennas, the cross polarised element is that part of the signal that is radiated as circular polarisation of the opposite sense to that intended. The relationship between wanted and unwanted signals is often expressed as an axial ratio or ellipticity, the defini-tions of which can be found in reference [1]. The smaller this figure, the better.

It is worth noting that with linearly polarised antennas,

particularly beams with complex polar diagrams, radiation from the side lobes can be of the opposite polarisation to the main beam, and will often be complex or elliptical, especially outside the principal planes. Hence the reception of signals from a cross-polarised station may often be stronger with the beam pointing away from, or at an angle to, the transmitting station.

Gain and directivity

The gain of an antenna is a basic property that is frequently used as a figure of merit. It is defined as the maximum signal radiated in a given direction relative to that of an isotropic radiator fed with the same power. An isotropic radiator is a hypothetical, lossless antenna that radiates equally in all directions. In practice, a half-wave dipole is often used as the reference radiator; if the dipole is lossless, it has a maximum gain of 1.64 (or 10 × $\log_{10}1.64 = 2.15$ decibels) relative to the isotropic antenna.

The directivity of an antenna is defined purely in terms of its radiation pattern, as the radiation intensity in a given direction to the radiation intensity averaged over all directions. A practical antenna may have good directivity, but poor gain if the antenna is lossy through poor design, use of lossy components or poor mechanical construction. If the antenna is lossless, the gain and directivity will be the same.

High directivity is achieved by compressing, or focusing the radiated power into a small solid angle, this is the product of the half-power beamwidths in the two principal planes. An isotropic radiator radiates equally in all directions, which can be imagined as equal illumination over the surface of a sphere. A good, directive VHF antenna will confine most of its radiation to a few tens of degrees around the main beam, corresponding to the beam of a pencil torch illuminating the inside of the sphere.

If antenna losses are small, and the side and back lobes are also much smaller than the main lobe (which we would expect for a well designed beam antenna), there is an approximate formula that relates the 3dB beamwidth of the antenna in the two principal planes (E and H) to the gain of the antenna:

Gain relative to a λ/2 dipole $\quad \dfrac{\lambda}{2} = \dfrac{27.000}{\theta_E \theta_H}$

where θ_E is the angular width, in degrees, between the half-power points in the E-plane, and θ_H is the angular width, in degrees, between the half-power points in the H-plane. The gain can be expressed in decibels relative to a half-wave dipole (dBD) by taking the logarithm of the expression:

$$G_{dBD} = 10\log_{10}\left[\dfrac{27.000}{\theta_E \theta_H}\right]$$

This formula is reasonably accurate (within 2dB) for well designed, efficient antennas with gains greater than 10dBi (8dBD), and can be useful for estimating the beamwidth

where a radiation pattern is only available for one plane and the gain of the antenna is also known. The gain in decibels relative to an isotropic radiator can be found by adding 2.15 to G_{dBD}.

Input impedance

The impedance presented at the feed point by an antenna is a complex function of the size and shape of the antenna, the frequency of operation, and its environment. The impedance is affected by the proximity of other conducting objects, where the induction of RF currents alters the impedance through mutual coupling between the antenna and object. The elements of a Yagi antenna are mutually coupled together, and the driven element would present a very different impedance if measured in isolation from the rest of the structure.

Input impedance is usually complex. The resistive part is composed of the radiation resistance, which can be thought of as dissipating power by radiating it as electromagnetic energy (desirable), and loss resistance, which dissipates power as heat (not desirable). The reactive part arises from the behaviour of antenna elements as resonators, or tuned circuits, and it can change rapidly with variations of frequency.

Impedance bandwidth

The impedance bandwidth of an antenna is defined as the frequency range over which the antenna impedance results in a voltage standing wave ratio (VSWR) less than some arbitrary limit. This may be typically 1.5:1 for amateur operation with solid-state transmitters or higher values for other applications. Ideally, an antenna should be impedance matched to the feed line and thence to the transmitter or receiver. Although tuned feed arrangements are sometimes used at HF, where a high standing wave ratio may be acceptable on the feed line, the losses in VHF feeders and tuning components usually preclude this approach at VHF and UHF. Feeders and matching arrangements are discussed later in this chapter.

Radiation pattern bandwidth

Antenna radiation patterns are also dependent upon the operating frequency. Using the analogy of the Yagi antenna's elements as tuned circuits, the loss of resonance away from the design frequency results in small currents in the elements and a consequently severe loss of performance. In the case of the Yagi antenna this results in a sharp decrease of gain, and destruction of the desired radiation pattern. For beam antennas, such as the Yagi, the radiation pattern bandwidth is often defined as the frequency range over which the main lobe gain decreases to 1dB less than its maximum.

It should be noted that the impedance bandwidth and radiation pattern bandwidth are independent of each other. It is quite possible for the impedance bandwidth to be greater than the radiation pattern bandwidth, especially with high gain antennas, and to be able to feed power into an antenna that then wastes it by radiating it in other than the desired direction!

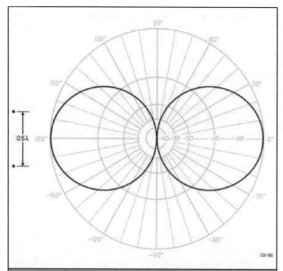

Fig 5.3: Array of two point sources and their radiation pattern.

Table 5.1: Calculations for the radiation pattern of a four element collinear dipole array.

Angle relative to normal (°)	Array factor	Dipole pattern (voltage)	Radiation pattern
0	4.00	1.00	4.00
5	3.74	0.99	3.71
10	3.00	0.98	2.94
15	1.98	0.95	1.88
20	0.89	0.91	0.81
25	-0.06	0.87	-0.05
30	-0.73	0.82	-0.59
35	-1.05	0.76	0.80
40	-1.06	0.69	-0.74

maximum achievable gain could be N times greater than one element fed with the same power (10 $\log_{10}$ N decibels) if there are N elements in the array. However, more complex feed arrangements can reduce the VSWR bandwidth and introduce losses, reducing the array gain. Arrays need care in construction and attention to detail, especially at UHF and above, but the results reward the effort expended.

Broadside arrays

If a pair of identical isotropic radiators or point sources are fed in phase with equal power, an interference pattern will be set up. The field will be a maximum at right angles to the array. However, cancellation will occur at other angles where the wave from one antenna has travelled an odd number of half-wavelengths further than from the other antenna, see Fig 5.3.

Antenna arrays

Purpose

The gain achievable with any antenna structure is ultimately limited by the fundamentals of its operation. However, higher gains can be achieved by using several antenna elements in an array. The array can comprise antennas stacked vertically above each other, or arranged side by side in bays, or a combination of both. These are broadside arrays, where most of the radiated power is projected at right angles to the plane in which the elements lie. An array can also be formed where the main beam is projected along the array of elements; these are endfire arrays, of which the HB9CV and Yagi antennas are examples.

An array of elements has a narrower beamwidth, and hence a higher gain than the individual antennas. The

The same principle can be applied to more than two point sources, which if they are equally spaced, produce a radiation pattern of the form:

$$E_\vartheta = \left[\frac{\sin\left(\dfrac{N}{2}\psi\right)}{\sin\left(\dfrac{1}{2}\psi\right)} \right]$$

$$\psi = 2\pi d \sin\theta + \beta$$

where θ is the angle measured normal to the line of the array, d is the separation of the point sources in wavelengths, β is the phase difference between the elements (usually zero) and N is the number of elements.

The electric field at any angle to the array is calculated by adding together the fields from each point source, taking into account the phase delay of the field from each source, i.e. vector addition of the fields. The resulting pattern for arrays of point sources is often known as an array factor.

In a practical array, each point source will be replaced by a real antenna i.e. a half-wave dipole or perhaps a Yagi antenna. Provided that all the antennas are pointing in the same direction, the pattern produced by such an array can be found by multiplying together, at each angle of interest, the array factor just calculated and the pattern factor or radiation pattern of the antennas used in the array.

This means that any nulls in the element pattern will be reproduced in the array pattern, which is why arrays of complex elements often result in many side lobes.

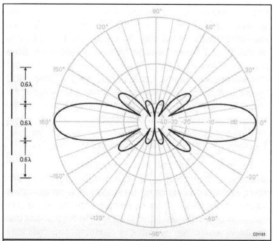

Fig 5.4: Plotted radiation pattern for a four element collinear dipole array.

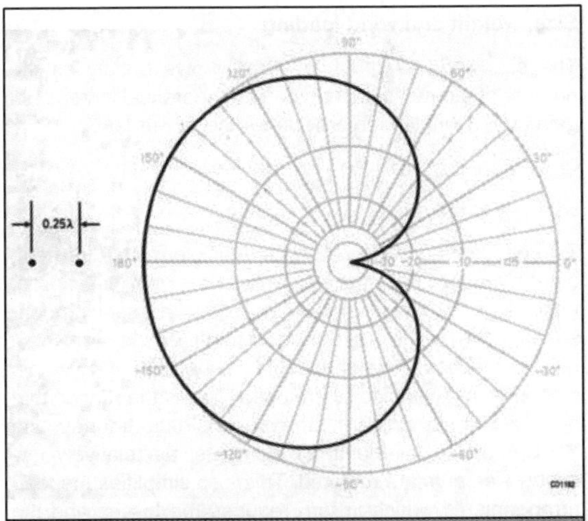

Fig 5.5: Radiation pattern of two point sources separated by one quarter wavelength and fed in quadrature.

The radiation pattern of such an array can be calculated by programming a computer, in a spreadsheet, or by hand by setting out a table as shown in Table 5.1.

Note that if working from antenna patterns or data expressed in decibels, the directivity at each angle must be converted to a fraction before multiplying by the array factor. For example, if the directivity at a given angle is -2.8dB relative to the peak of the main beam, the directivity in linear terms is:

$$10^{-2.8/20} = 0.7244$$

It is easiest to scale the directivity to the peak of the main lobe prior to carrying out the calculation.

Endfire arrays

If a pair of point source antennas are separated by one quarter wavelength, and are fed with a phase difference of 90° between them, the radiated field from one antenna will reinforce that of the second in one direction, and will completely cancel the field from the second in the opposite direction, see Fig 5.5.

The equation for the radiation pattern is the same as shown for the broadside array above, except that the phase angle β is now 90°. Other spacings may be used, provided that the phase difference is adjusted to ensure that the radiation is cancelled in the desired direction. Antennas such as the HB9CV (shown later in this chapter) use this technique to provide directivity and a good front-to-back ratio from mechanically compact structures. Both elements are fed by the transmitter. The Yagi antenna generates its radiation pattern using similar phasing principles, but only one element is fed as described later in this chapter.

Antenna array theory can be found in almost any book devoted to antennas. However, a good treatment with many radiation pattern examples can be found in references [3] and [4].

Practical considerations and limitations of arrays

Stacking separation

High gain cannot be achieved by simply stacking many elements close together. If we consider a dipole collecting power from an incident field for delivery to a load (receiver), it can be thought of as having a collecting area or effective aperture that is somewhat larger than the dipole itself. The higher the directivity of the antenna, the larger the effective aperture, as given by the relationship:

$$A_{eff} = \frac{\lambda^2}{4\pi} D$$

where D is the directivity of the antenna and λ is the working wavelength.

If the effective apertures of adjacent antennas overlap, the incoming RF energy is shared between them, and the maximum possible directivity (or gain) of the elements cannot be attained.

The optimum stacking distance is a function of the half-power beamwidth of the elements in the array, and is given by:

$$S_{opt} = \frac{\lambda}{2\sin\left(\frac{\phi}{2}\right)}$$

where ϕ is the half-power beamwidth. Note that this is usually different for the E and H planes, so that the spacing of the elements is also usually different in each plane.

Also, when antennas are placed close together, mutual coupling between elements occurs. This leads to changes in the current distribution on the elements, changing both the radiation pattern and the feed-point impedance of each element. The changes to the feed impedance often result in unequal powers being fed to the elements of the array, with consequential loss of gain. Optimum stacking rules are based on the assumption of minimum mutual influence that can be difficult to predict for composite antennas such as Yagis. However, antennas with low side lobe levels are less susceptible than those with high side lobes, as might be expected intuitively.

The coupling and effective aperture overlap problems cannot simply be solved by arbitrarily increasing the separation of the elements. As the element spacing increases, grating side lobes appear, which reduce the forward gain. The grating lobes are due solely to the array dimensions, and can be seen by plotting the array factor for the chosen configuration.

Power divider and transmission line losses

The usual arrangements for feeding an array of antennas require each antenna to be fed an equal amount of power in the same phase as all the other elements in the array. There are several ways that this can be achieved, as shown in the section on antennas for construction later in this chapter. The power can be divided N ways at one point, from which equal length transmission lines feed each element or groups of elements fed by another power divider. Each system has its merits but losses incurred in the power dividers and cables erode the gain provided by the array.

Each time a cable connection is required, whether to a power divider or an antenna, the connection usually creates a small impedance mismatch. Power will be reflected from this mismatch and others in the system, reducing the gain of the array. The cumulative degradation of the power distribution to each antenna element can be startling, and of course the same degradation occurs when the antenna is receiving. In general, the simplest feed arrangements incur lowest losses and best performance.

Phasing errors

The small mismatches described above can result in errors in the phase of the current injected into the array elements, again leading to loss of gain and filling of nulls in the radiation pattern. Incorrect line lengths can result in the same effect. In constructing feeds for UHF and above, care must be taken in cutting and connecting cables.

A knowledge of the velocity factor of the actual cable used is essential if good results are to be achieved. The velocity factor is the rate at which the RF propagates along the cable relative to the speed of light (or RF) in a vacuum, and is modified by the dielectric constant of the cable insulator. A cutting error of 2mm in a solid polythene dielectric cable (such as URM67) will result in a phase error of 5° at 1296MHz. Measurement of the cable characteristics as described in references [5] and [6] can help eliminate many of the uncertainties of cable harness fabrication.

Alternatively, the velocity factor can be found with a dip meter coupled to a very small loop at the end of an open circuit length of cable. At VHF, this loop should be no greater than 3mm radius. At higher frequencies, it is sufficient to trim the dielectric of the cable flush with the braid, fold the inner over the dielectric and solder to the braid, especially for larger diameter cables. The dip will appear when the cable is an odd number of quarter-wavelengths long; if the frequency is checked with a counter or calibrated receiver, the velocity factor can be accurately calculated from:

$$v = \frac{4Lf}{300n}$$

where L is the length of the stub in metres, f is the resonant frequency in megahertz, and n is 1, 3, 5, the length of the stub in quarter wavelengths. The lowest resonant frequency corresponds to n = 1.

Velocity factors are typically 0.66 for solid polyethylene, 0.72 for solid PTFE, and around 0.85 to 0.95 for foamed dielectrics or semi-air-spaced cables. Very low loss Heliax style cables that support the inner on small dielectric stand-offs can have velocity factors of 0.98.

Size, weight and wind loading

The size and weight of an array grows rapidly as the number of elements increases. The theoretical increase in gain over a single element follows the power law:

$$G_{max} = 10 \log_{10} N \quad \text{decibels}$$

where N is the number of elements.

Two elements provide 3dB gain, four elements 6dB gain, eight elements 9dB, 16 elements 20dB gain and so on, under ideal conditions. However, given the spacing constraints, the weight and wind loading of the array can quickly become unmanageable, especially if low-gain elements such as dipoles are used. This is the reason that most high-gain antenna arrays constructed today use Yagi antennas for the array elements, as relatively few driven elements are required. This also simplifies the feed arrangements, which in turn reduces the losses and the cumulative phase and mismatch errors that tend to occur as the feed arrangements become more complex.

Transmission lines

Antenna feeders or, more correctly, transmission lines, can make or break the performance of a station. At UHF and higher, the losses in the transmission lines feeding the antenna can be significant, dissipating RF power as heat, and requiring much larger antennas to achieve the desired radiated power. At these frequencies, there are essentially two useful types of transmission line for antennas: open wire and coaxial cable.

Open wire line

The open wire transmission line, comprising two parallel conductors held apart at intervals by spacers or spreaders, is still often used for feeding HF antennas. It provides a low loss, easily constructed feeder capable of handling high powers, and the characteristic impedance can be adjusted by changing the wire diameter or spacing. The characteristic impedance is given by:

$$Z_0 = 276 \log_{10}\left(\frac{2D}{d}\right)$$

where D is the spacing between the wire centres, both wires having diameter d.

At VHF and higher frequencies, dielectric losses can become significant, but are minimised in the parallel wire line. Apart from the spacers, the dielectric between the lines is air, and only a vacuum provides a better dielectric. The velocity factor is very close to unity. However, the spacing between wires must be much less than the wavelength if power is not to be lost through radiation. At VHF and above, this forces the selection of thinner wires or lower characteristic impedances if the feeder is to remain reasonably robust, and to some extent limits the uses of this type of transmission line to providing low loss feeds to antennas in arrays, where the ability to adjust the impedance by varying the spacing is useful. Open wire line is not really practicable for frequencies above 432MHz. This, and the difficulties of rigging long runs of closely spaced lines and of bringing them through the wall

Table 5.2: Attenuation of coaxial cables.

Cable type	Diameter (mm)	Velocity factor	Attenuation (dB/100m) at				
			50MHz	70MHz	144MHz	432MHz	1296MHz
URM76, RG58CU	5.0	0.66	12	14	19	32	N/A
URM43	5.0	0.66	8.1	10.2	16.1	28.5	N/A
URM67, RG213U	10.3	0.66	4.6	5.6	8.3	15.5	27.0
Westflex 103	10.3	0.85	2.0	2.5	4.5	7.5	13.0
3/8 in Flexwell	12.3	0.89	2.0	2.4	3.0	6.4	10.8
5/8 in Flexwell	23.0	0.92	1.25	1.5	2.5	3.8	6.8
7/8 in Flexwell	29.0	0.92	0.83	1.0	1.45	2.5	4.4

Table 5.3: Miniature and special impedance cables for stubs and transformers.

Cable type	Impedance (Ω)	Diameter (mm)	Dielectric	Velocity factor	Attenuation (dB/100m) at		
					100MHz	300MHz	1000MHz
URM95	50	2.3	Polythene	0.66	27	46	85
RG174U	50	2.3	Polythene	0.66	-	-	-
URM70	75	6	Polythene	0.67	15	27	52
URM111	75	2.3	PTFE	0.72	25	44	81
RG62AU	95	6	Air spaced polythene	0.83	-	-	-

of a building (or round the antenna rotator) have probably discouraged their more general use.

Where open wire line is required, use enamelled soft drawn copper wire and solid PTFE rod for spacers if possible. The wire should be stretched to straighten and work harden it immediately prior to assembly. Great care should be taken to ensure both wires are of equal length and made up/mounted symmetrically with respect both to dielectrics and conducting objects adjacent to the line.

Coaxial lines

Coaxial transmission lines, as their name implies, comprise an inner conductor mounted centrally within an outer conductor. The characteristic impedance for concentric circular conductors is given by:

$$Z_0 = \left(\frac{138}{\sqrt{\varepsilon}}\right) \log_{10}\left(\frac{D}{d}\right)$$

where D is the inside diameter of the outer conductor, d is the diameter of the inner conductor and ε is the dielectric constant of the insulator (1 for air).

A square section outer can be used to simplify connector mountings for home-constructed power dividers and transformer sections. The characteristic impedance is approximated by:

$$Z_0 = \left(\frac{138}{\sqrt{\varepsilon}}\right) \log_{10}\left(1.08\frac{D}{d}\right)$$

where D is now the inside dimension of the square outer conductor.

The principal advantage of coaxial transmission lines is that the surfaces carrying the RF current and the dielectric are inside, allowing robust, weather resistant design and simple mounting on metal surfaces or masts. The disadvantages are dielectric losses (which increase rapidly with frequency), cost and weight.

Flexible cable designs use a braided outer conductor that,

if it does not thoroughly cover the dielectric, will allow the RF to leak out through gaps in the braid. Cheap, so called "RG58" cable sold for Citizens' Band use should be avoided at all costs, as the braid coverage can be less than 50%, at VHF and above little power will reach the antenna. There are also cheap cables using a single wire and metallised plastic wrapping as 'braid' that are useless for VHF purposes.

Good quality flexible coaxial cables have thick, close woven single or double outer braids. Genuine RG58 or URM67 cables provide flexibility with acceptable losses, especially for short lengths. Where longer cable runs are necessary, cables with semi air spacing and copper foil outer conductors provide better performance, although some care is needed in sealing the ends of these types to prevent ingress of moisture which will rapidly degrade the cable irretrievably. The ultimate in coaxial feeders are the Flexwell or Heliax types of cable, with a continuous corrugated copper outer, and air spaced or PTFE foam dielectrics, together with special connectors to ensure good sealing and minimal mismatch. The performance of some typical 50Ω coaxial cables under impedance matched conditions is shown in Table 5.2. Note that losses will be higher if appreciable standing waves exist on the cable. There is further information in Chapter 12, "General Data".

An optimised installation would use rigid, low loss cable for the fixed runs, with a short section of flexible cable to bridge the antenna rotator.

Matching stubs and transformer sections (discussed below) often require cables with characteristic impedances other than 50Ω. Also, miniature cables are sometimes desirable for constructing matching networks and filters. The higher loss is usually acceptable, as the length of cable used is small. Characteristics of a few readily available special cable types are shown in Table 5.3.

Impedance matching circuits

At VHF and above it is usual to use transmission lines, rather than lumped components, to obtain an impedance

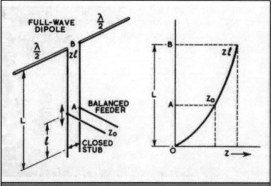

Fig 5.6: Stub matching applied to λ/2 dipole.

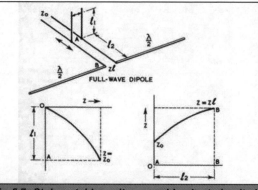

Fig 5.7: Stub matching wit a movable short circuited stub.

match between systems of different characteristic imped-ances. They can also be used to match arbitrary imped-ances (such as an antenna) to its feeder, of which a few techniques are shown below. Other methods addressing the design and calculation of matching circuits and components in detail are shown in references [7] and [8]. An excellent article on the behaviour of transmission lines and their use as circuit elements, together with some computer programs, can be found in reference [9].

Single stub matching

A short-circuited section of lossless transmission line behaves as a pure reactance at its input terminals. This impedance is given by the formula:

$$X_{in} = Z_0 \tan \beta l$$

where βl is the electrical length of the line (taking into account the velocity factor) and Z_0 is its characteristic impedance

The input reactance is inductive until the line length is a quarter wavelength. The input impedance is then infinite, i.e. an open circuit. As the line length is increased further, the reactance becomes negative, and the line behaves as a capacitor at the input terminals, although the remote end is a short circuit. When the line is exactly one half wavelength long, the input terminals appear to be short circuited with no residual reactance. This cycle is repeated as the line is extended further.

An open circuited stub behaves in a complementary

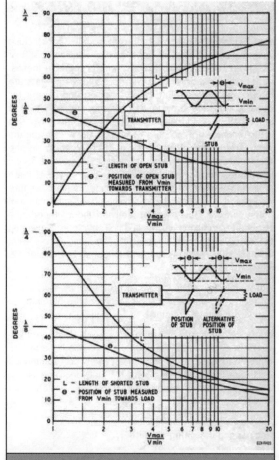

Fig 5.8: Impedance matching charts for a single stub.

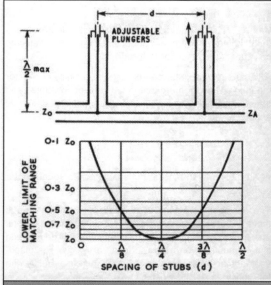

Fig 5.9: Two stub coaxial tuner graph. Z_0 is the characteristic impedance of feeder.

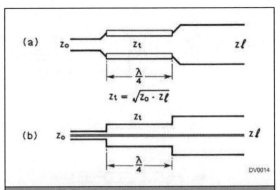

Fig 5.10: Quarter wave transformer construction in (a) open wire and (b) coaxial.

manner to the short-circuited line. The input impedance is given by:

$$X_{in} = \frac{Z_0}{\tan \beta l}$$

Now the short length of line appears as a capacitor at its terminals, becoming a short circuit at one quarter wavelength, appearing inductive as it lengthens further, and becoming an open circuit at one half-wavelength. The term matching is used to describe the process of suitably modifying the effective load impedance to make it behave as a resistance and to ensure that this resistance has a value equal to the characteristic impedance of the feeder used. To make a complex load (i.e. a load possessing both resistance and reactance) behave as a resistance, it is necessary to introduce across it a reactance of equal value and opposite sign so that its reactance is effectively cancelled. The stubs described above provide the means to supply this reactance. Although there is no need to make the characteristic impedance of a stub equal to that of the transmission line, it may be desirable to do so for practical reasons. In addition to tuning out the reactance, a match still has to be made to the transmission line characteristic impedance. The impedance at any point along the length of a λ/4 resonant stub varies from zero at the short circuit to a very high impedance at the open end.

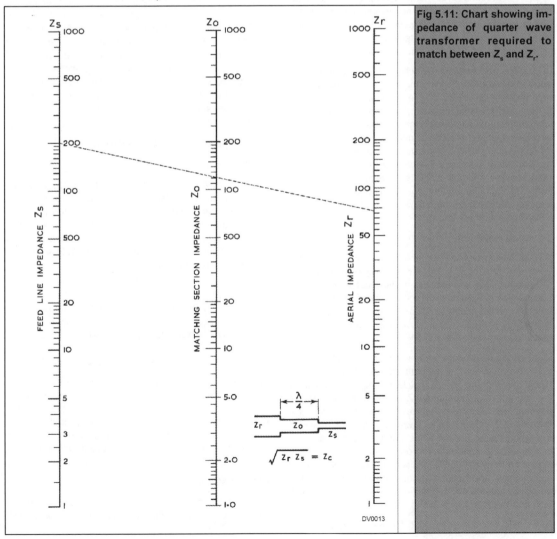

Fig 5.11: Chart showing impedance of quarter wave transformer required to match between Z_s and Z_r.

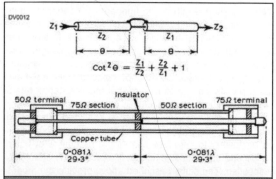

Fig 5.12 Transmission line transformer for matching 50Ω to 75Ω systems.

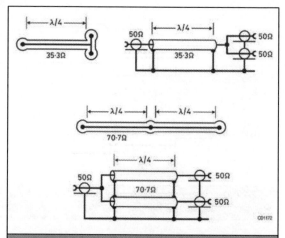

Fig 5: 13: Two types of quarter wave power divider.

If a load is connected to the open end and the power is fed into the stub at some point along its length, the stub may be used as an impedance transformer to give various values of impedance according the position of the feed point. This is shown in Fig 5.6. The distance L is adjusted to tune the antenna to resonance and will be λ/4 long if the antenna is already resonant. The distance l is adjusted to obtain a match to the line. However, it can be convenient to have a stub with an adjustable short circuit that can slide along the transmission line (see Fig 5.7).

In practice, matching can be achieved entirely by the 'cut-and-try' method of adjusting the stub length and position until no standing waves can be detected. The feeder line is then said to be flat. However, the frequency range over which any single stub matching device is effective is quite small, and where wide band matching is required some other matching system may be needed. Fortunately, for most amateur purposes the bandwidth required is relatively narrow and the single stub technique is usually sufficient. Fig 5.8 shows the positioning of open and short-circuited stubs when the VSWR and the position of the VSWR minimum are known.

Two stub matching

It is in making stub adjustments by 'cut-and-try' that the open wire transmission line comes into its own because of the relative ease of repositioning the stub and the short circuit. With coaxial line it is impracticable to construct a stub with an adjustable position. However, two fixed stubs spaced by a fraction of a wavelength can be used for matching purposes (see Fig 5.9).

The spacing usually employed is λ/8 or a multiple thereof. With this spacing, independent adjustment of the short circuit stub lengths gives a matching range over 0.5 times the characteristic impedance (Z_0) of the transmission line upwards. As the spacing between the stubs is increased towards λ/2 or decreased towards zero, the matching range increases, but the adjustments become extremely critical and the bandwidth narrow. The theoretical matching range limits cannot be realised in practice because of finite losses in the stubs, so attention should be paid to providing reliable short circuiting plungers in any home built adjustable two stub tuning units.

Adjustable stub tuners suitable for use at 144MHz have

largely disappeared from the professional inventory, and are therefore extremely scarce in amateur circles. However, if the impedance of the device to be matched can be measured, the position of the stub can be calculated from Fig 5.9, or by the methods described in detail in references [7] and [8]. Coaxial feeders and stubs carefully cut to length and checked (see 'Practical considerations and limitations of arrays' above) will usually achieve a reasonable match, which can then be adjusted by trimming the stub for best results. If trimming worsens the match, replace the stub with a slightly longer one, and start trimming again.

Transmission line transformers

Quarter wave transformer

A length of transmission line of a different characteristic impedance than the feeder can be used to transform impedance, providing an alternative technique that may be used to match a load to a transmission line. A special condition occurs when the length of the section of line is an odd number of quarter wavelengths long when the following formula applies:

$$Z_t = \sqrt{Z_0 Z_1}$$

where Z_t is the characteristic impedance of the section of the line and Z_0 and Z_1 are the feeder and load impedance respectively. For example, if Z_0 is 80Ω and Z_1 is 600Ω then:

$$Z_t = \sqrt{80 \times 600} = 219\Omega$$

This matching section is useful for transforming impedance, it is called a quarter wave transformer, see Fig 5.10. Note that the dimensions are in wavelengths and that allowance must be made for the velocity factor of the wave if dielectrics other than air are used to separate the conductors (see 'Practical considerations and limitations of arrays' above for typical velocity factors).

'Cot' transformer

The preceding methods require the use of special impedance cable sections that, although they may be readily

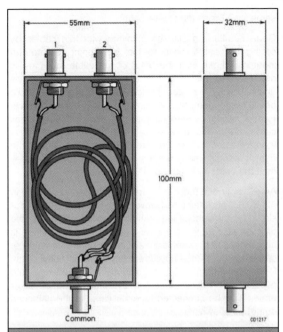

Fig 5.14: Compact two way power divider for 145MHz.

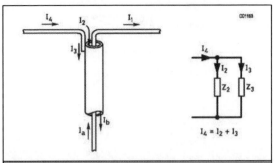

Fig 5.15: Currents inside and at the end of a coaxial cable.

matching device is called a delta match and is only really practical with open wire feeders.

Power dividers

The quarter wave transformers described above can be used to build power dividers to feed antenna arrays where interconnection cable lengths or available cable types will not permit transformation through the cables. This is especially valid for UHF systems, where it may be convenient to split the power at one place and feed the elements of the array with cables that have been cut to be of identical electrical length.

Two methods for achieving a two-way power divider are shown in Fig 5.13. A suitable single $\lambda/4$ transformer section can feed two outputs, connected together. This works well if the two loads are well matched both in magnitude and phase. The second method uses separate quarter wave transformer sections to feed each output, which can provide better overall performance if the two loads are well matched but not absolutely identical, as may be the case with the outer elements in an array. The separate transformer sections ensure that identical in-phase currents will be provided at the outputs despite minor differences in load impedance.

Construction of power dividers depends largely on the division ratio, the frequency of operation and the materials available. Square section tubing can provide faces for up to four output connectors if suitable inner conductors can be found to provide the correct transformation ratio. However, such dividers for 50 and 144MHz are large, and more compact but equally efficient dividers can be constructed from suitable coaxial cable, coiled up to fit within a box, see Fig 5.14. The example shown uses miniature 75Ω PTFE cable (URM111) for a 145MHz two-way power divider, it is suitable for powers no greater than 50W. For higher powers, larger diameter, lower loss cable should be used in a larger box.

constructed in open wire form, are difficult to realise in coaxial cable. There is another technique that can be used to transform between two cable systems of different impedance using short, equal length sections of the two types of cable in the sequence System1-Z_2-Z_1-System2 as shown in Fig 5.12.

The formula for the electrical length of the matching sections has been simplified by G3KYH to:

$$\cot^2 \theta = \frac{Z_1}{Z_2} + \frac{Z_2}{Z_1} + 1$$

where $\cot^2\theta = 1/\tan^2\theta$ and θ is the electrical length of each section in degrees. To transform between 50Ω and 75Ω or vice versa, $\theta = 29.3°$. The physical length must take into account the velocity factor of the sections imposed by their construction. One way of realising the transformer is shown in Fig 5.12.

Tapered line transformer

A section of tapered line can also be used to effect an impedance transformation. Again, a $\lambda/4$ section is only a special case, and to achieve a match in a particular installation the line length and the angle of taper should be varied until a perfect match is achieved. This form of

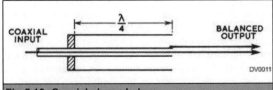

Fig 5.16: Coaxial sleeve balun.

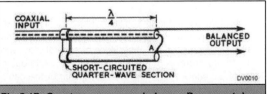

Fig 5.17: Quarter wave open balun or Pawsey stub.

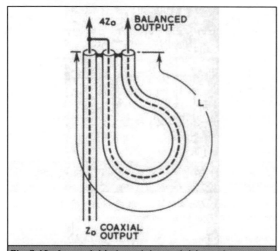

Fig 5.18: A coaxial balun giving a 4:1 impedance step up.

Baluns

In many cases, antennas require a balanced feed with respect to ground, with equal and opposite currents in each leg of the feed. Coaxial cables are not symmetrical and, if they are connected directly to a balanced antenna, current will usually result on the *outside* of the braid, see Fig 5.15. The effects of this current is usually unwanted radiation, manifested as distorted radiation patterns, or interference with other electronics (EMC problems) where the feeder outer carries the unwanted RF to the susceptible equipment. In extreme cases, it can result in 'hot shack' effects, e.g. RF burns or changes to the impedance seen by the transmitter as other pieces of equipment are connected to the transmitter. These effects can be eliminated by suppressing the unwanted currents on the outer of the feed cable through the use of a balance-to-unbalance transformer (*balun*).

Under normal operation, the RF current flows on *the inside* of the outer conductor and the *outside* of the inner conductor of the coaxial cable. Under these circumstances, I_a and I_b are equal and opposite. However, at the end of the cable braid, the current I_4 may divide into two parts: I_2 flowing on the inner of the braid (and hence not capable of radiation or interference) and I_3 which flows on the *outside* of the braid and can be a potential source of trouble. The fraction of current on the outside of the braid is directly related to the impedance presented by the path on the outside of the braid (Z_3) to the characteristic impedance of the cable (Z_2), as shown in Fig 5.15. Balun designs increase the value of Z_3 and may also provide impedance transformations that are not part of the true balun action.

A coaxial sleeve balun is shown in Fig 5.16. The short-circuited quarter wave stub surrounding the end of the coaxial cable presents an impedance of several thousand ohms to any currents that would flow on the cable outer. Most of the current then flows on the *inside* of the cable outer as required. Similar results are achieved with the Pawsey stub, Fig 5.17, which operates in exactly the

same manner as the sleeve balun.

Good results can also be obtained with thin cables by coiling the cable close to the feed point to form an inductive choke with the outer of the cable, but care is necessary to ensure that the capacitance between turns (increased by the cable jacket) does not tune the choke below resonance which will prevent it from being effective. Ferrite beads or sleeves may be used on very small cables but this is more appropriate for low power circuits than for antennas, where care is required in selecting the right materials; many ferrites are lossy at VHF and may melt the cable or shatter under even modest RF power.

An example of a much used transformer balun is shown in Fig 5.18. This uses a half wavelength of cable to invert the signal for the second leg of the balanced feed, and in the process also provides a 4:1 impedance increase. There is no connection between the balanced circuits and the outer of the feeder, hence no current flows on the outer of the feed. The length of the phasing cable should take into account the velocity factor of the cable, and all outer braids may be connected together close to the balanced output as shown.

Transmission line filters

The characteristics of transmission line stubs and transformer sections can be used to create effective filters and diplexers. An excellent series of articles by G4SWX [15, 16] covers the design and adjustment of a range of harmonic and TVI filters, together with diplexers for several VHF/UHF bands. The diplexers can be useful where several transmitters and receivers are connected to a single broad band antenna, or where concurrent transmission and reception on different bands are needed, as in certain types of satellite communications.

Selecting and installing antennas

This section deals with the essentials of choosing an antenna and its optimum location. Choice may be limited by the location of the station, planning considerations and the funds available, but is ultimately determined by the purpose of the station and the operator's interests.

Many of the decisions and trade-offs are between antenna beamwidth and gain. If interests lie with mobile stations or packet radio, steerable antennas can be a nuisance. Simple omni directional antennas, such as a monopole on a ground plane, will provide good local coverage, but higher gain omni directional antennas, such as collinear arrays, may be desirable for hearing stations further away. Most mobile and packet stations use vertical polarisation, placing another constraint on the choice of fixed antennas.

An antenna with very high gain will have a narrow beamwidth and few side lobes. This is fine if you know where to point the array, but many stations will not be heard because they are outside the beam. Gain can be achieved with a relatively wide beamwidth in the horizontal plane by stacking elements vertically. The horizontal beamwidth is then determined by the beamwidth of a single antenna element in the array, and the vertical beamwidth is narrowed by the array of elements in that

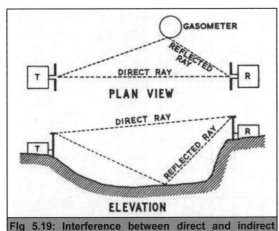

Fig 5.19: Interference between direct and indirect rays.

plane. Slot fed Yagi antennas are an efficient example of this type of antenna.

The converse may apply if using a steerable array for satellite communications; the azimuth angle is usually known, or can be found by steering the antenna, but the elevation varies as the satellite crosses the sky. A relatively narrow horizontal beamwidth and a broad vertical beamwidth with an antenna that is tilted upwards a few degrees will permit good communications without requiring the complexity and expense of elevation rotators and control equipment. Such an array can also be used for terrestrial communications with little loss of performance.

As the user's interests develop, the type of antenna or antennas required for optimum operation will become clearer. However, for beginners, relatively low gain antennas offer a low cost start with the greatest chances for success. The more complex the installation, the greater the chance it will not work first time, and the more difficult it is to find a fault which is often manifested as poor performance rather than total failure!

Polarisation

As stated above, most mobile and packet stations use vertical polarisation. However, at VHF and above, horizontal polarisation offers some advantages for long distance propagation. This is due, to some extent, to the way that waves are scattered and diffracted by the ground, a plane, buildings or a hill edge, and also by atmospheric refraction effects. However, the use of horizontal polarisation for directional arrays is largely driven by the difficulties encountered in mounting vertically polarised Yagi arrays on metallic support masts without the mast interfering with the radiation pattern or compromising the mechanical integrity of the array. Whilst a horizontally polarised Yagi may be mounted mid boom to a conductive vertical mast without ill effect, the radiation pattern of a vertical Yagi thus mounted would be completely destroyed. Dielectric masts of adequate strength also affect the radiation patterns at 144MHz and above, and so the antennas should ideally be supported from behind the reflector element. This presents considerable mechanical difficul-

ties, especially with long Yagis, unless counterbalancing weights are fitted. The whole structure becomes much larger and heavier than necessary for horizontal polarisation, and is generally not used by amateurs.

Man made interference, especially impulsive noise from motor vehicles and electric appliances, tends towards vertical polarisation, so the use of horizontal polarisation may also be beneficial in these circumstances.

Satellite communications do not require, but can be enhanced by, the use of circularly polarised antennas. Many satellites generate circularly polarised signals, and others may be spinning or tumbling whilst producing linear or mixed polarisations. A circularly polarised antenna will often reduce the short-term fading caused by satellite rotation, and by interfering rays scattered from the ground. There is a downside, if the available wave is largely of the opposite polarisation to the receive antenna, very little signal will be received (see 'Polarisation mismatch'), perhaps less than would be received by a linearly polarised antenna. Whilst the direction of polarisation can be reversed using suitable switching, this adds to the cost and complexity of the antenna. Circular polarisation can also be beneficial under conditions where the path is marginal and changing due to refraction or reflections, as in the case of communicating with mobile stations. However, the gain of a circularly polarised system against a linearly polarised source is 3dB less than would be obtained by correct linear polarisation at both ends under the same conditions.

What is of overriding importance in choosing antenna systems is that the polarisations of the source and receiving antennas are the same, i.e. matched. Cross polarisation between systems can result in losses of 15 to 20dB, which could completely negate the gain of the antenna system.

Height gain

When an antenna or array is mounted over ground, some radiation will strike the ground and be scattered or reflected by it. A remote receiving station may, in the simplest case, receive some power directly from the transmitting antenna, and some from the point of reflection, see Fig 5.19.

Similar effects occur when large reflecting objects such as electricity pylons or buildings are partially illuminated by the main lobe or side lobes of the transmitting antenna. The effect of the interfering ray will depend on its strength relative to the direct ray, the differential distance travelled, the nature of the reflecting object and other factors. However, if the reflection is relatively strong, the received signal will generally be improved as the height of the antenna is increased.

Several considerations apply when deciding the height of the antenna above ground. For optimum performance the antenna should be above any local screening from buildings and other obstacles. In addition, the rule-of-thumb figure of approximately 12m (40ft) is worth considering as it often raises the antenna above the layer of electrical interference and also the signal variations

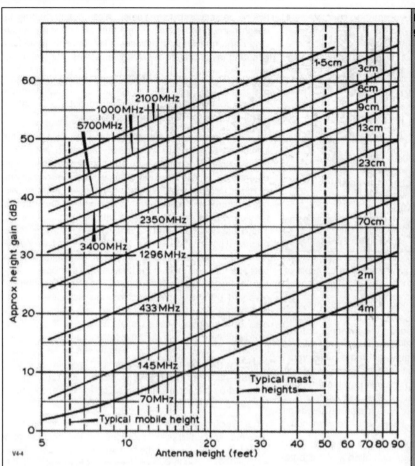

Fig 5.20: Antenna height gain correction factor.

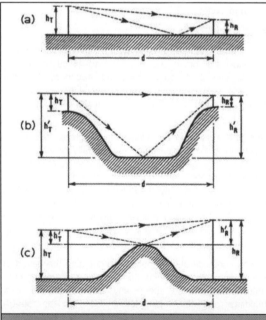

5.21: The effect of ground profile on direct and indirect rays.

caused (at higher frequencies) by the heat layer above buildings. Such a height may also reduce the problems that arise when RF is coupled into house wiring, or directly into consumer electronic equipment, causing TVI and EMC problems.

If there is no screening by buildings, and assuming the antenna is over ground that is reasonably flat for several miles, the main lobe radiation from it will tend to be raised in the vertical plane. As the antenna height increases, the direction of the main lobe will level off in the required horizontal plane. Secondary lobes from the antenna may degrade performance. In general, however, as height increases, the pattern improves, and an additional gain of 6dB is obtained each time the antenna height doubles.

Fig 5.20 gives the approximate height gain obtained at various frequencies for various heights above ground. For heights greater than 12m, and assuming all obstacles have been cleared, a 24m (80ft) mast would be required to increase gain by a further 6dB. The additional expense for the mast may not be justified by the 6dB gain improvement, and care should be taken that losses in the additional feeder length required do not cancel out any gain that may be expected from the increased height.

Should the station be well sited, on a hill for instance, increasing the mast height may make little or no improvement. The effective height above ground will relate to a point at the bottom of the hill, not the base of the mast under these circumstances. Conversely, a station in a valley or behind a hill may obtain a considerable increase in gain with height, much in excess of 6dB, as a more favourable angle to the hilltop or looking over it is achieved. A change of the vertical mounting angle (tilt) or a change of polarisation will also often provide a gain improvement.

The three basic configurations for receiving and transmitting antennas and the intervening ground are illustrated in Fig 5.21. The classic earth plane case is shown in Fig 5.21(a), and under ideal conditions the signal received at the distant antenna follows the relationship:

$$e = Const. \times \frac{h_T h_R}{\lambda d^2}$$

where h_T is the height of the transmitting antenna, h_R is the height of the receiving antenna, λ is the wavelength, and d is the distance between antennas. In this expression h_T, h_R and d must all be in the same units and d must be much larger than either h_T or h_R (by a factor of least 10) that is usually the case in practice.

From this expression it is clear that an increase in either h_T or h_R will result in a corresponding increase in e, and doubling the height will give an increase of 6dB. This is the 6dB 'height gain' rule.

Fig 5.21(b) may be that of the operator who has selected a good hilltop site for 'portable' operation. Here, the antenna height above immediate ground is relatively small compared with the effective height above ground level at the point from where the indirect ray is reflected. Now,

$$e = Const. \times \frac{h'_T h'_R}{\lambda d^2}$$

where h'_T and h'_R are the effective heights of the two antennas. There is still height gain to be achieved by increasing antenna height locally, but not at the same rate as in the first example. To obtain a gain of 6dB it is necessary to double h'_R, and this will require a large increase in h_R. In the limit it clearly is not worthwhile seeking any great antenna height improvement; this is often the case for portable stations on hilltops, when the increased loss in the feeders is less than offset by the small additional signal to be obtained by raising the antenna. The third case, Fig 5.21(c), is that of a station whose antenna is just able to 'see' over the surrounding higher ground, and is the reverse of case (b). The effective height h'_R is much less than h_R and only a small increase in the height of the antenna is required to bring massive improvements in signal level. To summarise, the antenna should ideally be positioned as high as possible, whilst taking into account the additional losses of the extra feed cable required. The signal improvements can be quite large if the station is in a location masked by hills or buildings.

EMC and location

The problems in achieving electromagnetic compatibility (EMC) are becoming ever more severe as ownership of electronic devices increase, together with housing densities. The problem is no longer solely one of television interference (TVI); amateur transmissions can interfere with the operation of telephones, audio equipment, and car security systems. There is also a growing reverse problem of domestic electronics interfering with amateur reception; line timebase noise from older large screen television sets, and more recently from personal computers, is adding to the general pollution of the RF spectrum. Whilst legislation is now in place to reduce emissions from, and the susceptibility of, domestic equipment, it will be many years before some of these equipments are replaced. In the meantime, it is prudent to design installations to minimise the mutual interference that may occur.

In positioning antennas, the following should be considered.

Avoid:

- Placing the antenna close to your neighbour's (or your own) TV antenna!

- Allowing arrays to 'stare' directly in the same plane at adjacent antennas; raising the array a few feet may reduce the potential for interference dramatically.

- Locating antennas where they can easily couple into mains wiring or plumbing.

- Placing antennas where they can couple into overhead telephone wires.

- Running feeders next to mains wiring or plumbing where coupling may occur.

Do:

- Use coaxial feeders with good screening indoors.

- Use chokes and baluns to minimise any RF on the (coaxial) feeders.

- Place the antennas as far away as is practicable from other antennas, TV feeders, mains wiring or telephone cables.

- Make friends with your neighbours and explain what you are doing, it is then easier to resolve any difficulties that occur.

- Choose materials that are electrochemically compatible to minimise corrosion and harmonic generation through the 'rusty bolt' effect.

- Overhaul antenna systems regularly to prevent 'rusty bolt' effects and deteriorating cable connections that can cause interference (also a good idea to preclude the antenna from deteriorating mechanically).

Installations

Internal installations

Whilst external installations are preferable, adequate VHF and UHF antenna systems can be installed successfully within a loft space. Space constraints will limit the size of antenna, especially if a rotatable array is considered, but omni directional antennas usually present few problems.

The roofing material can have a marked effect on signal losses, especially when wet. Slates shed water and dry out fairly quickly, but old and porous tiles, although adequately waterproof, can scatter and absorb much of the signal.

Measurements have shown a difference of more than 7dB for propagation through dry and wet weathered tiles at 435MHz.

Coupling into wiring and plumbing should be very carefully addressed and investigated with loft installations, and it is prudent to choose antennas that are not highly tuned or over sensitive to the presence of adjacent objects.

Chimney installations

The nature of these installations is usually determined by the strength of the chimney, the courage of the erector, and his willingness to revisit the chimney regularly.

An end chimney can provide an excellent antenna site provided it is not too close to adjacent property and antennas. A short mast is usually lashed to the stack at two or three places, and a fixed or rotating array fitted immediately above. Space and safety considerations dictate the size of the antennas, and whether they are assembled in situ. If the chimney is relatively accessible, complex antennas and systems that require maintenance or tuning are practicable. However, simpler, fixed systems are better if the site is difficult (or expensive) to access. In choosing the antennas, the wind load and overturning moment should be carefully considered, and if in doubt, someone with the necessary knowledge and qualifications should carry out a survey of the chimney; this could prevent expensive roof repairs! Lightweight fixtures and fittings can be bought from television antenna supply companies. Heavier duty fixtures are available from amateur antenna suppliers and professional antenna installers.

Masts and towers

Where suitable chimneys are not available, but wall and garden space can be used, a mast or tower may provide the best option, especially if the station is to be located in a garage or shed. Many varieties of mast are available commercially, both as freestanding and wall mounted designs, and hardware for fastening masts to walls and footings is available from a number of suppliers.

A mast can offer the freedom to experiment with antennas if suitable equipment for raising and lowering is provided. However, planning permission is nearly always required, and considerable thought is needed before installing freestanding towers, the foundation requirements can be considerable, and are not easily relocated. If garden space permits, a guyed mast may provide a good solution, although assistance and a great deal of care is required when erecting such structures, especially when loaded with antennas. The reader is referred to the articles by G3ZPF [17] for information outlining the size of founda-

tions and guy anchors required together with some methods for construction.

In addition, lightning protection should be installed to good earths with short, wide copper straps to minimise the current flowing into the radio equipment and house wiring if a lightning attachment does occur. Again, professional advice should be sought in this respect.

Wind loading

In all considerations for antenna design and erection, the wind loading of the array must be taken into account, so that the rotator (if used) and the supporting structures can be selected or designed to withstand the stresses to which the system may be subjected. It is prudent to allow a good margin for safety, to allow for wear and tear, corrosion and general deterioration in any calculation related to safety.

The articles by G3ZPF [17] provide the basis for estimating the loads experienced by antennas and masts. BS8100 and the earlier, but still useful, BSI CP3 Chapter 5 Part 2 provide information on basic wind speeds throughout the UK. This can be used with the given topography, ground roughness and height above ground factors to determine the dynamic pressure that is likely to be experienced by the structure under "worst case" conditions. Wind loading of masts and towers is now assessed under BS8100, and advice should be sought from the manufacturer for the appropriate information.

Safety

Masts and antennas are potentially dangerous structures especially during erection and dismantling. There are a number of safety rules that must be observed during these activities:

- Thorough checks must be carried out to ensure that there is no possibility of the mast or antenna coming into contact with overhead power wires, however it may topple or collapse.

- The job of erection or lowering must be planned carefully. Considerations must include the positioning of each part of the antenna and/or mast at every stage of the process. Enough persons should be available, wearing boots, gloves and safety helmets during the raising and lowering processes, and sufficient guiding ropes should be used to ensure control of the structure at all stages of the operation. There should be no possibility of tripping on ropes or equipment during the operation, which should not be attempted in strong winds or when it is getting dark.

- Before raising or lowering, all components and fastenings should be double checked for being fixed firmly and safely. The base of the mast must be firmly fixed to prevent slipping.

- Everybody involved shall have his or her role clearly defined. Those not needed to assist should be kept well clear. If any children are nearby, a person should be tasked to keep them clear of the area of operations, including those areas where the mast might topple or

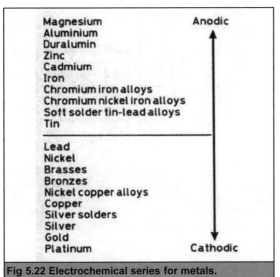

Magnesium	**Anodic**
Aluminium	
Duralumin	
Zinc	
Cadmium	
Iron	
Chromium iron alloys	
Chromium nickel iron alloys	
Soft solder tin-lead alloys	
Tin	
Lead	
Nickel	
Brasses	
Bronzes	
Nickel copper alloys	
Copper	
Silver solders	
Silver	
Gold	
Platinum	**Cathodic**

Fig 5.22 Electrochemical series for metals.

fall, and animals should be kept under control.

- One person should be in charge of the operation, and not take any part in the lifting activities themselves. He/she shall give clear concise instructions, which have been rehearsed before the actual lift or lowering.

- Safety precautions must be continued until all mast fixings and guys are secured, and any temporary ropes and equipment have been removed and stowed away.

- After erection, the mast should be inspected for tightness of bolts and for the integrity of any protective coverings. The mast and antennas should be regularly inspected for tightness of bolts, wear and/or damage to guys and fastenings, and integrity of protective coverings. The mast and antennas should be lowered for full inspection and overhaul at least every three years, or more often in exposed locations. Electrical continuity, sealing and painting/greasing should be checked, together with the replacement of items that weather or denature in sunlight (plastic covers and fittings).

Antennas – build or buy?

General considerations

A great deal of satisfaction can be obtained from building one's own antennas, either by following detailed instructions, or by experimenting with the materials available. However, as either the frequency or complexity of the antenna increases, so does the need for some test equipment or measuring facilities. There is little more frustrating than to have spent many hours in construction, and then be unable to make the antenna work.

Simple antennas such as whips and dipoles can be tuned with a low power transmitter and VSWR meter, by "pruning" element lengths for best VSWR.

As the frequency increases, variations in construction and the dielectric constant of materials used for insulators or

spacers can have a considerable influence on the performance of antennas. Tools to at least estimate the input impedance (resistance and reactance) can become essential to find out exactly why an antenna is not working. There are a number of commercially available antenna analyser that will operate up to 70cm. Noise bridges can provide the necessary information up to 70cm, beyond which second hand professional impedance bridges provide the best means for measuring antennas.

Single antennas with gains greater than, say, 10dB really require facilities for measuring changes of gain if experimentation is to be meaningful. This requires a reasonable amount of space with few unwanted reflections, and a calibrated signal generator and receiver. This is not as difficult as it may seem; the techniques, together with much other useful information on building test equipment and carrying out measurements are shown in The Antenna Experimenter's Guide by G3LDO [19].

Careful adherence to construction details will usually result in a working antenna with minimum tuning, so it can be well worth considering building your own if basic metal working facilities are available.

Arrays can also be assembled with a minimum of measuring equipment if ready built antennas are obtained (all antennas in the array should be identical), and care is taken in measuring and making up the feed cables. Some manufacturers can supply ready built (and phase matched) feeder harnesses for standard array configurations.

Decreasing cost and increasing power of personal computers has added a relatively new tool to the serious experimenter's armoury. A number of programs are available for modest cost that allows the electrical design of antennas on screen, followed by analysis of the current distribution, radiation pattern and gain. They can be useful to evaluate the effect of changes in dimensions or configuration, or to try out completely new structures. Some knowledge of antenna theory is necessary; the "garbage in, garbage out" syndrome certainly applies! Descriptions of the techniques and the results that can be obtained have been described by G3SEK and G3HCT [20, 21]. Special programs are also available for optimisation of Yagi antennas, see later section.

Choice of materials

The use of dissimilar metals in an antenna system is likely to cause considerable trouble due to electrolytic corrosion. Each metal has its own electro potential and, unless metals of similar potential are used, the difference will cause corrosion even when they are dry. When moisture is present, the effect will be much more severe and can be enhanced by atmospheric pollution.

If, for any reason, dissimilar metals must be used then considerable care should be taken to exclude moisture. The metals can be arranged in order of their electrochemical potential as shown in Fig 5.22.

Metals in each of the groups may be used together with little corrosive action, but metals from different groups will

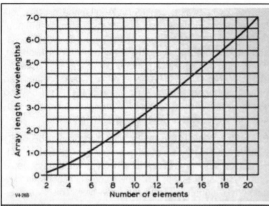

Fig 5.23: Optimum length of Yagi antenna as a function of number of elements (ARRL Antenna Book).

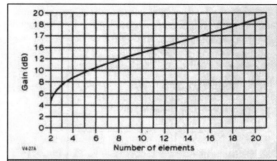

Fig 5.24: Gain(dB) over a λ/2 dipole versus the number of elements of a Yagi antenna (ARRL Antenna Book).

quickly corrode at the point of contact. The list is arranged in order, so that the greater the spacing between materials in the list, the greater the effect. The materials in the lower part of the list will corrode those in the upper. For example, brass or copper screws in aluminium will corrode the aluminium, whereas cadmium plated brass screws would cause less corrosion. Corrosion can cause weakening of mechanical structures and also increases in contact resistance between elements and feeders, resulting in dissipation of transmitter power as heat. Under some circumstances, the joint between corroded materials behaves as a semiconductor, generating harmonics and intermodulation products that cause interference to other radio users, both in and out of band. For this reason, selection of materials to minimise corrosion is important, and all antenna joints and weather protection measures should be inspected and refurbished at least every two years.

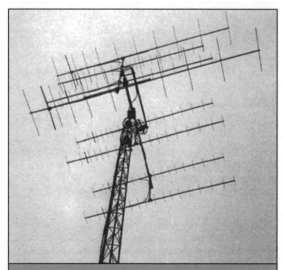

DL6WU has stacked two 11 element Yagis of his own design with six of the highly respected K2RIW 19 element Yagis for 432MHz.

Directional antennas for fixed stations

The Yagi antenna

This is one of the most useful antennas for VHF/UHF, as it can be compact, robust and provide good directivity and gain with a relatively simple structure. Unfortunately, it is also one of the most complex antenna structures to analyse, and it can be difficult to construct Yagis that really provide good performance, especially where high gain is required.

S Uda in Japan carried out the original research in 1926, but it was the review and translation into English by his professor, H Yagi, in 1928 that introduced the design to the West. The basic array comprises a driven dipole element with a passive dipole adjacent to it. If both elements are tuned to resonance, the currents in each element are approximately equal, and are in phase. By lengthening the passive (parasitic) element, the phase of the current is delayed, whilst the amplitude remains almost unchanged. When the phase delay complements the spacing between the elements, the radiated power will be directed away from the parasite, which is then known as a reflector. By similarly placing another, shorter director parasite in line with the driven element, but on the opposite side from the reflector, the directivity can be further enhanced. The principles for this phenomenon were addressed in the section on arrays.

Yagi antennas can be provided with large numbers of reflectors, the elements being excited by mutual coupling with the driven element and other elements according to their relative position. The magnitude and phase of the current on each element is influenced by their relative positions and lengths, the permutations of dimensions that can produce satisfactory performance become very large.

Until relatively recently, performance of the antenna was optimised by "cut-and-try" methods, as the mathematical analysis of the problem was too complex to afford numerical solution other than for small numbers of elements. Theoretical methods indicated the limits of performance that could be expected of the array for given constraints, e.g. Fig 5.23 and Fig 5.24, showing boom length and number of elements for "optimum" arrays. However, experimental work showed that these gains were rarely realised, usually falling short by 0.5 to 1dB, and very poor performance was sometimes obtained, especially from long Yagi antennas. Many independent investigations of multi element Yagi antennas have shown that in general the gain of a Yagi is directly proportional to the array length provided the number, lengths and spacing of the elements are properly chosen. However, to constrain the number of variables, the concept of equal length reflectors, or equally spaced reflectors was often used for elements well removed from the driven element.

P Viezbicke for the US Department of Commerce and National Bureau of Standards published a suite of results for several antenna geometries in 1976 [10], and it has become a reference document for many Yagi designers. It addresses:

- The effect of reflector spacing on the gain of a dipole

- Effect of different length directors, their spacing and number on realisable gain

- Effect of different diameters and lengths of directors on realisable gain

- Effect of the size of a supporting boom on the optimum length of parasitic elements

- Effect of stacking of antennas on gain

- Measured radiation patterns of different Yagi configurations.

However, as greater computing power has become available, it has been possible to investigate the theoretical optimisation of Yagi gain more closely, and to take into account the effects of mounting the elements on metallic and dielectric booms. Dr J Lawson, W2PV, carried out an extensive series of computations, collated in reference [11], which explain many of the disappointing results achieved by constructors. G Hoch, DL6WU, has especially studied the design and construction of long Yagis [12–14] and identified the pitfalls.

Generally, short Yagi antennas with less than six elements will perform reasonably well with a selection of materials and minor deviations from the optimum dimensions. However, higher gain Yagis need to be carefully constructed with minimum deviation from the design if the gain is to be realised. If it is necessary to use different diameter tubing from that specified, the length of the element must be adjusted to compensate for the change in self-reactance that results. Hoch gives a formula for the reactance of an element of arbitrary length (L) and diameter (D) for a given wavelength:

$$X = \left\{430.3 \log_{10}\left(\frac{2\lambda}{D}\right) - 320\right\}\left(\frac{2L}{\lambda} - 1\right) + 40$$

The modified length L' for a new element diameter D' can be calculated by rearranging the formula:

$$L' = \left[\frac{X - 40}{\left\{430.3 \log_{10}\left(\frac{2\lambda}{D'}\right) - 320\right\}} + 1\right]\frac{\lambda}{2}$$

Table 5.4: Typical dimensions of Yagi array components.

	Length		
	70.3MHz	145MHz	433MHz
Driven elements			
Dipole (for use with			
gamma match)	79 (2000)	38 (960)	12¾ (320)
Diameter range for			
length given	½–¾	¼–⅜	⅛–¼
	(12.7–19.0)	(6.35–9.5)	(3.17–6.35)

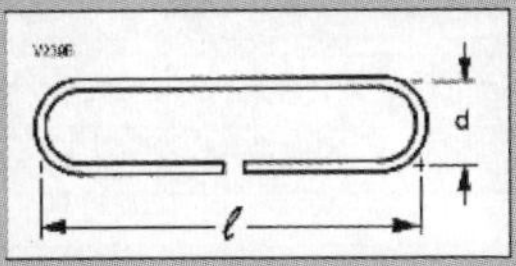

Folded dipole 70Ω feed			
l length			
centre/centre	77½ (1970)	38½ (980)	12½ (318)
d spacing			
centre/centre	2½ (64)	⅞ (22)	½ (13)
Diameter of element	½ (12.7)	¼ (6.35)	⅛ (3.17)

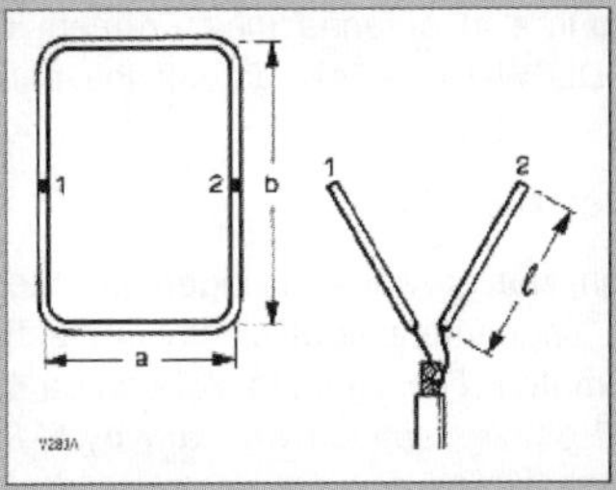

a centre/centre	32 (810)	15 (390)	5⅛ (132)
b centre/centre	96 (2440)	46 (1180)	152 (395)
Delta feed sections			
(length for			
70Ω feed)	22½ (570)	12 (300)	42 (110)
Diameter of slot and			
delta feed material	¼ (6.35)	⅜ (9.5)	⅜ (9.5)
Parasitic elements			
Element			
Reflector	85½ (2170)	40 (1010)	13¼ (337)
Director D1	74 (1880)	35½ (902)	11¼ (286)
Director D2	73 (1854)	35¼ (895)	11¹/₈ (282)
Director D3	72 (1830)	35 (890)	11 (279)
Succeeding directors	1in less (25)	½in less (13)	⅛in less (3)
Final director	2in less (50)	1in less (25)	¾in less
One wavelength			
(for reference)	168¾ (4286)	81½ (2069)	27¼ (693)
Diameter range for			
length given	½–¾	¼–⅜	⅛–¾
	(12.7–19.0)	(6.35–9.5)	(3.17–6.35)
Spacing between elements			
Reflector to			
radiator	22½ (572)	17½ (445)	5½ (140)
Radiator to			
director 1	29 (737)	17½ (445)	5½ (140)
Director 1 to			
director 2	29 (737)	17½ (445)	7 (178)
Director 2 to			
director 3, etc	29 (737)	17½ (445)	7 (178)

Dimensions are in inches with millimetre equivalents in brackets.

Table 5.4 shows typical component dimensions for a range of Yagi antennas for 4m, 2m and 70cm, using either

Photo showing how a driven element and first director are typically mounted on a boom.

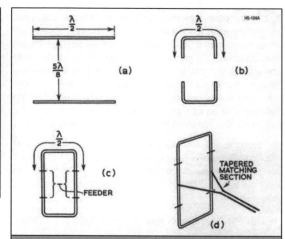

Fig 5.25: Development of the skeleton slot radiator.

open or folded dipole elements to drive the array. As stated above, antennas of this form can be expected to work reasonably well with up to six elements (12 elements for a skeleton slot array) if the dimensions are adhered to. Longer Yagis need to be constructed exactly as described, including the boom and fastenings used to secure the elements, if claimed performances are to be realised without recourse to antenna measurement ranges. The articles by DL6WU [12–14] address the construction of such antennas.

Skeleton slot Yagi stack

The skeleton slot provides an ingenious means to feed two stacked Yagi antennas efficiently and achieve a good impedance match. The skeleton slot can be thought of as a pair of $\lambda/2$ dipoles spaced vertically by $5\lambda/8$. Since the centre of the dipoles provides most of the radiation, their ends can be bent out of plane with little effect, and joined together with high impedance feeder so that end feeding may take place. To feed both dipoles in phase, the feed point must be midway between them; the high impedance is transformed to more manageable levels by a tapered section or delta match as shown in Fig 5.25.

The overall slot Yagi structure is shown in Fig 5.26. Element dimensions are taken from Table 5.4 and the radiation pattern, together with those of other typical Yagi antennas, is shown in Fig 5.27.

Table 5.5: Design dimensions for 70MHz and 144MHz quad antennas.

Band (MHz)	Reflector 1 total length	Reflector 2 total length	Director (if used)	Approximate length of stub if used Reflector s/c	Driector s/c
70 (a)	173 (4390)	165 (4190)	157 (3990)	-	-
70 (b)	166 (4190)	165 (4190)	165 (4190)	8 (203)	8 (203)
144 (a)	84 (2130)	80 (2030)	76 (1930)	-	-
144 (b)	80 (2030)	80 (2030)	80 (2030)	4 (101)	4 (101)

Dimensions are in inches with millimetre equivalents in brackets

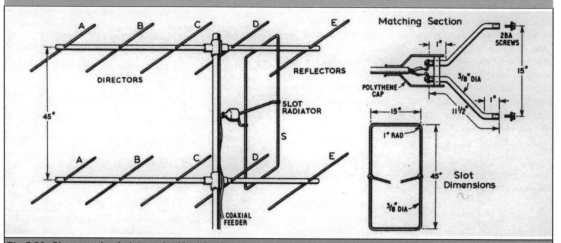

Fig 5.26: Six over six skeleton slot Yagi for 2m.

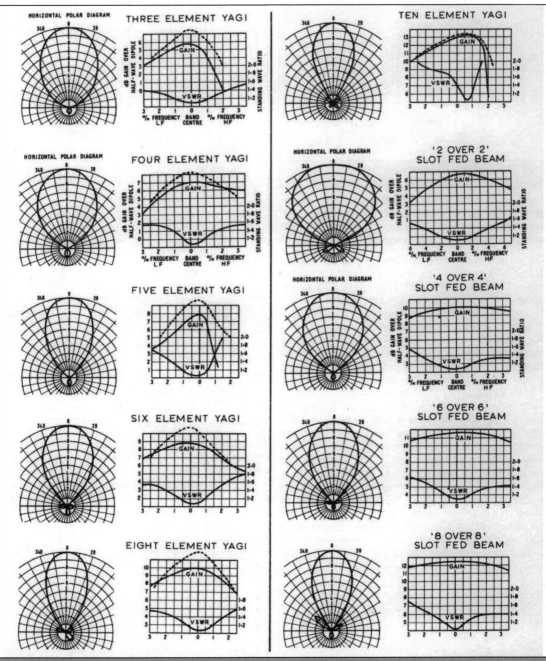

Fig 5.27: Charts showing voltage polar diagrams and gain against VSWR for various Yagi antennas with uniform directors. Dotted lines are for antennas optimised for maximum gain.

Quad antennas and arrays

The quad antenna offers a useful horizontally polarised alternative to short Yagi antennas at VHF and above, being both compact and lightweight with just a driven element and reflector, see Fig 5.28. Gains of 5.5 to 6dB are readily obtained, together with good front-to-back ratio. Arrangements for two and four antenna arrays of quads are described below.

Typical dimensions for quad elements are shown in Table 5.5. The input impedance is strongly affected by the spacing between the driven element and the reflector, and will be between 180 and 230mm for an input impedance of 72Ω. The elements may be made from 3mm or 6mm aluminium rod or bar, and if the vertical dimensions of both elements are made the same, two short cross pieces can be used to separate the elements and mount them to a mast. The cross pieces may be metal so that the whole

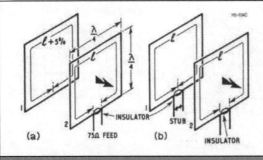

Fig 5.28: Quad antenna dimensions.

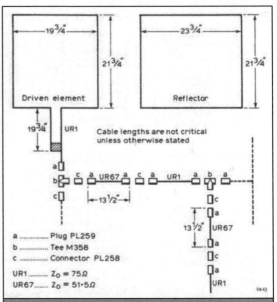

Fig 5.29: Arrangement for two or four antenna quad array with power divider and matching details.

structure with the exception of the feed point and reflector stub (if used) can be solidly built and bonded together. A balun should be used at the feed point, although this is not essential if the feeder is short and of low loss.

The antenna can readily be configured as a two element or four element array. Each antenna for 144MHz has the dimensions shown in Fig 5.29, spaced 178mm between elements. Two quads stacked vertically should be spaced $5\lambda/8$ between centres and paralleled through a single $\lambda/4$, 51Ω transformer. To obtain an input impedance of 72Ω (for further baying as a four antenna array), it may be necessary to increase the separation of the reflector and driven element to 230mm to overcome the effects of mutual coupling. The pair of antennas should provide a gain of 8.2dBD (10.3dBi) with a front-to-back ratio of 20dB. A four-antenna arrangement for the 2m band is shown in Fig 5.30. The layout is determined by the ease with which the feeder cables can be run, and the minimisation of unsupported (unguyed) sections of mast. Reflector-director spacing is 230mm, the vertical spacing remains 1650mm between centres, and the horizontal spacing is 2070mm, one wavelength in free space. The feed arrangements are shown in Fig 5.31. The design is based on a 72Ω main feeder; for 50Ω array impedance, the transformer in the feed line should be replaced with a 42Ω section or a "cot transformer" as described in the section on transmission line transformers. The more readily available URM57 may be substituted for UR1

cable with minor adjustments to the antenna element spacing.

The gain of the overall array should be 13.5dBD (15.6dBi) with a front-to-back ratio of 18dB. The radiation pattern is shown in Fig 5.32.

Quad element Yagi (quagi)

The quad element Yagi (Fig 5.36) offers better performance than a simple Yagi of comparable size, together with reduced side lobes. Up to five elements will perform satisfactorily, although larger structures can be made with

Fig 5.30: A 144MHz cubical quad array.

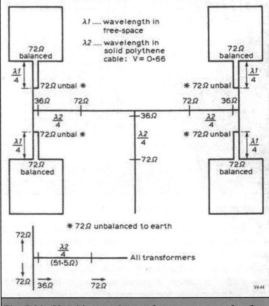

Fig 5.31: Matching and transformer system for four element quad array.

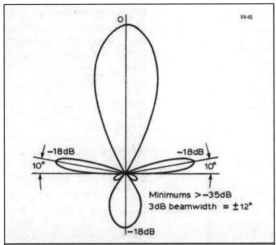

Fig 5.32: Horizontal radiation pattern of four element quad antenna array.

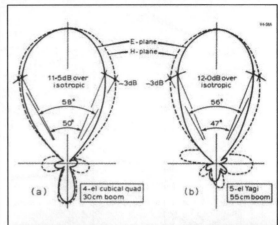

Fig 5.34 Measured voltage patterns of four element quad and five element Yagi showing approximately equivalent bandwidths.

care. The relative performance of Yagis with circular (loop) and conventional straight elements is shown in Fig 5.33. Loop Yagis with square and circular elements have comparable characteristics. Comparative measured radiation patterns for conventional and quagi antennas are shown in Fig 5.34 and Fig 5.35.

The only insulator required is that of the feed point, resulting in a simple and mechanically robust structure. 9mm aluminium rod or tube is satisfactory for elements for 144MHz and above.

Table 5.6 shows dimensions for several multi element quagi antennas for 144MHz; dimensions can be scaled for 432MHz. This antenna is relatively easy to construct, and will work well.

A quadruple quad antenna

This collapsible antenna, designed for portable use [18] but equally useable as a fixed antenna for use indoors or in a loft, can achieve gains of between 10 and 11dBi on

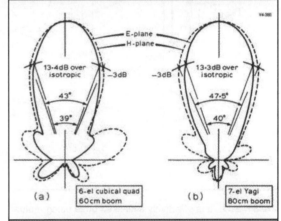

Fig 5.35: Measured voltage patterns of six element quad and seven element Yagi (ARRL Antenna Book).

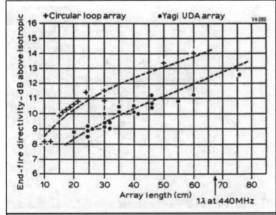

Fig 5.33: Comparative directivity of quad and conventional Yagi antennas as a function of array length (ARRL Antenna Book).

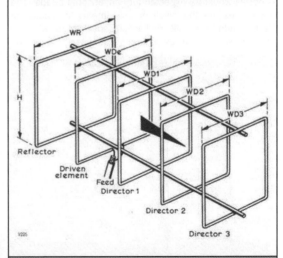

Fig 5.36: General arrangement of a multi element quad.

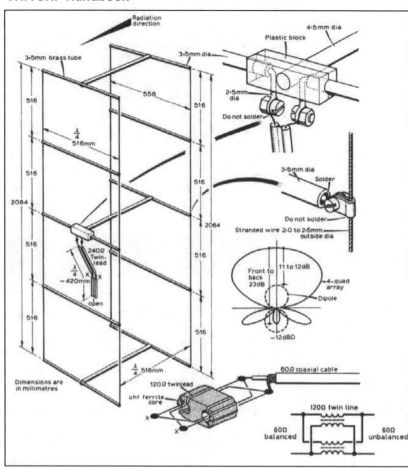

Fig 5.37: Quadruple quad. The match point xx should be found experimentally and will be approximately 200mm from the open end (VHF Communications).

the 2m band. It is effectively a stacked quad using mutual coupling instead of a phasing harness to excite the outer elements. Constructional details are shown in Fig 5.37.

Each section has a circumference of around 1.04λ, which is not as would be expected for conventional quads. The dimensions are the result of experiments to obtain the best front-to-back ratio and least sensitivity to adjacent objects, which can be important for portable or loft

operation, ensuring that the antenna will work without extensive adjustment.

Note that the antenna was designed for low power (1W) operation; the ferrite bead must not be allowed to magnetically saturate, or non linearities and harmonic generation may occur. The bead may also become hot and shatter.

Table 5.6: Cetre to centre dimensions for multi element quad Yagi.

Height H	21(533)	21	21	21
Width reflector WR	24½(622)	24½	24½	24½
Driven WD$_0$	20½(520)	20½	20½	20½
Director 1 WD$_1$	-	18(457)	18	18
Director 2 WD$_2$	-	-	16(406)	16
Director 3 WD$_3$	-	-	-	14(356)
Spacing				
Reflector to Driven	7(178)	19(483)	20(508)	20
Driven to Director 1	-	12(305)	14½(368)	14½
Director 1 to Director 2	-	-	14½	14½
Director 2 to Director 3	-	-	-	14½
Approximate Gain	5	7	10.5	12.5

Element diameters all 3/8 inch (9.35mm). Feed impedance in all cases is 75Ω. Dimensions are in inches with millimetre equivalents in brackets.

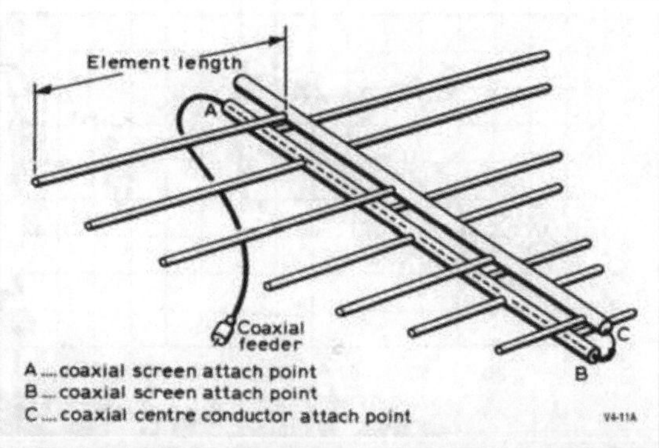

Fig 5.38: Typical log periodic antenna. Note that the bottom is fed from the coaxial outer while the top boom is fed from the centre conductor (Ham Radio).

A .... coaxial screen attach point
B .... coaxial screen attach point
C .... coaxial centre conductor attach point

Table 5.7: Spacing and dimensions for log periodic VHF antennas.

Ele-ment	21 - 55MHz array Length (mm)	Diameter (mm)	Spacing (mm)	50 - 150MHz array Length (mm)	Diameter (mm)	Spacing (mm)	140 - 450MHx array Length (mm)	Diameter (mm)	Spacing (mm)
1	3731	38.1	1050	1602	2.54	630	535	6.7	225
2	3411	31.8	945	1444	2.54	567	479	6.7	202
3	3073	31.8	850	1303	2.54	510	397	6.7	182
4	2770	31.8	765	1175	19.1	459	383	6.7	164
5	2496	31.8	689	1060	19.1	413	341	6.7	148
6	2250	25.4	620	957	19.1	372	304	6.7	133
7	2029	25.4	558	864	19.1	335	271	6.7	119
8	1830	19.1	500	781	12.7	301	241	6.7	108
9	1650	19.1	452	705	12.7	271	215	6.7	97
10	1489	19.1	407	637	12.7	244	190	6.7	87
11	1344	19.1	366	576	12.7	219	169	6.7	78
12	1213	12.7	329	522	9.5	198	149	6.7	70
13	1095	12.7	0	472	9.5	178	131	6.7	63
14				428	9.5	160	115	6.7	57
15				388	9.5	0	101	6.7	52
16							88	6.7	0
Boom	7620	50.8	12.7	5090	38.1	152	1823	38.1	152

For higher-power operation, ferrite rings could be considered for the balun transformer, or a sleeve balun constructed as appropriate.

Log periodic antenna

This antenna was originally designed and proved at the University of Illinois in the USA in 1955. Since then the military, in particular, have made considerable use of it. Its particular properties are a very wide bandwidth, governed only by the number of elements used, and the directive qualities of a Yagi antenna.

Tables 5.7 and 5.8 show typical dimensions for element spacings and length for log periodic arrays that are derived from a computer aided design produced by W3DUQ in Ham Radio, August 1970. Simple scaling of all dimensions can produce other frequency bands.

The tabulated parameters have a 5% overshoot in the working frequency range at the low end and a 45% overshoot at the high frequency end to maintain logarithmic response over the complete frequency range specified. In log periodic operation approximately four elements are active at any one specific frequency, hence the need for the high frequency and low frequency extension. The alpha or logarithmic element taper is 28° for all three antennas, which exhibit a forward gain of 6.55dBD with a front-to-back ratio of typically 15dB and a VSWR better than 1.8:1 over the specified frequency range.

The construction can be straightforward but it should be noted that the element lengths for the highest frequency antenna were calculated for the elements to be inserted completely through the boom. The two lower frequency antennas have element lengths calculated to butt flush against the element side of the boom. If the elements are to be inserted through the boom on the 21 - 55MHz and 50 - 150MHz antennas, the boom diameter must be added to the length of each element.

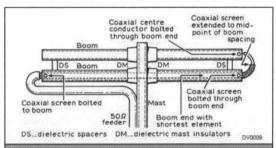

Fig 5.39: Feeding the log periodic is relatively simple. Remove the outer plastic jacket from the feed line for the entire length of the boom, so that the coaxial outer is permitted to short itself inside the boom as well as the solid electrical connection at each end of the boom (Ham Radio).

Table 5.8: Spacing and dimensions for log periodic UHF antenna (420 - 1350MHz array).

Element	Length (mm)	Diameter (mm)	Spacing (mm)
1	178	2.1	75
2	159	2.1	67
3	133	2.1	61
4	127	2.1	55
5	114	2.1	49
6	101	2.1	44
7	91	2.1	40
8	80	2.1	36
9	72	2.1	32
10	63	2.1	29
11	56	2.1	26
12	50	2.1	23
13	44	2.1	21
14	38	2.1	19
15	34	2.1	17
16	30	2.1	0
Boom	607	12.7	

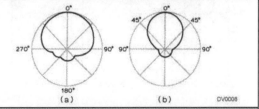

Fig 5.40: Typical log periodic voltage radiation patterns: (a) horizontal, (b) vertical (Ham Radio).

50MHz and 144MHz log periodic antennas.

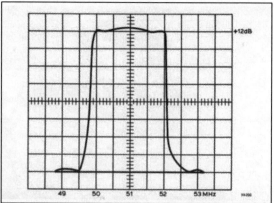

Fig 5.42: Gain versus frequency characteristics of the 50MHz log periodic Yagi.

As the supporting booms are also the transmission line between the elements for a log periodic antenna they must be supported with a dielectric spacing from the mast of at least twice the boom-to-boom spacing; otherwise discontinuities will be introduced into the feed system. Feed line connection and the arrangement to produce an "infinite balun" is shown in Fig 5.39. Any change in the boom diameters will necessitate a change in the boom-to-boom spacing to maintain the feed impedance. The formula to achieve this is:

$$Z_0 = 273 \log_{10} D/d$$

where D is the distance between boom centres and d the diameter of the booms.

The antenna can be orientated either horizontally or vertically (if a non metalic mast section is used) to suit the polarisation required. The horizontal half power beamwidths will be typically 60° with a vertical half power beamwidth of typically 100°.

Log periodic Yagi bandpass antenna

This is an antenna with an interesting and useful band pass characteristic, giving a flat response over a wide band, and significant attenuation outside. It is basically a combination of a log periodic driven section with a parasitic Yagi section.

The prototype 50MHz design gave a gain of 12dBD and a bandwidth of 2MHz. The details given in Fig 5.41 are for 144MHz, where the bandwidth would be around 5MHz.

This type of characteristic offers obvious advantages in terms of reducing adjacent channel interference; and also giving a more constant performance over the whole 144 to 148MHz band. The simple Yagi, by comparison, is essentially a narrow band antenna.

DImensions and construction details for 50, 70 and 144MHz have been developed by G3FDW [22].

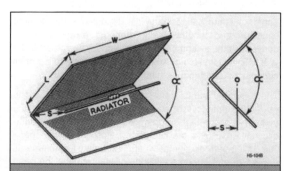

Fig 5.43: Corner reflector. The λ/2 dipole radiator is spaced parallel with the vertex or the reflector at a distance S; its characteristics are shown in Figs 5.44 and 5.45.

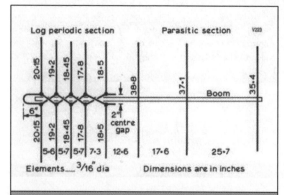

Fig 5.41: A log periodic Yagi bandpass antenna for 145MHz.

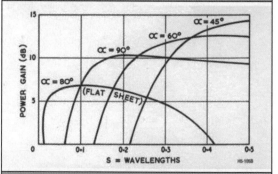

Fig 5.44: Theoretical power gain obtained by using a corner reflector with λ/2 dipole radiator.

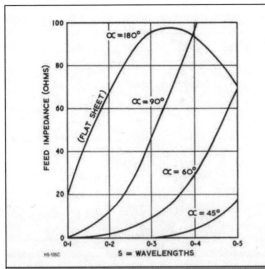

Fig 5.45: Feed impedance of a λ/2 dipole provided with a corner reflector: see Fig 5.43.

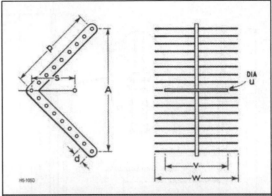

Fig 5.47: Dimensions for a 60° corner reflector antenna system giving a gain of about 13dBD. The feed impedance of the dipole radiator is 75Ω. The apex may be hinged for portable work.

Dimmensions in millimetres

Band	p	s	d	v	w	A	u	λ
144	2540	1016	152	965	1270	2540	9.5	2083
433	889	337	38	324	508	889	6.4	692
1296	305	114	12.7	102	203	305	3.2	232

The corner reflector

The use of an aperiodic plane reflector spaced behind a radiating dipole has already been discussed. If this reflector is bent to form a V, as shown in Fig 5.43, a considerably higher gain is achieved. The critical factors in the design of such an antenna array are the corner angle α and the dipole/vertex spacing S. The curves in Fig 5.44 show that as α is reduced, the gain theoretically obtainable becomes progressively greater. However, at the same time the feed impedance of the dipole radiator falls to a very low value, as can be seen from Fig 5.45. This makes matching difficult and hence a compromise has to be reached. In practice the angle α is usually made 90° or 60°; adjustments in a 60° corner are a little more critical although the maximum obtainable gain is higher. The final matching of the radiator to the line may be carried out by adjusting the distance S.

It does not greatly affect the gain over a useful range of variation but causes a considerable change in radiation resistance. A two stub tuner may also prove helpful in making final adjustments.

The length L of the sides of the reflector should exceed 2λ to secure the characteristics indicated by Fig 5.44 and 5.46, and the reflector width W should be greater than 1λ for a λ/2 dipole radiator. The reflecting sheet may be constructed of wire netting as described previously or alternatively may be fabricated from metal spines arranged in a V formation, all of them being parallel to the radiator; see Fig 5.46. The spacing between adjacent rods should not exceed 0.1λ.

A useful approximation for the power gain G referred to a λ/2 dipole is G = 300/α where α is the angle between the sides measured in degrees.

The maximum dipole/vertex spacing S included in the curves shown is λ/2. Spacings greater than this would require rather cumbersome constructions at lower frequencies, but at the higher frequencies larger spacings become practicable, and higher gains than would be suggested by Fig 5.44 can then be obtained; see Table 5.9. This indicates that the corner reflector can become an especially attractive proposition for the I.3GHz band, but the width across the opening should be in excess of 4λ to achieve the results shown.

HB9CV mini beam

An antenna that falls into the category of horizontally or vertically polarised, portable rather than mobile, or for base station use, is the HB9CV mini beam. Similar units

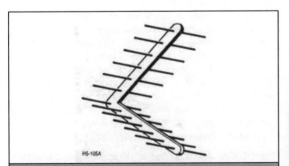

Fig 5.46: The corner reflector can be modified by using a set of metal spines arranged in "V" formation to replace the sheet metal or wire netting reflector.

Table 5.9: Corner/trough reflector.			
Angle α (degrees)	Value of S maximum gain (λ)	Gain (dBi)	T(λ)
90	1.5	13	1 - 1.25
60	1.25	15	1.0
45	2.0	17	1.9

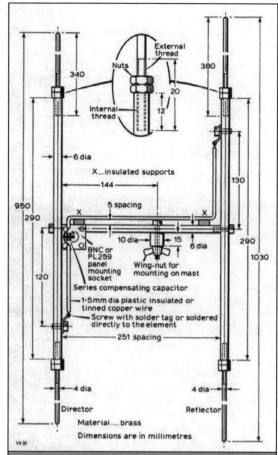

Fig 5.48: A collapsible HB9CV antenna for the 144MHz band (VHF Communications).

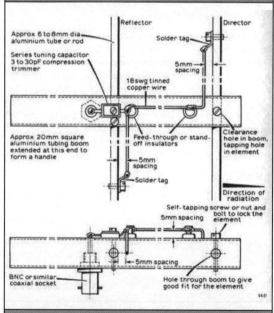

Fig 5.49: Alternative construction of the HB9CV. Dimensions as per Fig 5.48.

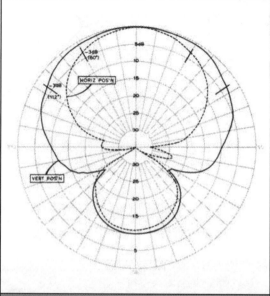

Fig 5.50: HB9CV antenna at 10m above ground.

are the lazy H and ZL special often used on the HF bands. The HB9CV version, however, has one or two mechanical advantages, which makes it particularly suitable for VHF portable use.

Figs 5.48 (taken from "The HB9CV Antenna for VHF and UHF", H J Franke, DK1PN, *VHF Communications* February 1969) and 5.49 show two methods of construction for the HB9CV antenna. A point that should be stressed is that a *series* capacitor of 3 - 15pF is required to finally adjust the gamma match/phasing combination to a VSWR of about 1.3:1 against 50Ω. The dimension of the element spacing and the transmission lines, particularly the spacing (5mm), is critical for optimum impedance matching and phasing, and hence gain and front-to-back ratio.

The principle of operation is as follows. If two dipoles at close spacing, typically 0.1 - 0.2λ, are fed out of phase, "end fire" radiation will occur in a direction at right angles to the line of the dipole elements. If the dipoles are resonant at the same frequency a bidirectional pattern with a gain of typically 3dB referred to a single dipole will be realised. However, if correct phasing between the elements is used, a unidirectional or beam pattern is produced. The different lengths found on most HB9CV antennas assist with bandwidth. The end at which the beam is fed designates the direction of radiation. A theoretical gain in excess of 6dBD should be possible. However, depending on the construction techniques, gains between 4 and 5.5dBD with front-to-back ratios between 10 and 20dB tend to be realised in practice. The radiation pattern shown in Fig 5.50 is for the antenna of Fig 5.48 that has a gain of typically 5dBD.

The HB9CV was mounted on a professional glass fibre radiation pattern measuring mast for the 10m test. This ensured a minimum disruption of the antenna radiation pattern when set up for vertical polarisation.

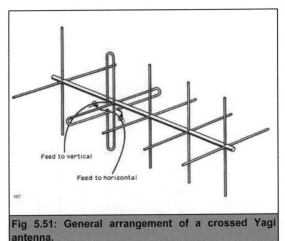

Fig 5.51: General arrangement of a crossed Yagi antenna.

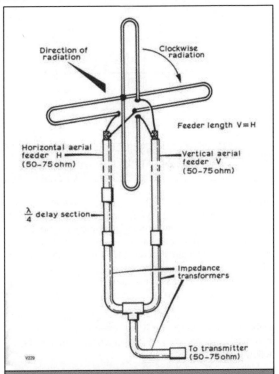

Fig 5.52: General arrangement of feeders with delay line (phasing) for clockwise radiation.

Crossed Yagi with adjustable polarisation

Vertical polarisation is popular for mobile operation in the UK, due to the basic fact that it is far easier to obtain omni directional radiation with a vertical antenna than it is with horizontal one. This is particularly important on a vehicle, where the mechanical simplicity of a short vertical rod considerably outweighs the complexity of a halo or crossed dipole, particularly when it is realised that the horizontal antenna must be at least $\lambda/2$ above the vehicle surface to ensure low angle radiation.

Repeaters using vertical polarisation for much the same reason of simplicity of antenna design means that operation of a fixed station, either direct to mobiles or via repeaters, can only be satisfactorily accomplished if a means of changing polarisation is available. It is of course quite possible to use two antennas, and ideally two rotating systems, but the cost becomes rather formidable.

Space communication, where control of polarisation is difficult or impossible, has forced the use of circular polarisation and it is surprising that it is not used more between fixed stations for long distance terrestrial work. The fundamental advantage of circular polarisation is that all reflections change the direction of polarisation, precluding the usual addition or subtraction of main and reflected signal; therefore there is far less fading and aircraft flutter when circular polarisation is used at each end of the link. The use of circular polarisation at one end only, with normal horizontal or vertical at the other end of the link, naturally results in a 3dB loss, and therefore to achieve the full advantages of circular polarisation it is necessary for all stations to use it.

The usual practice when using circular polarisation for terrestrial communications is to standardise on clockwise or "right-hand" in the northern hemisphere, and this may well become standard for the amateur by its regular adoption. The direction of polarisation is referred to as viewed from the rear of the antenna.

Changing all VHF operations to circular polarisation is obviously not practical, but if a system of switching polarisations were in use at all stations it would soon become evident that circular offers advantages, and there would of course be the added bonus that vertical would be available for operation with mobiles. Having used a system of polarisation switching, big variations are found in polarisation from stations, in particular mobiles. Quite often a mobile using a vertical antenna has been found to be of equal strength on all polarisations and in some cases a definite advantage for circular has been shown.

Circular polarisation normally brings to mind the helix antenna, which can only produce modes of circularity, depending upon whether the thread of the antenna element is wound clockwise or anticlockwise. Horizontal or vertical polarisation is possible from helix antennas, but only by the use of two helices and suitable phasing, with no real means of control. The simple means of changing polarisation is to mount a horizontal Yagi and a vertical Yagi on the same boom, giving the familiar crossed Yagi. Separate feed to each section of the Yagi brought down to the operating position will enable the user to switch to either horizontal or vertical, but it is perhaps not generally realised that it is a relatively simple matter to alter the phasing of the two Yagis in the shack and obtain four more polarisation options, namely two slant positions (45° and 135°), together with two circular positions (clockwise and anticlockwise) which with horizontal and vertical gives six positions altogether. This capability is also of great assistance for transmission and reception through satellites.

Although vertical polarisation is mechanically and electrically advantageous when using a simple dipole type of

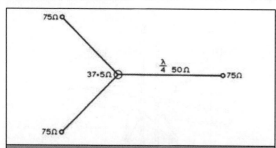

Fig 5.53: Matching two 75Ω antennas by parallel to 37.5Ω and increasing impedance to 75Ω again.

antenna, the presence of the mast in the same plane as the vertical elements on a Yagi considerably detracts from performance. This can be very simply overcome with a crossed Yagi with polarisation switching, mounting the antenna with elements at 45°. The mast then has little effect on the input impedance of the two Yagis, and feeding both antennas in the correct phase relationship can still produce vertical and horizontal polarisations.

Assuming therefore that a crossed Yagi is mounted at 45° with individual feeders to the operating position, the polarisation available and the phasing required is as follows:

- Slant position 45° and 135° Antennas fed individually

- Circular positions clockwise Both antennas fed with
  and anticlockwise 90°+ or 90°- phase
  relationship

- Horizontal and vertical Both antennas fed with 0°
  or 180° phase
  relationship

This all sounds very complicated, but in actual fact the desired result may be accomplished relatively simply with a three gang six position Yaxley type wafer switch. A coaxial switch is the "pure" way to do the job but, considering the cost of a three gang six way coaxial switch together with the necessary plugs and sockets, the difference in performance is just not worthwhile on 144MHz.

The first problem to overcome is simply that of providing the correct matching for feeding two antennas in parallel. Briefly, with 75Ω antennas the two feeders are simply

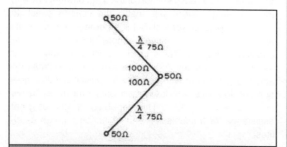

Fig 5.54: Matching two 50Ω antennas by increasing impedance to 100Ω and paralleling to 50Ω again.

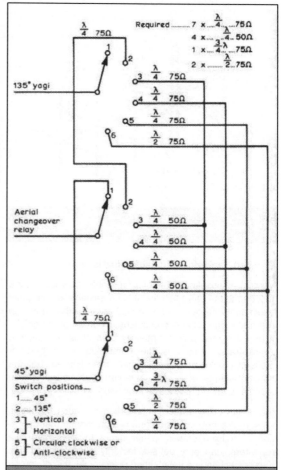

Fig 5.55: 75Ω phasing and matching switch.

paralleled, giving 37.5Ω, and λ/4 of 50Ω feeder used to transform back to 75Ω, as illustrated in Fig 5.53. 50Ω antennas are treated in a slightly different way in that λ/4 of 75Ω feeder is used in each feeder to transform up to

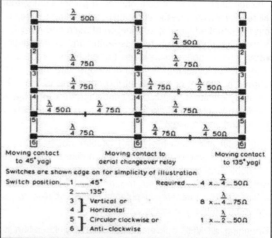

Fig 5.56: 50Ω phasing and matching switch.

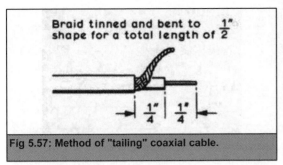

Fig 5.57: Method of "tailing" coaxial cable.

100Ω and the two are placed in parallel to produce 50Ω again, as shown in Fig 5.54.

Phasing is simply a question of altering the length of the feeders to each half of the crossed Yagi as the polarisation is changed. Where a 90° phase shift is required, λ/4 of feeder is inserted and where a 180° phase shift is required, λ/2 feeder is inserted. The polarisation switch must therefore arrange for correct matching by switching in the appropriate λ/4 impedance transformer and correct phasing by switching in the appropriate length of feeder. There is an added complication in that by no means all antenna systems are 50Ω, and a considerable number of 75Ω users still remain on VHF. 50Ω has become an international standard and is of course completely standard on low frequency; it can therefore only be a matter of time before all VHF installations are 50Ω.

Figs 5.55 and 5.56 show the necessary switching arrangements for 75Ω and 50Ω antennas respectively. The normal drawing of a switch makes the illustration of the 50Ω system extremely complicated, and Fig 5.56 is drawn as a side view of the Yaxley switch with the six contacts visible in a vertical line, the moving contact not being shown. It will be noticed that the 50Ω version is much simpler as there is no need to manufacture T-junctions in the cables.

It is very necessary for the phasing lengths of feeder to be accurately cut and this may be simply accomplished with a GDO. First, use the smallest possible diameter cable to minimise the mechanical problems of connection to the contacts of the switch. Types UR43 for 50Ω and UR70 for 75Ω are to be preferred and certainly a solid dielectric type should be used in the interests of uniformity. To obtain λ/4 of cable, cut off slightly more than the calculated length, which in the case of 144MHz will be 15in of solid dielectric cable, leave one end open circuit, and short the other end with the shortest possible loop that will produce a dip on the GDO. It is surprising just how small

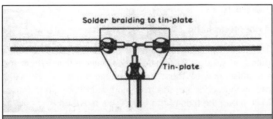

Fig 5.58: Method of joining three cables.

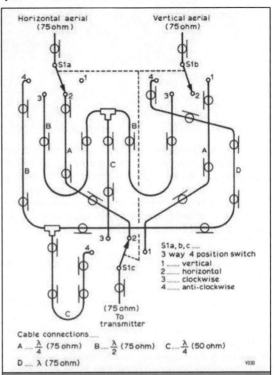

Fig 5.59: An alternative arrangement for feeding crossed Yagi antennas that provides various polarisations at the click of a switch.

that loop can be and, given a reasonably sensitive GDO, a virtual short circuit will still couple. Check the dip frequency, which will probably be around 120MHz, and carefully clip pieces off the open end of the cable until the dip occurs at 145MHz. Assuming that a solid dielectric cable of similar size is used throughout the switch, there is no necessity to dip each length. The uniformity of the cable is sufficient simply to copy mechanically this λ/4 and to double or treble it where λ/2 or 3λ/4 is required. The length in the switch contacts compensates the slight shortening of the cables when they are prepared for connection.

Remember when wiring the switch that every effort should be made to maintain impedance and all cable ends should be made up as short as possible to the configuration shown in Fig 5.57. All outer braids on each wafer of the switch must be joined together by the shortest possible route and not connected to the frame of the switch. The use of miniature switches with small diameter cable makes for a beautifully neat assembly, but very great care indeed is needed to deal with the many coaxial connections in a switch of this small size. The joining of a length of 50Ω and 75Ω is important, and here every effort should be made to maintain the coaxial nature of the cable by pushing the braid back away from the inner, making the inner connections carefully, taping up with polythene tape to avoid any possible short circuit, and then bringing the braids back again over the tape and binding securely with fine wire. Any attempt at soldering will probably be

Table 5.10: Received signals expected with various switch connections.

Switch position	Polarisation of signal (dB down)					
	Horizontal	Vertical	45°	135°	Clockwise	Anticlockwise
Horizontal	Max	20/30	3	3	3	3
Vertical	20/30	Max	3	3	3	3
45°	3	3	Max	20/30	3	3
135°	3	3	20/30	Max	3	3
Clockwise	3	3	3	3	Max	20/30
Anticlockwise	3	3	3	3	20/30	Max

disastrous, as the polythene will undoubtedly melt with the risk of short circuit. A layer of tape may give further protection over the entire joint. Similarly, the T-junctions on the 75Ω switch may be made up by cutting small triangular sections of tinplate and quickly soldering the outer of each cable to the tin; in this case short circuits may be seen and avoided. Fig 5.58 illustrates the method.

Assuming that the switch has been satisfactorily built, there is now the problem of whether the feeders to the halves of the crossed Yagi are of the correct individual length. Ideally, these feeders should be cut mechanically and electrically to equal length before installation, and the two halves of the crossed Yagi should be in exactly the same place on the boom. While the feeders may be cut accurately, it is mechanically difficult and almost impossible to mount the two halves of the Yagi in the same place. They inevitably have to be spaced by a few Inches. It is therefore necessary to correct this mechanical displacement of phase by an equal displacement of length of the feeders, and in practice it is far easier to simply connect everything up with unknown lengths of feeders and adjust the length of one or both feeders until the switch operates correctly.

A convenient method of adjustment is to receive a horizontally polarised signal of constant amplitude from a local station, ensuring that the transmitting and receiving antennas are beamed directly at each other. This point is vitally important; a beam antenna only radiates its intended polarisation from the main lobe, a fact that will become very evident in subsequent use of the switch. The feeder lengths should now be adjusted so that all slant and circular positions are equal, together with maximum

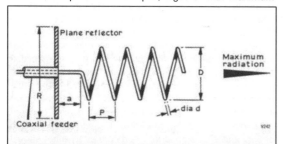

Fig 5.60: The helix antenna. The plane reflector may take the form of a dartboard type wire grid. The dimensions given in Table 5.11 are based on a pitch angle of 12°. The helix may be wound of copper tube or wire, the actual diameter is not critical, it must be supported by low loss insulators.

rejection in the vertical position of the switch. The choice of which shall be the horizontal and vertical positions can now be taken. Accurate S meter readings logged for each position of the switch after every feeder adjustment are essential. Typically, the slant or circular positions will be about one S point down on the horizontal, while the vertical position will be some six S points or 20 to 30dB down. To avoid the problem of the man trying to level the legs of a four legged table and finishing up with a 3in high table, when cutting feeder lengths cut only 1in at a time from one feeder. When the recorded readings indicate that the last cut as one too many, cut that last piece from the other feeder and the optimum situation will be restored.

With the Yagis mounted at 45°, it may appear surprising that a horizontal signal can produce differing signal strength on each antenna, but this will happen until the respective feeders are of equal length. The reason is the inevitable mismatch (sometimes deliberate to improve noise factor) that occurs at the input to the converter or receiver. Remember the object is equal signals, not maximum signals, converter mismatch can be compensated for and maximum signal strength achieved by altering the length of the main feeder after the switch, which will not affect the phase relationships between the antennas.

The question now arises as to which of the circular polarisation positions are clockwise or anticlockwise. This subject merits an entire article; it will be remembered that even the world's top telecommunication engineers got this one wrong on the first transatlantic TV broadcast via Telstar. Should the operator wish to define the circular positions, then with accurately cut equal feeders and an accurately made switch, position 5 will be clockwise and 6 anticlockwise, providing the antenna connections are as shown in Fig 5.56. If the antenna connections are not known, then the only way to calibrate the switch is to receive a known circularly polarised signal, when the respective positions will be immediately evident.

A correctly wired and phased switch should perform as in Table 5.10.

Axial mode helix

The helix antenna is a simple means of obtaining high gain and wide band frequency characteristics. When the circumference of the helix is of the order of 1λ axial radiation occurs, i.e. the maximum field strength is found to lie along the axis of the helix. This radiation is circularly polarised, the sense of the polarisation depending on whether the helix has a right hand or left hand thread.

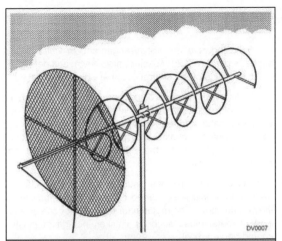

Fig 5.61: General arrangement to support a structure for a five turn helical antenna.

If a pick up dipole is used to explore the field in the direction of maximum radiation, the signal received by this dipole will show no change of amplitude as it is rotated through 360°, thus indicating true circular polarisation. At any point to the side of the helix the wave will be elliptically polarised, i.e. the horizontal and vertical components will be of unequal strength.

A helix may be used to receive the circularly polarised waves radiated from a transmitting helix but care must be taken to ensure that the receiving helix has a thread of the same sense as the radiator. If a thread of the wrong sense is used, the received signal will be very considerably weaker.

The properties of the helical antenna are determined by the diameter of the spiral D and the pitch P (see Fig 5.60) and depend upon the resultant effect of the radiation all along the helical conductor. The gain of the antenna depends on the number of turns in the helix. The diameter of the reflector R should be at least λ/2, the diameter of the helix D should be about λ/3 and the pitch P about λ/4.

A helix of this design will have a feed impedance of about 140Ω; this may be transformed to the feeder impedance

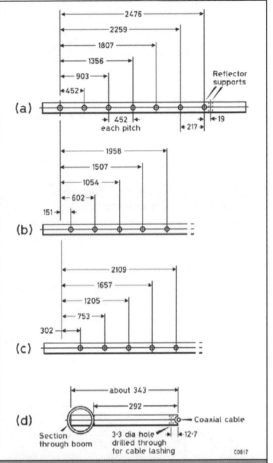

Fig 5.62: (a) First side drilling dimensions, reflector support holes are drilled at right angles. (b) and (c) are drilled at intervals of 120° and 240° respectively from (a). (d) Cutting and filing dimensions for the element stand offs.

by means of a λ/4 transformer. A typical helical antenna having a seven-turn helix has a gain of approximately 12dBi over a 2:1 frequency range. However, to achieve this gain fully it is necessary to use a circularly polarised

Table 5.11: General dimensions for 144, 433 and 1296MHz helix antennas as shown in Fig 5.60.

Band	Dimensions				
	D	R	P	a	d
Generral	0.32λ	0.8λ	0.22λ	0.1λ	
144MHz	25½(648)	64(1626)	17¾(450)	8¾(222)	½(12.7)
433MHz	8¾(222)	22(559)	6(152)	3(76)	3/16 - ½(4.8 - 12.7)
1296MHz	3(76)	7(178)	2(50)	1 1/8(28)	1/4 - 1/8(3.2 - 6.4)
Turns	6	8	10	12	20
Gain	12dB	14dB	15dB	16dB	17dB
Beamwidth	47°	41°	26°	31°	24°

Dimensions in inches, millimetres are given in brackets. The gain and beamwidth of the helical antenna are dependant upon the total number of turns as shown above.

Bandwidth = 0.75 to 1.3λ

Feed Impedance = 140 x circumference / λ Ohms (Note λ and circumference must be in the same units)

Beamwidth (degrees) = Square root of 12,300 / No of turns

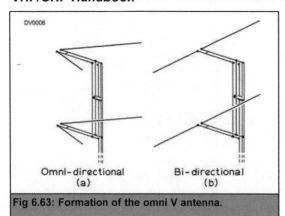

Fig 6.63: Formation of the omni V antenna.

antenna (e.g. a helix of the same sense) for reception. If a plane-polarised antenna, such as a dipole, is used there will be a loss of 3dB.

A practical helix antenna for 144MHz

The greatest problem to be overcome in this type of antenna for 144MHz, with its relatively large helix diam-

eter of 24½in, is the provision of a suitable support structure.

Fig 5.61 shows a general arrangement, in which three supports per turn (120° spacing) are shown, and details of suitable drilling of the central boom are given in Fig 5.62.

The helix may be made of copper, brass, or aluminium tube or rod, or coaxial cable. This latter alternative is an attractive material to use, being covered and substantially weatherproofed. If coaxial cable is used the inner conductor should connect to the outer at each end, or be removed completely.

The reflector is located at a distance "a" behind the start of the first turn, and is supported by crossed supports from the central boom. The material for the reflector can be any kind of metal mesh such as chicken netting or plastic coated garden mesh.

The central boom should be sufficiently rigid to adequately support the whole structure, and should ideally at the same time be of a non metallic material such as wood, thick wall plastic tube or thick wall glass fibre. Although glass fibre is more expensive it would undoubtedly be

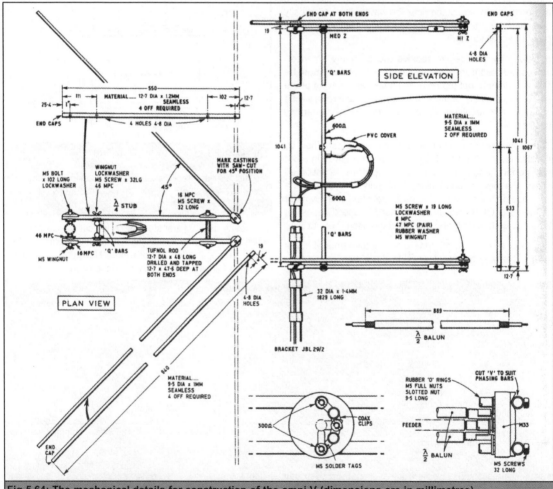

Fig 5.64: The mechanical details for construction of the omni V (dimensions are in millimetres).

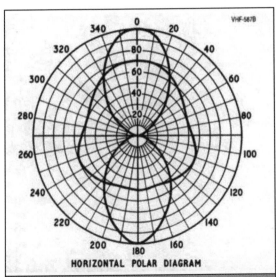

VHF-587B

HORIZONTAL POLAR DIAGRAM

Fig 5.65: The horizontal polar diagram for an average antenna, showing both the bidirectional and omni directional charts.

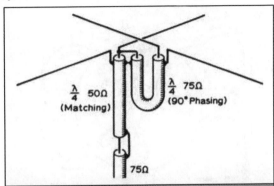

$\frac{\lambda}{4}$ 50Ω (Matching)

$\frac{\lambda}{4}$ 75Ω (90° Phasing)

75Ω

Fig 5.67: Phasing and matching arrangements of crossed dipoles.

worthwhile for a permanent installation.

The length of the final turn of the helix can be adjusted to obtain optimum circularity. This would entail rotating a dipole set up in line with the helix at a distance of, say, 10m, to be outside the near field and clear of all objects. The signal obtained from the dipole will be constant for all points of rotation when the helix is optimised for circular polarisation. Any variation of the signal is known as the polarisation axial ratio or bore sight ellipticity, and is usually expressed as a ratio or decibel figure. Helix antennas for higher frequencies are easier to construct and require little adjustment. Detailed instructions for building a 435MHz helix have been published by G3RUH [23].

Omni directional antennas for fixed stations

The horizontally polarised omni V

This antenna consists of a pair of λ/2 dipoles. The ends of the dipoles are physically displaced to produce quadrature

radiation and are supported on a λ/4 shorted stub. A pair of Q bars are tapped down the stubs to a point where the impedance is 600Ω so that when the two units are fed in parallel they produce an impedance of 300Ω at the centre. A 4:1 balanced to unbalanced coaxial transformer is fitted to the centre point of the Q bars so that a standard 75Ω coaxial cable feeder may be used.

A 50Ω feed can be arranged by repositioning the Q bars on the antenna stubs. This can best be achieved by monitoring the VSWR on the coaxial feeder whilst adjusting the Q bar position by small but equal amounts on both stubs.

The general arrangement is shown in Fig 5.63(a). Fig 5.63(b) shows how the antenna may be arranged to give a bidirectional radiation pattern.

Simple crossed dipoles

The ordinary turnstile, also known as crossed dipoles, provides a simple yet very effective horizontally polarised,

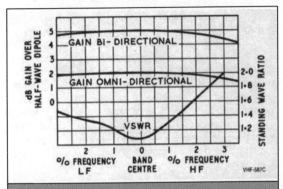

VHF-587C

Fig 5.66: Chart showing gain versus VSWR for the omni V.

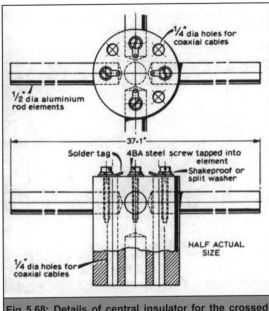

Fig 5.68: Details of central insulator for the crossed dipoles.

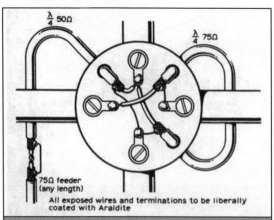

Fig 5.69: Connections of the coaxial section of the crossed dipoles.

omni directional antenna. It consists of two horizontal dipoles mounted at right angles and fed with equal power but at 90° phase difference (Fig 5.67). Matching to 75Ω is quite simple and with a little adjustment a very low SWR can be obtained. The radiation pattern produced tends to be square with the 'corners' at element ends being about 1dB up on a dipole's maximum radiation.

The 90° phase difference is readily obtained with a resonant λ/4 feeder between the dipoles and a further resonant series λ/4 section as a matching transformer for the characteristic line impedance. The antenna should be mounted at least 0.5λ above any conducting surface, otherwise much of the signal will be radiated upwards.

The λ /4 ground plane antenna

This is one of the simplest omni directional antennas to construct and usually yields good results. However, some unexpected effects may occur when the antenna is mounted on a conductive mast, or if RF current is allowed to flow on the outside of the coaxial feeder.

In its simplest form, the ground plane antenna comprises

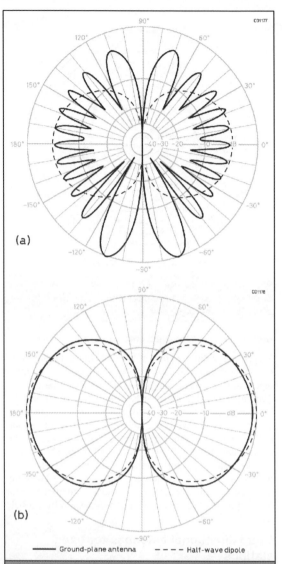

(a)

(b)

Ground-plane antenna   – – – – Half-wave dipole

Fig 5.71: Radiation patterns of quarter wave ground plane antenna. (a) On top of a 5λ (10m) mast. Note that the main lobes are directed downwards and would be prone to pick up man made interference. The pattern of a λ/2 dipole is shown for comparison. (b) In free space. A λ/2 dipole is again shown for comparison.

a λ/4 extension to the inner of a coaxial cable, with several wires extending radially away from the end of the outer of the coaxial cable, Fig 5.70(a). The input resistance will be quite low, of the order of 20Ω, although this may be transformed to a higher impedance by using a folded monopole radiator as shown in Fig 5.70(b). Equal diameter elements provide a 4:1 step up ratio to around 80Ω, and a smaller diameter grounded leg can reduce the input impedance to 50Ω.

Bending the ground plane rods downwards from the horizontal can modify the feed point impedance, Fig

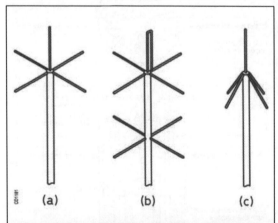

(a)   (b)   (c)

Fig 5.70: Quarter wave ground plane antennas. The folded monopole radiator may be used with any of the ground plane configurations.

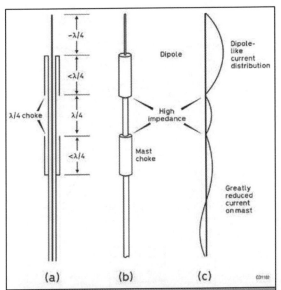

Fig 5.72: Skirted dipole antenna with mast choke. Note that the interior of the choke must be λ/4 in electrical length. Some designs use dielectric loading inside the dipole skirt to shorten its length which can be used to adjust the impedance of the dipole as a radiator.

5.70(c). If the radiating element and the ground plane rods are all λ/4 long, the input resistance is approximately:

$$R = 18(1 + \sin \theta)^2 \, ohms$$

where θ is the ground plane rod angle below the horizontal, in degrees. A 50Ω resistance is achieved when θ is 42°.

The ends of the ground plane rods are sometimes joined

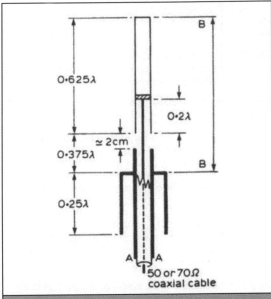

Fig 5.73: Gain sleeve dipole.

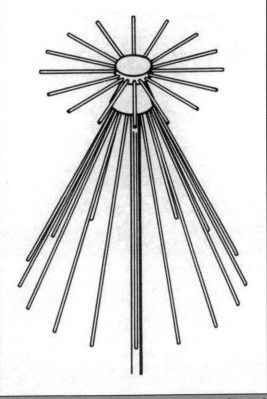

Fig 5.74: General arrangement of skeleton form of discone antenna.

together with a conductive ring to provide additional mechanical stability. The ring increases the electrical size of the ground plane, and the length of the radials can be reduced by about 5%.

The few rods forming the ground plane usually do not prevent current flowing on any conductive supporting mast or on the outside of a coaxial feeder. The mast or feeder can become a long radiating element that may enhance or destroy the radiation pattern of the antenna, dependent upon the magnitude and phase of the mast currents relative to that on the antenna. An example of this is shown in Fig 5.71(a), where the monopole and ground plane is mounted on a 5λ mast (about 10m). The corresponding radiation patterns without mast or cable influences are shown in Fig 5.71(b). The effects of ground reflections have been suppressed in both cases.

Some antenna designs make use of these currents to enhance the gain of the monopole; they sometimes have a second set of ground plane rods further down the mast, tuned to present a high impedance to reduce currents flowing below that point. Using more radials in the ground plane or extending their length to around 0.3λ can reduce the mast currents a little.

An open circuited choke sleeve can be more effective than radial wires for mast current control. This technique is used in the skirted antenna described below.

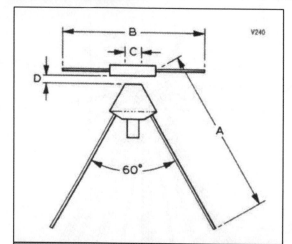

Fig 5.75: Primary dimensions of discone antenna.

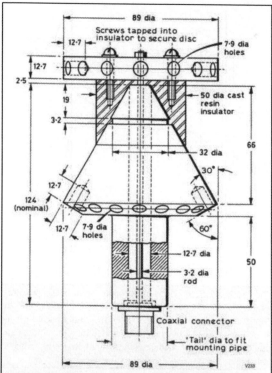

Fig 5.76: Details of the hub assembly of the discone.

The skirted antenna

The skirted antenna (Fig 5.72) does not require ground plane radials, and can be mounted in a cylindrical radome for better appearance and lower wind induced noise. The skirt forms the lower part of a λ/2 dipole and, being λ/4 long, presents a high impedance at its lower end, reducing unwanted currents on the mast. The current is further reduced by a second choke, with its open, high impedance end placed λ/4 below the dipole skirt for best effect. The radiation pattern of this antenna closely resembles that of a λ/2 dipole in free space.

The gain sleeve dipole (vertically polarised)

The gain sleeve dipole in Fig 5.73 is derived from the 1.8dBD shunt feed 5λ/8 mentioned later in the mobile antenna section.

The radiating element B - B is in principle a centre fed 1λ element but is fed coaxially to make it end fed. Having effectively twice the aperture of the λ/2 dipole, a gain of typically 2.5 - 3dB is achieved.

Mechanical construction is open to interpretation but a beer can or plastic water pipe format are two solutions. It should be noted that the mounting point should be at A - A and not on the 0.25λ sleeve.

The discone

This antenna has not found too much favour with amateurs in the past, though frequently used for commercial and military purposes. Unlike many other types this antenna is not only omni directional but also has wide band characteristics. It is capable of covering, say, the 70, 144 and 432MHz bands or 144, 432 and 1296MHz, although there will of course be some variation of the SWR over such a wide range.

Also, since the antenna can operate over roughly a 10-to-one frequency range, it will more readily radiate any harmonics present in the transmitter output. It is therefore important to use a suitable filter to adequately attenuate the harmonic outputs. The radiation angle tends to rise

after the first frequency octave.

The discone consists of a disc mounted above a cone, and ideally should be constructed from sheet material. Many amateurs would find this impossible to realise, but with little loss the components may be made of rods or tubes as illustrated in Fig 5.74, with a minimum number of rods of eight or preferably 16. Of course, open mesh may be used as an alternative, bearing in mind the windage increase, and that the current flows radially away from the feed point.

The important dimensions are the end diameter of the cone and the spacing of this from the centre of the disc, so that the terminating impedance is correct, e.g. 50Ω.

The primary parameters are shown in Fig 5.75 with dimensions as follows:

- A   the length of the cone elements, these are λ/4 at the lowest operating frequency, or 2952/f(MHz)in.

- B   the overall disc diameter, this should be 70% of λ/4.

- C   the diameter of the top of the cone, this will be decided to some extent by the diameter of the coaxial cable but for most purposes 0.5in will be suitable.

- D   the spacing of the centre of the top disc to the cone top, this is 20% of C, or 0.1in for 50Ω.

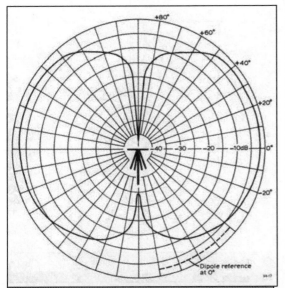

Fig 5.77: Typical discone and helicone radiation pattern, in dB, over the first 2:1 frequency range. As the frequency increases above 2:1 the pattern tends to rise above the horizon level until about 5:1 in frequency when the main direction of the radiation is above 45° from the horizon.

The detail given in Fig 5.76 of the hub construction will be suitable for any design using a 50Ω cable feed and may be taken as an example. There is likely to be some problem in producing a suitable insulator that may be made of a potting resin or turned from PTFE or other stable low loss material.

An extension of the discone is the helicone. The elements of the conventional discone can be replaced with helical

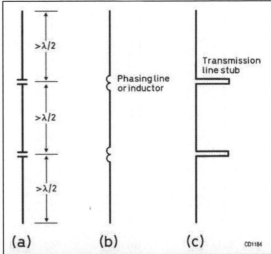

Fig 5.79: Realisation of collinear antennas. The antennas are end fed.

elements working in the normal mode as discussed later.

In its simplest form only eight elements are required for the disc and for the cone. Gain and the radiation pattern is essentially the same for both the discone and helicone but for the helicone the usable bandwidth is reduced to approximately one third.

Collinear antennas

Communication with mobile stations is best achieved with a vertically polarised omni directional antenna, as there is no need to point the antenna in the direction of the mobile. However, a fixed station is not as constrained by mechanical considerations as a mobile, and can thus be fitted with larger, and hence higher gain, antennas.

This can be achieved by stacking dipoles vertically above

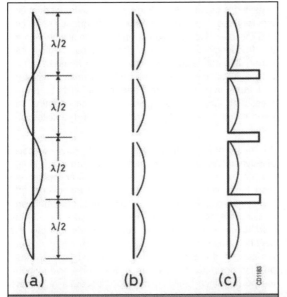

Fig 5.78: Current distribution on a wire and derivation of the collinear antenna.

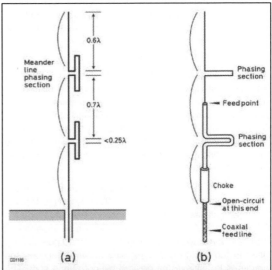

Fig 5.80: Franklin collinear antennas, end fed and centre fed.

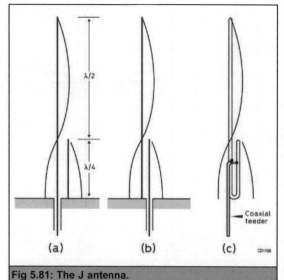

Fig 5.81: The J antenna.

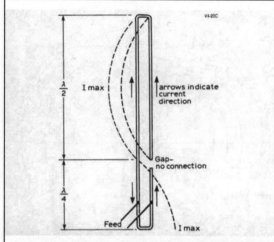

Fig 5.82: The basic Slim Jim showing direction of current flow and phase reversal in the matching stub (Practical Wireless).

one another in a collinear array, and feeding them with cables of equal lengths, as shown for the GB2ER repeater antenna later in this chapter. Another method of achieving gain with simpler feed arrangements is discussed below.

A formula was presented in the section on antenna arrays for calculating the radiation pattern of groups of elements. The radiation pattern of broadside arrays develops nulls as the elements are spaced further apart, so it is desirable to place the elements as close together as practicable, taking into account the capture area and mutual coupling effects also discussed in the section on arrays.

The current on a length of wire several wavelengths long will be distributed as shown in Fig 5.78(a). The wire shown is 2λ long. Radiation at right angles to the wire will be poor, as the successive half wavelength current maxima are in opposing phase, and if the currents were equal, there would be perfect cancellation of the radiation in that direction. However, if all the current maxima were in phase, the radiated fields would add, and a high gain could be achieved, Fig 5.78(b).

There are several ways of achieving this phase reversal. The simplest is to insert an anti resonant network or a non-radiating half wavelength of transmission line as a phasing section between the $\lambda/2$ radiating elements, Fig 5.78(c). The $\lambda/2$ transmission line can be realised as a quarter wavelength of ribbon cable, which can be wound around the insulator between the radiating elements (see the section on mobile antennas).

A more subtle approach uses radiating elements that are a little longer or shorter than $\lambda/2$. This helps the feeding arrangements, as it will be remembered that end feeding a $\lambda/2$ dipole is difficult because of its very high impedance. The self reactance of the longer or shorter dipole is then used in the design of the phasing network between the elements to achieve the desired overall phase shift. The non-radiating transmission line can then often be replaced by a capacitor or an inductor in series with the residual

element reactance, Fig 5.79(a) and (b). Again, a transmission line stub can be used to synthesise the required reactance, which may be more convenient or cheaper than a lumped component, especially if significant RF power handling is required, Fig 5.79(c). Sometimes a parallel tuned circuit is realised as an inductor resonated by the self-capacitance of the insulator separating the radiating elements, and on which it is wound.

A technique devised by Franklin that has been attractive to VHF antenna manufacturers folds parts of the radiating element to provide the phasing section as shown in Fig 5.80(a). Provided that the folded sections are significantly shorter than the radiating elements, the gain is not significantly degraded, although the whole structure is sensitive to capacitive loading by any housing and insulators required. The radiation pattern is frequency sensitive, and the main lobe will squint upwards or downwards as the frequency changes from the nominal. While these folded element designs look attractive for home construction, adjustments to optimise both the radiation pattern and input impedance are very difficult without proper measuring facilities. Poor gain and broken radiation patterns result if the sections are not properly excited and phased.

All these designs are end fed, which have practical disadvantages with longer, multi element arrays. If identical sections are used, the end elements carry less current than those close to the feed, reducing the overall efficiency of the antenna. While different length radiators and phasing elements can be used to equalise the current distribution, the design and adjustment is lengthy and definitely requires good radiation pattern measurement facilities. If the array can be centre fed, any residual phasing errors tend to cancel out and, for a given length, the performance tends to be better because of a more uniform current distribution. Fig 5.80(b) shows one means of achieving centre feeding with a Franklin array. Note the use of the $\lambda/4$ choke section at the base of the array,

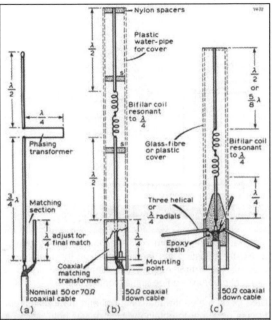

Fig 5.83: A collinear form of J antenna. (a) The addition of λ/4 sections as suggested by Franklin. (b) Use of a coaxial short circuit λ/4 transformer to give an unbalanced input. The tapping point in the matching transformer is approximately 0.15λ from the "earthy" end. (c) A variant of (b) with radials. With both (b) and (c) the λ/4 phasing transformer has been "wound up" as a bifilar coil (each coil being wound in the opposite hand). While the inductive component is cancelled, the mutual capacitance on the winding makes them physically shorter than λ/4.

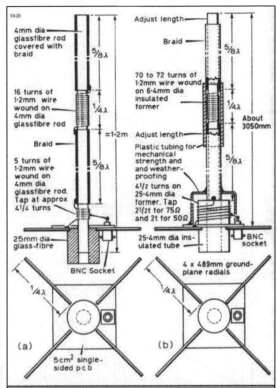

Fig 5.84: (a) A 432MHz collinear. (b) A 144MHz collinear (UK Southern FM Journal).

which is essential to prevent current flowing down the outer of the coaxial cable and destroying the performance of the collinear antenna. The practical gain limit of the singly fed collinear antenna is around 10dBi.

Practical collinears in radio amateur use tend to use variations on Fig 5.79. The radiating elements may comprise combinations of lengths up to 5λ/8, with or without ground planes.

The presence of a good ground plane increases the gain as the image or reflection effectively doubles the length of the array (see also the section on mobile antennas). However, good results can be achieved with collinears directly mounted on pipe masts, especially if care is taken to control unwanted currents from flowing on the mast.

None of the above considers the practicalities of feeding and matching the antenna. Collinear antennas, by virtue of their operation as end fed structures, have high feed point impedances. A good feed arrangement, valid for both ground plane and mast mounted antennas, is the use of a λ/4 short circuited transmission line, as described in the section on matching in this chapter.

Fig 5.81(a) shows such an arrangement to end feed a λ/2 dipole mounted over a ground plane. The matching

section should not radiate, and the overall effect is that of a λ/2 radiator raised λ/4 above the ground plane. Either leg of the λ/4 section can be fed, leading to the structure in Fig 5.81(b), which is identical to Fig 5.81(a) in terms of current distribution, and hence radiation performance. The evolution can be taken a stage further by removing the ground plane and feeding either leg of the λ/4 section as in Fig 5.81(c); this is the J antenna or J-pole antenna, which may use different diameters of tubing for the radiator and stub.

The Slim Jim antenna provides an elegant solution for a simple, mechanically robust antenna made from a single piece of tubing as shown in Fig 5.82. This antenna [24] comprises a folded, open circuit λ/2 radiator above a λ/4 transformer section, and is a derivative of the J antenna. The folded stub characteristics of the radiator provide some control over the reactive element of the input impedance. An insulator, e.g. a piece of stiff plastic tubing, to provide weatherproofing and enhanced mechanical rigidity, can join the two ends of the tube. Either balanced or unbalanced feeds can be used, tapped on to the λ/4 transformer section at the point that provides the best match to the feeder. Coaxial feeders should be strapped or bonded to the λ/4 section to reduce unwanted currents on the outer of the cable. The antenna has a maximum gain of around 2.8dBi in free space, although the main lobe is tilted up about 10°. The main lobe can be brought to the horizontal by reducing the length of the upper section to about 0.4λ. This reduces the peak gain to around 2.5dBi, and can make the feed impedance capaci-

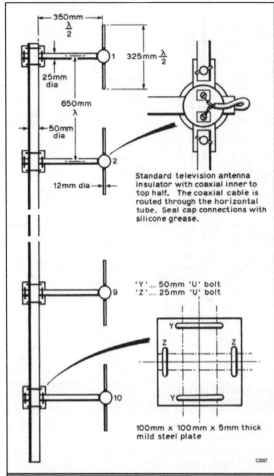

Fig 5.85: Mechanical details of GB3ER collinear.

tive.

Phasing sections and additional elements can be combined to produce a collinear form for the J antenna as shown in Fig 5.83(b). This antenna and that of Fig 5.83(c) have been used successfully to produce low angle radiation for the GB3SN 144MHz repeater.

A variation of the techniques described but using coils as with the original Marconi concept is shown in Fig 5.84(a) for 432MHz and Fig 5.84(b) for 144MHz. The expected gain is between 6 and 7dBD. Materials required for Fig 5.84(a) are as follows:

- One 2.5cm diameter 10cm long glass fibre tube

- One 40mm diameter 1.2m long glass fibre rod

- Four 20mm diameter 20cm long glass fibre rods

- Length of braiding from junk multicore cable

- Length of 18 SWG wire for matching coils

- Approximately 5cm square of singled sided PCB

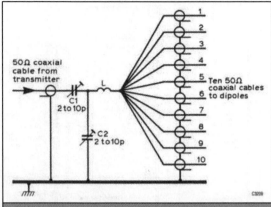

5.86: Matching unit from GB3ER collinear.

First, adjust the bottom $5\lambda/8$ element to give minimum SWR, by adjusting the tapping point on the bottom coil (approx $4\frac{1}{4}$ turns). Altering the length of the first $5\lambda/8$ element can make a fine adjustment.

Next fix on the centre matching coil and the top element. Please note that to obtain the best results both elements should be approximately $5\lambda/8$ and within reason the same length. A good SWR is obtained by adjusting the centre matching coil (the coil is spread over $\lambda/4$).

The matching coil provides the phase change necessary to feed the top element and so adjustment is quite critical. It has been found that if the matching coil has to be "squeezed up" to obtain a good SWR, then the coil has too many turns. The opposite is true if the coil has to be

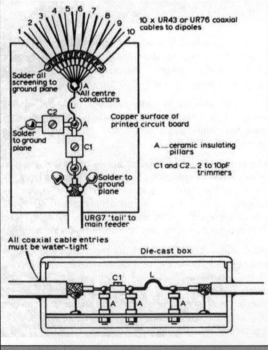

Fig 5.87: Matching unit layout for the GB3ER collinear.

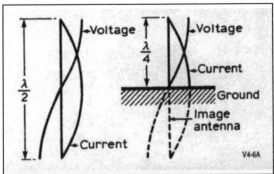

Fig 5.88 The λ/2 antenna and it's grounded λ/4 counterpart. The missing λ/4 can be considered to be supplied by the image in a ground plane of good conductivity.

greater than λ/2 for a good SWR.

To prevent the collinear going off tune once set up, the elements were secured to the centre glass fibre rod and the matching coil taped with self-amalgamating tape. Provided care is taken in setting up, an SWR of close to 1:1 to 1 can be obtained.

Materials required for Fig 5.84(b) are as follows:

- Two ½in diameter by 47½in ± ½in, 5λ/8 elements (adjustable)

- Four 19¼in rods for ground plane

- One 1in diameter by 30in insulated rod

- One 1in diameter insulated tube (a cotton reel can be used instead)

- 18 SWG wire for matching and phasing coils.

The diagram shows extra insulated tubing over the matching and phasing coils to give more mechanical strength and weatherproofing.

Setting up is carried out as follows. First, the length of the bottom 5λ/8 element must be adjusted to give the minimum SWR possible.

Next fix on the phasing coil and the top element that must be the same length as the bottom element. Then obtain the best SWR possible by adjusting the phasing coil.

This coil provides the phase change necessary to feed the top element, it is a length of 18 SWG wire, about 1λ long, coiled up to give 70 - 72 turns on a 4in former. It was found that the λ/4 spacing between the two elements is more critical than the number of turns. 68 turns gave satisfactory SWR on one version.

Some difficulty may occur in setting up the phasing coil. Before taking too many turns off, go back to the first stage to ensure that the bottom 5λ/8 element is correctly matched. If the bottom element is not correctly matched the collinear will not tune up. Careful adjustments in setting up should produce a SWR of 1:1 to 1.

A technique that has not been discussed but is widely

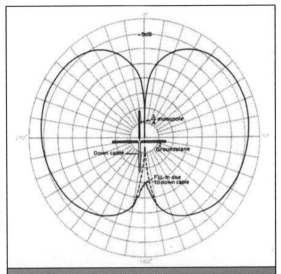

Fig 5.89: Radiation pattern of a λ/4 monopole over a λ/2 square ground plane at 145MHz.

used involves feeding conventional λ/2 dipoles in phase from a single source or adjusting the phase relationship of cable lengths between dipoles. There is a degree of interaction between cables and radiating elements but individual dipoles can be positioned to modify the pattern shape. The example given in Figs 5.85 - 5.87 is probably the simplest to implement and was devised for the GB3ER 432MHz band repeater.

Antennas for mobile and portable stations

The choice of an antenna for mobile VHF and UHF use is dependent on several factors. As the frequency increases the aperture of the antenna decreases. This means that larger gains are required for UHF than VHF to overcome the loss of aperture as well as the radiation path loss due again to the increase of working frequency.

As the direction of a vehicle, relative to the station to which it is transmitting or receiving, is continually changing there is a need for an omni directional antenna system. This will mean that to achieve gain in the horizontal plane, while retaining an omni directional pattern, will require considerable reduction of the pattern in the vertical plane. For example an omni directional antenna of 6dBD gain will have a typical half power point (-3dB) of less than 30°. The narrow beam or disc that is produced will result in considerable variation of transmitted and received signal strength as the vehicle or antenna tilts or where signals are reflected, as will always be the case, from nearby objects. A compromise has therefore to be arrived at to obtain maximum gain in the best direction that gives minimum disruption of signals when mobile.

The choice of polarisation is not only dependent on compatibility with stations being received and the optimum polarisation for the propagation path concerned, but the aesthetics and mechanical complexity of the antenna used and its mounting position on the vehicle.

Antennas, particularly when vehicle mounted, must al-

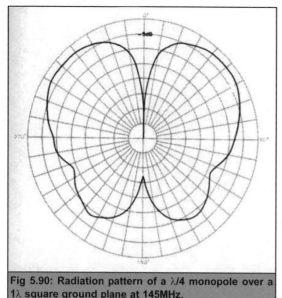

Fig 5.90: Radiation pattern of a λ/4 monopole over a 1λ square ground plane at 145MHz.

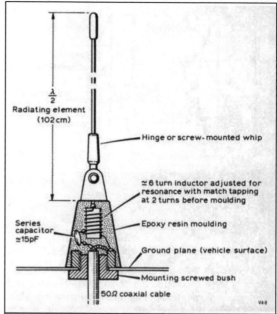

Fig 5.92: A typical home built λ/2 mobile antenna and mount.

ways be considered as an integral part of the environment in which they are to be used. Radiation patterns quoted by manufacturers can be completely different when an antenna is in use. Increased gain normally means an increase in physical size. This improvement of gain can be lost, with a probable loss of omni directivity, if, due to its physical size, the antenna is mounted at a lower point to facilitate access to a garage, for instance. The difference in mounting an antenna on the wing or boot of a car compared with mounting it on the top dead centre of the car roof can lose at least 3dB of gain with the variations of the expected radiation patterns.

There are several antennas in current use that are worth considering. In addition one or two specialised antennas are available or can be readily fabricated by the radio amateur that also merit consideration. Mobile antennas can be considered in three basic groups:

- Vertically polarised antennas, more often used for FM and repeaters.

- Horizontally polarised antennas, normally used for SSB transmission.

- Circularly polarised antennas.

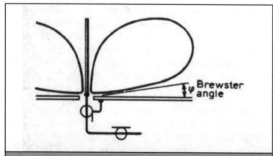

Fig 5.91: Radiation pattern of a whip on a large ground plane showing the elevation of the main lobe.

Quarter wave whip

This is the simplest and most basic mobile antenna. It is derived from the doublet or λ/2 dipole. Marconi, by replacing half of the doublet with a ground plane as shown in Fig 5.88, found that the image of the vertical λ/4 section was "reflected" in the ground plane, producing an antenna that was substantially the same as the original dipole. The theory of operation showed that if the ground plane was infinitely large and made of a perfectly conducting material, all of the radiation associated with the lower half of the dipole was radiated by the top half giving, in fact, a 3dB improvement over the dipole. In practice the size of the ground plane and its resistive losses modify the pattern and this 3dB is never realised. Figs 5.89 and 5.90 show optimum patterns of a λ/4 whip measured on a ground plane of λ/2 sides and 1λ sides. Although the pattern is raised from the horizontal, on a medium ground plane the loss of horizontal gain is relatively small (20° and 1dB at 0° in Fig 5.89 but 40° and 6dB at 0° in Fig 5.90).

However, as the ground plane size increases the main lobe continues to rise until the situation of Fig 5.91 occurs. When a radiator is mounted over a ground plane as described, the input impedance is typically halved. So for the λ/4 whip or monopole the input impedance is typically 36Ω + j, that is to say, approximately half the resistance of the dipole but with an additional reactive component.

Considering 50Ω as being the standard cable impedance used at VHF and UHF, this would produce a standing wave at the antenna base of about 1.5 to 1. The simplest way to overcome this mismatch is first to slightly increase the length of the whip to produce an inductive reactance to cancel the capacitive reactance normally obtained. In practice this also raises the resistive value of the whip and

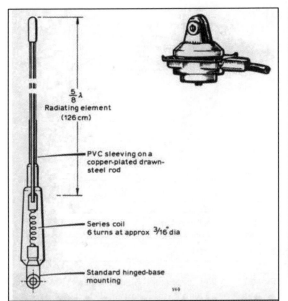

Fig 5.93: A typical commercial 5λ/8 mobile antenna and mount (top right).

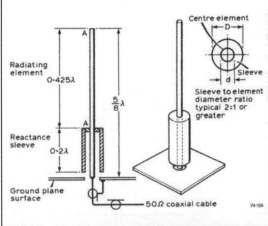

Fig 5.94: The reactance fed 5λ/8 monopole. Typical gain is 1.8dB (Ham Radio).

a close match can usually be obtained to 50Ω cable. Should a VSWR bridge or similar (of 50Ω characteristic impedance) be used to set up the whip, when a match has been achieved, the length of the cable should be changed and the match re-checked. If there is no change in the meter reading, then the antenna is matched to the cable. If a change does occur then the antenna/cable combination has been matched to the VSWR meter. The whip should be readjusted until changes in cable length have minimal or no effect. It is preferable that the added cable length is not an exact multiple of a λ/2 or λ/4 as this, particularly with a multiple of λ/2, will confuse the results.

The ground plane effects and aperture size of the λ/4 whip tend to limit its use at VHF and UHF. At UHF the aperture is small and the pattern tends to be raised in the vertical plane due to the large ground plane area. It is therefore not often used at those frequencies. At VHF, i.e. 144MHz, the compromise of the λ/4 whip's simplicity and size (about 49cm or 19¼in) often balances with its medium aperture and tendency on some vehicles to have a raised vertical pattern. At 70MHz the physical dimensions are such (about 102cm/40in) that this is the normal limiting factor to the use of the λ/4 whip as opposed to gain devices.

The aperture of the antenna at this frequency is compatible with path loss conditions, and the ground plane size is such that the radiation angle when roof mounted is fairly low. However, the shape of the radiation pattern can have a loss of 3dB in the omni directivity each side of the vehicle.

The λ/2 and 5λ/8 gain antennas

Using the ground plane techniques described for the λ/4 whip, gain antennas can be produced. If the λ/2 dipole is extended in length, maximum forward gain (before the pattern divides into several lobes) is obtained when the dipole is about 1.2λ. This becomes the maximum length of 5λ/8 for a ground plane antenna. A natural extension to the λ/4 whip is the λ/2 whip. However, such a radiator fed against a ground plane has a high input impedance. On the other hand, a 3λ/4 radiator fed against a ground plane has a resistive input of almost exactly 50Ω but is above the optimum length for a reasonable pattern shape.

If the λ/2 whip could be made to look like a 3λ/4 radiator then it would be possible to obtain a 50Ω resistive input. A series coil at the ground plane end of a λ/2 radiator can be used to resonate it to 3λ/4, but the input is still fairly high impedance and reactive. If, however, the coil is shorted to the ground plane a tapping point up the coil will provide the required impedance and the addition of a non critical capacitor in series will compensate for the reactive components. Fig 5.92 shows details of such an antenna.

As the aperture of the antenna has been doubled compared with the λ/4 whip, twice the effective radiation is obtained, i.e. approaching 3dB gain. This assumes however, that there is minimum resistance in the radiating element, i.e. it must be copper plated or similar.

The maximum radiator size of 5λ/8 for a single lobe pattern can also make use of the impedance characteristics of the 3λ/4 radiator. Construction is in fact simpler than the λ/2 antenna. If the radiating element is made 5λ/8 with a series coil equivalent to λ/8 at the ground plane end, an input impedance very close to 50Ω can be obtained. With correct materials a gain close to 4dBD can be achieved by the increase in aperture over the λ/2 antenna. The radiation pattern is often raised more than that of a λ/2 antenna so the slightly improved gain of the 5λ/8 may not always be realised.

Fig 5.93 gives details of the series 5λ/8 whip. One other advantage of this antenna is that over a wide range of mounting and ground plane conditions it will self compensate for impedance and resonance changes. It is preferable for both the λ/2 and 5λ/8 antennas to be on a hinge mount, particularly if roof mounted, to enable folding or

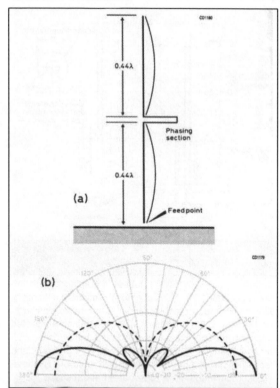

Fig 5.95: 7λ/8 whip antenna with the theoretical current distribution and radiation pattern on an infinite, perfectly conducting, ground plane. λ/4 whip pattern shown for comparison.

"knock down" with obstructions like trees and garages.

Various gain figures have been given for the "five eighth-wave". Unfortunately not all antennas use optimum materials. As previously stated, the DC resistive losses of the radiator must be a minimum, and in addition the use of a glass fibre rod changes the resonant length because the dielectric material changes the velocity factor by as much as 20%. This means the radiator has to be cut shorter than 5λ/8 with the accompanying loss of aperture.

Incidentally, the series coil with the true 5λ/8 whip must be held rigidly as movement of the coil turns will change the antenna's resonance, giving apparent flutter. For certain transceivers with VSWR activated transmitter close down this can produce a situation where the power output of the transmitter is continually being turned down or switched off, producing extremely severe flutter.

Apart from the above reasons for different gain figures, several ground plane antennas discussed in articles about the 5λ/8 system are in fact discussing antennas which are not truly of this nature. One of these devices worth considering for its own merits is that shown in Fig 5.94. It consists of a 5λ/8 vertical element with a reactive sleeve of 0.2λ at the ground plane end of the vertical as shown. The gain obtained from this antenna is typically 1.8dBD and, as can be seen, the actual radiating element A - A and therefore its aperture is under that of a λ/2 antenna.

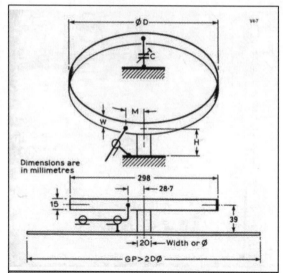

Fig 5.96: A low profile mobile antenna with vertical polarisation. Gain is 1dBD, termination 50Ω.

Other antennas with similar properties but different in construction are the "J" and "Slim Jim". These were described earlier in this chapter.

7/8 whip antenna

This is a variant of the 5/8λ antenna and its current distribution is shown in Fig 5.95. This antenna uses the principles of the collinear antennas shown earlier in this chapter, using either a phasing section or a series capacitor to ensure that the radiation from the upper and lower elements is approximately in phase. A stub phasing section, if properly adjusted, can enhance the gain by approximately 0.5dB over the capacitor variant, and can be realised as a short circuited piece of ribbon cable wrapped round the insulator separating the upper and lower elements. Phasing can also be achieved with a wound section along the lines discussed in the section on collinear antennas. Care should be taken in designing this insulator if the whip is for use on a vehicle, as it must withstand drag of the upper element at speed and the shock loads of the whip snapping from side to side.

For the dimensions shown, the stub length should be approximately 0.245λ. If a capacitor is used, it should

Table 5.12: λ/2 ring radiator dimensions.

	Theoretical	VHF antenna	UHF antenna
Frequency	f MHz	145MHz*	433MHz
Diameter D	52°	298mm	100mm
Height H	8°	39mm	15.5mm
Diameter d	nom 1 - 2°	15mm	10mm
		20 SWG strip	20 SWG strip
Match M	5° for 50Ω	28.7mm	9.7mm
Tuning Capacitor C	To give capacitive reactance nominally 200 - 500Ω	2 - 5pF	0.5 - 2pF

* Tuneable 137 - 148MHz

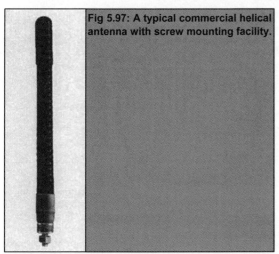

Fig 5.97: A typical commercial helical antenna with screw mounting facility.

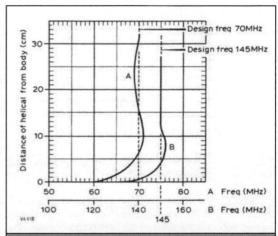

Fig 5.99: Frequency shift of a helical antenna on a typical hand held transceiver for various distances from the body.

present an impedance of around 500Ω at the working frequency (about 2.2pF at 145MHz). The base impedance will be high, between 200 and 400Ω, and capacitive. Base matching arrangements similar to those of the 0.5λ whip are suitable, although the series capacitor should not be necessary. Component values will depend on the materials and construction used, especially around the mounting base.

Low profile antennas

Alternatives to vertical ground plane antennas are devices to reduce the physical size of the system. Reduction of physical size normally implies loss of aperture and therefore gain. However, of the antennas discussed in this section, one in fact produces a gain referred to a dipole of +1dB.

The λ/2 ring radiator

Although called a "ring" radiator, in fact the slot formed between the horizontal λ/2 ring and the ground plane produces radiation.

Consider a λ/2 slot in a metal sheet. If the sheet is rolled into a cylinder such that the two ends of the slot come together, an omni directional vertically polarised radiator is produced. As with the conventional λ/2 slot an impedance match can be obtained by tapping along from one end. Also, if the slot is just under λ/2 a capacitor across the centre will resonate it to λ/2 again. As with the skeleton slot developed by G2HCG, if the ground plane sheet at the top of the slot is reduced to produce a ring and the lower ground plane section is bent into the horizontal plane the low profile of Fig 5.96 is produced. Dimensions

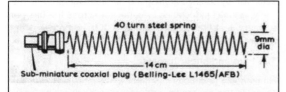

Fig 5.98: Details of a home made helical whip for 145MHz. A BNC plug could also be used.

in terms of electrical degrees and specific sizes for optimum performances for 144MHz and 432MHz are shown in Table 5.12. Halving the dimension H or the loop diameter D (with the necessary increase of capacitance and match point to re-tune to frequency) will halve the radiation capability.

The λ/2 ring radiator is a fairly high-Q antenna and has therefore a reduced bandwidth compared to a dipole (typically 3% compared to 10% for a monopole). Gain is 1dBD. If the ground plane is completely reduced, e.g. the top section previously described, a double ring radiator is produced. Both ring radiators lend themselves to discreet fixed antennas.

Normal mode helix

Typically less than 0.1λ high, this is described in the next section.

The normal mode helix antenna

Much has been said for and against what is termed the normal mode helix as used on hand held transceivers. Unfortunately the method of operation and the results obtainable for this type of antenna have been much misunderstood by amateurs and professionals alike. Most theoretical papers only consider the helical equivalent of the λ/4 whip while most users of this antenna are in fact using the equivalent of a physically reduced 3λ/4 whip.

A helix will work in the normal mode when the diameter and pitch of the helix is less than 0.1λ. When working in this mode the radiation is from the side of the helix, and when the diameter is considerably less than 0.1λ the resultant "spring" has a radiation pattern similar to a short vertical monopole or whip.

A 3λ/4 whip over a moderate ground plane has a resistive match very close to 50Ω. If this whip is coiled into a helical spring as previously described it will resonate to approximately 50Ω but at a somewhat lower frequency. If the spring is trimmed to the original frequency the result will be an antenna of about 0.1λ long matching to approxi-

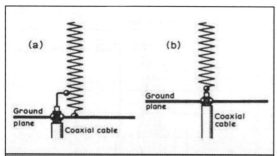

Fig 5.100 Two ways of feeding a helical antenna. (a) shunt fed. (b) series fed.

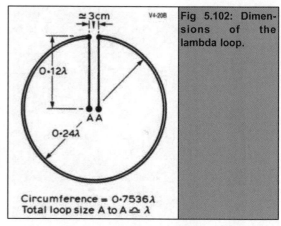

Fig 5.102: Dimensions of the lambda loop.

Circumference = 0·7536λ
Total loop size A to A ≏ λ

mately 50Ω. The actual wire length tends to be around λ/2 to 5λ/8 long at the working frequency. The capacitance formed between the turns of the spring has "loaded" the antenna such that it still resonates as a 3λ/4 antenna. This capacitance also tends to modify the matching under various conditions.

Because of its construction, the spring is very reactive off resonance and this makes it very important that it be resonated for the specific conditions that prevail in its working environment.

Fortunately it is only necessary to change the number of turns to resonate the spring over such diverse conditions as a large ground plane and no ground plane at all. However, the match referred to 50Ω can vary between about 30 and 150Ω at the extremities. Under typical hand held conditions, however, and depending on the frequency of operation, the spring tends to be fairly close to a 50Ω impedance match. This is shown in Fig 5.98 that also gives an indication of the number of turns required for a typical 9mm diameter helix for 3λ/4 resonance.

An important consideration is that since the helix is a reduced size and aperture antenna two factors arise. First, the radiation resistance is lower than the equivalent linear whip so the choice of a good conducting material is important to minimise resistive losses. A steel spring compared with a brass or copper plated helical can waste 3dB of power in heating up the spring. The aperture of the helical is a third the physical size of the λ/4 whip and would moreover indicate a loss of 4.77dB. However,

results obtainable with copper plated, Neoprene sheathed helical antennas, correctly matched to a hand held transmitter at 145MHz, are at worst -3dB and at best are +1dB compared to the equivalent λ/4 whip (which is -6dB compared to a λ/2 dipole). One thing that will be seen however is that the top of the spring on a hand held transceiver will often need to be raised to a position corresponding to the top of the equivalent λ/4 whip to receive or transmit the maximum signal strength.

A similar device resonated on to a λ/2 square ground plane could give results 2 - 3dB below a λ/2 dipole. An alternative arrangement using a bifilar wound helix gives identical results (within 0.2dB) to a λ/2 dipole.

The helix or spring has an interesting and difficult operating characteristic when supported close to the body, particularly at the higher frequencies. Fig 5.99 shows the typical results of a 145MHz or high band spring and a 70MHz or low band spring as it is brought closer to the body. The interesting effect that occurs at several centimetres from the body can be seen, where the resonance of the spring, instead of continuing to decrease due to body capacitance, suddenly increases the frequency of resonance. At 2cm and closer the operating frequency suddenly decreased due to body capacitance. Unfortunately this very changeable area occurs at the typical mounting distance of a body worn transceiver. However, many transceivers must be raised to the mouth when transmitting and this puts the antenna back to its best operating conditions.

The normal mode helical antenna can be vehicle or ground plane mounted if desired. The height is typically less than 0.1λ and the gain is around to 2 - 3dB below a dipole. An acceptable match to 50Ω can often be achieved by simply trimming the resonant length. Alternatively, a small inductance or capacitor across the base or a shunt feed as shown in Fig 5.100 will provide the required matching.

The halo and super turnstile

Horizontally polarised antennas for a mobile station become complex and bulky when gain is required. A simple antenna that produces an almost omni directional horizontal radiation pattern is the halo in its various forms.

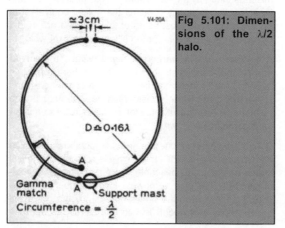

Fig 5.101: Dimensions of the λ/2 halo.

D ≏ 0·16λ

Gamma match

Support mast

Circumference = λ/2

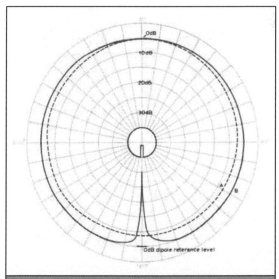

Fig 5.103: Decibel radiation pattern comparison of the halo (A) and the lambda loop (B) antennas.

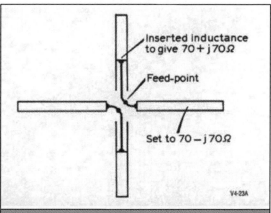

Fig 5.105: Achieving phase quadrature by introducing a reactance in one arm.

comparison of the halo and the lambda radiation patterns are shown in Fig 5.103.

Further extension to three loops can be produced to form the super turnstile but the complexity and sheer physical size tends to limit this sort of structure to only the most daring mobile radio amateur.

Both the lambda loop and the super turnstile should be at least 0.34λ above the ground plane surface to work satisfactorily.

Turnstile antennas along the lines of the crossed dipoles shown in the section on antennas for fixed stations were at one time popular for mobile operations, typically mounted on a λ/2 mast above the vehicle bodywork. However, the aerodynamic drag, wind noise, higher vehicle speeds and the danger of injuring pedestrians (the elements were often around eye height) have all discouraged the use of this and other horizontally polarised antennas for mobile use.

Basically this is a λ/2 dipole, often gamma matched, which is bent round into a circle or square. As can be seen in Fig 5.101, when correctly resonant the resultant radiation pattern is somewhat offset in favour of the direction of the gap. Best results are obtained when mounted at a minimum height of 70cm, 0.34λ at 144MHz, above the ground plane produced by the vehicle roof.

An extension of the λ/2 halo is the full wave or lambda loop. A 1λ loop is drawn in at one point to the centre to produce both a support and a match transformer, to approximately 50Ω (see Fig 5.102). The addition of a 1:1 Pawsey stub or similar balun (see earlier section on matching) produces a near omni directional pattern with a unity gain relative to the maximum radiation of a dipole. A

Antennas for satellite operations

For the average radio amateur satellite antennas fall into two groups, both of which are ground station antennas, that is, those on the ground rather than on the satellite itself. The two groups are steerable, which enable the passage of the satellite to be tracked across the sky, and fixed which, as they in the ideal case have a hemispherical radiation pattern, receive the satellite signals equally in any direction and do not require to track the satellite's passage. The tracking antennas are usually of high gain while the fixed antennas are usually relatively low gain due to the hemispherical coverage required. Fortunately, as signal losses between ground and satellite are low, being mostly line-of-sight path with no obstructions, relatively low gain antennas of the fixed variety are often acceptable for reception of amateur or weather satellites.

However, as the satellite tends to rotate, both groups of antennas are normally circularly polarised, right hand by convention, to compensate for variations in polarisation.

Of the higher gain tracking antennas, crossed Yagis and the helix are used in the main, with the crossed Yagis

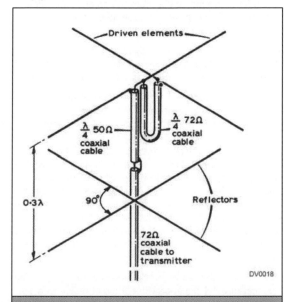

Fig 5.104 A crossed dipole antenna for 145MHz

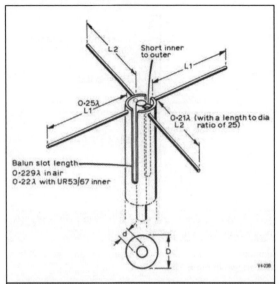

Fig 5.106: A starpole turnstile. D/d =1.86 for 75Ω and 1.5 for 50Ω.

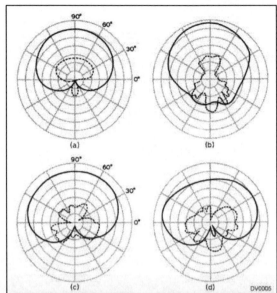

Fig 5.107: Volute radiation patterns. (a) Three quarter turn λ/4 volute. (b) Three quarter turn λ/2 volute. (c) Three quarter turn 3λ/4 volute. (d) Three quarter turn 1λ volute (Microwave Journal).

probably the easiest to construct and most readily available commercially. Details of crossed Yagis and the helix are discussed earlier in this chapter.

For fixed or low gain steerable antennas, several variations of crossed dipoles can be used and also the volute, which is a fractional turn four element helix that can be made to give either directional gain or hemispherical circular polarised coverage (see later). It is worth noting that a conventional single element helix requires two or more complete "turns" to obtain circular polarisation.

Crossed dipoles over a ground plane

Fig 5.104 shows a simple arrangement of crossed dipoles above a ground plane. This type of antenna can be scaled for use at 29, 145 or 432MHz. A suggested version for 145MHz is shown. Mechanical problems may make the reflectors inadvisable in a 29MHz version. The height above ground can be about 2m for 145MHz and 3m for 29MHz. Typical dimensions are:

29MHz	driven elements	(λ/2)	188in	477.5cm
145MHz	driven elements	(λ/2)	38in	96.5cm
	reflectors		40.5in	103cm
	spacing	(0.3λ)	24.5in	62.2cm

The phasing line comprises λ/4 of 72Ω coaxial cable, and the matching section λ/4 of 50Ω cable.

When calculating the length of the λ/4 sections, the velocity factor of the cable must be taken into account. Typically this is 0.8 for cellular and semi air spaced types, and 0.66 for solid dielectric cables, but verification of the correct figure for the cable used should be obtained. As an example, a matching section of RG59/U would be 13in (33cm) in length. To obtain a 50Ω input impedance, the 50Ω transformer section should be replaced by two pieces of 95Ω cable, λ/4 long, connected in parallel.

It is preferable to have a 1:1 balun included at each dipole

centre to ensure a consistent pattern through 360° of azimuth. Dependent on the spacing between the dipoles and ground plane the radiation pattern can be made to be predominantly to the side for satellites low on the horizon or up for overhead passes. By drooping the dipole elements at 45° and with a spacing of approximately 0.4λ of the dipole mounting boss about the ground plane, a compromise radiation pattern can be achieved that tends to be hemispherical. As horizontal and vertical polarisation is affected differently by ground reflections, low-to-horizon flight paths will not produce circular polarisation. This is due both to ground scatter from the satellite and ground reflections at low levels of incidence at the receiving antenna and its ground plane.

Circular polarisation is normally produced by feeding one dipole 90° out of phase to the second dipole by means of a phasing harness containing an extra λ/4 on one side.

An alternative approach to this method of phasing is to utilise the phase properties of a capacitive or inductive reactance. Suppose, for example, that the length and diameter of the dipoles are made to give a terminal impedance of 70 - j70Ω (capacitive). By introducing a series reactance (inductive) of +j70Ω at each terminal of one of the dipoles (Fig 5.105) the terminal impedance of this dipole becomes 70 + j70Ω. With the two dipoles connected in parallel the current in each dipole is equal in magnitude but, due to the opposite phase differences of 45° in each dipole, a total phase difference of 90° (phase quadrature) is achieved which produces circular polarisation.

The two impedances in parallel become 70 + j0Ω so the addition of a 1:1 balun provides a direct match to a 70Ω coaxial line. If the impedance of the balun is correctly

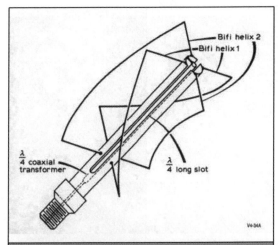

Fig 108: A quarter turn volute with split sheath or slot balun (Microwave Journal).

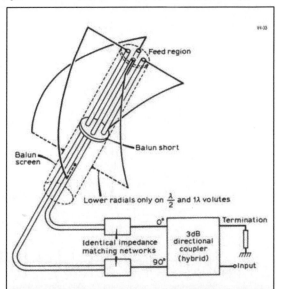

Fig 5.109: The general arrangement using Pawsey stub baluns. A half hybrid or λ/4 phasing harness as used for the crossed dipoles can be used in place of the directional coupler (Microwave Journal).

proportioned this match can be to the standard 50Ω coaxial line. Radiating elements can be drooped as previously described to improve the hemispherical coverage. An easier way of introducing the series inductance is simply to make one dipole long, therefore inductive, at the working frequency, and one dipole short, therefore capacitive at the working frequency.

Fig 5.106 shows a working example of the starpole turnstile arrangement. The reactive components were chosen as ±25Ω and dimensions were based on the reactive information for dipoles as shown in Fig 5.107.

Volute antennas

The volute can also make use of both phasing line or the reactance method to produce circular polarisation. The number of "turns" or part turns of the radiating elements combined with their length can be used to produce various radiation patterns. Radiation patterns produced for several combination of turns and resonant lengths are shown in Figs 5.107(a) to (d) with general details of the volute in Figs 5.108 and 5.109 [25, 26]. It must be noted that elements that are multiples of λ/4 have open circuit ends, while the elements that are multiples of λ/2 can be short circuited to the mounting structure.

Antenna CAD

The development of Computer Aided Design (CAD) software for antenna design has changed the way that VHF/UHF antennas are developed. The software has made the calculation of performance and fine-tuning of the design very easy but the inspiration for a new design still requires a human. Most of the software that is available today can be traced back to the original work carried out at The Lawrence Livermore Labs in 1981. They developed NEC2 (Numerical Electromagnetic Code). The basis of this is to divide the antenna into small elements and use numerical algorithms to calculate the current flow in each element and hence the electromagnetic effects. The smaller the elements are, the more accurate the results but more computing power is required. There is always a

trade off between accuracy and computing power. The original software was written in Fortran and required a fairly meaty (by 1981 standards) computer to run. That was before the PC had been developed and it took until 1989 for a useable version of the software to become available to run on a PC and hence making it available outside the walls of universities and large companies. The software was able to make the calculations but even then the display of the final design was a problem, now that more powerful computers are readily available, that problem has been solved and the design and performance of an antenna can be display in more ways than you can imagine. There are many variants of the original NEC software available to run on many operating systems including Windows, UNIX, LINUX and Macintosh, one of the best places to find out what is available is "The Unofficial Numerical Electromagnetic Code (NEC) Archive", maintained by Raymond Anderson [27]. You will find products ranging from expensive professional products to shareware. One encouraging trend is that "student" or "evaluation" copies of many expensive professional products are available free, these usually have some restrictions but are often quite capable of tackling antenna designs for amateur use.

To illustrate the use of some of the software available, three examples are described:

- YGO3 (Yagi Genetic Optimiser), uses NEC to calculate antenna designs selected by a genetic optimiser.

- EZNEC by Roy Lewallen, W7EL, illustrated by some design work carried out by Bob Hicks, W5TX

- Martin E Meserve's, (K7MEM) JavaScript Electronic Notebook, on line antenna design software

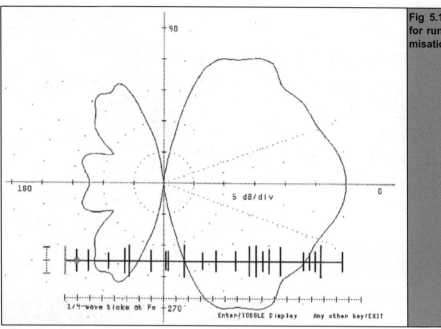

Fig 5.110: Radiation patter for run 1 of the YGO3 optimisation.

YGO3

Yagi Genetic Optimiser, version 3 (YGO3) is freeware [28] intended for serious amateurs who want to explore Yagi design using one of the most powerful techniques available. A full description by Richard A. Formato, WW1RF on installing and using YGO3 was published in VHF Communications Magazine [29]. YGO3 uses a genetic algorithm with state-of-the-art techniques, such as quadratic interpolation, auto grooming, coefficient perturbation, coefficient activation, several selection methods, and two crossover methods. It handles up to 150 element arrays at up to 50 frequencies. YGO3 is a DOS program that may be run in a DOS window in a Windows environment.

How Genetic optimisers work

YGO3 is a genetic algorithm (GA), a class of software that stochastically optimises a design problem by mimicking natural selection ("survival of the fittest"). In much the same way that Nature creates progressively fitter individuals in a species by passing along "good" genes and discarding "bad" ones, the GA produces progressively better designs by doing the same thing in a virtual world. Inside the computer, the species is "Yagi", an array of

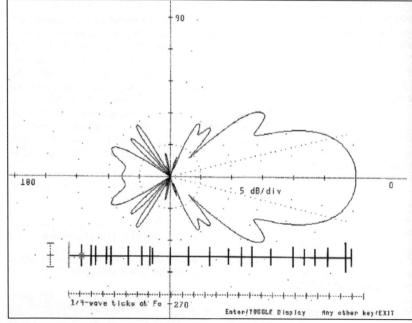

Fig 5.111: Radiation patter for run 2 of the YGO3 optimisation.

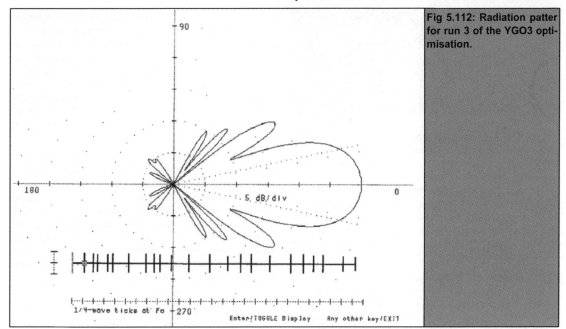

Fig 5.112: Radiation patter for run 3 of the YGO3 optimisation.

parallel, parasitic linear elements in which one is fed (the driven element, DE), one or more act as reflectors (REF), and the others serve as directors (D$_i$). The Yagi's structure is fully determined by a set of antenna genes that include all of its design parameters.

Because the Yagi is a simple antenna, at least geometrically, its gene structure is also simple. A Yagi is fully specified by listing the length, spacing, radius, and offset of each element in the array, so that each element has four genes. The total number of genes describing a complete design, N, is four times the number of elements.

In YGO3's virtual world, each Yagi array is a row vector of N real numbers; and every possible N vector defines a unique Yagi. These vectors are the chromosomes that YGO3 manipulates to select progressively better antenna designs.

GA's are fundamentally different from analytical optimization techniques, and often can be used when analytical methods utterly fail. Analytical optimisers usually compute derivatives to locate the extreme points (maxima and minima) of the function being optimised (so called gradient methods). GA's, by contrast, create random populations of

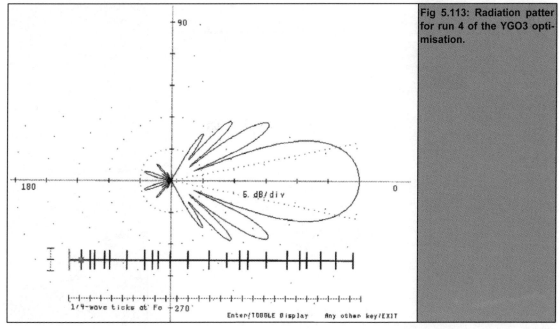

Fig 5.113: Radiation patter for run 4 of the YGO3 optimisation.

Table 5.13: Results of YGO3 optimisation.

Run	Gain dBi	SWR	Length λ	F/B Ratio dB
1	5.5	1.51	5.86	17.7
2	14.8	1.54	6.31	22.2
3	16.1	2.02	6.56	29.8
4	16.5	2.39	6.56	41.2

individuals (chromosomes) that are evolved to converge to an optimum solution. Gradient methods produce a single "best" answer; but they are often trapped in local extremes, which prevent the global optimum from being found, thus completely, missing the true best solution. By contrast, GA's produce groups of solutions, no one of which is necessarily the global optimum, but all of which are "good" solutions. YGO3 generates groups of Yagi designs, all of which are close to optimum antennas, even if not the absolute best one.

YGO3 evolves an initial population of random chromosomes by creating successive generations of chromosomes. The population size is constant from generation to generation, but the individuals comprising the population are genetically altered from one generation to the next using three genetic operators: selection, crossover, and mutation. The selection operator chooses the parent chromosomes that are used to create child chromosomes in the next generation. The crossover operator "mates" the parents to actually create the children. Selection and crossover may be implemented in many different ways; the details of how YGO3 performs these operations are discussed below. The mutation operator makes random changes in the gene values, usually with a low probability, replicating the random genetic mutations that occur in biological evolution.

One of the most important features of a GA is its ability to optimise a population using any desired measure of goodness or fitness. Unlike gradient methods that cannot optimise over discontinuities, GA's easily handle discontinuous functions. The only requirement for a figure-of-merit (FoM) is that it be calculable. A separate computer program called the calculation engine generates the data used to calculate the FoM. YGO3 uses NEC-2D as its calculation engine, but any suitable Yagi modeling program could have been used instead.

In every generation the GA computes an FoM for each of the chromosomes (specific Yagi designs), which are then ranked from best to worst according to the FoM values. GA's often minimise the objective function, but YGO3 maximises the FoM because it seems to make more sense to assign the highest value to the best antenna, not the worst. When a generation has been fully processed, the best antenna design (highest FoM) becomes the first row vector in the generation matrix, and the worst design (lowest FoM) becomes the last row vector.

Generation after generation is created in this way, with the expectation that each successive generation will contain better antenna designs. This expectation rests on a selection process that favors better parent chromosomes which presumably create better children. But, because of its stochastic nature, a GA may not create improved designs in every successive generation; the best FoM value may actually go down. Experience has demonstrated, however, that a well-designed GA will converge to an optimised solution if allowed to run for enough generations with a sufficiently large population size.

Table 5.13 shows the results of a design for a 23 element 2m Yagi, the optimization process can be seen taking place over a series of 4 runs with the gain an front-to-back ratio improving with each successive iteration. The polar

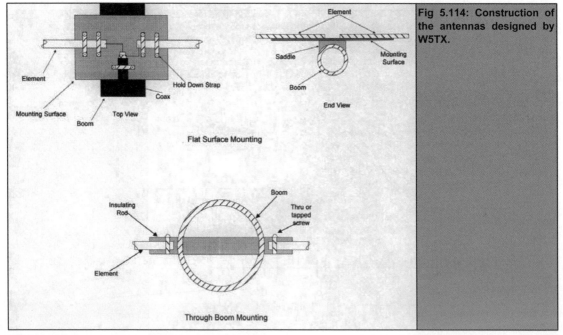

Fig 5.114: Construction of the antennas designed by W5TX.

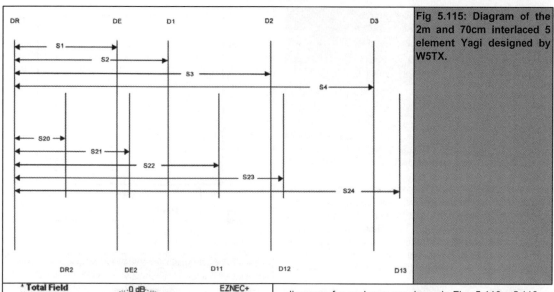

Fig 5.115: Diagram of the 2m and 70cm interlaced 5 element Yagi designed by W5TX.

diagrams for each run are shown in Figs 5.110 – 5.113.

YGO3 can generate optimised Yagi arrays that are not discoverable by any other method. Given the range of competing factors in choosing the right Yagi, genetic algorithms like YGO3 provide tremendous flexibility unavailable in traditional optimization methods. This flexibility comes at the expense of somewhat longer run times and perhaps more complicated set up. But the results are usually well worth the effort, not to mention that experimenting with GA's is fun!

EZNEC

This software falls into the category where an evaluation copy is available [30], this is restricted to 1500 elements which is useful for most amateur use, it is certainly enough to be able to understand how the program works and decide if you need to buy the full version. Bob Hicks, W5TX has done some interesting designs [31] for direct fed VHF Yagis. This means that they are intended to be

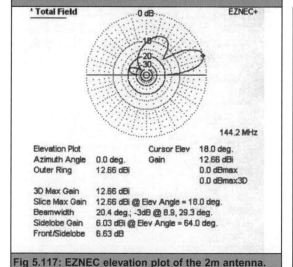

Fig 5.116: EZNEC azimuth plot of the 2m antenna.

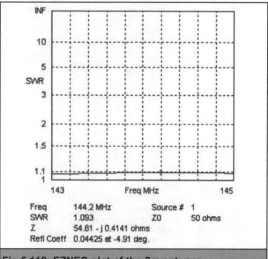

Fig 5.117: EZNEC elevation plot of the 2m antenna.

Fig 5.118: EZNEC plot of the 2m antenna.

Table 5.14: Dimensions for the 2m and 70cm interlaced 5 element Yagi designed by W5TX. The element diameter is 3/16 inch and the dimensions shown are half element lengths.

DR	20.75	S1	10.7
DE	19.76	S2	15.8
D2	15.53	S3	29.1
D3	14.86	S4	34.9
DR2	6.75	S20	5.3
DE2	6.26	S21	12.4
D12	6.03	S22	18.17
D22	6.26	S23	29.8
D32	5.74	S24	39.6

fed directly by 50Ω coax. The antennas are intended for light duty or portable use with the boom made from insulated material e.g. ¾ to 1½ inch PVC. Suggested construction is shown in Fig 5.114. There are 15 designs shown on the web site [31] the most interesting is a 2m and 70cm interlaced 5 element Yagi. It consists of two 5 element beams, one designed for 2m and one designed

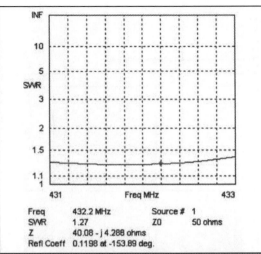

Freq   432.2 MHz   Source # 1
SWR   1.27   Z0   50 ohms
Z   40.08 - j 4.288 ohms
Refl Coeff 0.1198 at -153.89 deg.

Fig 5.121: EZNEC plot of the 2m antenna.

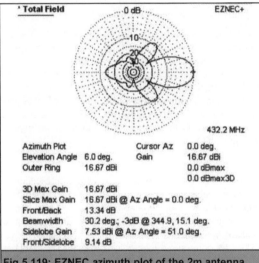

Azimuth Plot		Cursor Az	0.0 deg.
Elevation Angle	6.0 deg.	Gain	16.67 dBi
Outer Ring	16.67 dBi		0.0 dBmax
			0.0 dBmax3D

3D Max Gain	16.67 dBi
Slice Max Gain	16.67 dBi @ Az Angle = 0.0 deg.
Front/Back	13.34 dB
Beamwidth	30.2 deg.; -3dB @ 344.9, 15.1 deg.
Sidelobe Gain	7.53 dBi @ Az Angle = 51.0 deg.
Front/Sidelobe	9.14 dB

Fig 5.119: EZNEC azimuth plot of the 2m antenna.

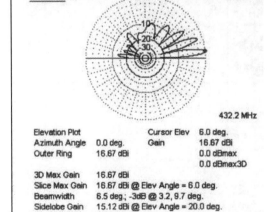

Elevation Plot		Cursor Elev	6.0 deg.
Azimuth Angle	0.0 deg.	Gain	16.67 dBi
Outer Ring	16.67 dBi		0.0 dBmax
			0.0 dBmax3D

3D Max Gain	16.67 dBi
Slice Max Gain	16.67 dBi @ Elev Angle = 6.0 deg.
Beamwidth	6.5 deg.; -3dB @ 3.2, 9.7 deg.
Sidelobe Gain	15.12 dBi @ Elev Angle = 20.0 deg.
Front/Sidelobe	1.54 dB

Fig 5.120: EZNEC elevation plot of the 2m antenna.

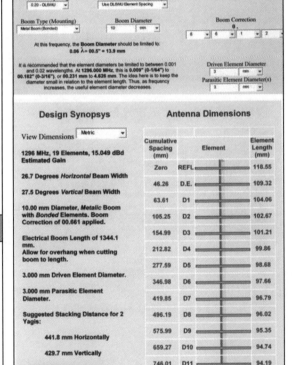

Fig 5.122: Quick mode JavaScript Notebook design of a 23cm 15dBi gain Yagi.

Introduction

The VHF/UHF Yagi Antenna Design page does a good job of calculating the lengths of all the antenna elements but it kind of leaves you flat for actually feeding the antenna. Although it's not really mentioned, the long boom yagis, designed from that page, are intended to use a **Folded Dipole** antenna feed. That is what this page is all about.

The **Folded Dipole** has several useful characteristics. It's easy to build and adjust, its bandwidth is good for over an octave. For example, 50 Mhz to 100 Mhz or 120 Mhz to 240 Mhz. And, its characteristic impedance is a more or less a constant 300 ohms. This doesn't mean that the whole yagi will have that kind of bandwidth. The directors and reflectors respond best for the design frequency, giving you an overall bandwidth of about 7% of the design frequency. So, an antenna designed for 145 MHz should give you an effective bandwidth of about 10 MHz.

Below is a somewhat exaggerated drawing of the basic **Folded Dipole**. But, it's only intention is to show you the configuration you are working with.

The most important dimension is the **Length**. You want to adhere as closely as possible to the calculated length from the VHF/UHF Yagi Antenna Design page.

The second most important dimension would be the element **Diameter**. For these designs, the diameter of the element should be limited to between 0.001 and 0.02 wavelengths. As an example, this would mean that for **2 Meters** you should keep the diameter between `0.081"` `(2.053 mm)` and `1.617"` `(41.068 mm)`. For **70 CM** the diameter should be limited to between `0.027"` `(0.681 mm)` and `00.536"` `(13.627 mm)`.

The **Spacing** between the horizontal sections can vary rather widely. This nicely accomodates do-it-yourselfers, but also give you some latitude for varying boom diameters and mounting methods.

The **Feed Gap** is exactly what it sounds like. This is where you break the loop for attaching the feed. An exact dimension is not necessary, but try to keep the gap as small as practicable. A good rule of thumb would be to keep it no larger than one boom diameter.

Fig 5.123: Details of the folded dipole driven element from the feed design section of the JavaScript Notebook.

The diagram on the right illustrates the assembly of the 1/2 **Wavelength Phasing Section** and **Folded Dipole Feed**. The feedline connects to one side of the **Folded Dipole Feed** section along with one side of the 1/2 **Wavelength Phasing Section**. The 1/2 **Wavelength Phasing Section** exits the plastic box through a rubber grommet and comes back in through another. This end is then connected to the other side of the **Folded Dipole Feed**. The shields tie all of the coax ends are tied together and soldered to a lug inside the box. If the boom is metal, and the screw holding the ground lug creates a physical connection, that's OK. If the boom is not metal, that's OK too.

You have a lot of space to get creative here. The drawings are only a suggested method. For example, if you had a box big enough, you could probably keep everything but the feedline in the box. But that is usually not the case, except for higher frequency antennas. Or, you could use coaxial connectors at the places where the coax enters the box.

In one of the drawings the 1/2 **Wavelength Phasing Section** is shown as a simple U shape, whereas, in the drawing above, it is shown looped at the bottom. Either way is acceptable. For lower frequencies, the 1/2 **Wavelength Phasing Section** may be quite long. Just roll it up into a 6 or 8 inch loop, secure it with electrical tape, and then lash it to the boom. Higher frequency antennas will have shorter 1/2 **Wavelength Phasing Sections** and may not need to be spooled up.

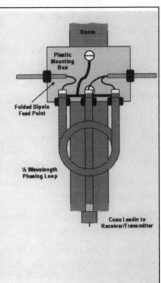

Fig 5.125: Details of the construction of the matching for the 23cm Yagi from the feed design section of the JavaScript Notebook.

cross platform and cross browser compatible, which means that it can be accessed by any computer e.g. Unix, PC or Mac, that has a suitable browser e.g. Internet Explorer, Firefox or Netscape. Choosing the Antenna section and then the VHF/UHF Yagi option takes you to an interactive design program for Yagi antennas. Just fill in the desired parameters and your antenna design is displayed immediately. There are two versions, a normal mode that has a description for each step and a quick mode that just has the parameters that are required for the design process. An example of the quick mode used to design a 23cm 15dB gain antenna is shown in Fig 5.122. The web site also contains a program to design the feed for the antenna, the design use a folded dipole driven element as shown in Fig 5.123. This can be matched to a 50Ω coaxial feed as shown in Figs 5.124 and 5.125.

for 70cm. The 70cm beam driven element is coupled to the 2m driven element by close spacing, only one feeder is required. A diagram of the antenna is shown in Fig 5.115 with the dimensions shown in Table 5.14. The performance predicted by EZNEC is shown in Figs 5.116 to 5.121

JavaScript Notebook

This is a very useful collection of programs for many radio related calculations. It is accessed by a normal Internet browser by going to Martin E Meserve's, (K7MEM) web page [32]. Martin has designed the web site so that it is

References

[1] Antennas, J D Kraus, 2nd edn, McGraw-Hill, 1988, pp 70–73.

[2] The ARRL Handbook for the Radio Amateur, any edition after 1986, antennas section.

[3] Antennas, J D Kraus, 2nd edn, McGraw-Hill, 1988, Chapter 4.

[4] Antenna Theory, Analysis and Design, Constantine A Balanis, Harper and Row, 1982, pp 204–243.

[5] "In Practice – Finding coax impedance", I White, G3SEK, RadCom February 1995, pp 40 - 41.

[6] "In Practice – Precise coax lengths", I White, G3SEK, Radio Communication July 1995, pp 60–61.

[7] Electronic Applications of the Smith Chart, Phillip H Smith, McGraw-Hill, 1969.

Frequency (MHz)	Type	Velocity Factor	Impedance
□	RG-59	.66	75 Ohm
□	RG-59/U Foam	.79	75 Ohm
□	RG-11/U	.66	75 Ohm
□	RG-11/U Foam	.80	75 Ohm
□	RG-6	.75	75 Ohm
☑	RG-58	.66	50 Ohm
□	RG-8	.66	50 Ohm
□	RG-8x	.78	50 Ohm
□	RG-8/U Foam	.80	50 Ohm
□	RG-213	.66	50 Ohm

Operating Frequency = 1296 M
Cable Type = RG-58
Velocity Factor = 0.66

1/2 Wavelength
Phasing Section (L)
0' 3' (7.6 CM)

Length Measured Over the Shielded Area

Fig 5.124: Details of the matching for the 23cm Yagi from the feed design section of the JavaScript Notebook.

[8] VHF Line Techniques, C S Gledhill, Edward Arnold Publishers, 1960.

[9] "The transmission line explained", Clive Smith, G4FZH, RadCom April 1994, pp 54 - 57, 61.

[10] Yagi Antenna Design, P Viezbickie, National Bureau of Standards Technical Note 688, 1976.

[11] Yagi Antenna Design, J L Lawson, ARRL, 1986.

[12] "Yagi antennas – principle of operation and optimum design criteria"?, G Hoch, DL6WU, VHF Communications 3/1977.

[13] "More gain from Yagi antennas", G Hoch, DL6WU, VHF Communications 4/1977.

[14] "Extremely long Yagi antennas", G Hoch, DL6WU, VHF Communications 1/1982.

[15] "Stub filters revisited", J Regnault, G4SWX, RadCom November 1994, pp 46 - 48.

[16] "Diplexers for the VHF bands", J Regnault, G4SWX, RadCom March 1996, pp63, 65 and April 1996, pp 61 - 63.

[17] "Wind loading", D J Reynolds, G3ZPF, RadCom April 1988, pp 252 - 255 and May 1988, pp 340 - 341.

[18] "A quadruple quad antenna – an efficient portable antenna for 2 metres"?, M Ragaller, DL6DW, VHF Communications 2/1971, pp 82 - 84.

[19] The Antenna Experimenter's Guide, P Dodd, G3LDO, 2nd edn, RSGB, 1996.

[20] "Antenna modelling on a PC", I White, G3SEK, RadCom August 1993, pp 39 - 41.

[21] "Antenna modelling with ELNEC", J Bazley, G3HCT, Radio Communication August 1993, pp 41 - 42.

[22] "The VHF log-periodic Yagi", M Gibbings, G3FDW, RadCom July 1994, pp 13 - 17.

[23] "Helical antennas for 435MHz", J Miller, G3RUH, Electronics and Wireless World June 1985, pp 43 - 46.

[24] "Slim Jim antenna", F C Judd, G2BCX, Practical Wireless April 1978, pp 899 - 901.

[25] "Resonant quadrifilar helix design", C C Kilgus, Microwave Journal, Vol 13 - 12, December 1970, pp 49 - 54.

[26] "Shaped-conical radiation pattern performance of the backfire quadrifilar helix"?, C C Kilgus, IEEE Trans Antennas and Propagation May 1975, pp 392 - 397.

[27] The Unofficial Numerical Electromagnetic (NEC) Archive, maintained by Raymond Anderson, www.nic.funet.fi/pub/ham/antenna/NEC/swindex.html

[28] YGO3, Yagi Genetic Optimizer, Version. 3, can be downloaded from: ftp://ftp.qsl.net/pub/wb6tpu/NEC/ygo3inst.exe or www.vhfcomm.co.uk/download.htm

[29] Designing Long Yagis with YGO3, Richard A For-mato, WW1RF, VHF Communications Magazine, 2001/3, pp 139 - 153

[30] EZNEC, http://www.eznec.com/

[31] Bob Hicks, W5TX web site, http://www.w5tx.com/

[32] Martin Meserve, K7MEM, JavaScript Notebook, http://www.w5tx.com/

Chapter 6

EMC

In this chapter :

- Good radio housekeeping
- Breakthrough of amateur transmissions
- Filters for radio and TV receivers
- Spurious signals from an amateur transmitter
- Interference to amateur reception
- Dealing with neighbours

Electromagnetic compatibility is the desirable situation where nearby electronic equipment is not affected by amateur transmissions and does not unduly affect amateur reception. Further information on EMC for radio amateurs is given in references [1] and [2]. The RSGB has a very active EMC committee who have produced several very useful leaflets on EMC for the radio amateur, a list of these is shown in Table 6.1, they can be downloaded from [17]

This chapter also deals with interference to amateur reception by non-radio equipment, particularly a computer in the shack.

If amateur transmissions affect a neighbour's TV or other electronic equipment, there are three possible causes:

- The affected equipment has insufficient immunity to the fundamental frequency of the transmitter.
- A harmonic or other unwanted emission from the amateur transmitter is not sufficiently well suppressed.
- A non-linear device somewhere else is receiving the amateur signal and re-radiating a harmonic.

The most common reason is the first one, while the second one is less likely and the last one is rare. If the affected equipment is a TV, video recorder or some sort of radio receiver then it is important to establish whether the cause is the first or second. If the amateur transmitter is producing an unwanted signal then adding a filter at the TV cannot remove it! Conversely, if a TV or other affected equipment has insufficient immunity to the fundamental frequency of the transmitter then filtering at the transmitter cannot solve the problem! If the affected equipment is an audio amplifier, wired telephone or other equipment that is not intended to receive radio signals at all, then clearly the problem is not due to harmonics.

Even if harmonics etc. are not causing a problem, it is wise to ensure that they are adequately suppressed in case of a visit from the Radiocommunications Agency. It is also important to realise that a VHF or UHF amateur station may be able to generate very high field strengths nearby.

Table 6.1: List of leaflets available from The RSGB on EMC.

No.	Description
01	Radio Transmitters and Domestic Electronic Equipment, general EMC information sheet about breakthrough on TV, radio, hi-fi etc.
02	Radio Transmitters and Home Security Systems, an informative sheet for neighbours or alarm installers about RF triggering of intruder alarms.
03	Dealing with alarm EMC problems, advice to members on how to deal with RF triggering of an intruder alarm.
04	Locating sources of interference to amateur radio reception, advice on how to identify and find sources of RFI in amateur bands.
05	Radio Transmitters and Telephones, all about RF breakthrough on telephones.
06	Automotive EMC for Radio Amateurs, advice on installation of mobile amateur radio equipment in vehicles.
07	Protective Multiple Earthing (PME), advice to those who have their electricity supply wired on the PME system.
08	TV Distribution Amplifiers, for neighbours and TV aerial installers about solving breakthrough on home TV distribution amplifiers.
09	Handling In-bound Interference.
10	Avoiding Interference to Nearby Electronic Equipment.
11	The Ofcom Procedure for the Measurement of the Field Strength of Amateur Stations.
12	Part P of the Building Regulations for England and Wales and what it means for Radio Amateurs.

Good radio housekeeping

The Schedule of the Terms, Provisions and Limitations Booklet BR68, which accompanies the full UK Amateur Licence or available from Ofcomm [11], lists a maximum output power level of 26dBW (400W) on most bands but this is subject to certain other conditions such as Note (1) which states:

"In densely populated areas sufficient separation of amateur equipment from surrounding transmitters, receivers and electronic equipment may not be possible to permit the amateur to operate with high power without the high probability of causing interference."

The above statement emphasises the need to plan with EMC in mind where an amateur station is to be installed in a typical urban environment in close proximity to neighbours. The RF from the transmitter should be kept under reasonable control, with the highest possible percentage going where it is wanted (in the direction of the distant station) and as little as possible going into the local environment. This is sometimes known as good radio housekeeping. Fortunately, installations designed to achieve this are also likely to minimise the pick up of locally generated interference.

Antennas

It is always good practice to erect any antenna as far from houses as possible, and as high as practical, subject to planning constraints. If possible, VHF/UHF beams should be located so that most of the power is beamed over the rooftops towards the horizon rather than towards neighbouring buildings or TV antennas. A mast away from the house (and neighbouring houses) is preferable subject to considerations of feeder loss.

Coaxial feeder should be well screened with good quality woven braid to minimise RF leakage into and out of the cable. When a balanced antenna is fed by coaxial cable, a balun should be used to minimise RF radiation from the braid of the cable. Passing the cable through some large ferrite beads or clip on ferrite chokes near the antenna can reduce any remaining RF currents on the braid of the cable.

Earths

Most VHF or UHF antenna systems do not require an RF earth for EMC reasons but don't forget the need for lightning protection. It should also be borne in mind that when antennas are mounted on an earthed tower, the braid of the coaxial feeder entering the radio shack is likely to be earthed via the antenna to the tower. In such cases, it is important to consider PME (protective multiple earthing) – see the warning in Table 6.2.

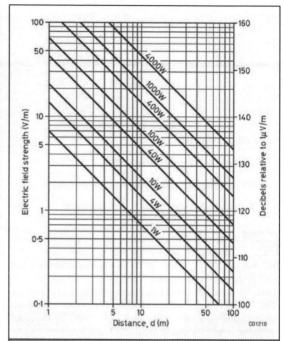

Fig 6.1: Field strength in the direction of maximum radiation from an antenna from 1W to 4KW ERP into free space.

Field strengths

Note (1) in the BR68 booklet mentions excessive field strength from an amateur station. It is therefore useful to be able to calculate the electric field strength generated near a transmitting antenna. The electric or E field strength at a certain distance is given by:

$$E = \frac{\sqrt{49.15 P_d}}{d}$$

This assumes far field "free space" conditions where E is the electric field strength in volts/metre, d is the distance from the antenna in metres and P_d is the effective radiated power. It should be noted that P_d is ERP, i.e. the input power to the antenna multiplied by the gain of the antenna relative to a dipole, not an isotropic radiator. Fig 6.1 shows the field strength generated by an antenna radiating between 1W and 4KW ERP at distances between 1m and 100m. For example, 100W (20dBW) into an antenna with a gain of 10dBd gives an ERP of 30dBW or 1KW. At a distance of 10m, this would produce a field strength of 22V/m in the direction of maximum radiation. This example shows that a high power VHF/UHF amateur station can easily generate a field strength that is higher than nearby electronic equipment can reasonably be expected to withstand. Field strength is also mentioned in leaflet RA234 (see below). It may therefore be necessary to avoid using maximum power in certain directions in order to avoid generating excessive field strengths in neighbours' premises. In any case, it is good practice to use only as much power as necessary for a contact. In the case of local contacts, the power necessary may only be

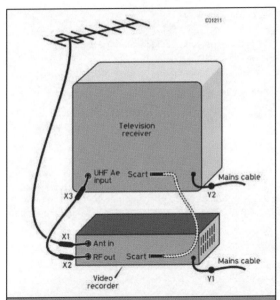

Fig 6.2: Fitting filters to a TV with a video recorder.

"1.1.2.3 Radio equipment used by radio amateurs is excluded unless the equipment is available commercially (Article 1.2(c) of the EMC Directive). This exclusion has been included because of the specific nature of the activities of radio amateurs. Radio amateurs are persons carrying out experimental activities within the field of radio communications, according to the definitions of the ITU (International Telecommunication Union) Radio Regulations. Amateur radio equipment which is commercially available comes within the scope of the R&TTE Directive. Commercial equipment which is modified by and for the use of radio amateurs and kits of components to be assembled by radio amateurs are not regarded as commercially available equipment, and therefore are outside the scope of the EMC and R&TTE Directives."

I understand this to mean that any home constructed equipment does not need to pass the appropriate tests to be used for amateur radio. This does not absolve us from the responsibility of making every reasonable effort to ensure that any such equipment is free from EMC problems. This is also covered by The Radiocommunications Agency leaflet RA234 discussed later.

Breakthrough of amateur transmissions

Television and video

If breakthrough occurs with a UHF TV set connected directly to an antenna, a suitable high pass filter should be plugged in at the TV antenna socket. If filtering the antenna input cannot cure the problem, it is possible that winding the mains cable through a ferrite core close to the TV set may help. At VHF, however, direct pick up in the actual TV set may occur and cannot be cured by external filtering. Possible causes include pick up in the vision IF amplifier circuitry or pick up in the internal loudspeaker cable. In the case of TV sets with external speakers, pick up in loudspeaker cables can be tackled in the same way as for audio systems (see below).

If breakthrough occurs when a TV is connected to a video recorder as in Fig 6.2, the first thing to establish is whether the TV set alone is immune. The addition of a video recorder makes breakthrough more likely because most video recorders contain a VHF/UHF amplifier with a bandwidth of typically 40 - 860MHz. A high pass filter should be fitted at X1 and another may be required at X2 or X3. In some cases, winding the mains cable through a ferrite core at Y1 or Y2 may help. If the TV and video recorder both have a SCART connector, the use of a SCART cable (shown dotted) provides a direct "baseband" audio and video connection on playback which bypasses the UHF modulator in the video recorder and the tuner and IF stages in the TV. This generally improves picture quality on video playback and also reduces the possibility of RF breakthrough. If the tuner or IF stages in the TV are susceptible to breakthrough but the video recorder is immune, it is possible to receive off air UHF signals without using the tuner and IF stages in the TV. The channel tuned on the video recorder can be viewed on the TV via the SCART connection. The only exception

one watt or less.

RF immunity standards

The UK EMC Regulations (Statutory Instrument 1992 No 2372) came into force on 1 January 1996. Almost all electronic equipment manufactured since that date must meet certain requirements for RF immunity and emissions and must also carry the CE mark to indicate compliance with all applicable European Directives.

This was a major step forward in EMC, as previously there was no requirement for consumer electronic equipment to meet any immunity standard in the UK. Nevertheless, the standards only set a basic level of immunity compared to the possible field strengths from an amateur station. In some cases it is argued that if immunity problems arise when an amateur station generates field strengths in excess of the levels specified in the relevant immunity standard, the amateur should take steps to reduce the field strength. In such cases, it is worth noting the standard, IEC 1000-2-5, Electromagnetic Compatibility *(EMC) – Part 2: Environment – Section 5: Classification of Electromagnetic Environments*. This lists various sources of RF fields (and other types of electromagnetic phenomena) that may exist in various classes of location including residential (urban), residential (rural), commercial etc. In most of these environment classes including residential (urban), the standard states that field strengths of up to 10V/m may be encountered in locations which are at least 20m from the nearest amateur radio transmitter.

Selected information about the RF immunity requirements of some current CENELEC harmonised European immunity standards are shown in Table 6.3. At the time of writing, there is a new standard in its draft stage called "EMC Directive 2004/108/EC", this is due to be ratified soon and should come into force in 2007. One interesting paragraph in the draft 2004/108/EC states:

Table 6.3: Some CENELEC harmonised European immunity standards.

EN 55014-2 : 2001 EMC – immunity requirements for household appliances, tools and similar apparatus

This standard specifies immunity requirements that are generally less demanding than the Generic Standard.

EN 55020 : 2007 Immunity of broadcast receivers and associated equipment

This is applicable to television broadcast receivers, sound broadcast receivers and associated equipment such as audio systems. Radio and TV equipment without a connection for an external antenna or without a mains power connection is not required to meet this standard.

The standard specifies various tests for immunity to radiated and conducted signals. For UHF TV receivers, VHF Band II (87.5–108MHz) sound broadcast receivers and audio equipment, the radiated immunity is tested up to 150MHz at a field strength of 125dB(μV/m) (1.78V/m) (carrier) with 80% AM at 1kHz. The modulated signal therefore has a peak envelope voltage (PEV) of 3.2V/m. There are some exclusion bands around IF frequencies and the tuned frequency. Long wave, medium wave and short wave sound broadcast receivers are only tested for immunity to common mode conducted currents on the antenna terminals (if any) at 26 - 30MHz.

EN 55024-1 : 1998 Information technology equipment – immunity characteristics – Limits and methods of measurement

Although the title refers to information technology equipment, this standard also applies to Telecommunications Terminal Equipment (TTE) such as telephones. EN 50082-1 : 1992 EMC Generic Immunity Standard – Part 1; residential, commercial and light industry

The Generic Standard EN 50082-1 : 1996 can be applied if no product specific standard exists although it may not be appropriate for all cases. This is a "watered down" version of the 1990 draft, prEN 50082-1. The 1992 edition referenced the IEC 801-3 standard for immunity to radiated fields but only tests from 27 - 500MHz at 3V/m with an *unmodulated* carrier. Immunity tests below 27MHz are not required and neither are tests for immunity to RF signals picked up on cables. The 1996 edition references the EN 61000 (IEC 1000) series of standards and specifies tests that are broadly similar to the 1990 draft. These include conducted immunity tests on interconnecting cables and mains cables with a 3V signal from 0.15 - 80MHz and radiated immunity tests at 3V/m from 80 - 1000MHz. In each case, a 3V or 3V/m carrier is modulated with 80% AM at 1kHz. The PEV (peak envelope voltage) on modulation peaks is therefore 1.8 times higher at 5.4V or 5.4V/m. There is also a new test at 900MHz with 200Hz pulse modulation to simulate GSM cellular telephones.

Section 3 of prEN 50082-1 : 1996 includes the following statements:

"The immunity requirements have been selected so as to ensure an adequate level of immunity for apparatus at the locations described. The levels do not however cover extreme cases which may occur in any location but with an extremely low probability of occurrence."

"In special cases, situations will arise when the level of disturbance may exceed the levels specified in this standard; for example, a hand held transmitter used in close proximity to an apparatus. In these instances special mitigation measures may have to be applied."

ETSI EN 301 489-1:2000 EMC Standard for Short Range Devices

This is an ETSI (European Telecommunications Standards Institute) standard for short range radio devices which includes specifications for RF immunity. Such devices include baby alarms, cordless household alarm systems etc. Immunity to radiated fields is not tested at 3V/m with 80% AM except within an exclusion band of ±5% of the receive frequency as performance within this range is considered to be a 'spectrum utilisation parameter' rather than an 'EMC parameter'. Narrow band spurious responses (such as image frequencies) can be declared outside the ±5% exclusion band.

to this is when recording one channel while watching another.

Satellite TV

In a satellite television receiving system, the LNB (low noise block converter) in the dish is unlikely to be affected by amateur signals directly, except on the 10GHz amateur band. The output of the LNB is at the first intermediate frequency covering 950 - 1750MHz or 950 - 2050MHz so there is a possibility of 23cm amateur signals causing IF breakthrough.

Fortunately, the cable between the LNB and the indoor receiver unit is normally quite well screened with foil and braid which minimises the possibility of IF breakthrough. Nevertheless, common mode signals can be picked up on the braid of the cable to the dish that may require a common mode ferrite choke.

The indoor satellite receiver unit normally contains a broadband amplifier and UHF modulator for use with UHF connections as shown in Fig 6.3. Such a set up may suffer breakthrough of amateur signals due to the cascaded broadband amplifiers in the satellite receiver and video

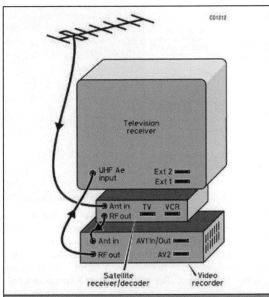

Fig 6.3: TV, satellite receiver and video recorder with UHF connections only.

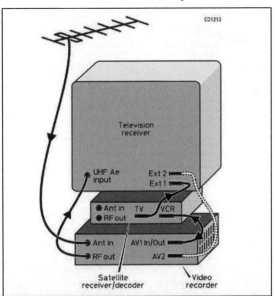

Fig 6.4: TV, satellite receiver and video recorder with SCART connections.

recorder. Fig 6.4 shows a possible set up that should reduce the chance of RF breakthrough while providing improved picture quality for satellite reception and video playback. With some satellite receivers, video playback via the SCART lead can pass through the satellite receiver to the TV but, if this is not possible, a third SCART cable (shown dotted) is required for video playback.

TV masthead preamplifiers

In a fringe area or where a long feeder cable is necessary, a TV masthead preamplifier can give a significant improvement in reception. Nevertheless, masthead preamplifiers are sometimes used inappropriately in areas of adequate reception in an attempt to compensate for a low gain antenna and/ or poor quality feeder cable. The use of a masthead preamplifier increases the chances of breakthrough of out-of-band signals from amateur transmitters or other radio transmitters nearby. Older preamplifiers may be unscreened and have broad bandwidth that can lead to breakthrough problems on any VHF/UHF amateur band. If strong amateur signals are picked up by the TV antenna and cause breakthrough, a filter is required at the input to the TV antenna but unfortunately, this is not easy to install with a masthead preamplifier! In such cases, the only solution may be to install a new preamplifier which is CE marked, adequately screened and covers UHF only.

TV distribution amplifiers

Indoor or loft mounted TV distribution amplifiers are available with two, three, four or more outputs. If any of the amplifier outputs are not used, these should be terminated with a 75Ω load otherwise the gain of the amplifier is increased. Distribution amplifiers are available in two types: broadband and UHF only. The broadband type typically cover 40 - 860MHz. These can distribute 88

- 108MHz Band 2 FM broadcast and Band 4/5 UHF TV signals simultaneously. In installations where the Band 2 capability is not used, a UHF high pass filter may be required at the input to the amplifier. If UHF TV and Band 2 antennas are both connected, a combiner is required and any UHF high pass filter must be fitted at the UHF input to the combiner. The Band 2 antenna may pick up 50, 70 or 144MHz amateur signals, in which case an 88 - 108MHz bandpass filter is required at the VHF input to the combiner. Amplifiers that are not CE Marked in unscreened cases may also be susceptible to picking up signals via the mains cable or directly in the amplifier itself. Such effects may be reduced by fitting the amplifier in a screened box grounded to the coaxial braid or by fitting a ferrite ring to the mains cable.

Fig 6.5 shows a "worst case" configuration from the EMC point of view. This configuration allows multiple TV sets to select the currently tuned satellite channel, video playback or any terrestrial channel. The same broadband amplifier and output cables also distribute band 2 FM signals. With three wideband amplifiers cascaded, the probability of breakthrough is clearly increased. To solve a problem with this type of set up, it is advisable to start with the satellite receiver feeding the TV alone and to cure any breakthrough problem. This may require a high pass filter at the input to the satellite receiver. The video recorder should then be connected, followed by the distribution amplifier alone. Finally, the combiner and Band 2 FM antenna should be added. It may be necessary to fit additional filters at the input to the video recorder or distribution amplifier and an attenuator may also be required to reduce the total gain.

Cable TV

The introduction of cable television (CATV) systems may reduce TVI problems because neighbours who subscribe

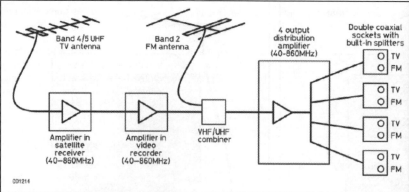

Fig 6.5: "Worst case" configuration with satellite receiver, video recorder and TV/FM distribution amplifier.

to the cable system no longer need to use their UHF TV antenna. There are, however, some potential EMC problems due to signals leaking into and out of CATV systems (known to cable TV companies as ingress and egress respectively). Many systems use harmonically related vision carriers on multiples of 8MHz, for example from 128 to 560MHz or higher with an FM sound carrier 6MHz above each vision carrier. Some systems use a vision carrier at 432MHz with sound on 438MHz. Although some UK cable TV operators avoid the use of 144MHz as a vision carrier, others use it for a leakage detection test signal or for programmes. This may lead to 144MHz breakthrough problems even with low power.

For cable TV systems, the permitted levels of radiated emissions are defined in the Radiocommunications Agency standard MPT 1510. This standard prohibits the use of certain frequencies and specifies low levels of leakage in certain bands including 50 - 54MHz, 144 - 146MHz and 432 - 440MHz [8]. It is anticipated that this standard will eventually be withdrawn and replaced by a harmonised European standard.

Many cable companies use fibre optic distribution systems that reduce the possibilities of ingress and egress but there are still points in the system where this can happen.

Filters for radio and TV receivers

The details below relate to filters for reducing breakthrough of 6m, 4m, 2m and 70cm amateur band signals. For details of filter performance on the HF bands and a filter which also rejects the 23cm band, see Appendix 3 of reference [1] or [2]. All the filters listed below are for use in the antenna input of TV and FM radio receivers and allow UHF TV signals to pass through. As with any filter, there is a small loss in the pass band. Only the HPF2 allows both VHF/FM broadcast radio (Band 2, 88 - 108MHz) and UHF TV (Bands 4/5) to pass through.

Unwanted pick up of amateur signals by a UHF TV antenna system can occur in two different ways. The first is where the TV antenna itself picks up VHF or UHF amateur signals that pass along the inner of the coaxial cable and return via the braid in the normal way. This is most likely to occur at 432MHz where a UHF TV antenna still has a moderate gain but it can still be a problem at 144MHz. Pick up by the UHF TV antenna itself tends to be

less significant on 70 and 50MHz, however. The second type of pick up is where the whole TV antenna with its down lead acts as a receiving antenna, resulting in signals which are on the braid and inner together relative to earth. If such signals cause breakthrough, some sort of "braid breaker" is required. The RSGB stocks a range of EMC filters [15]. There are four types, the transformer type such as the BB1 or HPFS, the capacitive type such as the HPF1, the resonant type such as the TNF range and the ferrite common mode choke:

HPF1 high pass filter and braid breaker

- Pass band: UHF TV.

- Stop band: All bands up to and including 144MHz (good performance on 50 and 70MHz, some effect on 144MHz).

- Braid breaking: Capacitive braid breaking at HF, some effect on 50MHz but little effect on 70 and 144MHz.

- Remarks: The HPF1 is not stocked separately by RSGB but is included in the RFK1 filter kit (see below).

HPF2 High pass filter (RSGB order code Filter 2)

- Pass band: FM radio broadcast (88 - 108MHz) up to UHF TV.

- Stop band: All HF bands plus limited effect at 50MHz.

- Braid breaking: None.

HPF6 high pass filter (RSGB order code Filter 8)

- Pass band: UHF TV.

- Stop band: All bands up to and including 430–440MHz.

- Braid breaking: None.

- Remarks: This high performance six-section filter has a very sharp cut off below 470MHz and is primarily intended for rejecting the 430 - 440MHz amateur band. It also offers a high degree of rejection at 144MHz and below.

BB1 braid breaker (RSGB order code Filter 1)

- Pass band: All VHF/UHF amateur bands plus FM Band 2 (88 - 108MHz), and UHF TV.

- Stop band: The BB1 does not give any rejection of any VHF/ UHF amateur band as it is a "braid breaker" rather than a filter.

- Braid breaking: A 1:1 transformer type braid breaker. Moderately effective on 50 and 70MHz, limited effect on 144MHz.

- Remarks: A BB1 on its own is only likely to be useful where the pick up is primarily on the braid of the coaxial cable. It can be cascaded with other filters such as HPF2 or HPF6 that do not have any braid breaking action, although this increases the total pass band loss.

HPFS high pass filter (special) (RSGB order code Filter 3)

- Pass band: UHF TV.

- Stop band: All bands up to and including 144MHz.

- Braid breaking: Includes 1:1 transformer type braid breaker (see BB1 above).

- Remarks: The HPFS is a BB1 combined with a high pass filter. Due to the relatively high loss in the pass band, it is not suitable for areas where the TV signal strength is low.

RBF1/70cms notch filter (RSGB order code Filter 5)

- Pass band: UHF TV

- Stop band: 430–440MHz.

- Braid breaking: None.

- Remarks: The RBF1/70cms is pre-tuned to reject 435MHz although the HPF6 is more effective on the 430 - 440MHz band. The RBF1/70cms also has a high pass action with some rejection at 70MHz and below.

TNF2 tuned notch filter range (VHF types)

- There are three filters available for the VHF bands: TNF2/145, Filter 4, notch tuned to 145MHz; TNF2/70, Filter 7, notch tuned to 70MHz and TNF2/50, Filter 6, notch tuned to 50MHz

- Pass band: UHF TV.

- Stop band: Only the specified band.

- Braid breaking: Only on the specified band.

- Remarks: These filters are designed to provide rejection of one particular amateur band. They have a parallel LC notch (band stop) filter in series with the inner conductor and with the braid. The manufacturers state that these notch filters are unsuitable for use with some TV distribution amplifiers.

Ferrite rings and cores

Unwanted breakthrough of RF signals into electronic equipment can occur in two ways. RF signals may be picked up directly inside the affected equipment or they may be conducted in via external cables such as loudspeaker cables, antenna cables and mains cables. If the pick up is on cables, it can often be reduced or eliminated by winding the affected cable onto a suitable ferrite core. This forms a "common mode choke" which presents a high impedance to unwanted RF signals without affecting the wanted signals. A common mode choke can also be used as a "braid breaker" for a TV or FM radio coaxial antenna cable. Compared to other types of braid breaker, it has the advantage that it introduces little or no loss to the wanted signal and maintains the integrity of the braid of the coaxial cable.

For the best chance of success, it is important to use a suitable grade of ferrite and a suitable number of turns in order to achieve the highest possible impedance at the frequencies of interest. Fair Rite Corporation in The USA makes ferrite rings in type 43 material, these are available from The RSGB. The inside diameter is 22.85mm (0.9in) and the width is 12.7mm (0.5in). They are equivalent to FT140-43. These rings give good results at VHF whereas some other grades of ferrite are poor at these frequencies.

At 50 or 70MHz, an impedance of 3kΩ or more can be obtained using 12 turns on two Fair Rite grade 43 ring cores wound separately, although in many cases one ring is sufficient. At 144MHz, six turns are recommended on a ring core. Further details of the characteristics of various ferrite rings are given in reference [3]. Stray capacitance between the ends of the winding core is critical at VHF and, in the case of a ring core, this should be minimised by keeping the ends of the winding separated and securing them to the core with cable ties. If the cable is very thick, or has connectors which cannot easily be removed or if it is not long enough, the best solution is usually to make up a short extension lead by winding a length of the thinnest suitable cable through a ferrite core and then fitting suitable connectors. This also has the advantage that it simply plugs in which is much more satisfactory when dealing with neighbours' equipment.

Normal TV coaxial cable has a minimum bending radius of typically 26mm so it should not be wound tightly through a ferrite ring otherwise it may collapse internally and short circuit. Instead, a one metre length of miniature 75Ω coaxial cable can be wound onto a ring core or a clip on core and fitted with coaxial connectors. Suitable cable is available from Maplin Electronics [12] (Stock No XR88V). To ensure that the cable grip in the coaxial plug grips reliably, sleeving or PVC tape should be fitted to the end of the cable to increase its outside diameter to 5 - 6mm.

Various types of clip on core are available but the type with 'U' shaped cores is not particularly effective unless four pairs of 'U' cores are stacked together. For best results, the core aperture should have a length that is two or three times its diameter. The split bead type of clip on ferrite core is available from several sources including Maplin Electronics [12] (BZ34M), Farnell Components [13] (535-904) or RS Components [14] (779-813 or 779-863). With such cores, three turns are recommended for all VHF bands.

Audio systems

A common cause of RF breakthrough in audio systems is RF being picked up in the loudspeaker cables and fed into the power amplifier where it is detected and comes out again as audio. A symptom of this effect is that turning the volume down does not reduce the breakthrough but it disappears if the speakers are unplugged and headphones are used. Fitting suitable ferrite ring cores or clip on chokes to the loudspeaker cables close to the outputs from the amplifier can often reduce this effect. RF may also get in to the amplifier inputs, in which case the breakthrough is affected by the setting of the volume control and may affect only one source such as cassette. In hi-fi systems composed of separate units, a plug in filter may be required for the appropriate audio input.

Telephones

There are large variations in RF immunity between different models of wired telephone. In many cases, breakthrough at VHF is caused by direct pick up in the telephone itself or in the handset cable so that it cannot be cured by means of a line filter. In any case, at the time of writing, telephone line filters that are available in the UK are not suitable for VHF use. For example, the BT 'Freelance' RFI filter LJU 10/14A and the BT80A/RF2 filtered junction box contain chokes with a self resonant frequency of around 1.3MHz for filtering medium wave broadcast signals and are little use at VHF.

As telephones used on the UK public telephone system should be approved for use on the system, they should not be modified to improve RF immunity and neither should home constructed telephone line filters be used. There is, however, no objection to winding the cable of the telephone through a ferrite core that may reduce RF breakthrough if this is caused by common mode RF signals on the cable. In the case of answering machines, fax machines or modems, a ferrite ring may also be required on the power supply cable or other cables.

Low power devices

Various low power devices, also known as short range devices (SRDs) are exempt from UK licensing provided they are UK type approved. Some devices such as vehicle radio keys or baby alarms operate on frequencies in or near amateur bands and can be susceptible to break-through.

Vehicle keys

Most radio controlled car alarms and immobilisers made since mid 1994 operate on a harmonised European frequency of 433.92MHz which is allocated to them on a secondary unprotected basis. Some cars contain superhet receivers with local oscillators that radiate a detectable signal at around 433.275 - 433.475MHz. These receivers use an IF centre frequency of approximately 500kHz and earlier types have no image rejection so they can be blocked by UK 70cm repeater output frequencies. Some types have a SAW RF bandpass filter to provide some image rejection.

Another type of receiver is the super-regenerative. Some types may have a SAW stabilised oscillator or SAW bandpass filter but those without either have a -6dB bandwidth of typically 6MHz.

In some systems, the radio key only controls central locking whereas in other systems, it also operates the immobiliser. If an amateur receives a complaint about blocking of vehicle radio keys by 70cm transmissions, the first thing to find out is whether there is an alternative way of disarming the immobiliser, for example by entering a code number manually. If there is no alternative to the radio key then it could be argued that the designers of such a system have used an unprotected frequency allocation for an unsuitable purpose.

Baby alarms

Devices that are UK approved to MPT 1336 are allowed up to 10mW ERP from 49.82 - 49.98MHz although many have an ERP of 1mW or less. This frequency allocation is used for wireless baby alarms, licence exempt walkie-talkies and cordless headphones. The receivers used in these low cost devices may have poor rejection of signals in the 50MHz amateur band, and in some cases only a few watts on 50MHz can cause breakthrough up to 100m away [4]. Some baby alarms have a switch to select one of two frequencies but this is unlikely to make much difference to breakthrough from 50MHz amateur signals. A few models have sockets to allow a cable to be connected between the units.

Users of wireless baby alarms should be aware that they are using an unprotected radio service. Models that are also sold in the USA include an FCC statement in the instructions stating that the device must accept any interference received, including interference that may cause undesired operation. The instructions for CE marked baby alarms may include a statement about possible interference from a nearby transmitter.

Intruder alarms and security lights

If RF triggering of a neighbour's intruder alarm system occurs, the radio amateur is in a strong position techni-cally, particularly if the alarm installation is claimed to meet BS4737 which refers to the "environmental condi-tions" at the protected premises. As these conditions include "electrical interference", a system that complies with BS4737 should be immune to radio signals from licensed transmitters nearby.

The most likely cause of RF triggering of an intruder alarm is insufficient immunity of PIR (passive infra red) sensors [5]. These use high gain operational amplifier circuits with DC bias conditions that may shift slightly when an RF carrier is keyed on or off. Most types use some form of pulse counting and can be set to count two, three or more pulse edges within about 5 - 10 seconds before sounding the alarm. This also provides some degree of immunity to RF triggering by an FM voice transmission but if the basic RF immunity is insufficient, amateur SSB, CW or packet transmissions will soon exceed the pulse count and trigger the alarm.

It is not advisable to attempt any modifications to PIR

sensors in a neighbour's intruder alarm and in any case, improving immunity at VHF may require changes to the PCB layout. Fitting filters or ferrite rings to the cables is unlikely to give a significant improvement in immunity so in most cases it will be necessary to replace the PIR sensors with a more immune type. If the make and model of the PIR sensor can be identified, it is worth approaching the manufacturer or importer to see whether they have a more immune model that they may be prepared to supply in exchange for the existing PIRs. Even if new PIRs have to be purchased, these need not be expensive because some low cost types are available with high RF immunity. Unless the system is a DIY installation, the replacement normally needs to be carried out by the installer, possibly under a maintenance contract.

PIR sensors used in security lights work on a similar principle to intruder alarm PIRs but generally have lower RF immunity and no pulse counting. In most types, the DC power supply to the electronic circuitry is not isolated from the mains so great care is required if modifications are attempted. Further details on how to improve the RF immunity of PIR security lights is given in reference [6].

Spurious signals from an amateur transmitter

Equipment with insufficient immunity to the fundamental frequency of transmission causes the majority of amateur radio EMC problems but it cannot be assumed that this is true in all cases. If interference occurs due to insufficient suppression of transmitter harmonics or other spurious outputs, it is likely to affect certain specific TV channels or FM broadcast stations. Every receiver within a certain distance is likely to be affected, although this depends on the directional properties of the transmitting and receiving antennas. Spurious emissions may also be generated if an RF power amplifier is unstable or has been incorrectly tuned. In the latter case, frequency halving may occur leading to strong spurious signals at half and 1.5 times the carrier frequency.

Harmonics

Clause 4.(1) of the UK Amateur Radio Licence Terms, Provisions and Limitations Booklet BR68 states:

"The Licensee shall ensure that: (a) the emitted frequency of the apparatus comprised in the station is as stable and as free from Unwanted Emissions as the state of technical development for amateur radio apparatus reasonably permits;"

In the USA, the FCC spectral purity regulations for VHF amateur equipment that reached the market since 1978 require spurious emissions at VHF to be at least 60dB below the level of the carrier (-60dBc) for power levels of 25W or more.

For commercially available amateur radio equipment manufactured or imported into Europe since 1 January 1996, the EMC standard ETS 300 684 specifies levels of emissions and immunity. Section 8.1.3 defines limits for unwanted emissions from the antenna port when the transmitter is active. From 50 - 1000MHz, the limit is of -

36dBm (0.25µW) or -60dBc, whichever is higher.

Even if all harmonics and other unwanted emissions are at least 60dB below the carrier level, this may not be sufficiently low for all situations. In the case of the 50 - 52MHz band, suppression of the second harmonic at 100 - 104MHz is particularly important. For example, even with only 10nW ERP of second harmonic power, the earlier equation shows that at a distance of 10m this would produce a field strength of 70µV/m or 37dB(µV/m). Within the service area of an FM broadcast transmitter, the field strength should be at least 54dB(µV/m) at a height of 10m above ground. Towards the edge of the service area, a spurious signal of 37dB(µV/m) within the pass band of the FM broadcast receiver would be more than enough to cause noticeable interference. Clearly, effective low pass filtering together with a second harmonic trap is required for 50MHz. It is also important to avoid any radiation of second harmonic from sources other than the antenna, for example from a power amplifier with insufficient screening or decoupling.

It is advisable to identify all FM broadcasts between 100 and 104MHz that are intended to serve your area and to check that you can transmit on or near half the frequency without causing interference. If sufficient suppression of the second harmonic is still not achieved after all possible steps have been taken, it will be necessary to avoid transmitting on or near certain frequencies.

In the case of the 144 - 146MHz band, the fourth harmonic falls at 576 - 584MHz in UHF TV channels 34 or 35. The fifth harmonic falls at 720 - 730MHz and could interfere with UHF TV channels 52 or 53. In areas where the above UHF channels are used, additional low pass or band pass filtering may be required at the amateur transmitter.

However, it should be noted that, if a TV antenna amplifier or the front end of a TV or FM receiver receives a sufficiently high level of amateur signal, this can cause harmonics to be generated within the antenna amplifier or receiver even though the amateur signal itself may be free of them.

Frequency synthesiser lock up

When constructing a synthesised transceiver or modifying synthesised ex PMR equipment, attention should be paid to the lock up characteristics of the synthesiser, particularly if the transceiver is to be used for packet radio where it is likely to transmit frequently for short periods. With most VHF transceivers, the PLL (phase locked loop) synthesiser must get into lock when switching from receive to transmit or vice versa. While it is locking, RF drive to the transmit amplifier chain must be inhibited for long enough to avoid a full power transmitted signal sweeping rapidly across other frequencies inside or outside the amateur band.

In a synthesised transceiver, out-of-lock detection should also be considered. If the VCO (voltage controlled oscillator) cannot reach the frequency required by the synthesiser IC, the loop fails to lock, resulting in an unstable transmission on an incorrect frequency. There are two reasons why a synthesiser may fail to lock. The first is if the VCO frequency range is incorrectly adjusted and the synthesiser is programmed for a frequency that the VCO cannot reach. The second that could affect a serially programmed synthesiser is if the microprocessor fails to program the synthesiser when switching to transmit, leaving the synthesiser programmed to an incorrect frequency. To protect against such error conditions, the out-of-lock condition should be detected and should inhibit transmission. Frequency synthesiser ICs intended for use in transceivers normally have a lock detector output but devices such as the Philips TSA 6057 which are intended for receive only applications have no lock detector which makes their use in a transceiver inadvisable.

Interference to amateur reception

In most cases where nearby electronic equipment causes RFI on amateur bands and the equipment complies with any RFI standards which were required at the date of manufacture, the owner is not obliged to take any action unless reception of a protected service UHF TV broadcasting or FM radio is also affected. There is, however, a possibility that a fault has developed, that screening/suppression components have been removed during servicing or that the equipment was not intended for the European market and was imported by the owner.

The first thing to check is whether any interference can be seen on TV or heard on FM radio when using a satisfactory receiving antenna within the intended service area of the broadcast transmitter. If so, the matter can be referred to the local office of the UK Radiocommunications Agency using form RA179 (see below). In such cases, it is worth trying to locate the source so that the unpaid service can be used.

In most cases, only amateur bands are affected and the RFI can only be reduced if the owner of the equipment in question is prepared to cooperate, so a diplomatic approach is recommended. In any case, it is difficult to be certain of the source unless the owner is prepared to cooperate in doing tests. Any RFI reduction should be restricted to measures that can be fitted by the owner without the need for you to touch or dismantle the equipment in question.

It is worth trying to find out details of the make, model number and date of purchase of the equipment so that a complaint can be made directly to the manufacturer or importer. A polite and technically well-informed approach is recommended when dealing with manufacturers. The most effective approach is to phone first to find out the name of the person responsible for EMC then follow up the phone call with a letter, fax or email. It is also worth finding out whether a newer model with reduced RFI is available. In some cases, the manufacturer may be prepared to exchange the equipment in question for a newer model at a reduced price.

In cases where it is not possible to reduce the RFI, cancellation techniques may be used. See for example, reference [7].

RF emission standards

Radio amateurs might wish for nearby electronic equipment to be so well screened and suppressed so that it emits no detectable signals in any amateur band but existing RF emission standards fall far short of this ideal. At VHF, emission standards were designed primarily to protect broadcast radio and TV reception with an outdoor antenna at a distance of 10m from the source of the emission. Consequently, they allow levels of RFI that are far higher than radio amateurs would like. Nevertheless the situation has improved for electronic equipment manufactured since 1 January 1996 because previously many types of electronic equipment were not required to meet the relevant emission standards in the UK.

BS EN 55022 that applies to information technology equipment covers radiated emissions above 30MHz. This not only includes computers but also other equipment containing microprocessors. Various other standards such as the Generic Standard EN 50081-1 are based on EN 55022. The EN 55022 Class "B" limits are specified as a field strength of 30dB(μV/m) at a distance of 10m over the range 30 - 230MHz, increasing above 230MHz. This is a very large signal compared to the minimum discernible signal in VHF/UHF amateur bands, but in practice the situation is seldom as bad as it might appear because emissions near the limit are only likely to be found at a few frequencies and in most cases these are not in an amateur band. Further information on RF emission limits in relation to received amateur signal levels can be found in reference [8].

For a VHF/UHF amateur station with a high gain antenna and low noise preamp in a quiet rural area, the MDS (minimum discernible signal) for 144MHz SSB corresponds to a field strength of about -30dB(μV/m). In an urban area, the MDS is likely to be higher on certain beam headings due to man made broadband noise sources. At certain spot frequencies, there may be significantly stronger narrow band signals from nearby electronic equipment.

Computer RFI reduction

Although many laptop computers generate little RFI at VHF, other types of computers and associated equipment can be a major source of RFI. The RFI reduction measures described below are primarily intended for desktop computers used in the radio shack but similar principles can be applied to other types of computer and to digital electronic equipment in general. Clearly, internal modification of a computer or monitor should not be attempted on someone else's computer or one that is still under guarantee. Further details of computer RFI reduction are given in reference [9].

If a computer is used in the radio shack, the antenna and computer should obviously be as far apart as possible. It is also worth checking that the RFI disappears when a dummy load is plugged into the antenna socket, proving that it is not getting into the radio by some other route.

A computer may contain many different clock oscillators, for example for the CPU, graphics controller, disc drives,

and the base all around the joints. If not, it may be necessary to add extra fixing screws.

Keyboard

On a PC, the keyboard cable can radiate RFI if the shell of the keyboard connector is not solidly grounded to chassis. Although PC main boards nearly always use four or more layers with power and ground plane, there can still be a small RF potential difference between "ground" at the shell of the keyboard socket and ground at the back of the case. The fixing hole on the main board nearest the keyboard socket ("D" in Fig 6.6), should be grounded via a metal pillar to minimise common mode emissions. On CE marked PCs, the shell of the keyboard socket is normally grounded directly to the back of the case using four spring fingers ("E" in Fig 6.6).

Another way of tackling common mode emissions is by means of a common mode choke using a ferrite core on the cable ("F" in Fig 6.6). Most keyboard cables already have one of these moulded on but with only one "turn"; they introduce a series impedance of only about 100 - 200Ω. Up to four times as much impedance can be introduced by threading the cable twice through a clip on ferrite core with 13mm inside diameter.

In some cases, the keyboard itself may radiate a harmonic in an amateur band. As the clock normally uses a ceramic resonator rather than a crystal, it may be possible to move the harmonic out of the band by "pulling" the frequency of the resonator by increasing its loading capacitors. If this is not successful, it may be necessary to substitute a new keyboard, as it is not easy to screen a keyboard effectively.

Serial and parallel I/O ports

Any unscreened serial or parallel interface cable can radiate RFI due to unwanted coupling inside the computer. Where possible, a screened cable should be used with the screen well grounded to the metal connector shell. For a computer mouse, however, unscreened cable is normally used and a clip on ferrite choke or a filtered connector may be required. Soldering a 1nF or 4.7nF ceramic capacitor from each pin to the connector shell can make a filtered "D" type connector. Filtered "D" connectors or adaptors with built in feedthrough capacitors are available ready made from suppliers such as RS Components [14] or Farnell Components [13] but are relatively expensive.

A filtered connector on a cable will only be effective if there is good electrical contact between the two halves of the connector shell which requires "dimples" on the male "D" type connector. The shell of the plug on the computer must also be well grounded to the case of the computer. This is likely to be true of connector "G" in Fig 6.6 but connector 'H' may not be well grounded because it is on an expansion card.

For a computer with an internal modem, the unscreened telephone cable can radiate or pick up RF, especially if connected to an overhead telephone line. The only feasible way of filtering the telephone line where it leaves

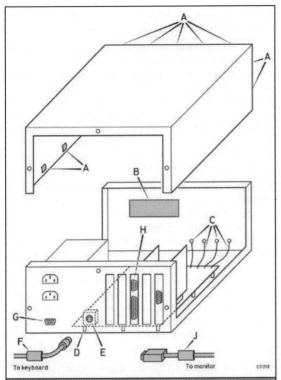

Fig 6.6: A typical PC case showing features which can affect EMC.

keyboard, mouse etc. Most of these oscillators are divided down to lower frequencies that can in turn produce many other harmonics.

Reducing RF leakage

Unwanted emissions may escape from a computer or other digital equipment via a number of routes so a step-by-step approach is normally required. It is best to monitor the level of RFI with an indoor antenna 2 - 3m from the computer, using an SSB receiver with an S meter if possible. Displaying a graphics screen with a lot of fine detail is recommended as a "worst case" test even when testing without the monitor. The starting point is to unplug the video lead from the computer, switch off the monitor and unplug the keyboard, mouse and all other interface cables. Any remaining RFI is likely to be a radiated emission due to insufficient screening of the case or a conducted emission via the mains cable. The latter is more likely to affect the HF bands than VHF.

On a CE marked computer, the case normally has several features to improve screening as shown in Fig 6.6. Arrows "A" indicate lugs or "pips" at intervals of about 50mm on the base or cover to ensure good electrical contact at many points. Holes for unused disc drive bays are usually filled with a metal blanking plate ("B"). The wires to LEDs and switches on the front panel come through the metal case ("C") and could cause a slight leak. In practice, however, the shielding of the case may not be the limiting factor so a metal case without these features may be adequate if there is good electrical contact between the lid

the modem card is by means of a ferrite ring or clip on choke. Connecting series inductors or shunt capacitors directly to the telephone line is not permissible, as it would invalidate the approval for the modem.

Graphics card

It is important that the shell of the video connector on a PC graphics card is well grounded to avoid a VHF common mode emission from the braid of the video cable. The shell of the video output connector is grounded to the mounting bracket but this is only grounded to chassis with one bolt at the top. If possible, the graphics card should be fitted in one of the end slots where grounding to the back panel is better. Some good quality cases for CE marked PCs have spring fingers around the expansion slots on the back panel to improve grounding but, if these are not fitted, RF grounding can be improved by bolting or clamping the mounting bracket of the video card to the back panel close to the connector. Another way of reducing RFI from a video cable is to clip on a ferrite choke ("J" in Fig 6.6) if one is not already fitted.

Computer monitors

Following the above steps should lead to a fairly quiet computer at VHF, until the monitor is switched on. RFI from a CRT monitor may have definite peaks at certain frequencies or may be broadband noise. There are large variations in the amount of VHF RFI emitted by different models of computer monitor. To reduce RFI from a monitor at VHF, it is normally necessary to make internal modifications to circuitry that operates at a high voltage. Only those with sufficient experience should attempt such modifications. Note that ferrite is conductive and any ferrite cores should be fitted so as to avoid causing a short circuit or flashover.

In many computer monitors, the switching frequency for the power supply is synchronised to the line timebase frequency that can make it difficult to distinguish between power supply harmonics, line timebase harmonics and video amplifier harmonics. If turning the brightness and contrast right down gives a large reduction in RFI, this could be due to reduced loading on the power supply, reduced loading on the line output stage or reduced output from the video amplifiers. The switch mode power supply in a monitor may be on an unscreened PCB in a plastic case leading to direct radiation, in which case adding additional mains filtering is unlikely to give much improvement at VHF.

The line output stage can radiate harmonics up to VHF due to the fast switching of the output transistor. As the collector of the line output transistor is usually connected directly to the "hot" side of the line scan coils, these coils and associated wiring can act as a radiating antenna. The only effective way of reducing VHF harmonics of the line timebase is usually to cut the track to the collector of the line output transistor and put in a series choke consisting of 2 - 3 turns on an FX1115 ferrite bead. As the added inductance in the collector could alter the operating conditions of this highly stressed device, such modifications should be regarded as experimental. A similar modification can be applied to the main switching transistor in the switch mode power supply if necessary.

If the video amplifiers are radiating, displaying a screen with a lot of fine detail will produce more RFI than a plain screen of the same brightness. The video output transistors are nearly always mounted on the base if the CRT on a small PCB with a tinplate screen. This screen should be grounded to the chassis by two short lengths of braid. The video cable from the computer should have its braid solidly grounded to chassis where it enters the monitor. Some CE marked monitors have two large ferrite beads on the video cable, one each side of this ground point.

Although it would be possible to coat the whole inside of a monitor's case with nickel RF shielding spray grounded to chassis, this is not recommended for several reasons. First, there are high voltages on the PCB that may flash over to any conductive coating inside the case. Secondly, the conductive paint may find its way through ventilation slots so that it can be touched from outside. This presents a shock hazard if part of the coating inside comes into contact with a high voltage. A third problem is that the coating may not adhere well to certain types of plastic unless a special primer is used. If the coating flakes off, this could cause short circuits.

Even the software set up of a PC can affect the emissions from a monitor. For example some Cirrus Logic VGA video cards operating in the 800 × 600 resolution modes use a pixel clock frequency of 36.088MHz or 72.176MHz. This produces a second or fourth harmonic at nominally 144.352MHz with sidebands either side. A VGA utility program such as CLMODE can be used to demonstrate the various graphics modes and identify any differences in RFI.

The increased use of flat screen monitors means that RFI generated by high voltage line timebase circuits is not a problem. These monitors can still cause RFI problems from their switch mode power supplies and video connections; the precautions suggested for CRT monitors can be used.

Other RFI sources

There are many possible sources of unwanted signals in the VHF and UHF bands apart from computers and associated equipment. Other domestic products that generally incorporate a microprocessor include intruder alarms and fax machines. Satellite TV receivers and decoders, video recorders and TV sets with NICAM stereo or digital signal processing can also generate RFI in the VHF bands. Many consumer products use a ceramic resonator rather than a crystal in the clock oscillator for the digital circuitry. Harmonics of ceramic resonators tend to drift with temperature and they may even be microphonic where nearby sound or other vibrations cause slight frequency modulation.

Some types of heating thermostat may develop a fault causing them to arc for several seconds or even tens of seconds when the contacts open. This may occur every few minutes and tends to occur more frequently in cold weather. In some cases, the same type of thermostat may have been installed in a number of houses and there could be several arcing thermostats.

Equipment in nearby commercial or industrial premises that may radiate RFI at VHF includes arc welders, computers and computer networks using unscreened twisted pair (UTP). Some types of fire alarm systems can also be a problem, particularly the "analogue addressable" type if these are wired with unscreened cable.

A broadband noise source that can affect all or part of the 70cm band is a super regenerative receiver on 433.92MHz. With a high gain 70cm antenna and low noise preamp, some types within 30 - 50m can cause a substantial degradation of signal-to-noise ratio. Noisy 433.92MHz super regenerative receivers are found on some after market car alarms manufactured in 1994 and 1995. Receivers manufactured from 1996 onwards have to meet ETS 300 220 and are therefore much quieter. Some particularly poor 173MHz garage door openers sold in the late 1980s also produced high levels of noise on 70cm and up into the UHF TV band.

RFI from noisy super regenerative receivers can take two forms. In the absence of a signal, they radiate broadband noise, possibly covering tens of megahertz. When the super regenerative receiver detects a carrier somewhere near its operating frequency, its emission changes to a number of discrete frequencies spaced at intervals of the quench frequency that may be around 800kHz. These emissions drift and are modulated by signals from other radio services such as radio paging. They can give the misleading impression that a paging transmitter has spurious outputs or that an amateur receiver has spurious responses.

Other radio users

If signals from other radio services such as radio paging or PMR are heard on a receiver tuned to an amateur band, a likely cause is a spurious response in the amateur receiver or overloading of any preamplifier. In particular, some 144MHz amateur transceivers with extended receive coverage can be susceptible to breakthrough of nearby radio paging signals at around 138 or 153MHz. This problem can often be cured by means of a 144 - 146MHz bandpass filter or a notch filter tuned to the pager frequency [10].

It is possible for radio paging transmitters to develop a fault that produces a number of unstable spurious frequencies either side of the carrier and, if this occurs, the interference typically drifts up or down the amateur band. Note that some types of super regenerative garage door receiver reradiating nearby pager signals can produce similar symptoms on 70cm.

If it is suspected that another radio service is radiating spurious signals in an amateur band, it is advisable to obtain conclusive proof of this before proceeding further.

Dealing with neighbours

With some amateur radio EMC cases, the technical problem is easy to solve but applying the solution is difficult because of a social problem. If relations deteriorate too far, even a simple matter like getting a plug in filter fitted could become a major issue. It is therefore well worth trying to maintain friendly relations even if the neighbour's initial approach is unfriendly. The neighbour's point of view may be that they have bought a good quality product that works perfectly well when the radio amateur is not transmitting, so they blame the amateur. The radio amateur's point of view is that he or she is operating within the terms of the amateur licence so the problem is caused by shortcomings in the neighbour's equipment.

To explain your point of view to a neighbour may not be easy and a diplomatic approach is called for. If you take the view that it is not your problem, there is a risk of a much bigger problem later on! Even if your station is "in the clear" technically, an uncooperative or, worse still, an alienated, neighbour could make life very unpleasant. Some radio amateurs have even resorted to moving house in such a situation.

It is wise to be prepared for the possibility of a breakthrough complaint before it happens. First of all, make sure your own house is in order by solving any EMC problems with your own domestic electronic equipment as far as possible. Being able to show that your TV, video recorder, hi-fi and telephone does not suffer breakthrough when you are transmitting should convince anyone that your transmitter is not at fault. Interference free radio and TV reception in your own house is also an additional check that any spurious outputs from your transmitter are adequately suppressed. It does not prove this conclusively, however, due to the directional properties of transmitting and receiving antennas.

Solving any breakthrough on your own domestic electronic equipment is also good practice and means that you will probably have a selection of suitable filters or ferrite rings to hand. Even if none are required for your own equipment, it is advisable to keep an "EMC first aid kit" consisting of at least one suitable TV filter together with a few ferrite rings. It is also worth having at least one RF immune telephone available even if your own telephone is never used while you are transmitting.

If a neighbour reports a problem, this could be your only chance to negotiate so great diplomacy is necessary. If there is any doubt about whether your station is the cause of the problem, you could ask the neighbour to keep a written log of dates and times when breakthrough occurs but they may be unwilling to do this so it is worth offering to conduct test transmissions immediately. If possible, the breakthrough should be solved promptly using a filter that you already have.

You are under no obligation to pay for filters for neighbours' TVs etc but in many cases, the neighbour is unwilling to pay, so it is in the interests of good relations to provide a filter on loan for as long it is needed. A small neat label with your name and address makes the point that it remains your property rather than being a gift (which might be taken as an admission of liability). It may also reduce the chance of a TV service engineer taking it away.

Regulatory issues

The Radiocommunications Agency produces a leaflet RA234, EMC and the Radio Amateur, this is available from the RA Document Distribution Centre [18]. RA234 states the following:

"What is EMC?

EMC, short for electromagnetic compatibility, is the capacity of equipment to function without causing excessive interference and without being unduly affected by emissions from other apparatus.

Why is EMC important?

Amateurs are privileged in being allowed to operate at high power levels in residential areas. This privilege brings responsibility. Interference can be immensely annoying. As a responsible amateur you will naturally take care not to interfere with television and radio reception, for example. Apart from general considerations of good neighbourliness, there are conditions in the Amateur Radio Licence on interference. In addition from 1 January 1996 an EC Directive will impose new EMC standards on virtually all electrical and electronic equipment.

Does the Directive apply to amateur equipment?

Self-built amateur equipment is not covered by the Directive but it will still be necessary when using it to abide by the Licence conditions on interference. Commercially available products will have to comply and carry the CE mark to show compliance.

What happens if an interference problem arises?

If a problem arises, as a first step, the amateur should check that his or her own equipment is not at fault. Poor immunity is often to blame for reception problems and it may be necessary to take steps to improve the immunity of the affected installation. The amateur should co-operate with the neighbour and/or the dealer to identify and resolve the problem. But, if this does not work, the Radiocommunications Agency is likely to become involved.

What happens then?

The Agency is empowered to vary the amateur's permitted power so that the amateur does not cause excessive interference. Before resorting to this, the Agency will take all relevant circumstances into account, including the immunity of the affected installation. In the final analysis, however, the Agency will be guided by the immunity required by the relevant European Standard. If poor immunity is not to blame and other steps to reduce interference have failed, the amateur may be required to take steps to stop the field strength exceeding the level that the relevant European standard requires the affected installation to be able to withstand."

Another useful RA publication is RA323, Guidelines for Improving Television and Radio Reception. It consists of 16 pages plus a colour section with photos showing various types of TV interference. It is primarily intended for radio and television dealers, service engineers and antenna installers rather than for the general public. Topics of particular relevance to amateur radio include TV antenna amplifiers, CE marking and effects due to lack of immunity.

Radiocommunications Agency involvement

The following information is believed to be correct at the time of writing (late 2007) but may be subject to change.

If a UK householder experiences a reception problem with UHF television, a video recorder or FM radio, they can refer the matter to the RA using form RA179, Advice on Television and Radio Reception. It is useful to keep an up-to-date copy of RA179 in case of a complaint from a neighbour. Copies are available from the Radiocommunications Agency [16]. RA179 is only applicable to domestic complaints. If a business is affected, there is a different procedure, details of which are available from the local offices of the RA.

Part A of form RA179 is used when reporting a known or suspected source of interference, for possible investigation by the RA. There is no charge for reporting a source but the RA does not visit the complainant to investigate the affected equipment. If a radio amateur is nominated as a source of interference, it is likely that the local officers of the Radiocommunications Agency (previously known as the 'Radio Investigation Service' or 'RIS') would visit the amateur's station. Such a visit may include checking for spurious emissions and ensuring that the station is being operated within the terms of the Amateur Licence. In some cases, the field strength produced by the amateur station could be measured.

A householder can use Part B of form RA179 to request a visit by the RA to investigate the affected equipment. There is a charge of £50 + VAT (at the time of writing) for this service unless the householder is eligible for a free TV licence.

Form RA179 states that the paid service is only available for UHF televisions, video recorders or FM radios. It does not cover long wave and medium wave radios, satellite TV, cable TV, telephones, fax machines or answering machines. Neither does it cover other equipment not intended to pick up radio such as record players, CD players, tape recorders, electronic keyboards, baby alarms, computers or monitors. PIR security lights and intruder alarm systems are not specifically mentioned but appear to come under the category of "other equipment".

References

[1] The Radio Amateur's Guide to EMC, Robin Page-Jones, G3JWI, RSGB, 1992.

[2] RSGB Guide to EMC, Robin Page-Jones, G3JWI, RSGB.

[3] RSGB Yearbook, EMC section.

[4] 49MHz baby monitors item in 'EMC' column, RadCom June 1996, p 74.

[5] Alarm PIR sensors item in 'EMC' column, RadCom December 1994, pp 75 - 77.

[6] PIR lights item in 'EMC' column, RadCom April 1994, pp 76 - 77.

[7] 'Two metre interference reduction system', T Day, G3ZYY, RadCom April 1992, pp 48 - 50.

[8] RF emission standards item in 'EMC' column, RadCom June 1995, pp 76 - 77.

[9] Computer RFI reduction items in 'EMC' column, RadCom December 1996, pp 77 - 78, and February 1997, pp 80 - 81.

[10] 'Intermod – A modern urban problem', E Hare, KA1CV, QST August 1996, pp 40 - 43.

[11] Ofcom, Riverside House, 2a Southwark Bridge Road, London, SE1 9HA, Tel: 020 7981 3000, Fax: 020 7981 3333, web: www.ofcom.org.uk/static/archive/ra/topics/amateur/amateur-index.htm

[12] Maplin Electronics Ltd, Valley Road, Wombwell, Barnsley, South Yorkshire, S73 0BS, Tel: 0870 4296000, Fax: 0870 4296001, Email: customercare@maplin.co.uk, web: http://www.maplin.co.uk

[13] Farnell InOne, Canal Road, Leeds, LS12 2TU, Tel: 08701 200 200, Fax: 08701 200 201, web: http://uk.farnell.com/jsp/home/homepage.jsp

 [14] RS Components, Birchington Road, Corby, Northants, NN17 9RS, web: http://rswww.com

[15] RSGB RFI filters details, www.rsgb.org/emc/filters.php

[16] Document Distribution Centre, The Radiocommunications Agency, Wyndham House, 189 Marsh Wall, London E14 9SX, Tel: 020 7211 0502 or 0505, web: www.ofcom.org.uk/static/archive/ra/publication/ra_info/ra179/sec1.htm

[17] RSGB EMC leaflets can be downloaded from www.rsgb.org/emc/emcleaflets.php

[18] Document Distribution Centre, The Radiocommunications Agency, Wyndham House, 189 Marsh Wall, London E14 9SX, Tel: 020 7211 0502 or 0505, web: http://www.ofcom.org.uk/static/archive/ra/publication/ra_info/ra234.htm

Data Modes

T he 1990s saw a major change in the number of data modes available for amateurs to use. The catalyst was the increase in the power of the Personal Computer (PC) and in particular the sound cards, making it possible to have a simple interface between your PC and your transceiver to open up a world of new data modes. The data modes used prior to this are still in use, the main one used on the VHF/UHF bands is AX25 packet that still gives amateurs a unique method of communication and has some very useful facilities. The other data mode used is of course CW; this is used on all amateur bands and is still the default method of communication when conditions are poor or for fun by dedicated CW operators.

With the number of software packages available by 2007 it is impossible to mention them all in this chapter, instead some are described to give a flavour of the modes that are being used together with some places to find more information. Broadly the modes available are divided into two categories, those that are designed for a QSO or chat and those that are designed to use the difficult propagation modes such as EME, Meteor scatter etc. or "Weak Signal Modes". You can have a QSO using these weak signal modes but probably not chat in the same way. The thrill of these modes is the ability to use your technical expertise and knowledge to have a QSO under very difficult circumstances; often the signals are not even detectable by the human ear.

In the early 2000s the use of the PC was taken one step further with the appearance on the amateur market of the Software Defined Radio (SDR) using Digital Signal Processing (DSP) to perform many of the tasks previously carried out with hardware. One such SDR is described in Chapter 4, The DSP 10. This can be used for many weak signal modes; some of these are described in this chapter.

It is surprising that any of the amateur data modes have survived with the increased use and speed of The Internet. It is not a surprise to see the two methods of communication merging. It is now possible to have a QSO over The Internet without even using a radio, that is not in the scope of this book, but linking amateur radio equipment with The Internet is becoming very common. Voice Over Internet Protocol (VOIP) is now possible and is described in this chapter.

Because of all these new modes, frequencies have been allocated for their use on the VHF/UHF bands, Table 1 shows these.

AX.25 packet radio

AX.25 packet uses an amateur protocol derived from X.25, defining the content, format and the handling of packetised data. Information on AX.25 and other amateur packet protocols is extensively covered in other RSGB publications [1, 2] as well as the ARRL Computer Network Conference documents, so only a brief description is given here, concentrating instead on the "physical layer" and user operation.

HDLC

Packet radio uses high level data link control (HDLC) to handle the forwarding of error free frames of data over a communications link. The transmission is based upon a series of "packets" of data, each packet containing a portion of the transmitted information preceded by routing information and ending with a cyclic redundancy check (CRC), which is a value calculated by the sending station based upon the content of the information in the transmitted packet.

At the receiving end, each packet is automatically checked for correct and valid information content. If a valid packet is received, an "ACK" (acknowledgement) is sent by the receiving end station to acknowledge that the packet has been received without errors. Otherwise, the transmitting station automatically repeats the transmission of that data packet.

By the use of this protocol, a number of packet radio stations may all use a common frequency, with individual data packets "interleaving" with others as required. Packet addressing, by callsign or a short "alias", ensures that the desired receiving station is correctly addressed, with each station ignoring packets not intended for that station's callsign or alias.

Terminal node controller

To handle the AX.25 protocol a terminal node controller (TNC) is usually used. This is a self-contained unit

Table 7.1: Data mode frequencies in MHz.

6m

50.385 ± 5kHz	PSK31/MT63 centre of activity
50.510	Slow Scan Television
50.520	Internet voice gateways (Unattended only)
50.530	Internet voice gateways (Unattended only)
50.540	Internet voice gateways (Unattended only)
50.550	Fax
50.570	20kHz packet channel
50.590	10kHz any digital mode
50.600	RTTY calling channel
50.610	10kHz any digital mode
50.630	20kHz packet channel
50.650	20kHz packet channel
50.670	20kHz packet channel
50.690	20kHz packet channel
51.910	Internet voice gateways
51.920	Internet voice gateways
51.930	Internet voice gateways
51.940	Internet voice gateways
51.950	Internet voice gateways

4m

70.0850	PSK31 centre of activity
70.3000	RTTY / Fax calling and working
70.3125	Any digital mode
70.3250	DX cluster
70.3375	Any digital mode
70.3500	Internet voice gateway
70.3625	Internet voice gateway
70.3875	Internet voice gateway
70.4375	Digital modes, special projects

2m

144.120 - 144.150	EME MGM (JT65)
144.370	MGM calling frequency
144.400 - 144.490	MGM beacons only

144.500	SSTV calling
144.600	RTTY calling / working
144.700	Fax calling
144.8250	Internet voice gateway
144.8375	Internet voice gateway
144.850	AX25 BBS user access
144.8625	For nodes and BBSs on application
144.8750	TCP/IP user access
144.8875	AX25 priority for DX cluster user access
144.900	AX25 DX cluster access
144.9250	TCP/IP user access
144.950	AX25 BBS user access
144.9750	High speed 25kHz channel
145.2125	Internet voice gateway
145.2375	Internet voice gateway
145.2875	Internet voice gateway
145.300	RTTY local
145.3375	Internet voice gateway

70cm

430.0125 - 430.0875	12.5kHz spacing voice internet
430.6000 - 430.6750	BBS / Node linking
430.7000 - 430.7750	High speed linking 25kHz channel
431.075 - 431.225	Voice internet linking
432.0850 ± 5kHz	PSK31/MT63 centre of activity
432.6250 - 432.6450	AX25 user access only
433.6250	TCP/IP user access only
433.6500	AX25 user access only
433.6750	DX cluster user access only
433.8250	TCP/IP user access 4800bps or faster
433.8500	AX25 user access 4800bps or faster
433.8750	DX cluster user access 4800bps or faster
433.900	DX cluster user access 1200bps or faster
433.9500	1200bps traffic
433.9625 - 434.5250	Voice internet linking
439.7625	BBS / Node linking
439.8250 - 439.8750	BBS / Node linking
439.9000 - 439.9750	Igh speed linking 25kHz channel

comprising of a modem and a microprocessor control system with the operating firmware stored in an erasable programmable read only memory (EPROM) IC. This allows firmware changes or upgrades to be accomplished as needed.

For the "user interface", the TNC has an RS232 serial data connector for connection to a terminal. This may either be a "dumb terminal", a computer operating in terminal emulation mode, i.e. running the Windows Terminal program, or a computer running a dedicated packet radio program to give added operating features such as automatic connections, logging, mailbox facilities etc. For personal use, many TNCs also have a self-contained message "mailbox" to provide storage facilities of personal messages to and from the TNC user.

For the radio interface, the TNC connects directly to your VHF/UHF transmitter/receiver although, depending upon the packet radio data rate, differing connections are required. Typical packet data rates used by individual amateurs are 1200 baud and 9600 baud, although "backbone networking" data rates typically use 9600 baud, 56kbaud, 64kbaud, or higher speeds still e.g. 2Mbits/s on the microwave bands. Note that the terminal baud rate you select for use between the TNC and your terminal does not affect the radio baud rate, the latter being dependent upon the type and speed of modem used within the TNC. See Fig 7.1 that shows these connections

diagrammatically.

Multiple users

The TNC receives audio from the packet station receiver, and on a given frequency used by a number of packet stations this is usually a sequential combination of many individual packets from differing stations, as well as packets from individual stations intended for a number of other "connected" stations. Up to 26 different connection streams can be handled by each TNC. In "monitor" mode, the TNC decodes all received packets, and transfers the decoded information to the RS232 terminal port for subsequent display and optional processing. However, in communication or "connected" mode, it still decodes all received packets but typically only transfers to the RS232 port packets addressed to the callsign or alias the user has manually stored (again via the terminal) into the TNC. It also automatically waits until the frequency is clear before transmitting a packet, to prevent interference to other packet stations on the same frequency. Pseudo-random wait timings prior to transmission give a degree of protection in preventing collisions of packets due to simultaneous transmissions from different stations on a given frequency.

Hardware

TNC kits of parts are still available from groups such as NWPUG [3] and TAPR [4]. A wide variety of commercial

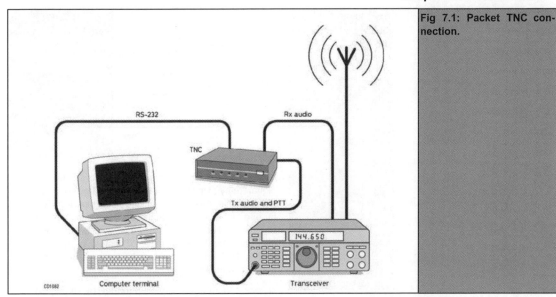

Fig 7.1: Packet TNC connection.

ready built TNCs are of course available. Many of these are based upon a TNC-2 clone e.g. some PacComm and AEA TNCs, whilst others use proprietary firmware to provide additional features e.g. some Kantronics TNCs. Fig 7.2 shows the inside of a typical TNC.

TNC connection and operation

The TNC requires a suitable RS232 connection link to your terminal for operation. Note, however, that some TNCs may employ otherwise unused connections on the 25 way D type connector for other purposes, e.g. alternative supply voltage input, test points etc. If in doubt, follow the instructions supplied with your TNC. Tables 7.2 and 7.3 show the most commonly used connections required for typical TNCs, and Figs 7.3 and 7.4 the serial port connector wiring diagrams.

Transceiver connection

For 1200 baud packet, the TNC transceiver interface may connect simply to the receiver external speaker audio and to the transmit microphone and PTT connections. Unless

your TNC has a software DCD incorporated and enabled, i.e. it has intelligent data detection of packet data to differentiate from receiver squelch noise and other signals, you should ensure that your receiver squelch is suitably adjusted. This is because the TNC will not transmit if the TNC's front panel DCD LED is illuminated, this being controlled by the detection of a received signal by the TNC modem. 9600 baud packet requires connection to the flat, i.e. unprocessed, audio points in your transceiver. On receive, this means that the received audio needs to be taken directly from the receiver discriminator, prior to any audio de-emphasis filtering. On transmit, an audio response down to a few hertz, preferably down to DC, is required, together with an essentially flat i.e. unprocessed, transmitted frequency response.

Table 7.2: TNC-2 "clone" RS232 connections (25 pin D type).

Pin	Function	Signal direction
1	Frame Ground (FG)	Common
2	Transmit Data (TXD)	PC O/P
3	Receive Data (RXD)	TNC O/P
5	Clear To Send (CTS)	TNC O/P
6	Data Set Ready (DSR)	TNC O/P
7	Signal Ground (SG)	PC O/P
8	Data Carrier Detect (DCD)	TNC O/P
20	Data Terminal Ready (DTR)	PC O/P
22	Ring Indicator (RI)	Not connected

Table 7.3: PacComm Tiny-2 connections (9 pin D type)

Pin	Function	Signal direction
1	Data Carrier Detect (DCD)	TNC O/P
2	Receive Data (RXD)	TNC O/P
3	Transmit Data (TXD)	PC O/P
5	Signal Ground (SG)	PC O/P
6	Data Set Ready (DSR)	TNC O/P
7	Request To Send (RTD)	PC O/P
8	Clear To Send (CTS)	TNC O/P
9	Ring Indicator (RI)	Not connected
Shell	Frame Ground (FG)	Common

Fig 7.2: Inside view of a typical packet TNC.

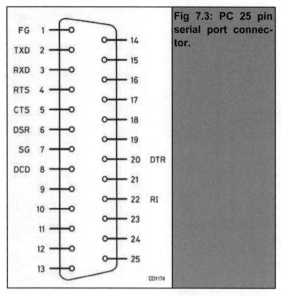

Fig 7.3: PC 25 pin serial port connector.

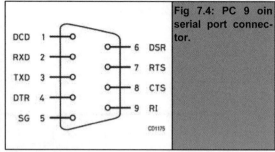

Fig 7.4: PC 9 oin serial port connector.

using the packet station of G0SBV as an intermediate digital "relay". Up to eight intermediate digipeaters may be used for this. Any error checking here is performed at the far end of the link, individual digipeaters simply retransmitting the packet information to the next station along. The digipeater facility is an inherent feature in every current packet TNC, although it may be enabled or disabled by the TNC operator as required.

A packet "node" goes one step further, by employing local error checking and repeats transmission requests. A simple node facility is occasionally an inherent feature of some TNCs, e.g. the "KA-Node" in Kantronics TNCs. One stage further is that of a "network node", which usually uses dedicated firmware or a PC running appropriate node software such as that written by John Wiseman, G8BPQ.

A network node system has automatic networking abilities, including automatic routing using the best possible transmission quality path between two remote points. A typical network node station arrangement could use multiple transceivers and TNCs, e.g. operating on 4m, 2m, 70cm and 23cm, with the TNCs locally interconnected either via an RS232 matrix or with the host computer running appropriate node software, see Fig 7.7. In the latter case, the individual TNCs are commanded to run in "KISS" mode, with the computer handling packet routing.

Some commercially available FM transceivers are fitted with 9600 baud packet data connections for this. However, many amateurs also use dedicated low cost crystal controlled transceivers, often ex PMR equipment, for packet radio use, to avoid permanently tying up a high value commercial transceiver on a given BBS or DX cluster frequency. The RSGB PMR Conversion Handbook [5] gives more details on typical equipment and comprehensive conversion information. Transceiver connections for both 1200 and 9600 baud are shown in Fig 7.5 and a typical FM modulator modification circuit in Fig 7.6.

Packet digipeaters and nodes

For individual one-to-one amateur communication via your terminal you simply issue a "connect" command to your TNC to directly link to the intended station that is operational on the same frequency and in communication range of your station. An example command would be "CONNECT GB7SMC" (or "C GB7SMC") to connect to the GB7SMC DX packet cluster node.

However, the AX.25 protocol also allows "digipeating", where a third party packet station can automatically retransmit packets by remote command. Thus, "CONNECT GB7DXW VIA G0SBV" would attempt a link to GB7DXW,

Bulletin boards

Although individual contacts are made using packet radio for live "chats", the most common use of packet radio is by the use of a bulletin board system (BBS). These systems consist of a computer running appropriate BBS software, linked to the packet radio network, usually through individual TNCs and radios at the BBS station.

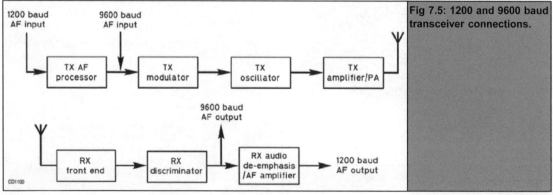

Fig 7.5: 1200 and 9600 baud transceiver connections.

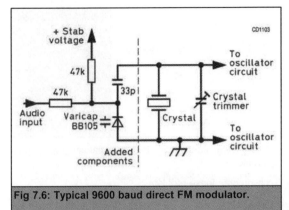

Fig 7.6: Typical 9600 baud direct FM modulator.

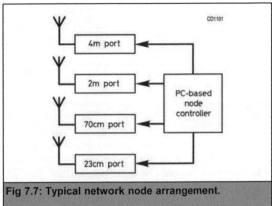

Fig 7.7: Typical network node arrangement.

Two common types of BBS are in use, the "normal" BBS and, of greater interest to the DX operator, the DX packet cluster system.

Network BBS

Differing from the "personal" BBS you may have in your TNC or computer software, which is used for personal messages to and from your station only, a network BBS operates as a linked national and international message storage and forwarding system for third party messages and bulletins to and from radio amateurs, many have facilities for Internet links.

After you have connected to your local BBS, you can then list message titles, either all stored messages or to any given subject, callsign, or whatever, view and download message texts and stored files, as well as uploading files of interest to others, and enter messages addressed to other amateurs. Each BBS is part of the worldwide network, linked via nodes on HF, VHF and UHF, as well as via store-and-forward amateur satellite gateway stations. Thus, you can send and receive messages worldwide, the BBS network routing your messages to the intended recipient. You may read and send general "bulletins", subject to licensing restrictions, which are intended for general reading, e.g. to seek help or informa-

tion on a given subject from other amateur on the packet network.

Each BBS is normally run by an individual, or occasionally by a club, with all running costs being met by him or her and not by any national organisation. This is worth bearing in mind as, due to current UK licensing conditions, the BBS system operator (sysop) usually refrains from directly soliciting donations to pay towards the running costs.

DX packet cluster

A DX packet cluster is a network of interconnected individual DX cluster "nodes", each of which is located in a given area to serve a local amateur population. Similar in many physical respects to a network BBS, the controlling PC instead runs specialised DX cluster software which has enhancements for DX station activity reporting, propagation information etc. A typical area configuration is shown in Fig 7.8, with local stations each connected to their local DX cluster node, which are in turn linked to each other, and to those further away (not shown here) either via dedicated RF links or via the national and international AX.25 packet network.

In operation, the users are all part of a shared information resource, where one station can enter an announcement, i.e. a DX "spot" with DX station details, operation fre-

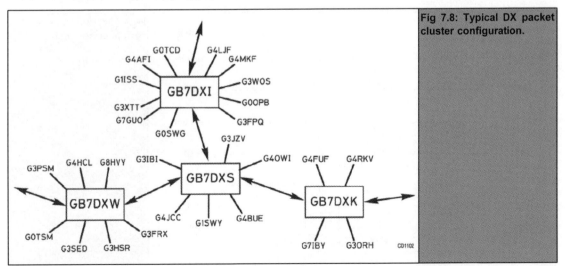

Fig 7.8: Typical DX packet cluster configuration.

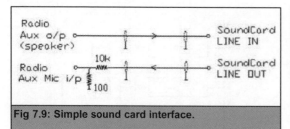

Fig 7.9: Simple sound card interface.

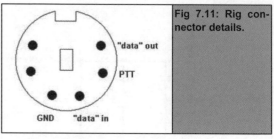

Fig 7.11: Rig connector details.

quency and a short comment, usually when he's heard or worked a station worthy of reporting to others. This announcement is then forwarded throughout the DX cluster system and passed to all other connected stations. A filter is available, where if you wish you can choose to only receive announcement spots relating to certain bands, e.g. the VHF/UHF bands, you are specifically interested in, or indeed any combination including HF. This system can be an excellent way of obtaining and sharing real time information on sporadic E or tropospheric activity with other amateurs, as well as arranging skeds for meteor scatter, EME etc.

As with a network BBS, each DX cluster node is usually financed by an individual amateur or local club, which should be borne in mind if you are a regular user of a particular one.

PC sound card Interface

Much of the current software for data modes uses a PC sound card to process the audio signal to and from a transceiver. To connect your transceiver to your PC you need an interface. In its simplest form this is just a cable connecting the line out socket on the PC sound card to the microphone socket of the transceiver and the headphone/loudspeaker socket on the transceiver to the microphone socket on the sound card, see Fig 7.9. This has a number of disadvantages:

- To transmit the VOX in the transceiver must be used, this can add an unacceptable delay.

- The transceiver and PC are electrically connected by

the ground connection; this may cause ground loop problems.

To overcome these problems:

- The RTS signal on an RS232 (Serial) ports is used for PTT, this too can have its problems if your PC does not have an RS232 port. Many PC, particularly laptops do not have RS232 ports but do have USB ports, using a USB to RS232 converter can solve this problem.

- An isolated interface is needed, Ross Wilkinson, G6GVI has a design for an isolated interface using transformers for the audio signals and an opto isolator for the PTT signal [6]. The circuit diagram for the isolated interface is shown in Fig 7.10. Suitable transformers are available from Farnell [7] type 309-8-11 or Maplin [8] type N92CC. To test the interface, first try out a program on receive. The simplest way is to connect the transceiver loudspeaker or headphone output to the PC microphone or line input, adjusting the input level on the PC sound card to give the correct signal level. This will work, but has the following disadvantages:

  - You can't hear the receiver output

  - The setting of the receiver volume control is critical.

A better alternative is to use an auxiliary audio output from the transceiver. See Fig 7.11 for details of this connection using the FT817/857/897, IC703 and IC706 mk2 transceivers. If you do this, you can adjust the receiver's volume control for a comfortable monitor level without affecting the signal level going to the PC

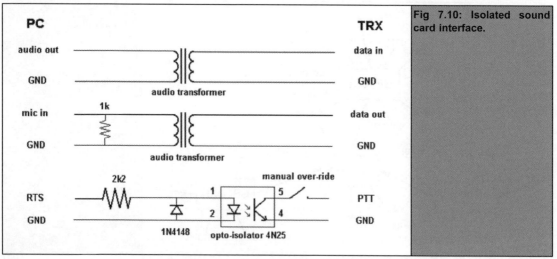

Fig 7.10: Isolated sound card interface.

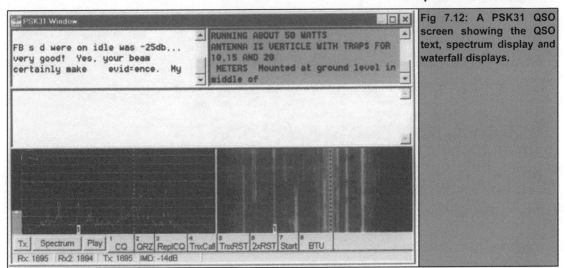

Fig 7.12: A PSK31 QSO screen showing the QSO text, spectrum display and waterfall displays.

sound card. If the received audio fed into the PC is very quiet, then the programs decoding performance may be limited by noise (although they will still work OK with strong signals), but if the input signal is too high (generating distortion), then the programs will be unable to decode any signals correctly. It will be necessary to adjust the microphone slider on the PC sound-card's "Audio Properties" menu, to achieve the correct level. Most soundcards have an extra microphone pre-amp (sometimes labelled "boost"), accessible on the "Advanced" menu: try switching this out if you're having trouble with overloading.

In order to transmit, the interface must be connected to the transceiver input. It is possible to use the microphone input, but this is usually a very low level signal, so the PC output needs to be attenuated down, and then becomes more susceptible to noise and interference, leading to possible RF feedback problems. A better way is to use the external mod input to the transceiver, and to switch its PTT line from the PC serial port. This removes the need to rely on the VOX control. The microphone can then be left connected so it is possible to go back to using telephony by just operating the mode switch. However, beware that if the PC crashes, the transceiver could end up stuck in transmit!

If your PC only has a USB serial port, you'll need to get an adaptor to RS232. Some of the USB/RS232 adapters have a lower current output than a dedicated serial port, so it may be necessary to reduce the 2k2Ω resistor accordingly.

In order to be sure that you've got the modulation level into your transceiver set correctly, it will be necessary to get a report from another station, who can observe your signal off air using his spectrograph or waterfall display: this will show up any distortion or over-wide signals.

There are many commercial sound card interfaces available, probably the best known are the Rigblaster range from West Mountain Radio [9] or the Tigertronics [10]

range. RadComm published a special computer supplement in the April 2004 issue with a lot of useful information about computer interfaces etc. The advantage of a commercial unit is they are ready to plug and play.

PSK31

PSK31 is probably the best known of the "new" digital modes that uses a PC sound card interface. The modulation system was introduced by SP9VRC and implemented on Windows PCs by Peter Martinez, G3PLX [11]. The name stands for Phase Shift Keying 31 baud. It was designed as a chat mode and is the modern equivalent of RTTY. The original implementation used BPSK modulation with two-phase changes to transmit the data giving good weak signal performance. No error correction was included so any error correction was "manual" by the operator interpreting any garbled of missing characters. In 1977 QPSK modulation was added, this uses four phase changes to transmit the data that improves the performance and enabled some error correction to be added.

The PSK31 mode is available in many of the software packages that are available. It is used widely on most of the amateur bands. A typical screen display of a QSO is shown in Fig 7.12, it shows the QSO text in two windows at the top of the screen and a spectrum display at the bottom left and a waterfall display at the bottom right. The waterfall display shows several QSOs taking place in the bandwidth of the display.

Software packages for data modes

There are so many software packages available for amateur radio data modes that it is impossible to mention them all. Most of the software is free or freeware where it is possible to make a donation to the author. It is all very comprehensive and usually covers many of the chat modes and weak signal modes in one package. I have chosen two packages to mention, MULTIPSK and MixW but please use recommendations from other amateurs, your radio magazines or The Internet to seek out other software.

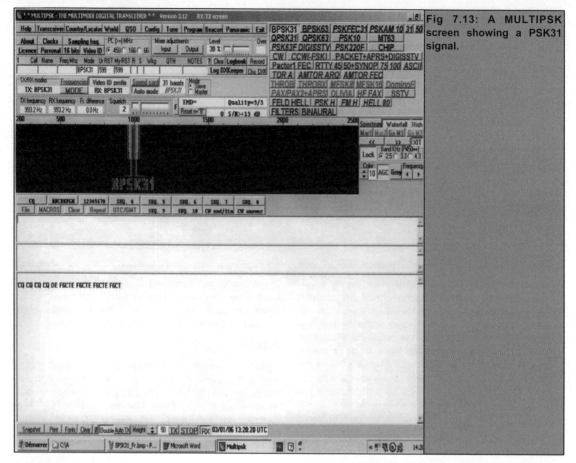

Fig 7.13: A MULTIPSK screen showing a PSK31 signal.

MULTIPSK

This was written by Patrick Lindecker, F6CTE [12], a restricted version can be downloaded free and an unrestricted version is available for €30. It has an impressive range of modes:

- PSKFEC31, an experimental new mode. This mode is derived from PSK10 mode using the set of characters from PSK31 for the 31.25 baud.

- PSK10 mode is designed to assure communications with weak Signal-to-Noise ratios down to -17.5dB with less than 2% errors. The speed is 18 wpm. This mode is very sensitive to ionospheric Doppler modulation.

- BPSK31 and QPSK31 modes are designed to assure communications with Signal-to-Noise ratio down to -11.5dB, for a PC at 166MHz or more. The speed is 37 wpm for capitals letters and 51 wpm for lower case letters.

- CHIP (64/128) is a new PSK mode which uses the "Spread Spectrum" modulation technique and particularly the Direct Sequence Spread Sequence (DSSS) using an original algorithm. The minimum Signal-to-Noise ratio is -8dB.

- BPSK63 and QPSK63 modes derived from

BPSK31/QPSK31 but they are twice as faster. The minimum Signal-to-Noise ratio is about -8dB.

- BPSK125 and QPSK125 modes derived from BPSK31/QPSK31 but they are four times as faster. The minimum Signal-to-Noise ratio is about -5dB.

- PSK63F mode has a same speed (62.5 bauds) as PSK63 but with different encoding. It is a powerful mode in the presence of noise. The minimum Signal-to-Noise ratio is about -12dB.

- PSK220F mode is a PSK63F mode carried at 220 baud. It allows a very rapid transmission speed. The minimum Signal-to-Noise ratio is about -7dB.

- DIGISSTV "Run" in PSK63F or in PSK220F: it is possible to send and to receive small pictures in digital SSTV during a QSO in these modes.

- CCW (Coherent CW) created for amateur radio by Ramond Petit, W6GHM in 1975. CCW is derived from the traditional CCW with some modifications by F6CTE and DK5KE.

- CW, RTTY, ASCII and AMTOR are traditional modes used by radio amateurs.

- PACKET is an AFSK mode used for access to the VHF

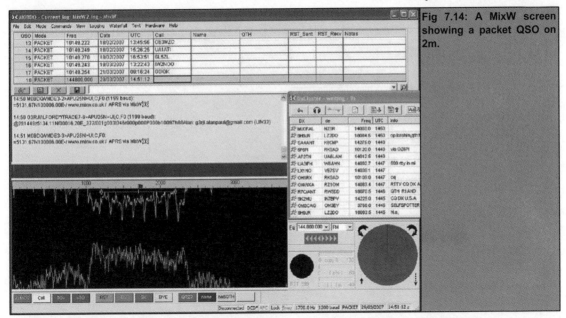

Fig 7.14: A MixW screen showing a packet QSO on 2m.

packet network. This mode allows the transport of APRS (Automatic Position Reporting System) frames. It is possible to send and to receive small pictures in digital SSTV ("Run" protocol), during a QSO in this mode.

- PACTOR 1 is an AFSK mode using an ARQ protocol.

- PAX is a robust MFSK mode derived from Olivia. The minimum Signal-to-Noise ratio is about -10dB.

- The PAX2 is the PAX mode but modulated twice as rapidly. The minimum Signal-to-Noise ratio is about -7dB.

- THROB and THROBX are experimental multi-tone frequency shift keyed (MFSK) modes, good for low power transmission without being sensitive to Doppler like PSK transmissions. The use of raised cosine shaped tones pulses applied to each character gives a characteristic "throbbing" sound, hence the name of the modes. THROBX is an improved THROB mode but only for speeds of 1 and 2 bauds. The minimum Signal-to-Noise ratio is about -18.5dB for THROBX at 1 baud.

- MFSK16 and MFSK8 are powerful modes MFSK (Multi Frequency Shift Keying) modes designed specifically for DX. They use FEC (Forward Error Correction) coding and an interleaving that disperses the symbols over a long period of time, in a way that counters the effects of noise and multi path that affect reception. Bits are sent on a carrier chosen among 16 (MFSK16) or 32 (MFSK8). The minimum Signal-to-Noise ratio is about -13.5dB for MFSK16 and -15.5dB for MFSK8. It is possible to send and receive small pictures during a QSO in MFSK16.

- MIL-STD-188-141A is a broad band MFSK mode which is used for ALE (Automatic Link Establishment) communications. It uses a Golay coding. The minimum

Signal-to-Noise ratio is about -4dB.

- OLIVIA is an MFSK mode designed for QRP and QRM (due to a large bandwidth, up to 1000Hz). It uses Walsh-Hadamard functions, an interleaver and a scrambler that makes it robust. The minimum Signal-to-Noise ratio is about -13dB (in the standard mode).

- CONTESTIA is an MFSK derived from Olivia. The minimum Signal-to-Noise ratio is about 1.5dB less than Olivia. It is a bit less robust than Olivia but it is twice as fast.

- RTTYM is an MFSK mode derived from Contestia. The minimum Signal-to-Noise ratio is about 1.5dB less than Contestia. It is much less robust than Contestia but it is almost twice as fast.

- VOICE is an MFSK mode designed for blind or partially sighted Hams and SWL's, derived from Olivia. The minimum Signal-to-Noise ratio is about -14.5dB. All received characters can be pronounced.

- DominoF DF is a sensitive mode due to its incremental frequency keying and thanks to its interleaved multiple tone sets it is easy to tune and is not sensitive to interference and ionospheric effects. The minimum Signal-to-Noise ratio is -12dB.

- DominoEX DF is a development of the Domino F mode allowing an extended set of characters. The minimum ratio Signal-to-Noise ratio is -12dB (in the standard mode).

- MT63, 64 carrier frequencies are phase modulated. This mode is not sensitive to fading and, due to its interleaving, is considered as a very robust mode. The minimum Signal-to-Noise ratio is 10 baud is -5dB.

- Hellschreiber FELD HELL, PSK HELL, FM HELL and HELL 80 modes are graphical modes where characters

Fig 7.15: A picture received on August 13th 2006 by David Worboys, M0ZLB / KG4ZLB from The International Space Station (ISS). Received using MMSSTV software.

are drawn and the interpretation done by the user.

- SSTV (Slow Scan Television) allows the user to send fixed pictures, with a bandwidth similar to HF Fax.

- HF Fax.

A typical MULTIPSK screen is shown in Fig 7.13.

MIXW

Steve Ford described MixW in QST magazine as "The Swiss Army Knife of Digital Communications Software". Not only does the software operate with a wide range of digital modes using a sound card interface, it can control a CAT capable transceiver or other hardware like a rotator via a serial interface on the PC, it has a built in logging program with special digital contesting facilities, DX cluster link and QSL card printing. One of the only things not in the list of facilities is tea and coffee making! All of this can be tried out with a 15 day free trial download [13], the full product is £39.

The list of modes is not as impressive as MULTIPSK but because it has a macro mode and DDE interface there are lots of add on modes appearing on the Internet from other amateurs. The digital modes included are in the standard software are:

- CW

- BPSK31, QPSK31, FSK31, RTTY, Packet

- Pactor, AMTOR, MFSK

- Hellschreiber, Throb, Fax, SSTV

- MT63

A typical screen shot from a Packet QSO on 2m using MixW is shown in Fig 7.14

The software is now being sold bundled with a range of hardware called RigExpert [14], this extends the Swiss Army Knife concept a bit further. RigExpert does not use the sound card in your PC but plugs into a USB port and provides all of the facilities plus several others like voice recording and playback.

SSTV

I was not sure where to put this description of Slow Scan Television (SSTV), should it be a data mode, should it be ATV or should it be satellite communications because of Fig 7.15. So it is in this chapter with references from the other two chapters.

Copthorne Macdonald invented SSTV in the 1960s for use by radio amateurs but it has been adopted by organisations like the police and security services. It takes a television picture and transmits it at a line speed of 16.6Hz and 120 or 128 lines per frame. The bandwidth is 2.3KHz with 1500Hz being the black level and 2300Hz being the white level and a 5ms 1200Hz tone as a sync pulse at the end of each 30ms frame. This results in a complete picture every 7.2 or 8 seconds. Most of the data software available will decode and display SSTV pictures.

To illustrate what can be achieved using SSTV, Fig 7.15 shows a picture received on August 13th 2006 by David Worboys, M0ZLB/KG4ZLB from The International Space Station (ISS) [15]. In early 2006 a new mode of operation, dubbed "SpaceCam 1" was developed and delivered to the ISS to allow amateurs and anyone with a suitable receiver and a personal computer to receive fairly high quality SSTV images direct from the orbiting Space Station. The SSTV developments for the ISS are being carried out by the MAREX group that contributed and gained much valuable experience in the very successful Mir SSTV System. Whilst the Mir SSTV System consisted

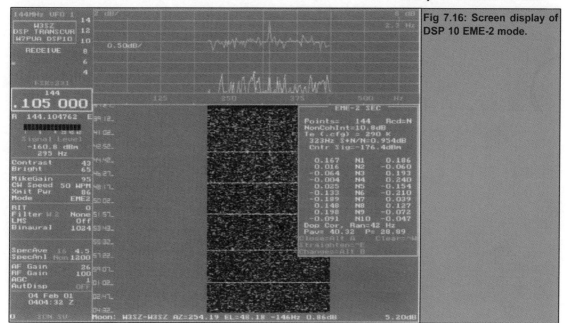

of a hardware package, ISS SSTV utilises a laptop computer that was already aboard the ISS and the software and interface was mated to the already present Ericsson HT radio aboard the station. That Ericsson radio is also the one being used for packet and voice communications. It is worth mentioning at this point that there is no funding available for this project, the generous contributions of amateur radio operators worldwide having made this idea a reality. The idea is that eventually the system will be transmitting pictures 24 hours a day on a slideshow basis which should allow three or four pictures to be downloaded in the time that it takes for the ISS to pass over your QTH. That is providing that the pass is high enough in the sky. A library of some 400 images will be available and ultimately it is hoped that amateurs will be able to upload their own images. At the end of July 2006, Pavel Vinogradov, RV3BS, the Commander of the Expedition 13 mission, initiated some testing of the system by activating the SSTV program that proved that the basic configuration was set up correctly.

The real beauty of this mode of operation, from a recipient's viewpoint, is the ease and simplicity and inexpensiveness of the equipment needed to receive images. If you have 2m receive capability and a personal computer equipped with a soundcard, you can get in to this new mode of ISS amateur radio with the minimum of fuss. You do not need az/el rotators, high gain yagis and computer controlled tracking. It is nice, but not actually a requirement for any ISS mode of transmission. Better still, for those experienced satellite operators, there are no worries about Doppler effect, the strength of the signal from a craft that is not spinning away in space combined with a large footprint, means that you can set your equipment up, wait for an ISS pass over your location and let the equipment do all the work.

Two programs are needed on your computer, one being a satellite-tracking program to tell you where and when the ISS will be passing you and the second is a program that will decode the signal received to provide the image. The good news is that both of these are available free on The Internet. David uses a program called "Nova" [16] for satellite tracking that is available to be downloaded on a trial basis; the only difference between the trial version and the registered version is the inability to save as default, certain end user preferences, but it is a clean and clear program that is extremely user friendly. For SSTV, David uses "MMSSTV" [17] that is extremely popular with SSTV enthusiasts. A radio or scanner that has 2m capabilities and an antenna is all that is needed to receive the transmissions. It can be done with a handheld and a rubber duck antenna, the strength of the signal from the ISS is such that basic antennas are adequate. Initially SSTV images were received on the ISS normal downlink frequency of 145.800MHz. When the system is running at full capacity this may be changed because 145.800MHz is the worldwide downlink frequency for voice and packet.

Weak signal modes

Weak signal modes covers QSOs using meteor scatter, E and F layer propagation modes and Earth-Moon-Earth (EME). Again there is lots of software available, I have chosen those available for the DSP 10 hardware described in chapter 4 and WSJT to illustrate what is available.

DSP 10 weak signal modes

The DSP 10 hardware lends itself very well to working the weak signal modes. Bob Larkin, W7PUA wrote the software for four special weak signal modes for the DSP 10:

- EME-2 is a mode for determining system performance and path conditions. A typical screen for this mode is

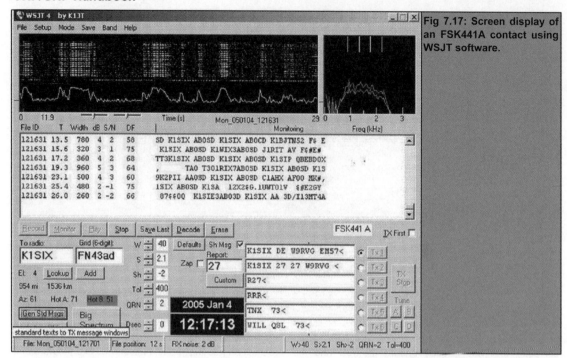

Fig 7.17: Screen display of an FSK441A contact using WSJT software.

shown in Fig 7.16. In this mode the DSP 10 transmits a CW pulse for 2 seconds. There is a delay of 2.6 seconds from the start of the transmitted pulse to allow for pulse travel, followed by a 2 second receive period. (The actual pulse travel time will vary from about 2.4 seconds at perigee to about 2.7 seconds at apogee). The cycle then repeats (every 5 seconds) for as long as desired, and the DSP 10 averages the received signal to gain the "square root of n" increase in signal-to-noise ratio. An averaged spectrum is displayed at the top of the DSP 10 spectrum display area. With this technique Bob W7PUA has detected well-defined EME echoes using 5 watts of transmit power and a 4 x 12 element array! The software automatically applies EME Doppler correction.

• PUA43, named because Bob W7PUA created it, and because there are 43 defined characters in the PUA43 code. These are the letters A - Z, the numerals 0 - 9,

Space, Period, the comma, the forward slash, the pound sign, the question mark, and the Dollar sign. The pound sign is defined as "message received" and the Dollar sign is used to shift the meaning of the following character. This mode is the mode generally used for two-way low power level EME communications. With this mode Bob, W7PUA and his brother Beb, W7SLB have completed a two-way EME contact on 144MHz using single yagis and 150W transmitter power at each end. Ernie, W7LHL and Larry, W7SZ completed an EME contact on 10GHz with TVRO dishes and 5 – 15W at each end with this mode [18].

• LHL-7. This is essentially an FSK Morse code method with much greater tolerance for frequency errors than PUA43. It can be used with either human or automatic decoding. Dots are sent at 750Hz tone frequency, dashes at 900Hz, end of character at 600Hz, and "times two" at 1050Hz, "times three" at 1200Hz, "times four" at 1350Hz, and "times five" at 1500Hz. Thus "e" would be 750Hz, 600Hz. The numeral "5" would be 750Hz, 1500Hz, 600Hz. Each tone can be sent for 2, 4, 10, 20, or 60 seconds. Automatic Morse ID can be sent periodically.

• LTI (Long Term Integration mode), this mode is able to detect signals in the range of -180 to -190dBm. Such signals are of the order of 30 - 40dB below audibility. This mode operates much like EME-2, with alternating transmit and receive periods, but the transmit and receive cycle lengths are adjustable variables, and either CW or a continuous tone can be transmitted, with automatic CW ID possible as well. There is a "noise blanker" function that will discard the data from a given period if the noise in the noise measurement bins for that period exceeds the running average of the noise

Table 7.4: WSJT modes best suited to various propagation modes.

2m and higher Meteor Scatter	FSK441
6m short burst Meteor Scatter	FSK441, JT6M may be too slow for vet short bursts
6m long burst Meteor Scatter	JT6M
Steady signal tropo	JT65
EME	JT65
Spradic E	JT6M (JT44 more sensetive but much slower, JT65 is much too slow
F layer propagation	JT6M (JT44 more sensetive but much slower, JT65 is much too slow

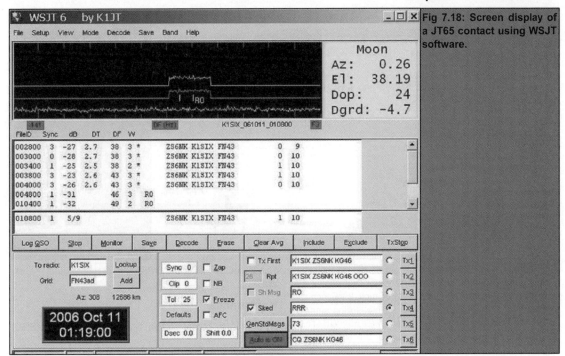

Fig 7.18: Screen display of a JT65 contact using WSJT software.

by "x"dB. This mode is most useful for determining path performance between two stations, and for exploring the possibility of a link between two sites where conditions are expected to be at most marginal. It is an excellent experimental propagation tool.

WSJT

Joe Taylor, K1JT has developed the software package WSJT (Weak Signal communications by K1JT) . At the present time, there are four modes built into WSJT, all are FSK. The first mode is FSK441 optimised for short ping meteor burst communications utilising a transmission rate of one character every 2.3 milliseconds. From 3rd March 2003, the JT44 like JT6M enhancement to WSJT was released which included an averaging feature for improved weak signal detection of up to 13dB over FSK441. The new mode is slower than FSK441 but faster than JT44 and has already shown promising results on 6m

meteor scatter where the ionisation tends to last longer than 2m meteor scatter. In addition, JT6M shows great promise for Es communications on any band and for 6m F2. The third mode is JT44 that uses a very slow transmission rate of 5.38 baud and can detect "sync" as low as 29.9dB below noise (in a 2500Hz bandwidth) making it extremely useful for EME and other weak signal work. However, due to the very slow transmission rate, attempting to use JT44 for meteor scatter can be extremely frustrating. In November 2003, the latest JT65 modes were released showing even further enhanced weak signal EME capability over JT44. This mode is the slowest of all and therefore not recommended for weak signal Es and F2 propagation. Therefore, WSJT contains four two-way communications applications, each optimised for a particular task: FSK441/JT6M for Meteor Scatter work, JT6M for E and F layer propagation modes and JT44/JT65 for extreme weak signal work when

Table 7.5: The main characteristics of each WSJT mode.

Mode	Transmission rate	Bandwidth	Sensitivity	Features
FSK441A	147 characters per second	1323Hz	-2dB (SH msg)	Highest speed of all
FSK441B	110 characters per second	1379Hz	-5dB (SH msg)	FEC used = less falsing (no longer supported in WSJT)
FSK441C	63 characters per second	1379Hz	-5dB (SH msg)	Strongest FEC of all three = less falsing (no longer supported in WSJT)
JT6M	14.1 characters per second	925.93Hz	-13dB	Much slower than 441 but more sensitive, uses averaging
JT44	5.38 baud (0.7 char. per sec.)	485Hz	-20dB to -29dB	Relies on averaging over time
JT64A	2.69 baud	177.6Hz	-23dB to -29dB	Least forgiving re frequency stability, averaging and FEC
JT65B	2.69 baud	355.3Hz	-22dB to -29dB	More forgiving re frequency stability, averaging and FEC
JT65C	2.69 baud	710.6Hz	-21dB to -29dB	Most forgiving re frequency stability, averaging and FEC

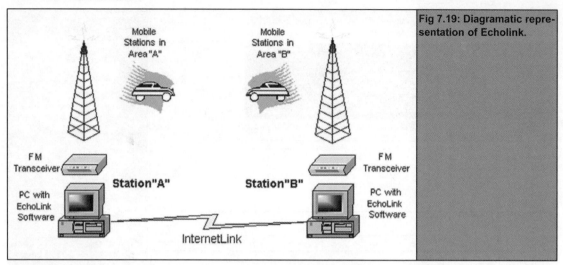

Fig 7.19: Diagramatic representation of Echolink.

signals have a relatively constant amplitude. WSJT also includes a fifth mode: EME ECHO mode that allows the user to measure the received level of their EME echoes and an embedded measure mode for measuring signals, noise, etc. that can be very useful even for non WSJTers. To operate all modes, two releases of the software are required because the latest revision no longer contains JT44.

Table 7.4 shows the WSJT modes best suited to the various propagation modes. Table 7.5 shows the main characteristics of each WSJT mode

Bob Mobile, K1SIX who wrote the description of WSJT is a keen 6m operator and user of WSJT, Fig 7.17 shows one of his QSOs using FSK441A and Fig 7.18 shows him using the JT65A mode.

VOIP

Radio amateurs have used Voice Over Internet Protocol (VOIP) for many years. It started life with the Internet Radio Linking Project (IRLP) to make a voice link over the amateur packet radio network; it used specialised hardware to link computers running LINUX to the network. Ilink designed by Graeme Barnes, M0CSH, was the next product that used special hardware but a Windows PC. Unfortunately Ilink did not last long and has been overtaken by Echolink [19] developed by Jonathan Taylor, K1RFD in 2002. The Echolink software can be downloaded free. The software runs on a Windows PC and uses a standard sound card and interface to connect to an amateur radio. Once the software is installed on your PC you must logon to the Echolink server to be verified as a radio amateur and be added to the system. From then onwards you can use the Echolink server like a telephone exchange and telephone book to see who is logged on and contact them. The system enables contact to be made from either your PC or a transceiver connected to your PC to any of the other amateurs logged in to the system either to their PC or their transceiver connected to their PC as illustrated in Fig 7.19

There are other similar systems becoming popular, these

include eQSO [20] and WIRES-II [21] that is a Yaesu system.

References

[1] Your First Packet Station, Steve Jelly, G0WSJ, RSGB 1996

[2] Packet Radio Primer, 2nd edition, Dave Coomer, G8UTZ and Martyn Croft, G8NZY, RSGB 1995

[3] North West Packet User Group (NWPUG), Whitchurch, Salop., SY13 2PX , Tel: 01939 235357, web: http://www.merseyworld.com/nwpug/bsxinf.htm

[4] Tucson Amateur Packet Radio (TAPR), PO BOX 852754, Richardson, TX 75085-2754, USA, Tel: 972-671-TAPR (8277), Fax: 972-671-8716, web: http://tapr.org/packetradio.html

[5] PMR Conversion Handbook, Chris Lorek, G4HCL, RSGB 1997

[6] Computer-to-transceiver interfacing for digital modes, Ross Wilkinson, G6GVI, web:

http://homepage.ntlworld.com/jon.mossman1/digimodes/interface.html

[7] Farnell In One, www.farnell.co.uk

[8] Maplin Electronics Ltd, National Distribution Centre, Valley Road, Wombwell, Barnsley, South Yorkshire, S73 0BS, Tel: 0870 4296000, web: http://www.maplin.co.uk/

[9] West Mountain Radio, 18 Sheehan Avenue, Norwalk, CT 06854, USA, Tel: 203.853.8080, Fax: 203.299.0232, web: http://www.westmountainradio.com/RIGblaster.htm

[10] Tigertronics, P.O. Box 2490, Grants Pass, Oregon 97528, USA, Tel: (541) 474-6700, web: http://www.tigertronics.com/

[11] The official PSK31 homepage, web: http://aintel.bi.ehu.es/psk31.html

[12] Patrick Lindecker, F6CTE, Software homepage, web: http://f6cte.free.fr/index_anglais.htm

[13] MixW Distributor, Konstantine Kisselev, KMK UK Limited, email: mixw@mixw.co.uk, web: www.mixw.co.uk

[14] RigExpert Distributor, Konstantine Kisselev, KMK UK Limited, email: mixw@mixw.co.uk, web:http://www.mixw.co.uk/product/product.htm

[15] Chelmsford Amateur Radio Society contact with the International Space Station (ISS), web: http://www.g0mwt.org.uk/events/iss-qso/iss-qso.htm

[16] Northern Lights Software Associates, P.O. Box 321, Jamesville, NY 13078, USA, Tel: (315) 345-6991, email: nlsa@nlsa.com, web: http://www.nlsa.com/nfw.html

[17] MMSSTV, web: http://mmhamsoft.amateur-radio.ca/

[18] EME-2 contacts, web: http://www.proaxis.com/~boblark/wksig1.htm

[19] Echolink, web: http://www.echolink.org/

[20] eQSO, web: http://www.eqso.org/

[21] WIRES-II, web: http://www.vxstd.com/en/wiresinfo-en/

VHF & UHF Linear Power Amplifiers

50MHz/70MHz/144MHz/432MHz/1.3GHz/2.3GHz, 1W to 100W, kit or ready built & tested

Some examples :-

PA432-45 - 432MHz, 45W

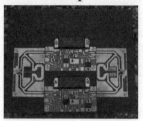

PA1.3-50 - 1.3GHz, 50W

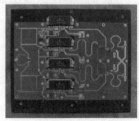

PA1.3-100 - 1.3GHz, 100W

All power amplifiers operate from 12V DC with reverse polarity protection. The use of RF MOSFET technology means very low input power required, thus suitable for driving direct from transverter. SMA connectors supplied as standard, heatsink can be pre-drilled and tapped if required . Optional attenuator allows for input powers up to 3W.

Mitsubishi Semiconductors

All the popular Mitsubishi power amplifier modules and GaAsFETs in stock, including :-

RA30H0608M	70MHz	30W						
			RA13H1317M	144MHz	13W	RA30H4047M	432MHz	30W
			RA30H1317M	144MHz	30W	RA45H4047M	432MHz	45W
RA18H1213G	1296MHz	18W	RA60H1317M	144MHz	60W	RA60H4047M1	432MHz	60W

GaAsFETs :-   MGF1302   MGF1402   MGF1801   MGF0906   MGF4953

12.5GHz, divide by 10 prescaler

Ideal for extending the rage of frequency counters.
Operates from 50MHz to >12.5GHz.

XP12-10

Unique broaband input buffer ensures high sensitivity of better than -15dBm at 12.5GHz

In development - ultra low noise VHF crystal oscillator

Using a unique dual-resonator circuit resulting in ultra-low levels of phase noise, this is an ideal replacement Local Oscillator for use in VHF transverters or as the first stage of a microwave oscillator/multiplier chain. Can be locked to GPS and FSK modulated if required. Available late 2007.

Coming soon - Ultra low noise UHF/microwave source

Using the ultra-low noise VHF oscillator above, this source comprises a series of low-noise frequeny multipliers with buffers and filters to give an extreemly clean output. The output can be taken from any of the multiplier stages, allowing for a number of uses on bands from 432MHz to 2.3GHz, or higher with an external microwave multiplier.

GH Engineering

The Forge   tel 01256 889295
West End   fax 01256 889294
Sherborne St. John
Hants
RG24 9LE   www.ghengineering.co.uk
                 sales@ghengineering.co.uk

Also available - semiconductors from Avago, Mini-Circuits and others, SMA and N-type connectors, high power resistive terminations. Semi-rigid and coaxial cable *and much more........*

Chapter 8

Amateur Television

In this chapter :

- Video equipment
- ATV transmitters

- ATV receivers
- Operating techniques
- Digital Amateur Television (DATV)

O f all our senses, sight is probably the most precious to us. Almost every activity we involve ourselves in has a degree of searching, moving and manipulating which require visual cues or feedback at some point. It seems logical that visual communication using television, which has become so much a part of our domestic lives, should also be applied to amateur radio. Listen to any voice conversation on the amateur bands and before long you will hear someone describing a piece of equipment in their shack or asking if anybody knows what a "grey thing with an odd looking connector in the top corner" is. It's much easier to explain the gadget in your hand when you can hold it up to a camera and let the people see it for themselves. The adage "a picture is worth a thousand words" is proven true with amateur television (ATV).

ATV activity really started in the mid 1940s with experiments by amateurs. I am familiar with one of the early public demonstrations of ATV because it took place in my local Radio Society; The Shefford and District Amateur Radio Society (Then the Shefford and District Short Wave Society), it is still talked about today as one of high points in the activity of the society. On April 21st 1950 Ivan

Howard, G2DUS demonstrated his 250 line Iconoscope camera equipment to an audience or 250 people. Fig 8.1 shows the "studio" for the demonstration. A full account of the can be found in issue 4 of CQ-TV [1]. CQ-TV is the magazine of the British Amateur Television Club (BATC) [2], a full archive of the magazine is available on a DVD containing all issues of the magazine and is an invaluable source of information.

The majority of ATV contacts are picture and sound in one direction with "talkback", usually on 144.750MHz in Europe and 144.34MHz in The USA, these frequencies are also used as a calling channel. Full duplex operation (sound and vision both ways simultaneously) is becoming more popular as activity grows and repeater coverage is extended. The use of Digital transmissions (DATV) means that more sound channels are available.

What gets broadcast?

ATV and voice communication are similar in that they both tends to be unprepared and unrehearsed. Some people use television as an extension of photography; their interest lies in the picture content and production rather than its technical aspects. Others are experimenters,

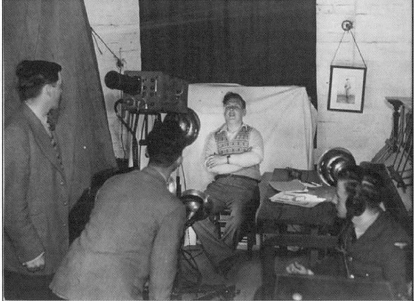

Fig 8.1: The "studio" for an early public demonstration of ATV organised by Ivan Howard. G2DUS in 1950 at Shefford and District Short Wave Society.

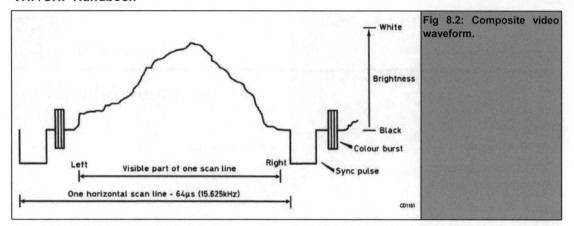

Fig 8.2: Composite video waveform.

preferring to try new electronic techniques and exotic components. The blend of art and technology works well and provides a wide variety of enjoyable material.

Local shows and events are often tape recorded with camcorders and replayed to an audience over the air and occasionally, depending primarily on location, the transmissions are sent "live". Having an ATV station at a public event always attracts attention and is a good way of introducing newcomers to the hobby. The view through a camcorder lens will often make a more rewarding transmission than one from a professional camera team or editing suite. More adventurous amateurs are no fitting ATV equipment on model aircraft or hang gliders to give an aerial view of events.

Of course, many ATV transmissions are simply "shack shots" with the camera pointing at the operator, this may not always be the prettiest of sights but at least it adds a more personal touch to the contact. There are a few ATVers who prefer not to send camera shots at all and concentrate their efforts on transmitter and video circuit designs; the only evidence on air of these devotees is an occasional test card transmission.

Like other aspects of amateur radio, ATV has its contests and contest groups. The challenge in ATV contests is to send a four digit number over the greatest distance and receive confirmation of its total from the recipient. The numbers themselves are never repeated back in case other competitors overhear them but they are entered in the contest log sheets for checking by the adjudicator. Some contests allow slow scan television (SSTV), while others only allow normal fast scan TV on 70cm and above. See chapter 7 for a description of SSTV. Striving to exchange pictures as well as voice enhances the competition. Picture quality reports are also exchanged using the "P" system, where P0 corresponds to an unrecognisable picture through to P5 for a perfect, blemish free picture.

A close look at a television signal

Unlike a voice transmission that only carries a single modulation at audio frequencies, TV signals are a composite of several different component parts. Before getting too deeply involved in transmitter and receiver functions, let's look at exactly what these video components are and their purpose.

The intention is to measure the amount of light falling at each point in the source image and faithfully recreates it on a screen some distance away. Two of the requirements are already defined: a way of measuring the intensity of light and some way of defining its position within the image. If colour is being used, a third signal is needed; this is itself a composite of two colour difference signals modulated onto a common carrier. This method of carrying colour information ensures compatibility with monochrome monitors that can simply ignore the colour difference signals and use the intensity (also called luminance) signal alone.

In the camera, the source image is focused by a lens and made to illuminate a light sensitive pick up. In older cameras this was a sensitised layer that was electrostatically charged; some of the charge was displaced when hit by light. The layer, or target as it is correctly named, was also hit by an electron beam which was magnetically or electrostatically scanned to make it sweep side-to-side and top-to-bottom over the image area. You may find it useful to think of the scanning process as moving your eyes over these lines of text. The combination of electron beam, fixed charge and light impact made the target voltage change according to the light intensity at the point hit by the beam, and after amplification this was used as the video signal.

More modern cameras use charge coupled devices (CCDs) to convert the image to an electrical signal. The image is focused onto the CCD that consists of an array of photosensitive cells; the charge on the cell depends upon the amount of light falling onto it. To retrieve the image as a usable voltage, the cells are read sequentially, usually as a long shift register (aka bucket brigade). The process is analogous to the electron beam scanning in an older camera in that at any point in time the signal from the CCD corresponds to a particular position in the image.

Once a video signal has been generated, it can be used to modulate a carrier and be sent over the air. At the receiving station, the signal can be demodulated to recover the original voltage. The final step is to use the video signal to change the intensity of a dot of light on the monitor screen.

If the position of the dot and its intensity match that

Fig 8.3: Of air capture of the Bristol 24cm repeater test card over 25km distance.

and decoding colour information is beyond the scope of this text; see [2] for further reading on this subject.

The final component added to the composite video before transmission is the sound carrier. Audio is first pre-emphasised by increasing the volume at high frequencies while at the receiving end these higher frequencies are attenuated to bring them back to their original levels. This roll off of the frequency response also reduces the effect of noise from other sources, thus improving the overall signal-to-noise ratio. The transmission audio is used to frequency modulate a carrier at a nominal 6MHz. This carrier is then added at low level to the picture signal and the total is then used to frequency modulate the transmission carrier. The carrier-in-a-carrier principle is called intercarrier sound. In the receiver, the 6MHz is recovered from the demodulated video, filtered and fed to its own amplifier and demodulator.

Video equipment

The vast majority of ATV operators rely on commercially available cameras and monitors so the complications of generating the composite video source are largely circumnavigated. One area where home brew video is still the norm is the test card. Most operators use an electronic test card generator to identify themselves. Typically this will have a callsign in large letters, the operator's name and Locator Square. Many fancy and varied designs can be seen on the air, originating from a variety of electronic designs and sometimes generated by computer.

A typical ATV station consists of a camera, test card generator, a video and sound source switch, a TV and of course a transmitter and receiver. Some operators utilise more advanced gadgets such as video effects and "wipe" generators or units to display one picture in another. Almost all the commercially available home video equipment can be applied to ATV because the transmission standards used are almost the same as those of domestic broadcast television. The narrower bandwidth used on the 70cm band does not permit colour or sound to be sent but on higher frequencies amateur TV sound and picture quality can surpass that of professional broadcasters. It follows that on the 70cm band a low pass filter must be employed to ensure the transmission bandwidth is restricted to prevent out-of-band radiation from the signal sidebands. Even with the reduced bandwidth, perfectly acceptable pictures can be sent. For those of us who can remember 405 line television, the 70cm band can still give picture quality superior to a good VHF BBC signal!

ATV repeaters

Although a great deal of point-to-point operating goes on, particularly during contests, the majority of ATV activity is through repeaters. The directional nature of long Yagi arrays and dishes makes it difficult to find new contacts unless locations and headings are known before hand. Repeaters provide a central target to aim at and their omni directional output ensures their reception in the widest possible area. Unlike voice and data repeaters, ATV repeaters are normally operational all the time. Instead of shutting down when not in use, they show a test card (Fig

generated in the camera, the image has been successfully reproduced. The process of ensuring the same position within the image is being used at the sending and receiving stations is called synchronisation or 'sync' for short. The sync pulses are generated in the camera at the sending end and are included in the transmitted waveform. There are two main types of sync pulse; one occurs just before the start of the horizontal sweep and the other before the vertical sweep; their lengths can distinguish them. Horizontal sync pulses are relatively short compared to the vertical ones, and the difference in length is used in the monitor to decide which sweep should be reset to its start position.

The combined video and sync pulses are known as composite video and are shown diagrammatically in Fig 8.2. Also shown is a part of the signal called the colour burst – this is only present when colour information is present in the picture. The burst is a 10-cycle sample of the colour subcarrier oscillator from the camera's colour encoder. It is used to ensure the colour demodulator at the receiving end stays in exact phase lock with the sending one. Inside the monitor, a timing circuit triggered by the horizontal sync pulse opens a gate allowing only the colour burst through. It is then compared to the phase of the monitor's own colour decoder oscillator and any phase errors between them are detected and eliminated. As an extra precaution, the phase of the burst signal is shifted +45 then -45° relative to centre on alternate lines. The monitor averages the phase shift to derive a single central phase for demodulating and uses the instantaneous difference in phase to decide the polarity of one of the colour difference signals. This system is called phase alternation line (PAL). The advantage of PAL over the North American NTSC colour system, which does not alternate the burst phase, is that phase errors taken over any two line average tend to cancel out. Phase errors manifest themselves as shifts in the hue of the colour, for example making flesh tones take on a green or blue tinge. This can be quite important in ATV where poor signal paths are common and can cause considerable distortion to both amplitude and phase. The full process of encoding

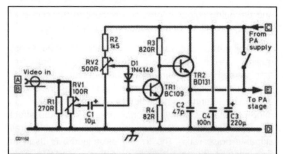

Fig 8.4: 70cm AM modulator. BD131 will require a small heatsink (minimum 10°C/W).

8.3) or page of descriptive text instead. The presence of a steady constant signal is an enormous help when setting up a receiving system, making it easy to optimise antenna position and receiver tuning. Some repeaters have facilities for reporting the strength of incoming signals, displaying a graphic S meter to assist with transmitter alignment. During the early 2000s several digital repeaters have been installed, these will often have both analogue and digital capability with the ability to switch modes by remote control, usually using DTMF commands. The wide separation between repeater input and output frequencies, usually 50MHz or more, also makes it fairly easy to filter out transmitted RF from the receiver input, allowing "look-through" while sending.

Repeater input and output signals are horizontally polarised, generally using Alford slot antennas, although some allow the selection of a directional antenna to improve reception at the repeater by sending command tones (usually telephone dialling tones) over the sound channel.

ATV transmitters

The methods employed depend upon the band being used. On the 70cm band, where space is very limited, transmissions are normally amplitude modulated and ideally will have one of the sidebands reduced in amplitude by filtering; this asymmetrical spectrum is called vestigial sideband. Sound and colour carriers are normally not used on 70cm because they would result in sidebands spreading wider than the band allocation allows. Control of the final amplifier supply voltage is normally used to achieve the amplitude modulation of the carrier. On the higher-frequency bands, FM is the predominant mode of operation, the combined composite video, colour and sound signals being used to directly control the transmission frequency. Some operators have experimented with reduced bandwidth FM in the 70cm band and achieved good results but unfortunately the techniques used are somewhat incompatible with domestic television sets and are therefore not very popular. An ATV transmitter for 70cm is described in chapter 4.

ATV construction guidelines

The frequencies present in a video waveform span DC up to about 5MHz and therefore need to be treated rather like a HF band signal. Screening is important, not only to prevent pickup of magnetic or radio signals but to prevent

radiation of the same. A strong signal entering the video signal chain will show as a pattern overlaid on the picture; this may be stationary or random depending on the type of interfering signal. Interference escaping from video circuitry manifests itself as a buzzing sound on nearby radio receivers. The picture content changes level and harshness of the buzz.

Always use screened cables to carry video signals; 75Ω cable is generally used rather than the 50Ω type used to carry RF. Unfortunately, the quality of domestic UHF TV feeder cables leaves a lot to be desired and in many cases is unusable. Use a cable with a properly woven braid to ensure signal leakage is minimised. Cables should be correctly fed and terminated with resistive loads; mismatch causes standing wave problems that show as "ghosts" or repeated images side by side as the signal bounces back and forth along the cable. Very short reflections can cause phase cancellation of certain frequencies that may result in loss of colour or sound subcarriers.

Most ATV stations will have more than one video source on hand, probably at least one camera and a test card generator. Because these are probably not synchronised with each other, if any cross coupling occurs between them, the weaker signal will probably appear as a faint image drifting slowly through the dominant one. Care is needed to minimise this breakthrough, particularly in source switching or mixing units. Standard CMOS signal switch ICs can be used at video frequencies but grounding and decoupling needs to be very efficient to keep the signals apart. Note also that switching between unsynchronised signals will almost certainly cause monitor "jump" until the new sync pulses are recognised and cross fading will wreak havoc while two sets of sync pulses appear together.

Unlike audio where a potentiometer can control the volume, video fading requires the reduction of the visible part of the waveform while leaving the sync pulses and colour burst at the same amplitude. Reducing sync level will result in an unlocked picture, while reducing burst level will cause severe colour noise and eventually no colour at all. Several designs for video faders or "fade to black" units are available from [1]. Basically they use the sync pulses to operate a changeover switch; syncs pass straight through while the picture information alone is routed through an attenuator. The two paths are then recombined.

Practical design for an AM modulator

The circuit shown in Fig 8.4 is a simple AM modulator for use in the 70cm band and can be used to convert a low powered (no more than 3W) conventional voice transmitter to transmit ATV. Ideally the transmitter should use CW mode but FM will work just as well if the microphone audio is disconnected. Although a small amount of audio frequency deviation will not affect the picture, it will be receivable on a conventional FM receiver. To use the modulator, the power supply to the PA stage (and possibly driver stage) is redirected through TR2. The switch across TR2, when closed, will restore normal operation so the

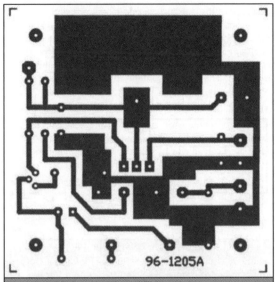

Fig 8.5: PCB for the 70cm ATV modulator.

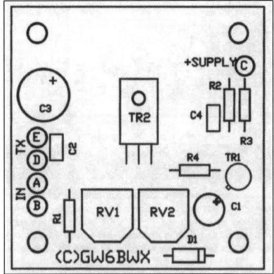

Fig 8.6: Component layout for the 70cm ATV modulator.

transmitter can be used as before when not using ATV mode. Before adding the circuit, it will be necessary to locate and disconnect any large value decoupling capacitors that will almost certainly be present across the PA supply lines. A small capacitance, no more than 470pF, should be left in place to provide a low impedance to RF and to help attenuate any high frequencies in the video signal. PCB and component layouts for the modulator are shown in Figs 8.5 and Fig 8.6 and the parts list in Table 8.1. A picture of the completed modulator is shown in Fig 8.7.

Fig 8.7: Picture of the 70cm ATV modulator.

Adjustment is straightforward. Initially set RV2 to mid position and tune the transmitter to the desired frequency; 435.5MHz is a commonly used frequency but avoid moving too close to the band edges as sidebands will start to radiate out of band. With the switch closed, check that the transmitter is working normally. If all is well, open the switch; the output power should drop and be adjustable by setting RV2. Apply a video signal, preferably of a stationary image or test card, and set RV1 to mid position. While monitoring on a receiver, adjust RV2 for optimum picture; at one end of its range the sync pulses will "crush", causing the monitor to lose synchronisation. At the other end the brightest parts of the picture will "wash out", rather like the appearance of an over exposed photograph. The correct setting is midway between these two points. Once the optimum setting is established, adjust RV1 for best contrast; its setting will have some effect on RV2 so it may be necessary to repeat both adjustments until best results are obtained.

If an oscilloscope is available, the circuit in Fig 8.8 will help with the alignment. It is a simple RF pick up probe and detector. If used, the oscilloscope should display the same video waveform as the one fed into the modulator. This circuit can also be used as a field strength meter by connecting a millivolt meter instead of the oscilloscope and will work over frequencies from about 10MHz up to about 1GHz.

Table 8.1: Parts list for the 70cm ATV modulator.

R1	270Ω	R2	1.5kΩ
R3	820Ω	R4	82Ω
RV1	100Ω	RV2	470Ω
C1	10µF	C2	47pF
C3	220µF	C4	100nF
D1	1N4148		
TR1	BC109	TR2	BD131

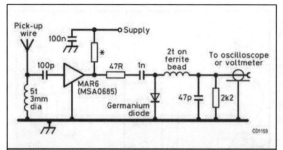

Fig 8.8: Simple RF pick up probe and detector. * Use 330Ω for 12V supply, reduce to 270Ω for 9v battery.

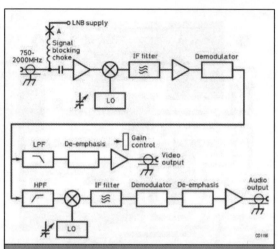

Fig 8.9: Functional block diagram of a typical satellite receiver. Cut at "A" to isolate the voltage from the input socket if connecting directly to an antenna.

As with all transmitters, before connecting the antenna, check for spurious emissions and that the signal is confined within the band edges. If the sidebands are wide enough to reach the band edges, a low pass filter should be fitted in line with the video input; a roll off starting at about 2.5MHz should be adequate. Remember the filter response must be relatively flat right down to DC to avoid video distortion. Use a linear amplifier after the transmitter to boost the power output if necessary; one suitable for SSB should do the job but under no circumstances use one designed for FM only. 70cm ATV transmissions are AM, so linearity is important.

23/24cm (1.3GHz) transmitter designs

Several excellent and inexpensive kits and ready built modules are available for 23/24cm ATV transmitters. A system built from ready built modules is described in chapter 4.

Most designs use a varactor diode (varicap) to tune a VCO at the transmitted frequency. The alternative of using a lower frequency oscillator and passing it through frequency multiplying stages is sometimes used but the relatively wide deviation can cause problems, especially as the deviation is multiplied along with the carrier. After the oscillator there is usually a buffer stage and then a modular power amplifier block. Several amplifiers are available at affordable prices. Some amplifier designs are described in chapter 4. Frequency stability is usually controlled using a PLL and frequency divider (normally in one IC); the Plessey SP5060 and SP5070 are popular, containing the phase detector, a divide by 256 prescaler and the reference oscillator circuits. For example, a crystal cut to 4.902MHz will result in a carrier 256 times higher in frequency on the 1255MHz simplex TV frequency.

ATV receivers

As with transmitters, receiver techniques depend very much on the band being used. On the 70cm band, where AM is the predominant mode, most stations use up converters to shift the band so it can be received on a normal UHF broadcast TV. Some televisions and VCRs will tune low enough to receive the band without any additional converter or modification but the later generation synthesised tuners are less generous when it comes to out-of-UHF-band reception. Some manually tuneable TV sets have a resistor in series with the low voltage side

of the tuning control, shorting it out will usually allow the bottom end of the tuning range to extended down to the ATV frequencies. Domestic terrestrial broadcasts in the UK are AM so the mode used commercially and in 70cm ATV are completely compatible.

On bands above 70cm the mode usually used is FM that makes a separate receiver mandatory. This isn't as bad as it first sounds because domestic satellite broadcasts are FM and surplus receivers are inexpensive and only require minor modification before being usable for ATV. To see what changes are needed to convert a satellite receiver it is first necessary to understand how one works. In essence they are nothing more than a normal superheterodyne receiver with a tuneable IF and an additional intercarrier sound demodulator.

Fig 8.9 shows the structure of a typical system; the satellite signal is typically in the 11GHz (K) band and is down converted inside the LNB by mixing with a 10GHz local oscillator and filtering to accept the subtractive product. After amplification, this signal is sent down a coaxial cable to the indoor unit which is tuneable across the filter bandwidth, typically 750MHz to 2GHz. Sometimes the LNB local oscillator can be switched to different fixed frequencies so a wider range of input bands can be converted to the same IF. Note that the whole of the 23/24cm band falls within the tuning range of the indoor unit; many receivers even give a direct frequency readout of the IF and therefore the frequency being received.

Satellite units can be used without any modification at all but making a few small changes can significantly enhance performance. First, a warning; when used for satellite reception, the DC supply to the LNB is fed from the receiver via the coaxial cable. If an antenna utilising a looped dipole or balun is directly attached it will short out the supply and may cause damage. There are several ways to avoid this problem; the simplest is to cut the supply feed wire inside the receiver but alternatively a small capacitor can be wired in line with the input socket.

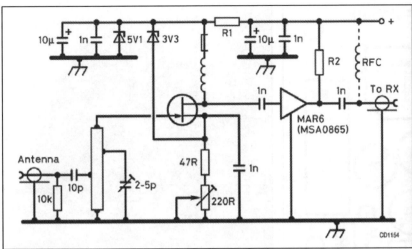

Fig 8.10: A high gain 23/24cm preamplifier using a GaAsFET and MMIC from a dismantled LNB. For 12V operation, R1 = 150Ω (0.5W), R2 = 560Ω (0.5W). To power from a satellite receiver, R1 = 270Ω (1W), R2 = 560Ω (1W) and connect RFC (5t on 3mm former) as shown to link receiver supply from the coaxial output cable.

If a capacitor is used, make sure it is a type suitable for use at UHF or losses will be incurred. Probably the most satisfactory solution is to use the feed to power a preamplifier because, as receivers are normally preceded by an LNB that provides 50dB or more gain, they are relatively insensitive when used alone. Many designs for preamps exist; the single GaAsFET followed by a MMIC seems popular and yields excellent results. If the preamp includes a filter, it should have sufficient bandwidth to allow a 12MHz wide TV signal through. A narrow band filter will result in poor sound and colour performance because both of these use the higher frequency contents of the video signal.

A simple and inexpensive design is illustrated in Fig 8.10. The GaAsFET and MMIC devices can be salvaged from a broken LNB; typically there are three low noise FETs and two MMICs inside an LNB so they make an excellent source of RF amplifier components, yet are usually thrown away when they break down. A trip to the local TV dealer to ask for discarded LNBs can be very rewarding. Before removing semiconductors from an LNB, mark them to identify the input pin, once removed it can be difficult to tell their original orientation. Hint: use sharp scissors to cut the PCB around the component before unsoldering, it reduces the heat dissipation into the board and shortens the time the component is heated by the soldering iron.

It should be noted that satellite broadcasts use a much higher modulation index than used in ATV and this will result in a lower than expected video voltage from the demodulator. Almost all satellite receivers have an internal video gain control that can usually be advanced to maximum to increase the video level. There may be a penalty to pay for increasing the level control; the amplifier stage in some receivers will exhibit poor HF response due to bandwidth reduction, as more gain is demanded. If this happens, little can be done with the existing amplifier and another stage will have to be added in series; this can be in line with the video output socket and external to the receiver if desired.

A suitable external amplifier with two identical output channels is shown in Fig 8.11 with the PCB and component layout show in Figs 8.12 and Fig 8.13 with the parts list in Table 8.2. A picture of the completed amplifier is shown in Fig 8.14. The derivation of a split polarity supply from a DC-DC inverter unit eliminates the need for

Fig 8.11: A video amplifier suitable to raise the video level from a satellite receiver.

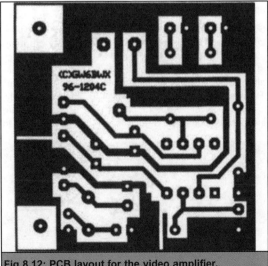

Fig 8.12: PCB layout for the video amplifier.

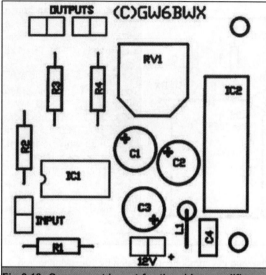

Fig 8.13: Component layout for the video amplifier.

Fig 8.14: Picture of the video amplifier.

coupling capacitors, so ensuring a near perfect LF response. Do not be tempted to use normal op amp ICs in this application; purpose designed video amplifier ICs have a wide bandwidth, low phase distortion and are designed to feed 150Ω loads (75Ω in series with the cable and 75Ω terminating load at the far end). Also, note that large value coupling capacitors should normally be used to carry video signals; the relatively low impedance used and requirement to convey frequencies close to DC makes a low reactance essential. It is also a good idea to connect a low value ceramic capacitor in parallel with large value electrolytic capacitors as their internal inductance can reduce their effectiveness at carrying high frequencies. Poor low frequency response will be seen as a brightness gradient across large areas of dark or light picture and in extreme cases will lead to poor vertical synchronisation or field roll. A poor high frequency response causes a loss of definition and makes the picture appear smudged.

Some older satellite receivers expect fixed sound carrier frequencies, usually 6.5MHz, but modern ones are tuneable usually between 5.5MHz and 8MHz. If the frequency is fixed, the sound IF filter needs to be replaced; they are all a standard size and 6MHz ones, as used in domestic TV sets, are inexpensive and easy to obtain. Obviously, satellite receivers are not ideal for ATV use but they are inexpensive and make a good "base" system on which to build. Experience shows that the performance of a modified satellite receiver is almost indistinguishable from a purpose designed ATV receiver.

Operating tips

To check for local activity, try calling on 144.750MHz; it's used throughout the UK and much of Europe as a "talkback" frequency so it is likely to be monitored by active ATV stations. In The USA 144.34MHz is used.

When sending live pictures, try to send sound with them, particularly when talking to the camera. Do this even if you are also using a separate "voice" transmitter to talk to another station; watching someone's lips moving but not hearing what they are saying is impolite to say the least. Remember there could be people watching who cannot hear the voice transmission.

Try to keep the camera in the same line of view as the monitor; if possible place it immediately above the centre of the monitor screen as a slight downward glance while you watch the picture is hardly noticeable. If the camera and monitor are spaced too far apart, there is a natural tendency to look toward the monitor rather than the lens. At the receiving end this looks like the conversation is with someone out of camera view in the shack instead of the station in contact.

Be aware of the background; avoid bright lights or reflections that can result in flare or a silhouette image. The rules are pretty much the same as with photography; keep the light source behind the camera, not behind the subject.

If the camera is in a position where other members of the family can be seen, make sure they are aware that they can be observed and overheard by a third party. Embarrassing situations when people are unaware of the camera being used are not uncommon!

Table 8.2: Parts list for video amplifier.

R1	1kΩ	R2	220Ω
R3, R4	75Ω		
RV1	470Ω		
C1, C2, C3	33µF	C4	100nF
L1	100µH		
IC1	EL2020	IC2	NMA1212S

Fig 8.15: Comparison between analogue (left) and digital (right) reception.

Digital Amateur Television (DATV)

Amateur television has always kept pace with, or even set the pace of, developments in broadcast television. This is true of the move to digital broadcasting. The main benefits of DATV are the much improved quality of the received pictures and the ability to control the bandwidth so that colour picture transmission is possible even on 70cm. Fig 8.15 shows the comparison between an analogue transmission and a digital transmission from the GB3HV repeater [3] Experiments with DATV started in the mid 1990s, the first choice was which transmission standard to use. There are three main standards:

- DVB-C, this standard was developed for cable networks. It uses Quadrature Amplitude Modulation (QAM). It requires highly linear transmitter and receiver amplifiers and is not suitable for amateur radio use.

- DVB-S, this standard was developed for satellite broadcasting. It uses Quadrature Phase Shift Keying (QPSK). It was designed for an environment where nonlinear amplifies would be used so it is suitable for amateur radio use.

- DVB-T, this standard was developed for terrestrial broadcasting to tolerate multi path propagation. It uses Orthogonal Frequency Division Multiplexing (OFDM). Whilst this is ideal for amateur radio use the problem is that the signal processing is very complex.

Initially radio amateurs used DVB-S systems by more recently several DVB-T systems have been used.

DVB-S

The main reason that this mode was chosen for the first DATV experiments is because a standard digital satellite receiver can be used. The pictures shown in Fig 8.15 were received using a Technomate E5500 "Free-to-air" digital satellite receiver. This transmitter is more of a challenge because there are two main signal-processing stages to be implemented as shown in Fig 8.16. The first is MPEG2 compression, fortunately there are encoder ICs available for this task. The second is the DVB-S baseband processor that is more difficult to implement and needs some complex digital circuitry, usually using a Field Programmable Gate Array (FPGA). The final step is to convert this to the amateur band frequency required.

Uwe Kraus, DJ8DW has been working with DATV since 1995 when he transmitted signals at 1.5Mbits/s over 50km. He demonstrated live DATV at the Ham Radio 2000 exhibition in Friedrichshafen at 1.5Mbits/s using Gaussian Minimum Shift Keying (GMSK) modulation on 70cm. GMSK is a constant envelope modulation that can be used with non linear power amplifiers but needs a special receiver. In 2002 4Mbits/s DVB-S was transmitted over 30km from a mountain hotel to the Freidrichshafen exhibition hall and in 2003 live broadcasts were transmitted from a Zeppelin flying around Fredrichshafen. The transmitter used is available as a two PCB solution.100 sets of PCBs were produced at The University of Wuppertal, at the time of writing (April 2007) there are still PCBs available [4]. Fig 8.17 and 8.18 show the completed PCBs, they support DVB-S, 2Mbits/s GMSK, 5MBits/s GMSK and the American digital HDTV standard ATSC (8-VSB). Uwe is now working on the next generation DATV that will be compatible with the current version but on a single PCB, it will include DVB-T and controlled via a USB port on a laptop or by joystick and an LCD display.

DVB-T

Because there are many digital set top boxes (STBs) available for terrestrial television it would seem that the receive side of this mode would be as simple as DVB-S. This is not quite true because they are often designed to work with OFDM systems where many different video signals (channels) are multiplexed onto the same multiple carrier system. For amateur use there will generally be one video signal. The STBs available for UK use are generally not suitable but some of the boxes available for wider European use are ideally suited. The Technisat Interdigital-T [5] is a comprehensive STB with automatic and manual channel search capabilities. The manual channel search can set a channel number or frequency to 1kHz. Unfortunately the menu is not in English but it is not difficult to master. Ian F Bennett, G6TVJ/D reviewed the Technisat Interdigital-T in CQ-TV 204 [6].

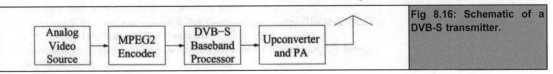

Fig 8.16: Schematic of a DVB-S transmitter.

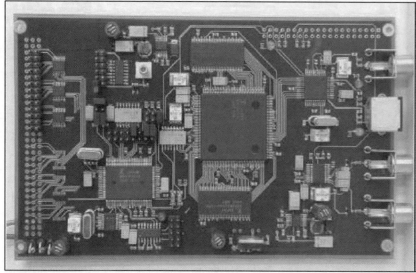

Fig 8.17: The DATV encoder board from Uwe Kraus, DJ8DW.

The transmitter for DVD-T is also more of a challenge to produce and the RF must be very well designed to prevent signal degradation. A ready built transmitter is available from SR-Systems [7], it was review by Ian F Bennett, G6TVJ/D in CQ-TV 203 [8]

References

[1] CQ-TV Magazine, a complete archive is available on DVD, web: http://www.cq-tv.com/index.htm

[2] The BATC (British Amateur Television Club), The BATC Membership Secretary, The Villa, Plas Panteidal, Aberdyfi, Gwynedd, LL35 0RF, web: http://www.batc.org.uk/index.htm

[3] Home Counties Amateur Television Club digital repeater GB3HV, web: http://www.gb3hv.com/gb3hv/digital.htm

[4] DJ8DW DATV project, web:http://www.datv-agaf.de/DATV_Boards_V1.pdf

[5] Technisat DVB-T receiver, web: http://www.technisat.com/datasheets/de/Interdigital_T.pdf

[6] Digital Terrestrial Set Top Boxes for DATV, Ian Bennett, G6TVJ/D, CQ-YV 204, November 2003, pp 15 - 17

[7] SR-Systems, Brüder-Grimm-Straße 126, 36396 Steinau a.d. Straße, Tel: +49 (66 63) 91 88 66, Fax: +49 (66 63) 91 88 67, web: http://www.sr-systems.de/

[8] SR-Systems DATV Transmitter, Ian Bennett, G6TVJ/D, CQ-TV 203, August 2003, pp 37 - 43

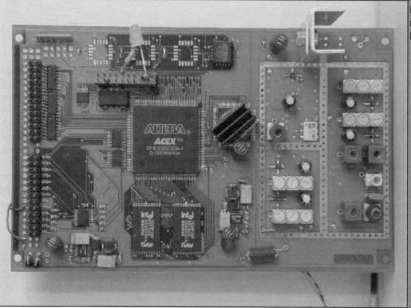

Fig 8.17: The DATV transmitter board from Uwe Kraus, DJ8DW.

Chapter 9

Satellite communications

In this chapter :

- Sources of information
- Types of satellite

- Satellite operating

Very early in the "space race" a group of Californian radio amateurs managed to persuade the US Air Force to replace ballast on the Agena rocket upper stage with the first amateur satellite. It was launched from Vandenberg Air Force Base on 12th December 1961 and the acronym OSCAR (Orbiting Satellite Carrying Amateur Radio) was born. It was a 4.5kg box shaped satellite shown in Fig 9.1 with a 140mW battery powered transmitter sending out "Hi Hi" in CW on 144.983MHz. The batteries lasted for three weeks but in that time 570 amateurs in 28 countries sent signal reports to the OSCAR project centre. The satellite now named OSCAR-1 re-entered the atmosphere and burnt up on 31st January 1962 but it was the start of a remarkable series of satellites that has involved amateurs from all around the world.

Sources of Information

The definitive source of all information on amateur satellites is one of the AMSAT (Amateur SATellite) organisations. The main one is AMSAT-NA [1] (AMSAT North America) was formed in 1969 but there is are AMSAT organisation in many countries around the world, these are listed on the AMSAT web site [2]. There have been over 70 OSCAR satellites so far, with many more planned. Not all satellites that are built are launched and not all that are launched make it into orbit, once a satellite makes it into orbit and is working it is given it's final name such as AO-51 (AMSAT OSCAR satellite 51). Table 9.1 shows the operational satellites when this text was written in April 2007, the operational status changes all the time, current status information is maintained on the AMSAT web site [3]. The table is really included to show the names and organisations involved in amateur satellite development; it is a truly international effort.

Types of satellite

There are many different types of satellite and many different modes of operation, to find the exact details refer to the AMSAT web site [4] but as an overview:

- The capabilities of a satellite are broadly described by the build phase:

  - Phase 1, these were battery powered thus short lived and really built to test the technology. OSCAR-1 to AO-5 were all Phase 1 satellites.

  - Phase 2, these are designed for longer life and equipped with solar cells to recharge the on board batteries. They are in a Low Earth Orbit (LEO) which is a low circular orbit passing over the poles, they typically take 100 minutes to orbit the earth and give 10 – 15 minutes of operation per pass. AO-6 was the first phase 2 satellite

  - Phase 3, these are designed for long life with solar cells to recharge the on board batteries. They generally have more modes and better telemetry control from the ground. They are placed in High Elliptical Orbit (HEO), also called a Molniya orbit, this gives much longer operational time for each pass of the satellite, typically 7 – 10 hours. AO-10, launched in June 1983, was the first successful phase 3 satellite.

Fig 9.1 OSCAR-1, the first amateur radio satellite.

Table 9.1: List of operational satellites in April 2007, showing name, organisation and frequencies.

Name	Organisation	Uplink Frequencies	Downlink Frequencies	Status
AO-7 (AMRAD OSCAR 7)	AMRAD, Washington	145.850 – 145.950 linear transponder 432.125 – 432.175 linear transponder	29.400 –29.500 linear transponder 145.975 – 145.925 linear transponder 29.502 telemetry beacon 145.9775 telemetry beacon	Semi operational
AO-16 (AMSAT OSCAR 16)	AMSAT North America	145.900 MFSK 1200bps 145.920 MFSK 1200bps 145.940 MFSK 1200bps 145.960 MFSK 1200bps	437.026 MFSK 1200bps 437.051 MFSK 1200bps 2401.143 MFSK 1200bps	Semi operational
AO-27 (AMSAT OSCAR 27)	AMSAT North America	145.850 FM voice repeater	436.795 FM voice repeater	Operational
AO-51 (AMSAT OSCAR 51)	AMSAT North America	28.140 PSK31 145.860 AFSK 9600bps 145.880 FM voice repeater (QRP) 145.920 FM voice repeater 145.920 FM voice repeater 1268.700 FM voice repeater 1268.700 FM voice repeater 1268.700 FM voice repeater 1268.700 AFSK 9600bps	435.300 PSK31 435.150 AFSK 9600bps 435.150 FM voice repeater (QRP) 435.300 FM voice repeater 2401.200 FM voice repeater 435.300 FM voice repeater 435.150 FM voice repeater 2401.200 FM voice repeater 2401.200 AFSK 9600bps	Operational
ANDE	USA Navy	145.825 1200bps APRS	145.825 1200bps APRS	Operational
ARRIS (Amateur radio on the International Space Station)	International	144.490 FM crew contact (region 2 & 3) 145.200 FM crew contact (region 1) 145.990 AFSK 1200bps	145.800 FM crew contact (region 2 & 3) 145.800 FM crew contact (region 1) 145.800 AFSK 1200bps 144.490 SSTV	Operational
CO-55 (CubeSat 55)	Tokyo Institute of Technology		436.8375 CW beacon 437.400 AFSK telemetry 1200bps	Operational
CO-56 (CubeSat 56)	Tokyo Institute of Matunaga LSS	1268.500 GMSK 9600bps	427505 GMSK 9600bps 437.385 CW beacon	Operational
CO-57 (CubeSat 57)	University of Tokyo		436.8475 CW beacon 437.4900 AFSK telemetry 1200bps	Operational
CO-58 (CubeSat 58)	University of Tokyo		437.3450 AFSK telemetry 1200bps 437.4650 CW beacon	Operational
FO-29 (Fuji OSACR 29)	Japan Amateur Radio League	145.900 – 146.000 linear transponder	435.800 – 435.900 linear transponder 435.795 CW beacon	Operational
GeneSat-1	GeneSat USA		437.075 AFSK telemetry 1200bps	Operational
HO-59 (HITSat OSCAR 59)	Hokkaido Institute of Technology		437.275 CW beacon 437.425 AFSK beacon 1200bps	Operational
LO-19 (LUSAT OSCAR 19)	AMSAT Argentina		437.125 CW beacon	Operational
NO-44 (Navy OSCAR 44, PCSat)	US Navy	145.827 AFSK 1200bps	145.827 AFSK 1200bps	Semi operational
PO-28 (POSAT OSCAR 28)	Portuguese consortium		429.950 GMSK beacon 9600bps	Operational
RS-22 (Radio Sputnik 22)	Mozhaisky Military Space University		435.352 CW beacon	Operational
RAFT	US Naval Academy	145.825 1200bps APRS 28.120 PSK31	145.825 1200bps APRS 145.825 PSK31	Operational
SO-50 (Saudi OSCAR 50)	KACST, King Abdul Aziz City for Science & Technology	145.850 FM voice repeater	436.795 FM voice repeater	Operational
SO-33 (SEDSat OSCAR 33)	Students for the Exploration and Development of Space (Alabama USA)	1266.687 FSK 9600bps	437.910 FSK 9600bps	Semi operational
UO-11 (UoSat OSCAR 11)	University of Surrey		145.826 AFSK 1200bps beacon	Semi operational
VO-52 (VUSat OSCAR 52, Hamsat)	Indian / Dutch amateurs	435.220 – 435.280 linear transponder	145.870 – 145.930 linear transponder 145.860 CW beacon	Operational

Table 9.2: Frequency designators and their band.

V	2m	U	70cm
L	23cm	S	13cm
C	7.5cm	X	3cm
K	1.5cm	Q	5mm

- Phase 4, these will be geosynchronous i.e. they will appear stationary in the sky giving continuous operation within their footprint. No Phase 4 satellites have been launched to date.

- Phase 5: these will be fitted to spacecraft on lunar or planetary missions, these will only happen when such spacecraft are launched.

• Satellites are equipped with one or more transmitters and receivers, on the larger satellites these can be configured from the ground so you need to find out the current operating mode or modes before you try to use the satellite. The early satellites just had a single transmitter (downlink) that broadcast a beacon message. OSCAR 3 was the first satellite to have a receiver (uplink) and a transmitter (downlink) these were linear transponders where a signal transmitted to OSCAR 3 on 145.9750 - 146.0250MHz SSB/CW was re-transmitted by the satellite on 144.3250 - 144.3750MHz SSB/CW. Following that three modes were defined:

- Mode A 10m uplink to a 2m downlink

- Mode B 2m uplink to a 70cm downlink

- Mode J 70cm uplink to a 2m downlink

• With the increase in different frequencies the modes are now specified as a two-character mode indicator e.g. U/V that is a 70cm uplink and 2m downlink. Table 9.2 shows the letters designated to each frequency band. The transmission modes vary and include PSK31, FM, AFSK, SSB, SSTV and APRS, details can

be found for any satellite on the AMSAT web page [3]

There are too many satellites to mention individually, some examples are:

• AO-51, Fig 9.2 shows Lyle Johnson, KK7P with the satellite (the cube shaped one on the left) in the clean room at the launch site, Baikonur Cosmodrome, Kazakhstan. This shows the size of the satellite that was successfully launched on 29th June 2004 and is still in full operation.

• ARISS (Amateur Radio on the International Space Station), this is probably the best-known satellite, many of the crew are radio amateurs and they use spare time to chat to fellow amateurs on earth. The crews particularly like to chat to groups of school children in the spirit of extending the hobby of amateur radio. One recent addition has been SSTV that is described in Chapter 7.

• SuitSat (AO-54), this was a spacesuit ejected from The ISS on 8th September 2005. It was equipped with a 144.990MHz FM voice beacon and transmitted for several orbits. A second SuitSat is being planned.

• CubeSat, these are very small satellites, usually 10 x 10 x 10cm, as shown in Fig 9.3. Because of their small size it is easier to find launch space and they are much cheaper being aimed at research projects by universities etc. They usually only have downlink capability with a CW beacon and FSK telemetry beacons.

Satellite operating

Things to know about a satellite

Before you can start using one of the operational satellites there are a number of things you need to know:

Fig 9.2: Lyle Johnson, KK7P with AO-51 (cube on the left) at the launch site.

Fig 9.3: A CubeSat being held by hand.

Two very good software packages are Nova by Northern Lights Software Associates (NLSA) [5] and SatPC32 by Erich Eichmann, DK1TB [6].

• What modes are in operation on the satellite? Many satellites can be configured in different ways, make sure you know how it is configured, often this information is broadcast on one of the satellite's downlink frequencies.

Things to know about your equipment

Having decided on which satellite you are going to try to use you must make sure you have the correct equipment:

• You must have a transceiver that can operate in full duplex mode on the two bands that you want to use i.e. for AO-51 you must be able to transmit on 435.300MHz and receive on 145.920MHz at the same time. Many modern transceivers are capable of this. An alternative is to use two transceivers, one for 70cm and one for 2m.

• One problem when working satellites is Doppler shift. This happens because the satellites are constantly moving towards or away from you. This causes the frequencies used to change in the same way that the pitch if a train horn changes as it passes you on the track. To maintain a QSO you must follow this frequency by changing your transmit and receive frequencies as the QSO progresses. This can be done

• Which satellite are you going to use? To start working with satellites it is best to chose an FM voice repeater, using FM reduces the effects of Doppler shift. The full list of the operational satellites and modes can be found on the AMSAT web site [3]

• Where is the satellite and when can you use it? The AMSAT web site has an interactive page to calculate this information from your locator or longitude and latitude. The alternative is to install some software on your own PC to calculate the information from the published Keplerian elements (Keps) for the satellite.

Fig 9.4: The fully steerable satellite antenna array of Matthias Bopp, DD1US.

manually or by computer control via a CAT interface between your transceiver and your computer. This is more difficult than it sounds for FM because it is more tolerant of frequency change but for SSB and digital modes it is more important. John Heath wrote a good article in RadComm [7] that describes this and much more about satellite operation in more detail, the same article can be found on many of the AMSAT web sites including AMSAT UK [8].

- Since the Satellite moves across the sky you may need a method of tracking it with a directional aerial. If the angle of the satellite is fairly low and the signal is quite strong e.g. for LEO satellites, a fixed antenna may be sufficient. It is quite possible to work some satellites such as the ARISS using a handheld transceiver and its rubber duck antenna, I remember well a local 2m DF hunt being interrupted by a contact from the Space Shuttle! If you need a directional antenna a simple low gain Yagi is a good start because it has a wide beamwidth and will probably be acceptable when pointed in the right direction and not moved. The 2m and 70cm antenna on the same boom shown in chapter 5 is a very useful design. For the HEO satellites the recommended type of antenna is a circularly polarised with a mounting that has motorised control of both elevation and azimuth such as the array belonging to Matthias Bopp, DD1US [9] shown in Fig 9.4. This comprises of crossed X-Quad antennas on 2m and 70cm and helical antennas on 23cm and 13cm. Care must be taken to ensure that the rotation of polarisation is the same as the satellite; it is an easy mistake to make. In the array shown the X-Quad antennas can be switched from RHCP (right hand circular polarisation) to LHCP (left hand circular polarisation). A computerised tracking program can be used to control the antenna for the satellite pass, both Nova [5] and SatPC32 [6] can control the antenna. Make sure that the real time clock in your PC is properly set!

Things to know about operating procedure

Before you start operating there are a few guidelines to note:

- Probably the most important operating procedure is to use just enough power for the contact. This saves the scarce power resource on the satellite.

- Most satellite passes are short, so do not hog the whole pass, once you have made a successful QSO let someone else take a turn.

- Use headphones, you are working full duplex so it is easy to set up an audio feedback loop.

References

[1] AMSAT North America (AMSAT-NA), 850 Sliogo Ave. Suite 600, Silver Spring, MD 20910, USA, Tel 1-888-322-6728, web: http://www.amsat.org/amsat-new/

[2] List of AMSAT organisations around the world, web: http://www.amsat.org/amsat-new/links/index.php

[3] AMSAT satellite status page, web: http://www.amsat.org/amsat-new/satellites/status.php

[4] AMSAT list of all satellites, web: http://www.amsat.org/amsat-new/satellites/all_oscars.php

[5] Nova satellite tracking software, Northern Lights Software Associates, P.O. Box 321, Jamesville, NY 13078, Tel: (315) 345-6991, email: nlsa@nlsa.com, web: http://www.nlsa.com/

[6] SatPC32 satellite tracking software, Erich Eichmann, Kiewningstr. 57, D32756 Detmold, Germany, Tel: 49-5231-359130, Fax: 49-5231-359132, email: dk1tb@amsat.org, web: http://www.dk1tb.de/indexeng.htm

[7] Getting started on amateur radio satellites, John Heath, RadCom March 2007, pp53 - 56

[8] AMSAT-UK, Jim Heck, G3WGM, Hon Secretary, AMSAT-UK, "Badgers", Letton Close, Blandford, Dorset, DT11 7SS, web: http://www.uk.amsat.org/. RSGB article under the How Do I Start menu.

[9] Matthias Bopp, email: dd1us@amsat.org, web: http://www.dd1us.de/

Repeaters

R epeaters have been described as the second greatest development in amateur radio since the Second World War. The first was, of course, the advent of SSB that is firmly established as the speech DX mode on all bands.

What is a repeater?

It does exactly what it says on the tin, it repeats radio signals. They were introduced to help mobile stations make more reliable and longer distance contacts. Once accessed the repeater re-transmits the incoming signal on a slightly different frequency. In the Amateur Service mobile-to-mobile contact is very common but the difficulty is that range is restricted; why not put a base station on the biggest hill in the county so that many mobiles can make contact through it? See Fig 10.1.

Careful design has meant that repeaters can receive and transmit on the same band, and this means that the same antenna can be used for both reception and transmission at the mobile station. In effect, the receiving and transmitting coverage of the mobile station becomes that of the repeater and, since the repeater is favourably sited on high ground or a tall mast, the range is greatly improved over that of unassisted, or simplex operation. The coverage areas of two mobile stations continually change shape, whereas the coverage of a repeater will stay constant, and can even be published (Fig 10.2).

The Amateur Service has specific bands and repeaters are confined to fairly small segments of these bands by international agreement so that the needs of all users can be accommodated in the limited amount of spectrum available. The repeater uses two frequencies simultaneously, one for transmit and one for receive.

UK repeaters are operational on all of the VHF bands except for 70MHz because of the small amount of space available. The difference between receive and transmit frequency is 500kHz on 50MHz, 600kHz on 145MHz, 1.6MHz on 432MHz and 6MHz on 1.3GHz. Channel spacings are 10kHz, 12.5kHz, 25kHz and 25kHz respectively. On the 50MHz and 433MHz bands the input frequency is higher than the output frequency but in the other bands it is lower.

During the late 1960s and early 1970s FM came into widespread use on the VHF bands mainly because of its cheapness and the ease of construction of FM equipment compared with that for SSB. Surplus ex-private mobile radio (PMR) equipment was cheaply available and this was frequently converted from high band PMR use to FM on 2m.

The improvement of FM on mobile communications system performance is quite dramatic. Although the range is potentially less, the quality of reception is much better. This is because of the limiting effect of an FM signal that eliminates much of the ignition noise from surrounding

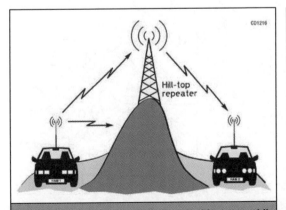

Fig 10.1: A repeater on a hill being used by two mobile stations.

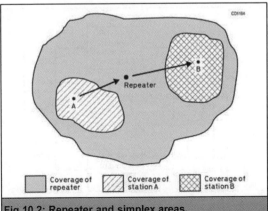

Fig 10.2: Repeater and simplex areas.

Table 10.1: Total number of UK repeaters by band.

10m repeater	1
6m repeaters	20
2m repeaters	115
70cm repeaters	156
23cm speech repeaters	12
23cm TV repeaters	28
13cm TV repeaters	13
3cm TV repeaters	11
Total (April 2007)	355

vehicles. Although an individual may have satisfactorily suppressed his/her vehicle the problem is all those other unsuppressed vehicles around. It is also advantageous for the repeater in that when a receiver is close in frequency to an adjacent transmitter a lot of amplitude noise is generated which is easier to eliminate in an FM system by the nature of the limiting action of the FM detector.

Because of the limited spectrum available in the amateur bands it is customary to use a much narrower spacing between the receive (input) and the transmit frequency (output) compared to commercial systems, e.g. on the 430MHz band the spacing is 1.6MHz and on 144MHz band is 600kHz. There are 355 repeaters in the UK (April 2007), as shown in Table 10.1. A full list of repeaters with their location and operating frequencies is available on the UK Repeater Net web site [1] and is published annually in the RSGB Yearbook [2]. Some of these repeaters now have Internet linking to enable the use of Echolink as described in chapter 7. Many of these repeaters are extremely popular and are in use for many hours a day whereas the corresponding PMR system might only be in use for a few minutes per hour. This continuous service aspect of repeaters makes greater demands on power supplies and other components that have to be continuously rated rather than for intermittent use. Further information on these repeaters is available in the Amateur Radio Operating Manual [3].

The fact that large numbers of amateurs use any repeater system means that the coverage area of the unit is very quickly established. This large number of users highlights another problem. How do you share out the available air time to all potential users on what is basically a single channel device? Although many can listen, only one person at a time can transmit. In order to provide an incentive for short transmissions it is normal to provide a limitation to the talk-through time permitted. After a given period of time, usually one to two minutes on the busiest VHF repeaters and five minutes on the UHF repeaters, the user times out, i.e. the repeater will no longer relay the input signal.

The simplest sort of repeater needs an antenna or antennas, a receiver, a transmitter, something to control it (usually referred to as the logic), and an arrangement of filters to enable it to receive and transmit at the same time (Fig 10.3). A further difficulty for the repeater builder is that Ofcom have stipulated that repeaters should not be triggered by a spurious transmission on their input frequency. Access to the repeater, i.e. switching on of the transmitter, is accomplished by either a short tone burst of 1750Hz or by the transmission of a sub-audible tone. This is often called CTCSS that stands for "Continuous Tone Coded Squelch System". The user has to transmit a tone that is below the audible range all the time. The CTCSS frequency used depends on the area and has the advantage of preventing a station accessing a repeater out of its area except in exceptional conditions. For example, all the London repeaters have the same CTCSS tone (82.5Hz) but the Brighton repeater (GB3SR) on the same frequency as the East London repeater (GB3EL) would not be accessed at the same time because its tone is 88.5Hz. For convenience of mobile users, repeaters that are using the sub-audible tone transmit an appropriate letter after their callsign in Morse code to indicate which tone should

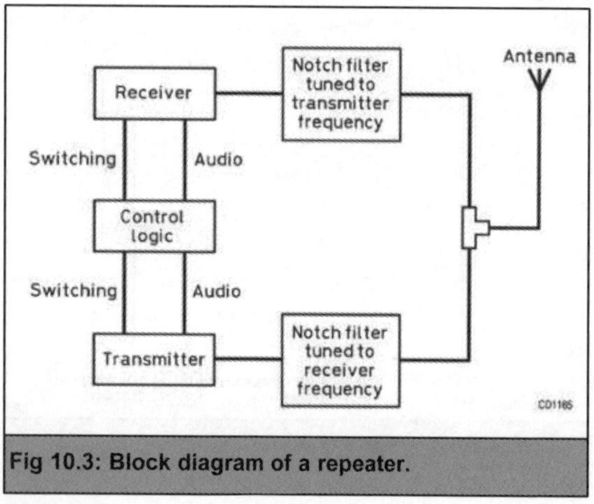

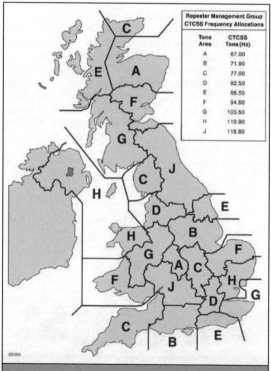

Fig 10.3: Block diagram of a repeater.

Fig 10.4: CTCSS tones in The UK.

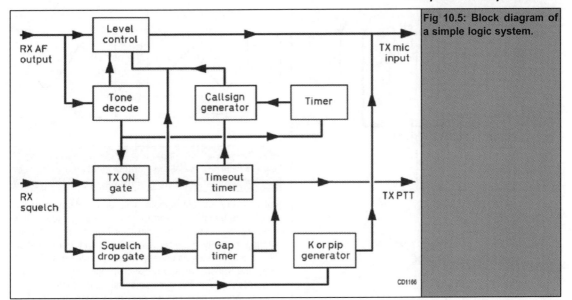

Fig 10.5: Block diagram of a simple logic system.

be used. The tones used and the geographic areas are co-ordinated by the RSGB's Repeater Management Committee (RMC) [4]. The tones for each area of the UK are shown in Fig 10.4.

If the repeater receiver hears a valid tone on its input frequency it will relay the transmission. If either the carrier or sub-audible tone ceases then after a short time the transmitter will send a "K" or "E" in Morse that signals the input of the repeater is clear and is an invitation for another user to make a transmission. If no further valid transmission is received then after a short period of time the repeater will close down. The repeater transmitter must identify itself in Morse code at intervals not exceeding 15 minutes. Often repeaters respond with their callsign when accessed. The repeater needs to be able to decide whether suitable conditions have been met before it can relay an incoming transmission, to know when to send an identifying callsign and when to close down.

Because the repeater has to respond to various situations it needs to be able to "think" for itself especially because it is often remotely located. This means that a logic system has to be built into the repeater. The repeater users often refer this to simply as the logic. Several sorts of logic systems can accomplish the control of the repeater. Dr Tony Whitaker, G3RKL designed one of the most popular logic control systems; the Mk1 version was described in RadCom 1980 and 1982 [5] and the Mk2 version was described in 1983 [6]. This is still popular with over 130 PCBs being supplied. There are other more sophisticated systems available and in operation such as the G8CUL and G1SLE logic systems. Further details of logic control systems can be found on the UK Repeater Net [4].

How a simple logic system works

The block diagram in Fig 10.4 shows the simplest sort of repeater logic system that provides the basic minimum to cover the mandatory requirements for a working repeater as well as a user-friendly system that is simple to

understand. Here is a general description of what it does. The receiver audio is fed to the tone burst decoder, producing an output which:

• keys the transmitter

• feeds audio to the transmitter via the audio control

• starts the time out timer

• activates the callsign timer

When the user has finished talking the receiver squelch closes:

• activating the "K" or "pip"

• activating a timer determining the interval after which a callsign will be sent

• resetting the timeout timer.

Thus the repeater will send a "K" and may send a high level callsign if there is no receiver audio present and close the repeater transmitter down. If a further transmission takes place after the "K" then once again the timeout timer begins to time the length of the transmission. The callsign will be sent at a time governed by the callsign timer at low deviation so as not to interrupt the audio through the repeater. Many repeaters also send what is known as a beacon callsign when they are not in talk-through mode that serves to notify listeners that they are within range of a particular repeater. This is relatively simple to incorporate, as there is already the timer and the callsign generator available. Repeaters may send other information such as their location and signal strength of received signals, or even a busy tone to indicate that a user has timed out but is still transmitting. There are numerous possibilities including speech messages but before incorporating any of these ideas a prospective repeater builder must seek the advice of the Repeater Management Committee of the RSGB [4] that handles

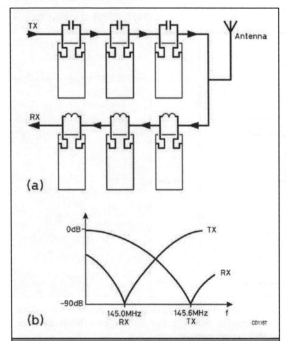

(a)

(b)

Fig 10.6: (a) Block diagram of a duplexer, three cavity receive/three cavity transmit. (b) Response curves.

repeater applications on behalf of Ofcom.

Many repeater builders make some of these parameters variable so that they can tailor the repeater to the needs or wishes of local users. It has to be pointed out that the vast majority of UK repeaters conform to the pattern of logic outlined above and this has evolved after many years of experimentation by repeater builders and users. VHF repeaters tend to be very busy and the timeout is almost universally set at one or two minutes. It can all be summed up in the KISS acronym; "Keep it simple, stupid!" The system outlined is easy to understand and logical to use!

How a repeater transmits and receives at the same time without de-sensing itself

De-sensing is a term referring to the problem of a receiver trying to listen in the same band as the local transmitter. A transmitter never transmits a single frequency but a range of frequencies distributed either side of the carrier frequency. This results in wide band noise that is received by the adjacent receiver and prevents it from receiving any

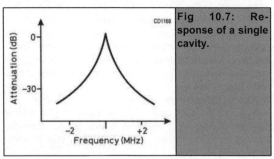

Fig 10.7: Response of a single cavity.

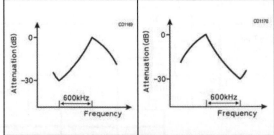

Fig 10.8: Response of single cavity with parallel capacitor.

Fig 10.9: Response of a single cavity with parallel inductor.

but the very loudest signals. This desensitisation of the receiver is usually referred to as de-sensing. How is this problem overcome? The answer is to use very selective filtering, not only in the receiver but also in the transmitter. The filtering system is usually called a duplexer, the filters allow the transmitter and receiver to operate on their two separate frequencies simultaneously, i.e. duplex operation, as opposed to simplex operation where the receiver and transmitter cannot operate simultaneously.

A typical duplexer is made up of three cavity filters in the receiver input and three cavities in the transmitter output (see Fig 10.6). Each cavity is a very high Q filter which therefore has a very high attenuation either side of its resonant frequency. See Fig 10.7. A design that a lot of 2m repeaters use was published in QST and can be found on The Internet [7].

The three cavities in the receive leg are tuned to the transmitter frequency to give maximum rejection of the transmitter. This ensures that the strong carrier does not drive the receiver front-end circuits into overload. The transmit cavities are tuned to the receiver frequency so that they attenuate the wideband noise generated by the transmitter as much as possible on the receiver input frequency. This enables the receiver to hear weak signals.

Fig 10.6(b) shows the response curve of each set of cavities at receive and transmit frequencies. For the purposes of this diagram it has been assumed that the repeater receiver frequency is 145MHz and the transmitter frequency is 145.6MHz. There is a slight difference in the set of cavities used in the receive leg compared with those used in the transmit leg. Those in the transmit leg are wired up with a capacitor in parallel whilst those in the receive leg have an inductor in parallel. These additional components have the effect of skewing the skirt of the filters so that the attenuation effects can be adjusted to allow little or no attenuation of the transmit frequency by the transmitter cavities and little or no attenuation on the receiver input frequency by the cavities in the receiver input. In practice this is usually adjusted on site to give the performance necessary. See Figs 10.8 and 10.9.

As a typical receiver sensitivity is of the order of -130dBm, if the transmitter generates noise on the receiver frequency at about -40dBm it is necessary to achieve an attenuation of about 90dB, i.e. -130 - (-40) = -90 in order

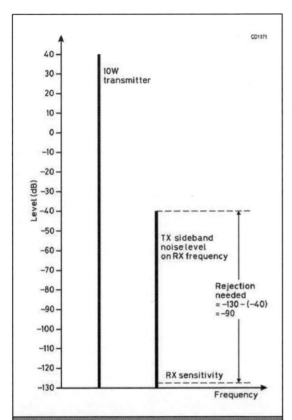

Fig 10.10 Transmitter and receiver levels for a repeater.

for the receiver not to be desensitised.

In practice each cavity is capable of producing a rejection notch of 30dB so the repeater needs three in each leg to provide approximately 90dB. See Fig 10.10.

Using repeaters

There is a user's code of practice. First, repeaters are primarily intended for mobile or portable users. It is definitely unacceptable to "hog" them for long lengths of time. Always welcome newcomers to join in, encourage membership of the group, and remember your normal amateur codes of practice are as valid on repeaters as on simplex operation (use of callsign, courtesies etc).

Before attempting to transmit, ensure that:

- Your transmitter and receiver are on the correct frequencies (remember the repeater split).

- Your tone access (if fitted) is operating correctly.

- Your peak deviation is set correctly (some repeaters will not relay your signal if this is incorrect!)

- Any adjustments you have to make should be done into a dummy load, not on-air!

- Avoid using the repeater from your base station; it is really intended for the benefit of local mobile and portable stations. If you really do intend to try it from a fixed station, then use the lowest power to get into the repeater (under 1W is acceptable in the majority of situations where you can hear the repeater well).

- Always listen before transmitting. Unless you are calling another specific station, simply announce that you are "listening through", e.g. "GM8LBC listening through GB3CS". On the other hand, if you are responding to someone specific, try something like "GM0ZZZ from GM8LBC".

Once contact is established:

- At the beginning and the end of each over, you need give only your own callsign, e.g. "from GM8LBC".

- Change frequency to a simplex frequency at the first opportunity, especially if you are operating from a fixed station.

- Keep your overs short and to the point, or they may time out, and do not forget to wait for the "K or "pip" if the repeater uses one.

- Do not monopolise the repeater when busy; others may be waiting to use it.

- If your signal is very noisy into the repeater, or if you are only opening the repeater squelch intermittently, finish the contact and try again later.

Joining a repeater group

Repeaters have initiated many newcomers to the amateur radio hobby. Repeater outputs can be monitored easily, either using widely available amateur equipment, or perhaps by a scanner. Repeater groups themselves have been able to enrol new users through local meetings and newcomers are shown how to proceed. Many amateurs use repeaters in addition to their other amateur activities, perhaps using their local repeaters whilst travelling to and from work, then doing something entirely different in the evenings!

If you enjoy operating through your local repeaters then remember that they do cost money. They are operated on a purely voluntary basis, sometimes by individuals but mostly by groups who would appreciate contributions towards the cost of running the repeater. Apart from the initial costs of the equipment there are the on going costs of electricity and site rental. Site rentals for advantageous sites such as those of commercial transmitters can cost several hundreds of pounds a year even at the favourable rates negotiated either by the local repeater group or by the RSGB.

References [1] gives details of the repeater keeper who is the person to contact to offer your help.

Amateur radio "purists" have, particularly in the early years of repeater growth, shunned their existence, believing them not to be truly in the "ham spirit". Thirty-five years on, this is very much a minority view. The presentation of so many strands for devotees to find their niche is the strength of our hobby. Repeater builders are amongst the most technically competent and experienced people in amateur radio, and many are professionally employed in PMR or other communications jobs. Repeaters are often co-sited with other major broadcasters or PMR users, and so have to be of a sufficient technical standard to co-exist.

Repeaters have sometimes become the target for abuse, generally by people with limited vocabularies (using profanities) or with strange voices, ("squeakies"). The only way to treat the abuse in whatever form it takes is to ignore it completely. Any attempt to remonstrate with them encourages them since they know they have an audience. If possible, take a bearing on the repeater input frequency, make a tape recording of the abuser and note the time, date, frequency etc. This information should be sent to the Repeater Abuse Co-ordinator at RSGB Headquarters. Further information on how to deal with abuse problems is available from the same address.

If you feel there is a need for a repeater in your area then make sure you contact the Repeater Management Committee of the RSGB, c/o RSGB HQ and read reference [8] before you do anything else.

References

[1] The Repeater List, a csv file can be downloaded from the UK Repeater Network web site: http://www.ukrepeater.net/index.html

[2] RSGB Yearbook, published annually by the RSGB

[3] Amateur Radio Operating Manual, 6th edition, Don Field, G3XTT, the RSGB

[4] The RSGB Repeater Management Committee (RMC), they can be contacted via their web site: http://www.ukrepeater.net/index.html

[5] A J T Whitaker, G3RKL, Radio Communication 1980, pp34–42; A J T Whitaker, G3RKL, Radio Communication 1982, pp30–31.

[6] A J T Whitaker, G3RKL, Radio Communication 1983, pp882–885 and pp990–993.

[7] Duplexer design by W1GAN, published in July 1972 QST, the article is available on the Internet: http://www.repeater-builder.com/rbtip/2mduplexer.html

Chapter 11

Test Equipment, Methods and Accessories

In this chapter :

- Antenna measurements

- Measurement of RF power

- Frequency measurement

- Power amplifier measurement

- Receiver measurement

In the VHF region and above there is still a fair amount of scope for experimentation and home construction as well as the use of the so-called "black box". There are many items of ex-commercial equipment that can be obtained at reasonable prices for modification.

Amateurs often have to use their ingenuity to use the test equipment that is available to make measurements on their equipment. The availability of modern ICs means that test equipment can now be built to rival the performance of expensive commercial equipment. This chapter contains some designs using modern ICs as well as some more traditional designs.

Antenna measurements

To keep the performance of any VHF/UHF station as near optimum as possible the antenna system should be properly tuned to start with and maintained in that condition.

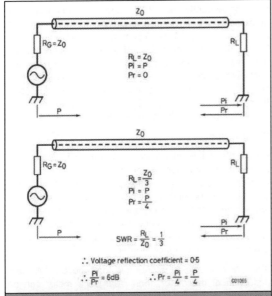

Fig 11.1: Effects of bad termination on a transmission line in terms of the incident and reflected power at the load.

To tune up any antenna system, it is essential to keep it away from large objects such as buildings, sheds and trees, and the array itself should be at least two wavelengths above the ground. It is useless to attempt any tuning indoors since the change in the surroundings will result in a completely different performance when the array is taken outside.

Undoubtedly the most effective apparatus for tuning up any antenna system is a standing wave indicator or reflectometer. If there is zero reflection from the load, the standing wave ratio (SWR) on the antenna feeder is unity (1:1). Under this condition, known also as a flat line, the maximum power is being radiated. All antenna matching adjustments should therefore be carried out to aim at a standing wave better than about 1.5:1 (some 4% reflected power). Many modern transceivers have SWR internal protection circuits and these may cut in and start to limit power output. Consult the manual for your equipment if in doubt.

If suitable apparatus is not available, the next best course of action is to tune the antenna for maximum forward radiation. A convenient device for this is a field strength meter comprising a diode voltmeter connected to a $\lambda/2$ dipole placed at least 10λ from the antenna. When adjustments have resulted in a maximum reading on the field strength meter, the SWR may not be unity and therefore some power may be wasted. However, if the best has been done with the resources available it is highly likely that good results will be achieved.

Reflectometer for VHF

When power at radio frequency is fed into a transmission line that is correctly terminated at its far end, this power is propagated along the line in terms of voltage and current waves and is all absorbed in the load at the far end of the line. This represents the ideal condition for the transfer of power from a transmitter to an antenna system. Such a condition is rarely, if ever, achieved due to the impossibility of presenting the transmission line with a perfectly matched load. In practice, it is possible only to terminate the line with an antenna or load that approaches the perfect condition. Under these circumstances a certain amount of power is reflected and is propagated back down the line again by means of further waves of voltage and current travelling in the opposite direction, to be either

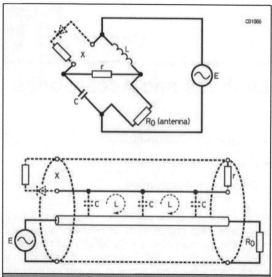

Fig 11.2: Maxwell bridge representation of a transmission line coupler

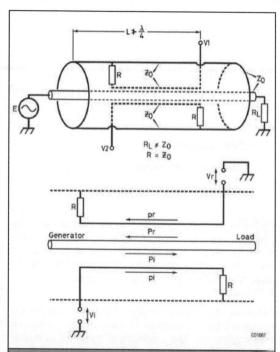

Fig 11.3: Arrangement of sampling lines to respond to incident and reflected powers.

absorbed or re-reflected at the generator depending on the match presented by the generator.

The amount of power reflected from the antenna or load is directly proportional to the magnitude of the mismatch on the line. Therefore, the mismatch on the line, or in more practical terms, the standing wave ratio, may be expressed in terms of the ratio of the forward or incident and the backward or reflected powers (Fig 11.1).

If the SWR = S, then the voltage reflection coefficient K is given by:

$$K = \frac{S-1}{S+1}$$

Clearly, if a device can be constructed which will differentially respond to power in terms of direction, it can be used directly to measure standing wave ratio, and the ratio M of incident to reflected power is given by:

$$M = 20 \log_{10} \frac{1}{K} \, dB$$

It can be shown that if a line whose length is short compared with a wavelength is introduced into the field of, and parallel to, another line which is carrying power, then an amount of power is coupled into the secondary line which is directly proportional to the magnitude of the power travelling in either or both directions on the main line. The configuration of main and sampling lines may be regarded as a Maxwell bridge, the reactive arms of which are provided by the distributed capacitance C and mutual inductance L of the coupled lines, and the effective load on the bridge is r (Fig 11.2). Then, if $r^2 = L/C$ the bridge is effectively balanced at all frequencies, and now power from the generator E appears in the load r, but a proportion appears in the detector load.

If two such subsidiary lines are coupled to a main

transmission line carrying power and are respectively terminated at opposite ends, an output can be taken from each line which is respectively proportional to the incident and reflected power in the main line.

This is the principle behind the reflectometer shown in Fig 11.3. The accuracy of such an instrument depends on the correct termination of the sampling lines. Any mismatch on those lines will result in a standing wave along them, and consequently the RF voltages appearing at their output terminals will not be proportional to the forward and reflected powers. This parameter of performance is termed the directivity of the reflectometer, and is measured as the ratio of the voltage developed on the backward sampling line, when the instrument is itself correctly terminated, to the voltage on the same line when the instrument is reversed. The directivity is usually expressed as a ratio in decibels (dB).

Design aspects

Before the details of construction can be finalised, it is necessary to consider one or two design aspects of the instrument itself. It has already been shown how two voltages may be obtained which are proportional to the forward and backward components of power respectively. However, these voltages are still at radio frequency and it is necessary to convert them to DC before they can be used to drive a moving coil meter.

If the forward voltage is arranged to produce a full scale deflection of the meter, then clearly the meter can be calibrated directly in SWR by observing the deflection produced by the backward voltage and making due allowance for any differences in coupling between the two

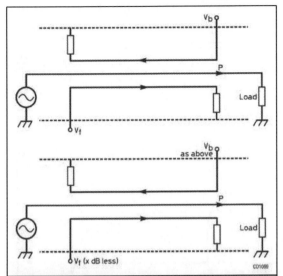

Fig 11.4: Instrument sensitivity and coupling ratios. (a) Sampling couplings equal. V_f gives meter FSD, so V_b/V_f (say y dB) which corresponds to a given meter deflection. (b) Sampling couplings different by x dB. V_f gives meter FSD less x dB for same power, SWR V_b/meter FSD, so for same deflection as (a) SWR = x + y dB.

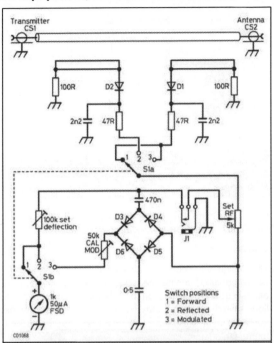

Fig 11.5: Circuit diagram of the reflectometer. D1, D2: OA91; D3 - D6: 1N4148. D3 - D6 should be bypassed by 1nF ceramic capacitors across each diode.

sampling lines and the main line. The calibration will be valid independent of the actual transmitted power, since in each case the meter is adjusted for FSD.

In practice, it is easier to arrange for identical sampling lines, in which case the calibration of the meter becomes a simple question of the ratio of RMS voltages applied to the rectifier diodes. This places an inherent limit on the sensitivity of the instrument at low SWR. However, provided that the relative couplings can be measured, it is possible to improve the overall sensitivity for a given power and meter sensitivity by arranging for an appreciably greater degree of coupling on the backward sampling line than on the forward, and thus providing an immediate improvement of x dB in the lowest SWR which can be measured for a given deflection of the meter (Fig 11.4).

Care must be exercised that the coupling from either line is not increased to the point where the presence of the sampling line distorts the electromagnetic field around the inner of the main line sufficiently to cause an effective change of Z_0 of the main line and hence introduce an inherent SWR in the instrument itself.

As a general rule the coupling should not be greater than 30dB to maintain an inherent reflection coefficient of less than 3 - 4%.

When the main line is carrying power which is subject to amplitude modulation, the sampling voltage from the forward (and backward) line will also be subject to amplitude modulation at the same modulation depth. Since this voltage has already been rectified and arranged to deflect the meter to full scale, if a rectified (or detected) signal is once more rectified, a DC voltage will be obtained

that is proportional to the audio frequency voltage modulating the carrier. This voltage can then be used to deflect the meter and this can be calibrated directly in percentage modulation. This calibration will also, to a first order, be independent of the transmitted power, since the meter has been adjusted for FSD on the sampled detected carrier.

In practice it is necessary to resort to full wave rectification of the detected carrier, although this does not really provide sufficient DC voltage to cause large excursions of the meter reading under full modulation conditions, i.e. it is not possible to advance the meter to FSD for 100% modulation. It is recommended therefore that the "modulation meter" aspect of the instrument be regarded only as of an arbitrary quantitative nature.

A circuit diagram for a typical reflectometer is given in Fig 11.5. The diodes used must be capable of the frequency range that the instrument is to cover.

The introduction of the instrument into a transmission line requires the use of plugs and sockets, and this in turn will lead to a discontinuity in the lines at the ends of the reflectometer proper due to the sudden transition from the relatively large inner of the instrument line to the inner of the coaxial fitting. The size of the inner conductor of the instrument must be large to maintain the line characteristic impedance while at the same time providing sufficient room to accommodate the sampling lines between the inner and outer conductors, i.e. this is a physical requirement. These discontinuities are of the right angled step type (Fig 11.6), and there is an optimum arrangement of dimensions to provide minimum reflection at the step for any given characteristic impedance and inner conductors

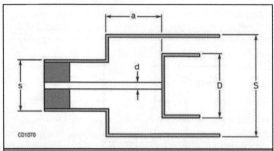

Fig 11.6: The characteristic impedance Z₀ is given by 138 log₁₀ s/d which is also 138 log₁₀ S/D. The optimum step length "a" is a function of Z₀ and D/d.

ratio. There is no simple mathematical formula relating the step length a to these parameters.

Construction

The design is based on a diecast box 114 × 89 × 55mm, with a partition running the length of the box to form an almost square cross section (51 × 51mm) to form a trough line. Any other spacing may be used but this complicates

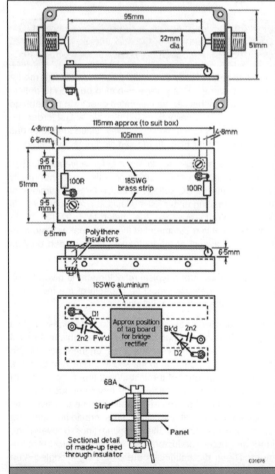

Fig 11.8: Arrangement of strip line on partition and tag board.

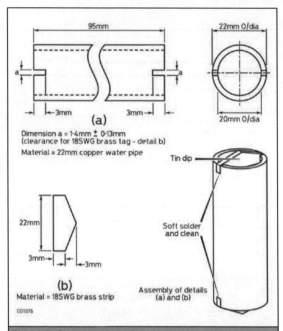

Dimension a = 1·4mm ± 0·13mm
(clearance for 18SWG brass tag - detail b)
Material = 22mm copper water pipe

(a)

(b)
Material = 18SWG brass strip

Fig 11.7: Construction of main line inner conductor.

the calculation of Z₀ of the line.

The characteristic impedance of a coaxial line with a cylindrical inner conductor and a square outer is given by:

$$Z_0 = 138 \log_{10} \frac{L}{d}$$

where L is the length of the side and d is the diameter of the inner conductor. It is assumed that L/d > 1.5. For a 50Ω line, substitution of 51mm in this formula gives d = 22mm.

The RF connections to the box can be made from N type, BNC, TNC or SO239 type connector, the last being a non-constant impedance type. When soldering to these it is wise to insert a plug, this will hold the middle pin central as prolonged soldering usually softens the surrounding insulation.

The sockets are mounted centrally at each end of the 51mm square section of the box, and their spigots are cut down so that the overall dimension from the inside face of the box to the end of the spigot is about 6.5mm. The inner conductor detail (Fig 11.7, detail a) is slotted at each end for a depth of 3mm and wide enough to accept 18 SWG (1.4mm) brass sheet as a tight fit. It is important to ensure that the slots at each end lie in the same plane.

The small end pieces (Fig 11.7, detail b) are cut from 18 SWG (1.4mm) brass sheet and pushed into the slots at each end as shown and soldered in position. The pointed end of each tab is then tinned, any surplus solder being removed in order to keep the cylindrical shape at the ends. The inner assembly may then be rested between the spigots of the coaxial sockets and soldered into position (Fig 11.8).

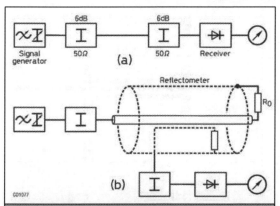

Fig 11.9: Insertion method of measuring coupling. (a) Set a signal to give an arbitrary deflection K on receiver meter. Note the signal generator attenuator setting, say x dB. (b) Repeat the exercise with reflectometer in circuit and readjust the signal generator to give the same deflection K on the receiver meter. Read the attenuator setting, say y dB. Then the coupling of the main line to the sampling line is x - y dB.

The sampling lines are formed from a strip line of 18 SWG (1.4mm) brass lying parallel to the partition. The formula for the characteristic impedance of a strip line over an infinite plane is:

$$Z_0 = 230 \log_{10} \frac{4D}{W}$$

where D is the distance from the plane, W is the width of the strip and the ratio D/W has a value between 0.1 and 1.0. As already explained, it is necessary to terminate the sampling lines correctly in order to preserve the directivity of the instrument, and a characteristic impedance of 100Ω is used, based upon the use of available 100Ω, 2% tolerance 0.5W resistors as the terminating loads. This figure substituted in the above expression gives a value of D/W of 0.68. This provides a whole possible range of dimensions for the strip line and in order to achieve the required degree of coupling to the main line a value of D = 6.5mm and hence W = 9.5mm was chosen by experiment. The sampling lines were made as long as conveniently possible, care being exercised to make them as near as physically identical as possible.

The partition is made from 16 SWG (1.6mm) aluminium sheet and the sampling lines mounted in the positions shown in Fig 11.8. The spacing of the sampling lines may be trimmed by adjustment at the terminated end when the instrument is being set up. The partition is assembled with sampling lines, tag board on the rear, and all components, before being fitted in the box. Connections from the other side of the partition to the various controls are made up as short flying leads to facilitate this assembly. An alternative and neater solution would be to mount most of the components on a PCB instead of the tag board, but keeping D1, D2, C1 and C2 in approximately the positions shown.

The position of the various potentiometers and switches is not critical, and some alteration to the suggested layout is permissible. Alternatively there is no objection to extending the DC outputs of D1 and D2 via a three core cable to another position. D1 and D2 must be fitted as per Fig 11.8.

Calibration

Accurate calibration of the reflectometer requires a signal generator with calibrated output, a receiver with some form of carrier level meter, and a load of known reflection coefficient suitable for direct connection to either end of the reflectometer test line (this load should be as near matched as possible). The procedure is then as follows:

First terminate the antenna end of the instrument and measure the coupling of each sampling line in turn by the insertion method (Fig 11.9). Adjust the sampling line spacing for identical coupling.

Using the signal generator injecting directly into each sampling diode in turn (with sampling lines disconnected), calibrate the indicating meter in terms of decibels relative to the injection voltage for FSD. This also provides a check on the match of the diode characteristics of each sampling circuit. These must be matched if the instrument is to read accurately at all transmitted power levels. Two diodes at random from the box provided the results quoted for the prototype.

The instrument is then calibrated directly in terms of the ratio of backward to forward voltages, expressed in decibels, for all transmitted powers, provided it is always adjusted to FSD on the forward position using the SET RF control. (The SET DEFLECTION control should be set, for any particular meter, to such a value to allow the SET RF control to function over the whole range of transmitted powers expected).

Many amateurs will not have the necessary test equipment outlined above. However, this need not detract greatly from the appeal of the instrument since, even without any calibration at all, the output from the backward line will usually reduce as the SWR on the main line is reduced. Thus the reflectometer may be used qualitatively to indicate best SWR when adjustments are being made to, say, an antenna system.

It is possible, without any test equipment other than a low power transmitter, to make some basic checks on the instrument as follows:

With an open circuit on the antenna end of the instrument, vary the power from the transmitter in steps, and take the forward meter readings at each level with the instrument connected normally, and then the backward meter readings with the instrument reversed. This will check the characteristics of the diodes, and also enable slight adjustments to be made to the sample lines to equalise the coupling. The latter adjustment should be carried out at the normal transmitter power only, for the best performance in practice.

Care must be exercised, when carrying out such checks, to avoid damaging the PA device through excessive

Table 11.1: Reflectometer calibration figures.

Meter reading			
Forward	Backward	Level dB	SWR
50	50	0	infinite
43	44	-2	8.8
37	36	-4	4.4
30	29	-6	3.0
23	21	-8	2.3
18	17	-10	1.92
14	13	-12	1.67
11	10	-14	1.5
8	7	-16	1.37
6	5	-18	1.29
4	3	-20	1.22
3	2	-22	1.16
2	1	-24	1.13

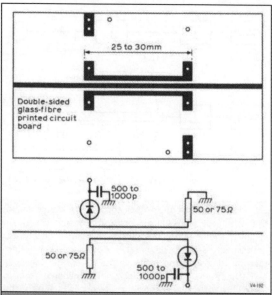

Fig 11.10: Printed circuit directional coupler.

dissipation on no load. Provided that the dimensions given have been followed closely, the errors introduced due to stray differences in the final instrument should not be more than 2 - 3dB. Inspection of the calibration table shows that for the lower values of SWR such an error results in a very small error in SWR, this becoming increasingly worse as the SWR gets larger. Therefore, an un-calibrated but carefully built instrument can be expected to indicate SWR to an accuracy of ±0.5 up to values of 2:1, becoming as poor as ±1.0 at 4:1. This should be quite adequate for most amateur uses.

The SWR column of Table 11.1 represents the conversion of backward meter readings for a forward reading of 50. For a given input level, the difference between the lines was less than 1dB over the full range. Zero level is equivalent to 1V RMS in 100Ω.

Power limitations

The sensitivity of the instrument is such as to provide FSD on a 50μA meter for a carrier power of 5W. The upper limit is set by the dissipation in the resistors terminating the sampling line. These are rated at 0.5W and, since the forward line is dissipating power 32dB down on the incident transmitted power, the maximum transmitted power should not exceed 500W carrier.

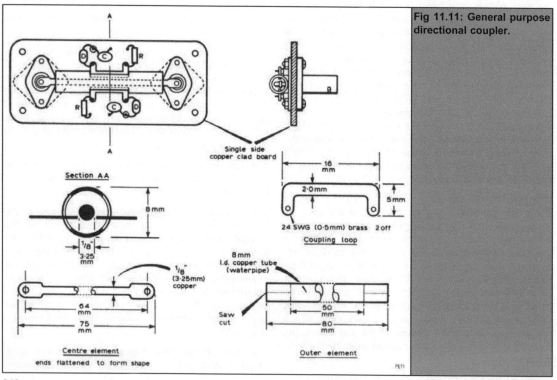

Fig 11.11: General purpose directional coupler.

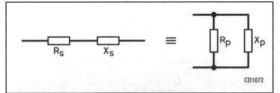

Fig 11.12: Series and parallel equivalence.

Frequency range

The performance of the instrument is constant over the 144MHz band. The sensitivity will fall linearly with decrease of frequency since the coupling lines are short. The impedance match of the instrument itself will deteriorate with increasing frequency due to the presence of the step discontinuities and also the variations in the terminating loads on the sampling lines, which will become increasingly reactive.

Printed circuit directional coupler

A simple method of constructing a directional coupler is by use of a printed circuit board as shown on Fig 11.10. The line impedance can be made in accordance with the design information given in the appendix. The coupling lines may be of any convenient length to suit the meter in use but they should be short compared with λ/4.

The diodes should be a signal type such as a silicon Schottky barrier type (e.g. BAT83, 1N6263 etc) or a germanium type (e.g. OA47, OA91 etc) which have low forward voltage drop and suitable for the frequency range concerned. The terminating resistors should be as far as possible non-inductive types of good stability. The bypass capacitors may be disc, plate or feedthrough type, the latter having the advantage of providing a terminal for connection to the meter. It is important that the actual value should be suitable for the frequencies to be used.

General-purpose directional coupler

A reliable directional coupler can be made employing readily available items as an alternative to the above PCB type and without recourse to machine tools. A short section of air spaced coaxial line is used with the coupling loops inserted into the line through the slots in the outer tube.

The general arrangement is shown on Fig 11.11. The whole unit is assembled on a piece of single sided, copper clad PCB made to fit a diecast box, say, 92 × 38 × 31 mm. The size is not too important but should be kept small. The outer of the coaxial line is made from a piece of 8mm copper tube with its ends opened out by cross-sawing and slitting. This is attached to the copper side of the PCB. The inner conductor is made from a piece of brass or copper rod/tube; for 50Ω use 3.5mm rod and for 75Ω use 2.5mm.

The coupling loops are made from 24 SWG (0.5mm) brass or copper strip mounted on four small stand-off insulators. The spacing between them and the inner line should be equal and adjusted so that each provide the same readings when used either way it is connected. This

should be carried out with the output socket connected to an appropriate dummy load.

Representation of an antenna system using circuit components

An antenna system (including feed cable if necessary) represents an impedance at the feed point to whatever is driving it. This can either be considered as being made of a series circuit or a parallel circuit as shown in Fig 11.12.

It is possible to convert between these circuits, the equations being given below. Please note that these values are only true at one particular frequency.

$$R_P = \frac{R_S^{\ 2} + X_S^{\ 2}}{R_S}$$

$$X_P = \frac{R_S^{\ 2} + X_S^{\ 2}}{X_S}$$

$$R_S = R_P \times \frac{X_P^{\ 2}}{R_P^{\ 2} + X_P^{\ 2}}$$

$$X = X_P \times \frac{R_P^{\ 2}}{R_P^{\ 2} + X_P^{\ 2}}$$

For optimum power transfer, the resistive part should equal the source resistance and the reactive part should cancel with the source reactance; in effect the condition for resonance. Thus it is important to be able to make these measurements at the frequency of concern. Also remember that power can only be dissipated in a resistive element.

Thus, if serious work is to be undertaken on antennas, it is important to determine feed point impedances. Commercial equipment to perform this function is available but the following two circuits will give a good indication of conditions.

Also, don't forget that what the transmitter "sees" is an impedance represented by the antenna and the associated transmission line. If, and only if, the transmission line is a multiple of half wavelengths (taking into account cable velocity factor) will the feed point impedance be that of the antenna. Ideally measurements should be made directly at the antenna terminals if at all possible.

An RF bridge

This is a Wheatstone type bridge suitable for use on frequencies up to the 70cm band (430 - 440MHz). It

Table 11.2: Component list for the RF bridge.

R1, 2	100Ω ±1% metal oxide
R3, 4	4k7Ω ±1% metal oxide
R5, 6	100Ω
VR1	50kΩ miniature pot
VR2	2k5Ω miniature pot
C1, 2	1000pF ceramic disc
C3 - 9	10nF ceramic disc
D1	OA91, CV2290, BAT85 (low volt drop diode suitable for frequency range)
Z$_{known}$	50Ω, fitted in a coaxial plug

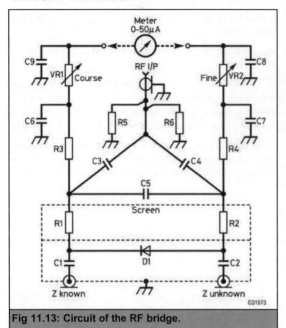

Fig 11.13: Circuit of the RF bridge.

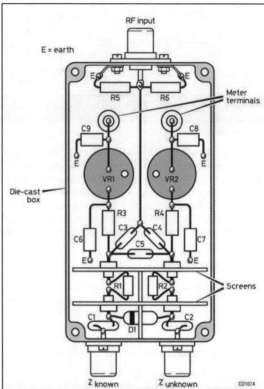

Fig 11.14: Component layout of the RF bridge.

requires care in construction to ensure absolute symmetry of the component layout together with the use of miniature components and matched pairs where necessary. This will then give a bridge that has accuracy of the order of ±1% of full-scale deflection of the meter that is good enough for practical purposes and should fulfil most amateur needs.

The circuit of the bridge shown in Fig 11.13 is given in the same form as shown in Fig 11.14 and is self-explanatory. The whole unit, which uses an external meter, should be built in the smallest size diecast box. The component list is given in Table 11.2.

Operation

The method of operation with this bridge is to start with the value of impedance known and adjust the length of stubs,

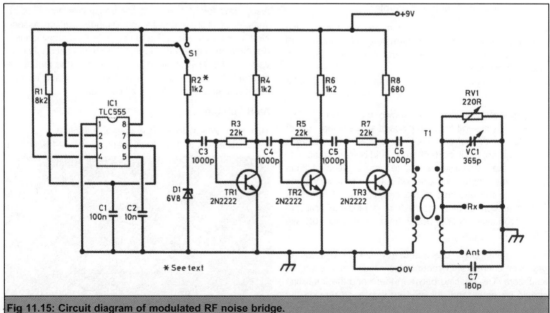

Fig 11.15: Circuit diagram of modulated RF noise bridge.

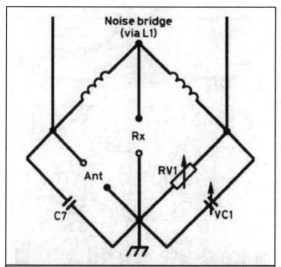

Fig 11.16: Diagrammatic representation of the noise bridge.

Table 11.2: Component list for the RF noise bridge.	
R1	8k2Ω
R2, 4, 6	1k2Ω
R3, 5, 7	22kΩ
R8	680Ω
RV1	220Ω pot (see text)
C1	100nF 50V ceramic
C2	10nF 50V ceramic
C3 - 6	1000pF 50V ceramic
C7	180pF silver mica
VC1	365pF Jackson type 01 gang
D1	6V8 400mW zener
TR1 - TR3	2N2222 or equivalent
IC1	TLC555
D1	SPCO switch
T1	T50-6 dust iron core, 4 windings, each 14 turns or 596100001 ferrite core, 4 windings 6 turns
Resistors are 0.25/0.5W, ±5% unless otherwise stated	

matching device etc. until a balance is achieved. This unit will be found ideal for cutting coaxial cable to quarter and half wavelengths, where the known Z is either an open circuit or a short circuit.

RF noise bridge

The circuit described here is from reference [1]. It is a useful circuit for measuring the R and X components of an impedance or antenna system at a given frequency. It also allows a modulated signal to be obtained, if desired, by pulsing the supply to the noise generator. Such modulation may aid detection of the balance point, especially if an AM receiver is used. The circuit consists of a wide band noise generator followed by a bridge for making the measurements. The bridge allows the measurement of the parallel components of an unknown impedance to be measured. The circuit requires 9V DC at about 25mA.

Circuit description

The circuit is shown in Fig 11.15. The white noise is generated by the zener diode D1 operating at low current. It may be possible to maximise the noise by suitable choice of the zener diode and R2. The frequency range of this noise should extend up to at least 200MHz. A three-stage wide band amplifier raises the noise level to the order of 100μV follows, this enables a receiver to be used as a null indicator.

The noise output from the amplifier is applied to a quadrifilar-wound toroid that forms the transformer T1. This provides two arms of a bridge circuit that has a variable resistor and capacitor in the third arm to obtain a balance against the impedance (e.g. antenna system) in the fourth arm. The bridge circuit is shown diagrammatically in Fig 11.16.

When the noise across the RV1/VC1 arm equals the noise across the antenna/capacitor combination, the bridge is "balanced", and this occurs when the received noise

signal is at a minimum. The values can be obtained from the settings of RV1 and VC1. The inclusion of C7 allows an offset to be used so that inductive reactance can be measured. The mid point setting of VC1 is equal to zero reactance. If a noise bridge is only required to measure the resistive part of the antenna impedance then omit C7 and VC1.

Timer IC1 is in astable mode and runs at about 850Hz with a 50% duty cycle, and this can be used to provide current for the zener circuit via S1, so modulating the noise source. The zener diode can be alternatively fed from the constant voltage power supply line.

Construction

The component list is given in Table 11.2. The toroid transformer consists of a dust iron core, type T50-6, which is wound as follows. Cut four lengths of 26 SWG enamelled copper wire about 120mm long, twist them together and then thread them through the toroid to give 14 turns and evenly spaced to cover the circumference. Divide the turns into two pairs, each pair consisting of two windings connected in series, the end of one winding connecting to the start of the other. Check that the two pairs are insulated from each other. Endeavour to keep the lead lengths in the bridge as short as possible and symmetrical. The variable resistor RV1 should be of high quality and with a carbon, cermet or conductive plastic track; not wire wound!

When constructing the circuits, ensure that the noise generator and amplifiers are well away or screened from the bridge transformer and measuring circuit. The potentiometer case should not be earthed and, if it has a metal spindle, this should be isolated from the user and should not contact ground.

The complete circuit should be mounted in a screened box such as a diecast type with appropriate connectors e.g. UHF type or BNC. In order to avoid coupling into the measuring circuit of noise by way of current in earth loops, the earthed side of the noise source should not be joined to the general chassis earth of the bridge but should be taken by an insulated lead to the frame of the variable capacitor.

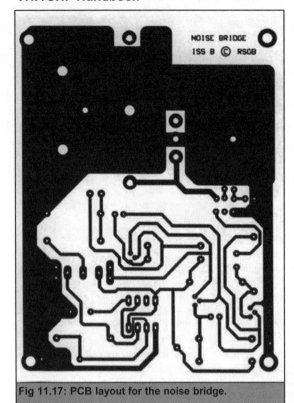

Fig 11.17: PCB layout for the noise bridge.

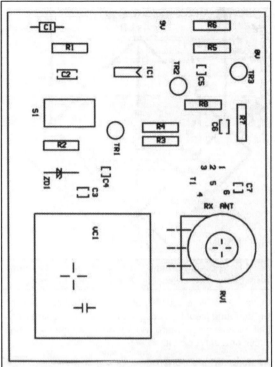

Fig 11.18: Component layout for the noise bridge.

As in all high frequency measuring circuits, lead induct-ance should be kept to an absolute minimum and, where any lead length more than a few millimetres is unavoid-able, copper foil at least 6mm wide should be used. All earth returns should be taken to the capacitor frame. Capacitor C7, which should be silver mica, can be soldered directly across the "unknown" socket. PCB and component layouts are shown in Figs 11.17 and 11.18.

Calibration

Connect a test resistor (a carbon type) across the "unknown" socket with the receiver tuned to 3.5MHz. Adjust RV1 and VC1 to give a null. The value of RV1 is at the position equal to the test resistor and the capacitor should be at approximately the mid mesh position or the zero reactance condition; mark these positions. Repeat with different values of test resistor up to 220Ω in order to provide a calibration scale for RV1. Repeat this operation with known values of capacitance in parallel with the test resistor, up to a maximum value of 180pF. Mark the corresponding null positions on the VC1 scale with the value of this capacitance. Repeat this procedure at 28MHz to check the accuracy of the bridge. If the layout has been carefully attended to there should be little difference in the null positions.

To calibrate VC1 for negative capacitance values (i.e. inductance) it is necessary to temporarily place given values of capacitance in parallel with VC1. Gradually decrease the value of these capacitors (CT) from 150pF towards zero, obtaining null positions and marking the

VC1 scale with the value of -(180 - CT)pF, i.e. if 100pF is substituted then the negative C value is 80pF.

Using the noise bridge

For work on an antenna, a noise bridge should ideally be connected across the antenna terminals. This is usually not practical, in which case a noise bridge should be connected to the antenna by a length of line that is a multiple of a half wavelength at the frequency of interest (taking into account the velocity factor of the cable).

Connect the impedance to be measured to the "unknown" socket, switch on the noise generator and tune the receiver to the frequency at which the test is to be made. Use RV1 and VC1 to obtain a minimum noise reading on the receiver S meter. The values must now be converted to circuit components. The value recorded from RV1 is the resistive part of the impedance. The value from VC1 is the parallel reactive component of the impedance and, de-pending on the sign, is either inductive or capacitive. If it is positive, then the value of shunt capacitance is read directly from the VC1 scale. If it is negative, the VC1 reading represents the value of the shunt inductance and must be calculated as below.

If a negative value of capacitance (C) is obtained this can be converted to an inductance value using the formula:

$$L = \frac{1}{4\pi^2 f^2 (180 - C)}$$

where f is in megahertz and C in picofarads.

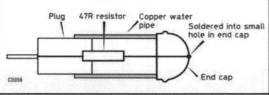

Fig 11.19: Typical construction of a low power dummy load.

Measurement of RF power

Power measurements when running into a dummy load can be made directly using RF voltmeters, oscilloscopes etc, taking into account their frequency limitations. The use of a reflectometer or directional coupler is preferable for monitoring power when coupled to an antenna system as they also give an indication of what is happening on the feed system.

The effect of modulation on power output

In a carrier wave situation (CW) or with a frequency-modulated signal, the output is of constant amplitude and so it is relatively easy to measure the output power. Key the transmitter and determine the RMS voltage (VRMS) of the resulting carrier across a dummy load (R). The power is given by:

$$P = \frac{V_{RMS}^{2}}{R} \; watts$$

If the signal is amplitude modulated (double sideband with carrier) then the overall output power increases. The power is divided between the sidebands and the carrier component. With 100% modulation the output power increases to 1.5 times the unmodulated condition; the power contained in each of the two sidebands is one quarter that in the carrier. It is suggested for this form of modulation that the carrier power is measured (i.e. with no modulation) as described above, this can be multiplied by 1.5 to give the maximum output power.

With single sideband modulation, no power is output until modulation is applied. The output envelope is non-sinusoidal in appearance. The normal method for measuring output power is by observation of the modulation envelope and determination of the peak envelope power (PEP).

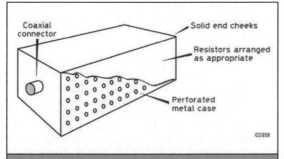

Fig 11.21: Possible construction of a higher power dummy load.

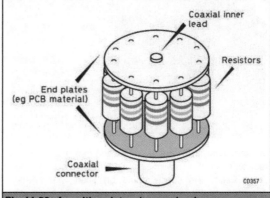

Fig 11.20: A multi resistor dummy load.

Dummy loads

A dummy load is a resistor (or group of resistors) that has the same resistance value as an antenna system. It should be purely resistive and so should provide an SWR of 1:1. The dummy load is normally constructed so that it provides minimal radiation when a transmitter is operated into it. Transmitters should always be set up into dummy loads before connecting them to the antenna system.

A resistor, no matter what type, will always have an associated inductance and capacitance, and the way it is mounted will also affect these values. The ideal resistor is one that has no associated capacitance and inductance, and is also one that does not change its value appreciably with frequency and power dissipation. This is unfortunately difficult to arrange in the real world, and the best one can do is to choose a resistor that minimises these adverse effects. In practice, impedance presented by the dummy load changes with frequency and hence will not provide an SWR of 1:1; this effect is more pronounced as frequency increases. This is why any dummy load that is purchased should have some information included with it concerning frequency range and expected SWR values.

The best type of resistor to use is made from carbon. Unfortunately it is becoming increasingly difficult to obtain power ratings in excess of 2W from distributors but tubular carbon resistors of higher power ratings will often be seen at rallies. Never use wire wound resistors for RF. However, these may be adequate for measuring AF power.

A low power dummy load can be made from a single 47Ω resistor with surrounding shield as shown diagrammatically in Fig 11.19, and this is obviously easier for those with mechanical skills and some ingenuity. To increase the power dissipation it would be possible to make the metal container a tight fit around the resistor. However,

Table 11.3: Resistor values for 50Ω dummy loads.

Resistance Ω	No. in parallel	Approximate value
100	2	50
150	3	50
390	8	49
560	11	51
1000	20	50

Table 11.4: Typical impedances of MP820/821 resistors.

R (Ω)	10MHz	100MHz	500MHz
10	10 + j0.43	10 + j4.3	10 + j21.7
25	25 +j0.4	25 + j4	24.8 + j20
50	50 + j0.3	50 + j2.8	48.4+ j14.3
75	75 + j0.09	74.8 + j0.9	69.9 + j5.3
100	100 - j0.2	99.6 - j1.9	91 - j6.6
120	120 - j0.5	119.3 1 j4.6	105 - j17.6
150	150 - j1	148.7 - j9.6	122.5 - j35.8

this may pose problems if conduction can occur from the resistor case. If a small clearance can be ensured around the resistor, the space could be filled with heatsink compound that is thermally but not electrically conducting. Alternatively one could fill the case with cooling oil and/or put fins onto the outside of the case. The use of the metal shield prevents unwanted radiation and also provides a low inductance path.

To increase the power rating it is possible to use resistors in parallel; Fig 11.20 shows a typical arrangement. This should, if at all possible, be encased in a metal shield to prevent unwanted radiation, possibly a perforated shield to permit airflow; see Fig 11.21.

The characteristics can be improved by arranging the resistors in a coaxial manner. Ideally the pitch circle of the resistors and centre coaxial conductor should be carefully calculated but as this arrangement tends to be very short compared to a wavelength it has little effect until the higher frequencies are reached. The characteristic impedance can be calculated using:

$$Z_0 = 138 \log_{10}\left(\frac{D}{d}\right)$$

where D is the pitch diameter of the resistors and d the diameter of the inner coaxial connector. Typical arrangements to make approximately 50Ω are shown in Table 11.3. The overall power rating is the sum of the power ratings of each resistor used.

To obtain higher power ratings it may be possible to place the load resistors in a perforated screened container and air blow them. This could be accomplished by placing a thermal switch on the resistors and using it to switch a fan on once the temperature has risen above a certain point.

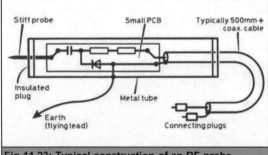

Fig 11.23: Typical construction of an RF probe.

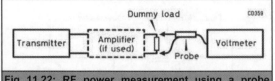

Fig 11.22: RF power measurement using a probe voltmeter.

Sometimes large tubular carbon resistors come onto the surplus market, these can make excellent dummy loads. Try to form them in a coaxial manner with the feed up the centre. Again, air blowing can be used to increase the power dissipation.

When using a dummy load, remember that it may be possible to dissipate a much higher power for a short period of time, providing a long cool down period is allowed between applications of power. A commercial dummy load may often be provided with advice on this method of use.

An interesting development is the production of power film resistors in TO126 and TO220 packages with power ratings of 20W at +25°C case temperature when mounted on a heatsink of some 6°C/W. These resistors show good characteristics up to at least 300MHz. Typical of these are the MP820/821 from Rhopoint Ltd. Lead impedance is estimated to be 0.39 to 0.47nH per millimetre. Other manufacturers such as Welwyn and Meggitt CGS also produce these.

For the type quoted above, the equivalent series inductance of the internal resistance film is about 7nH and has a shunt capacitance of about 1pF. These values will be affected to some extent when the device is mounted on a heatsink. Table 11.4 gives typical design guidelines and assumes the leads are terminated 2.5mm from the body of the resistor.

Use of RF voltmeters and/or probes

You can obtain an RF voltmeter, e.g. as surplus equipment, or make a probe as suggested in the next section. In fact, the commercial instrument may well use a probe. However, the measuring equipment must cover the frequency range in which the power measurements are being undertaken. If a peak reading voltmeter is being used do not forget to convert the peak voltage to RMS voltage by dividing by √2 and don't forget to take into account any attenuators used. This method of measuring power should be used for carrier power only. Fig 11.22 shows the basic arrangement for these measurements.

RF diode probe

This device allows the scope of a DC voltmeter to be extended to measure AC voltages in the VHF range, and by careful construction probably higher. The probe essentially rectifies the AC immediately and then only has to pass a DC voltage to the meter. The diode is often the limiting factor; to get high-speed operation the diode junction must be narrow and hence this reduces the breakdown voltage. Using a BAT46 Schottky barrier diode the maximum input voltage is about 35V RMS; with the 1N914/1N4148/OA91 it is about 45V RMS. Using a

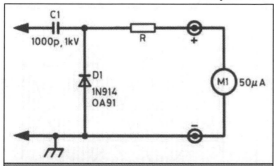

Fig 11.24: RF probe circuit. For R = 270kΩ, the meter scaling is 0 - 10V and full scale power in 50Ω is 2W. For R = 820kΩ + 27kΩ, the meter scaling is 0 - 30V and full scale in 50Ω is 18W.

Schottky or germanium diode the forward voltage drop is of the order of 0.2 to 0.3V but with a silicon type it is about 0.6V. The probe should be mounted in a small metal cylinder which is well screened and the resulting DC signal fed via a coaxial cable to the DC meter, see Fig 11.23.

A typical circuit is shown in Fig 11.24 with component values for feeding a 50µA meter movement. The advantage of arranging the capacitor and rectifier in this manner is that the capacitor also acts as DC blocking.

An alternative when the circuit is to be fed into a high-input-impedance DC voltmeter such as an electronic analogue meter or a digital meter is shown in Fig 11.25. The input resistance of the meter should be such that it is 10 times the value of R2. Also, the value for the series resistor (R1) should be approximately 41% of the combined resistance R2 in parallel with the meter input resistance. This then allows the meter to read the RMS value of the RF signal. The values shown are suitable for a meter with an input resistance of at least 10MΩ. For a meter of input resistance of 1MΩ, reduce the values of R1 and R2 by a factor of 10.

To measure higher voltages and hence higher power levels, one suggestion is to use a resistive divider across the load using resistors suitable for the frequencies encountered. Fig 11.26 shows a divide-by-10 unit suitable for a 50Ω system. Remember, the actual voltage is 10 times the value as read on the meter.

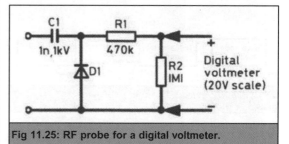

Fig 11.25: RF probe for a digital voltmeter.

Use of the oscilloscope for power measurement

This requires the use of an oscilloscope with a timebase or a CRT monitor. It should be stressed, however, that oscilloscopes working into the VHF range are expensive. This section deals solely with the measurement of power, e.g. voltage display on an oscilloscope. An oscilloscope can also be used for some modulation measurements. At 100W (CW) the peak-to-peak voltage across a 50Ω dummy load is 200V and at 400W PEP, the maximum peak to peak voltage that will be measured is about 400V! You have been warned.

As with the RF voltmeter, the most straightforward measurement is of carrier power that is obtained from the key down condition for CW operation or the constant amplitude of a frequency-modulated signal. Connect an oscilloscope instead of a voltmeter (Fig 11.22) bearing in mind any frequency or voltage limitations of the oscilloscope and probe. Measure the peak-to-peak amplitude Vpp (Fig 11.27) across the known dummy load R. The average power is then calculated from:

$$P_{avg} = \frac{V_{pp}^{\ 2}}{8R} \ watts$$

The same physical connections are made across the dummy load with the oscilloscope for PEP measurements. The transmitter should be driven by a two-tone oscillator, see Fig 11.28. The output of the oscillator should be fed into the microphone socket and be of amplitude equivalent to that from the microphone.

Set the timebase on the oscilloscope to be in the audio range and a waveform similar to that shown on Fig 11.29

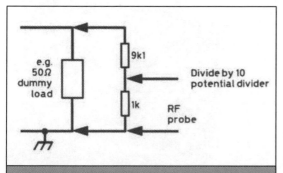

Fig 11.26: Suggested method for higher voltages.

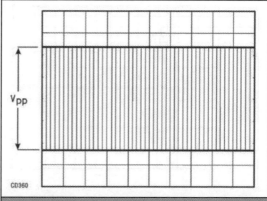

Fig 11.27: Oscilloscope display for carrier only.

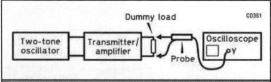

Fig 11.28: RF measurement for SSB work.

will be obtained. Measure the peak-to-peak voltage Vpp at the peak of the envelope (as shown); the power is given by the previous formula.

The input capacitance of an oscilloscope can start to have an appreciable effect at 30MHz; the reactance of 25pF is 212Ω at 30MHz, and obviously affects the readings. It may be better to use a divide-by-10 probe that will decrease the parallel capacitive loading to about 12pF. This still represents a capacitive reactance of 442Ω at 30MHz and the voltage read from the screen will be lower than in reality. To reduce these effects some high quality oscilloscopes have 50Ω Inputs; use these at higher frequencies but remember that these will have significant loading on a circuit and may have to matched into the latter.

If the same oscilloscope is continually used to monitor output power on SSB, then note should be made on the graticule or display of the positions corresponding to various power levels. The peak of the speech modulated waveform should then never exceed the maximum permitted level, see Fig 11.30.

If it is possible to feed the Y signal directly to the plates, then the capacitive loading is much smaller, the readings are therefore more accurate and it will be possible to use the oscilloscope to higher frequencies.

Low power RF wattmeter using and AD8362 detector

This design is by Wolfgang Schneider, DJ8ES [2]. Low power wattmeters are still expensive even if it is a second hand instrument from a surplus market. Fortunately it is possible to make a suitable measuring instrument yourself with the help of modern integrated circuits such as the

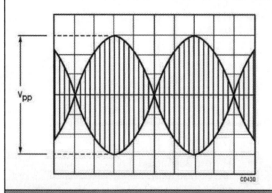

Fig 11.29: Two tone test display.

AD8362 True-Power detector, in combination with a standard LCD voltmeter. The readings obtained from such equipment are in no way inferior to those from commercial products.

Analog Devices [3] have developed the AD8362 for measuring power over a wide frequency and power range. Thanks to special internal compensation, it can also be used over a wide temperature range. The IC forms part of a whole family of power detectors that were originally developed for mobile telephones and wireless LAN applications in a frequency range from 1MHz to more than 8GHz. They are normally used for regulating the transmit power in such systems. According to the manufacturer's specifications, the AD8362 detector displays entirely linear behaviour over a very wide frequency range, going up as far as 2.7GHz. From the data sheet, the best results are obtained with a 1:4 balun at the input. The circuit suggested here does not use a balun so it displays certain irregularities in the frequency response and cannot be used for frequencies below 10MHz and falls off above 1.9GHz by 1dB or more.

Circuit description

The measuring instrument is split into two parts, a measuring head and a display unit shown in Fig 11.31. The circuit diagram for the measuring head is shown in

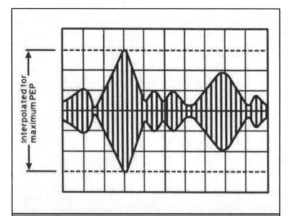

Fig 11.30: Speech waveform and interpolated maximum PEP.

Fig 11.31: Picture of the low power RF wattmeter.

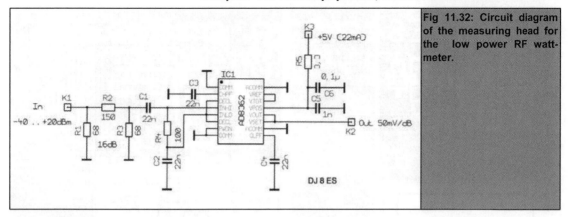

Fig 11.32: Circuit diagram of the measuring head for the low power RF watt-meter.

Fig 11.32, the main component is an AD8362 True-Power detector (IC1). The external components consist of a few blocking capacitors (C2 to C6) and the input matching and a 16dB input attenuator used to establish the measurable input power range between -40dBm and +23dBm. This range of values can vary slightly, depending on the component tolerances. Thus, for example the prototype displays power levels of between -37dBm (0.5µW) and +27dBm (500mW).

The display unit is made very simply using a ready built LCD voltmeter module. The circuit for the display unit is shown in Fig 11.33, it is operated directly from a 9V battery. The 5V voltage regulator, IC2 (78L05) generates the reference voltage for the zero point calibration and the supply for the measuring head. The output voltage of the measuring head is matched to the input voltage range of the LCD module (-200mV to +200mV) using an OP90P operational amplifier (IC1) followed by a voltage divider. The amplification can be adjusted precisely by means of the 20kΩ precision trimmer (R6). The offset voltage

required (approximately 40mV) for the zero point adjust-ment is obtained using a diode connected to the trimming potentiometer, R7 (5kΩ).

Assembly instructions

The measuring head is assembled on a 34mm x 34mm double-sided copper clad epoxy printed circuit board; the layout is shown in Fig 11.34. Only SMD components can be used because of their RF characteristics. They are all mounted on the top side of the board as shown in Figs 11.35 and 11.36, while the underside is an earthing surface. Low inductance earth connections are made using feedthroughs at the relevant points. The unit is mounted in a suitable metal box e.g. from Mini Circuits, see Fig 11.37. The board must be cut to the required size before the components are mounted.

The display unit is assembled on a 52mm x 34mm single-sided copper clad epoxy board; the layout is shown in Fig 11.38. Only wired components are used as shown in Figs 11.39 and 11.40. The components are mounted in no

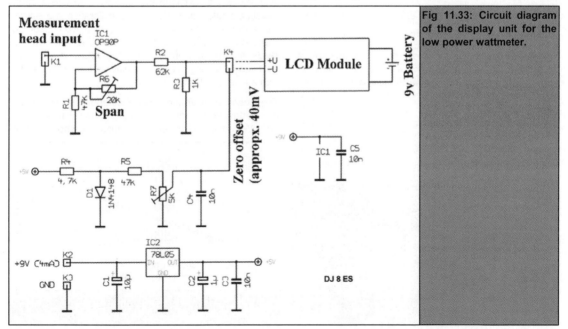

Fig 11.33: Circuit diagram of the display unit for the low power wattmeter.

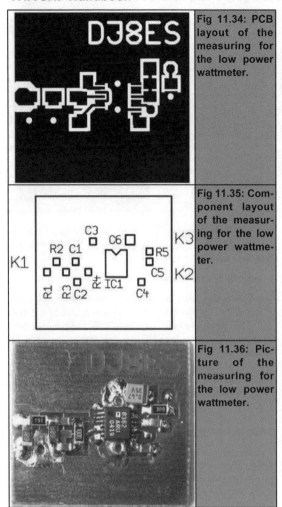

Fig 11.34: PCB layout of the measuring for the low power wattmeter.

Fig 11.35: Component layout of the measuring for the low power wattmeter.

Fig 11.36: Picture of the measuring for the low power wattmeter.

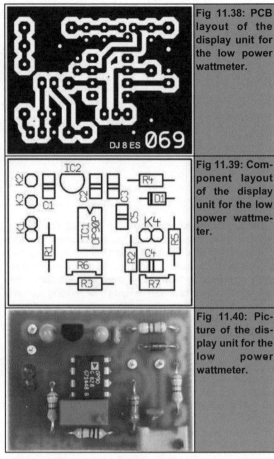

Fig 11.38: PCB layout of the display unit for the low power wattmeter.

Fig 11.39: Component layout of the display unit for the low power wattmeter.

Fig 11.40: Picture of the display unit for the low power wattmeter.

particular order. The parts lists are shown in Table 11.5.

Calibration

The measuring head itself does not require any special calibration. Once it has been switched on, check the current consumption (approximately 22mA) and the presence of an output signal. The output should be approximately 50mV per dB of input level, Fig 11.41 shows the characteristic of the prototype. The current consumption for the display assembly is only 4mA, or 26mA when the measuring head is switched on. An important point is that the LCD voltmeter module should be operated from its

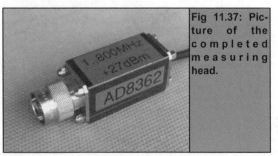

Fig 11.37: Picture of the completed measuring head.

own battery. First, the offset voltage (zero point adjustment) is set using R7 to approximately 40mV. Then set R6 to its mid position to start the calibration procedure. The simplest way to calibrate the linearity is to use a 20dB switchable attenuator. During the calibration procedure, the absolute value of the reading displayed is of no importance. It is only the difference between the two test levels that is relevant. Finally, the offset is precisely adjusted by setting the LCD display to 0 for a test signal with a level of 0dBm

The measuring instrument described above is a low power RF wattmeter for the power range from <1µW up to 500mW, though in this version the display is shown only in

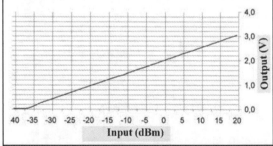

Fig 11.41: The output characteristic of the measuring head.

Table 11.5: Parts lists for the low power wattmeter.

Parts for measuring head

IC1	AD8362, Detector, SMD
C1- C4	22 nF, ceramic capacitor, SMD 0805
C5	1 nF, ceramic capacitor, SMD 0805
C6	0.1µF/16V, tantalum electrolytic capacitor, SMD
R1, R3	68Ω, SMD 0805
R2	150Ω, SMD 0805
R4	100Ω, SMD 0805
R5	3.3Ω, SMD 0805

1 x printed circuit board DJ8ES 068

Parts for display unit

IC1	OP90P, Operational amplifier
IC2	78L05, Fixed voltage regulator
D1	1N4148, Diode

Resistors 0.25 W, RM 10 mm:

R1, R5	47kΩ
R2	62kΩ
R3	1kΩ
R4	4.7kΩ

Precision trimmer:

R7	5kΩ, Model 64 W,
R6	20kΩ, Model 64 W,
C1	10µF/25 V, tantalum, RM 2.5 mm,
C2	1µF/25 V, tantalum, RM 2.5 mm,
C3-C5	10nF, ceramic capacitor, RM 2.5 mm
K1, K4	Pin-and-socket connector 2-pin
K2, K3	Soldering iron 1 mm

1 x printed circuit board DJ8ES 069

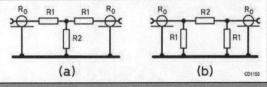

Fig 11.42: (a) T type attenuator. (b) Pi type attenuator.

standard resistors and can be put to a variety of uses. For example, attenuators at RF can be used as pads between interacting stages, e.g. varactor multipliers, or to follow noise or signal sources to bring their output close to 50Ω. At IF they can be used for calibrating attenuators, since their attenuation is fairly predictable at lower frequencies. They may also be used for calibrating S meters etc. and as a reference for noise measurements, e.g. Sun and ground noise. An attenuator might also be useful between a transmitter and transverter.

Design and construction of simple attenuators

Attenuators are normally made from T or pi networks; see Fig 11.42. For this exercise it is assumed that load and source impedances (R_0) are equal and resistive. The design of these is covered by the following formulae.

T network

$$Attenuation(dB) = 20\log_{10}\left(\frac{R_0 + R_1}{R_0 - R_1}\right)$$

When:

$$R_2 = \frac{R_0^2 - R_1^2}{2R_1}$$

Pi network

$$Attenuation(dB) = 20\log_{10}\left(\frac{R_1 + R_0}{R_1 - R_0}\right)$$

When:

$$R_2 = \frac{2R_0^2 R_1}{R_1^2 - R_0^2}$$

"dBm". The range can be extended using either attenuators or directional couplers when making measurements. Alexander Meier, DG6RBP has developed a digital display unit and an improved measuring head [4].

Attenuators

The need for good attenuators capable of working at frequencies up to several hundred megahertz or higher often arises. These are relatively easy to construct out of

The greatest problem in constructing a good attenuator is the radiation and leakage of signals from within the unit. Because of this, the attenuator should consist of a good RF tight metal box with high quality connectors.

Two methods of construction are illustrated in Fig 11.43. A pi type is shown in (a) and the T type in (b), but either type could be used in either design. The resistors should be a low inductance type, the common form of carbon film resistors being particularly suitable. Lead lengths should be as short as possible. For higher power attenuators at lower frequencies, parallel combinations of 0.5W carbon resistors can be used to increase dissipation. A 10dB attenuator built in this way to handle 10W measures 9.5dB attenuation at 432MHz with low SWR.

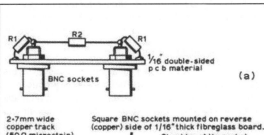

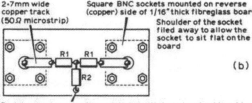

Fig 11.43: Method of constructing attenuators: (a) below 500MHz, (b) above 500MHz.

Table 11.6: Design data for 50Ω T type and Pi type attenuators.

Attenuation (dB)	T type R1	T type R2	Pi type R1	Pi type R2
1	2.9	433.0	870.0	5.8
2	5.7	215.0	436.0	11.6
3	8.6	142.0	292.0	17.6
4	11.3	105.0	221.0	23.9
5	14.0	82.0	178.0	30.4
6	16.6	67.0	150.0	37.4
7	19.1	56.0	131.0	44.8
8	21.5	47.3	116.0	53.0
9	23.8	40.6	105.0	62.0
10	26.0	35.1	96.0	71.0
12	30.0	26.8	84.0	93.0
14	33.4	20.8	75.0	120.0
16	36.3	16.3	69.0	154.0
18	38.8	12.8	64.0	196.0
20	40.9	10.0	61.0	248.0
25	44.7	5.6	56.0	443.0
30	46.9	3.2	53.0	790.0

Provided that care is taken, these attenuators can be used up to 1 - 2GHz. The biggest error is likely to arise in the higher value attenuators, where stray coupling may reduce the attenuation below the expected value. For this reason it is better to use several low value stages in cascade when a high value of attenuation is required. Table 11.6 shows some attenuator values. The Javascript Notebook [5] by Martin E Meserve, K7MEM contains a very useful on line attenuator calculator.

Switched attenuator

A switched attenuator has a number of applications in the amateur station; it may be made either wide or limited range depending on the intended application.

The simple three-section unit illustrated (Fig 11.44) is intended for use between the output of a VHF transceiver having an output in the range 10 - 20W PEP and a following linear amplifier. With the three stages of 2, 4 and 8dB available, various levels between 0 and 14dB are available.

In an attenuator that is to be used with a power source such as a transceiver, it should be remembered that a significant proportion of the input power will be dissipated in the resistors in the attenuator. The proportion is increased with the level of attenuation. In this case a 2dB

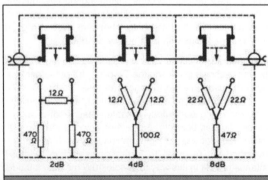

Fig 11.44: Circuit of a switched attenuator.

attenuation will dissipate 36% of the input power, 4dB 52% and 8dB 84%. Therefore adequately rated components are essential if the unit is to be used continuously.

For a continuous carrier input of 10W, after a 2dB attenuation 6.3W is available to the next stage, after 4dB there is 4W, after 6dB there is 2.5W and after 8dB just 1.6W. The remaining power is dissipated within the attenuator.

Although the switched attenuator may be used, for normal general-purpose operation a single stage fixed type is more likely to find favour once the degree of attenuation has been established. Such a unit can more readily be built using suitable components and where necessary adequate heat dissipating construction.

Frequency Measurement

One of the most important things for a radio amateur to know is the frequency that his working on. Digital frequency counters have made this very easy and a design for such a counter is shown in this section. The frequency measurement range can be extended with a prescaler, these divide the input frequency by a suitable factor e.g. 10, 100 or 1000 to reduce the frequency to be measured to suit the input range of the counter being used. The counter described here has a maximum input frequency of about 45MHz, most prescaler designs use microwave counters that do not work below a few hundred megahertz. The prescaler design shown in this section uses a divider that will work down to 50MHz with a division factor of 1000.

When frequencies at the top of the UHF range are being measured it is most important that the reference frequency for the counter is accurate. One method to ensure this is to lock the reference to the GPS system. A small unit based on a readily available GPS receiver is described in this section

Digital counters are not suitable for some jobs, the tried and tested Dip Oscillator is invaluable for measuring tuned circuits and setting up multiplier chains. The design shown in this section may be old but it still works extremely well.

Digital frequency counter

A digital frequency counter is a valuable piece of test equipment, the design described here was produced by Ron Taylor, G4GXO [6]. It uses a PIC programmable microcomputer that is easily used by the home constructor and in fact radio clubs have used this design as a club project. A ready build and more sophisticated PIC counter is available from Ron's company [7]

PIC counter designs have been around for several years. The use of a PIC instead of discrete logic offers enormous savings in circuit complexity, cost and assembly time. Whilst PIC counters are not new this one has an interesting feature in that it can be use to either measure and display frequency directly or display the sum or difference of the input signal frequency and a user definable IF offset. The IF value is programmed on power up by holding the two frequency set buttons down as the unit is

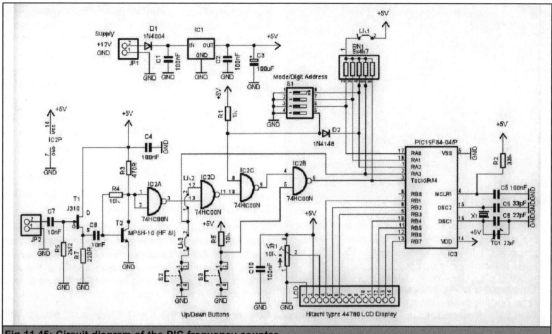

Fig 11.45: Circuit diagram of the PIC frequency counter.

switched on to put the PIC into Programming mode. Each digit of the 8 digit offset value is addressed by a binary address on DIP switches 1 - 3.

The circuit diagram for the counter is shown in Fig 11.45, the PCB layout shown in Fig 11.46 and a picture of the completed PCB is shown in Fig 11.47. The PCB design can be downloaded from Ron's web site [6] Despite the 35MHz quoted upper limit of the PIC16F84 prescaler, all three prototypes of this counter operate to just over 46MHz when driven from a GDO loosely coupled to the input amplifier via a 4 turn coil (less than ideal!).

Counter software

The software can be downloaded from Ron Taylor's web site [6]. To use these files you will need a copy of MPLAB, a PIC Programmer and a PC. First make any modifications such as IF offset value using a text editor or MPLAB's editor. Then compile the file into a hex file via MPLAB. The hex file is loaded into the PIC using a PIC

programmer and it's associated software. There is an enormous volume of information on The Internet about programming PIC's and a wide range of programmers available ready built or as kits. Data sheets and programming information for the 16F84 are available on Arizona Microchip website [8]. Downloads of MPLAB and other utilities are also available from the web site.

The software re-uses ideas from several sources, most notably:

- The NJQRP Club who in their DDS designs demonstrate the use of the PIC16F84 EEPROM area for holding variable user definable data, in this case Hex calibration words for computing DDS steps.

- Dr Peter Halicky OM3CPH, who has provided several excellent examples of how to use PIC16F84's as frequency counters, the approach used in this design

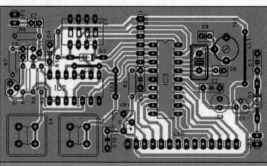

Fig 11.46: PCB and component layout for the PIC frequency counter.

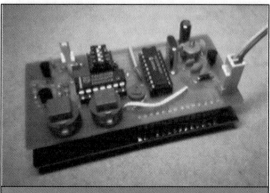

Fig 11.47: Picture of the completed PIC frequency counter.

Table 11.7: Switch settings for normal mode operation of the PIC frequency counter

Dip switch	ON	OFF	Function
1		OFF	MSB digit address (must be OFF for measurement mode)
2	Difference	Sum	Add / subtract IF offset value
3	Direct	IF offset	IF offset enable
4		OFF	Mode selection (must be OFF for measurement mode)

Table 11.8: Switch settings for IF offset frequency in program mode operation of the PIC frequency counter

Switch	Frequency in (M)Hz, (k)Hz and Hz							
	100M	10M	1M	100k	10k	1k	100	10
1	x	x	x	x	√	√	√	√
2	x	x	√	√	x	x	√	√
3	x	√	ξ	√	x	√	x	√

x = OFF, √ = ON

- Hold down the two UP/DOWN push buttons

- Power on the unit

- After one second the "Offset Prog" message will be displayed.

follows Peter Haliky's approach of using the TMR0 and two registers to hold the frequency count. The nested timing loop concept used in Peter's software has also been adapted for this design.

- Ed Skelton EI9GQ, for ideas on the external gate circuit. In this design the external gate circuit uses a 74HC00 that is modified to allow gating, frequency programming and clocking out of the TMR0 register content.

The IF Offset routines are adapted from those Ron developed for his DDS software.

Counter operating instructions

This section describes how to operate and program the PIC Counter. There are two modes, normal operating mode and programming mode. In normal operating mode the IF offset feature can be selected or disabled without needing to perform any form of reset. This allows the feature to be controlled by a switch or relay in applications where the IF offset or direct frequency-counting mode needs to be under the control of an external circuit. An example might be a CW transceiver with a superhet receiver and a "straight through" transmitter. The IF offset feature would be enabled during receive and disabled during transmit. Similarly the IF offset can be added or subtracted from the input frequency during normal operation. Table 11.7 shows the switch settings for normal operations and the IF offset feature. In normal operating mode a status message is displayed briefly on each change of the IF Offset switches.

Note that in normal mode, DIP switches 1 and 4 MUST be set to OFF to correctly configure the input circuit to the counter.

In programming mode, switches 1 to 3 are used to form a binary address of the each of the 8 IF Offset frequency digits, (see Table 11.8). Switch 4 allows selection of programming mode. To place the unit into programming mode follow these steps:

- Ensure that the unit is powered off

- Set DIP switches 1 to 4 ON

The Unit is now in programming mode, holding down either push button will increment or decrement the least significant IF Offset frequency digit. Other digits may be changed by setting up the digit address in binary on DIP switches 1 to 3 as follows, note that ON = logic 0 (pull down) and OFF = logic 1 (pull up):

Operating and holding the Up/Down push buttons will cause the selected digit to increment or decrement, note that incrementing a digit above 9 and decrementing below 0 will cause a carry and borrow respectively.

Once the desired IF Offset has been programmed it is saved to EEPROM by briefly pressing both buttons simultaneously. The IF Offset Frequency will be saved, even during powered off states, and will be recalled when IF Offset mode is used. The save operation is not permanent and other new IF Offset frequencies may be programmed to suit future applications or projects. To skip over the IF Offset Programming mode press both buttons simultaneously (as in the save action).

Once the IF Offset Frequency has been saved the unit will select Multiplier program mode. This is an unusual but useful function designed to allow the counter to be used with frequency multiplier chains. The input frequency is multiplied by a programmable factor after which the IF Offset function may be applied. A typical application might be a VXO driven multiplier chain in a VHF transceiver. The multiplication factor would be set to that of the frequency multiplier chain and the input for the counter would be taken from the source VXO. The input frequency (up to 45MHz) is multiplied by the Multiplication Factor to produce a displayed representation of the VXO multiplier chain output frequency.

On entry to the Multiplier Function Mode the message "Mult Factor" will be displayed together with the programmed value. Operating and holding the Up/Down buttons changes the value. For direct frequency display the "Mult Factor" should be set to "01". (Note that on newly programmed PIC's random symbols may be displayed; use the UP/Down buttons to reach the permitted range of 0 - 98). Once the desired Multiplication Factor has been set, simultaneously operate both push buttons to save the value to EEPROM. The message "Saved" will be displayed.

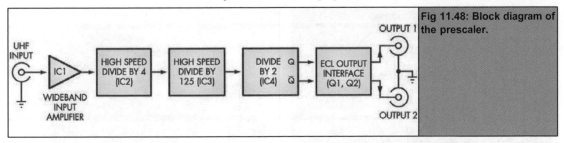

Fig 11.48: Block diagram of the prescaler.

Prescaler

Here is a high speed prescaler that can extend the range of virtually any frequency counter to over 2.8GHz. It divides frequencies by exactly 1000, so gigahertz can be read directly in megahertz. It was designed by Jim Rowe and is reproduced by arrangement with SILICON CHIP Magazine, from the October 2006 issue [9].

The UHF bands go up to 2.4GHz, so now can you check your operating frequency with the prescaler described here. This simply connects "in front" of your existing counter and divides the frequency of the signals you want to measure by exactly 1000. So 1.5GHz becomes 1.5MHz, 2.45GHz becomes 2.45MHz and so on, allowing you to read the incoming frequency directly and without any mental arithmetic.

The prescaler uses some special high speed ECL (Emitter Coupled Logic) ICs to perform the 1000:1 frequency division and these are able to operate at input frequencies up to at least 2.8GHz. Because the output frequency of the prescaler is still only 2.8MHz for an input of 2.8GHz, this means that it should be suitable for extending the range of just about any counter. In fact, it would be a good companion for the PIC counter described in this section.

Circuit description

The operation the Prescaler is pretty straightforward, as you can see from the block diagram of Fig 11.48, and the circuit diagram Fig 11.49. The parts list is shown in Table 11.9. The input signal is fed through an input termination and overload protection circuit formed by two 100Ω resistors and diodes D1 & D2. The two resistors are in parallel to provide an input termination of 50Ω, while D1 & D2 are very low capacitance Schottky barrier diodes, having a very low forward voltage drop. Because they're connected in inverse parallel, they limit the input signal level to no more than 2V peak-peak.

The signal is then coupled to the input of IC1 via a 10nF capacitor. IC1 is an MMIC (Monolithic Microwave Integrated Circuit), with about 12dB of gain up to over 5GHz. IC1 is fed with DC power via its output (pin 3), with the 47Ω resistor chosen to set the correct operating current. As the power feed is effectively in parallel with the output of IC1, choke RFC3 is used to provide a reasonable load. This choke is a special very wideband device chosen because it has a very low parasitic capacitance and is

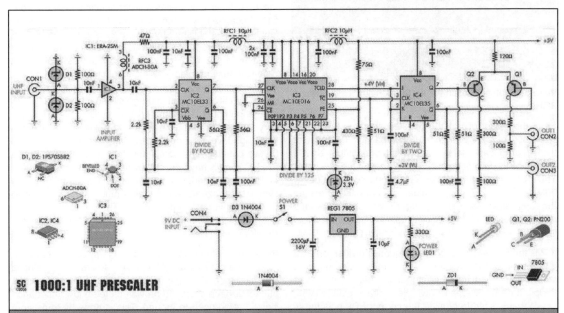

SC 1000:1 UHF PRESCALER

Fig 11.49: Circuit diagram of the prescaler. Reproduced by arrangement with SILICON CHIP magazine [9].

Table 11.9: Parts list for the prescaler.

Semiconductors

IC1	ERA-2SM UHF monolithic amplifier
IC2	MC10EL33 divide-by-4 ECL divider
IC3	MC10E016 ECL programmable counter
IC4	MC10EL35 ECL JK flipflop
REG1	7805 +5V 3-terminal regulator
Q1, Q2	PN200 PNP transistors
ZD1	3.3V 1W zener diode
LED1	3mm green LED
D1, D2	1PS70SB82 UHF Schottky diode
D3	1N4004 1A diode

Capacitors

1	2200µF 16V RB electrolytic
1	10µF 16V RB electrolytic
1	4.7µF 16V tantalum
3	100nF multilayer monolithic ceramic (leaded)
6	100nF X7R dielectric 1206 SMD chip
8	10nF X7R dielectric 1206 SMD chip

Resistors (0.25W 1%)

2	2.2kΩ 0805 SMD chip
1	430Ω
1	330Ω
2	300Ω
1	120Ω
2	100Ω 0805 SMD chip
2	100Ω
1	75Ω
2	56Ω 0805 SMD chip
3	51Ω
1	47Ω 0805 SMD chip

Hardware

CIN1	reverse polarity PCB mount SMA socket
CON2, 3	PCB mount BNC sockets
CON4	PCB mount 2.5mm concentric DC connector
S1	PCB mount DPDT toggle switch
RFC1, 2	10mH RF chokes
RFC3	ADCH-80A UHF wideband RF choke, SMD
1	double sided PCB, code 04110061, 81 x 111mm
1	diecast aluminium box, 119 x 93.5 x 34mm
1	TO220 heatsink, 6073 type (19 x 19 x 9.5mm)
1	12 x 12mm aluminium sheet (1mm thick, heatsink for main divider chip)
1	small quantity of thermal grease
1	M3 x 6mm round head machine screw
6	M3 x 15mm countersunk machine screws
6	6mm long untapped metal spacers
7	M3 nuts & star lockwashers

Fig 11.50: Picture of the completed prescaler.

tary outputs (pins 7 & 6) that both need to be tied to ECL low logic level via termination resistors of close to 50Ω. 56Ω chip resistors are used, because this value is more readily available than 51Ω.

From pin 7 of IC2 the signal (now 1/4 the input frequency) passes directly to the clock input of IC3, an ECL 8 bit programmable synchronous binary counter able to count/divide input frequencies up to at least 700MHz. It is programmed to divide by 125, by tying its parallel load inputs (P0 - P7, pins 3 - 7 and 21 - 23) to the appropriate ECL logic levels. For division by 125, the parallel inputs are set to the binary code for 256 - 125, or 131 i.e. 10000011. Note that the ECL high or "1" level is established by the 75Ω and 430Ω resistors, forming a voltage divider across the 5V supply rails.

The output signal from IC3 (1/500 of the input frequency) appears at the terminal count pin (19) that must be tied to the ECL logic low level via a terminating resistor (here 51Ω, because it is a standard leaded part). The ECL logic low level is established by ZD1, a 3.3V zener diode. The output signal from IC3 is low in frequency (below 8MHz) but it is in the form of very narrow pulses that would probably pose problems for the input circuitry of many low frequency counters. That is why IC3 is not programmed to divide by 250. Instead it is programmed it to divide by 125 and its output is fed to a third ECL device, IC4. This is a very fast JK flip-flop with its J and K inputs tied to ECL logic high level so it operates in toggle mode as a divide-by-two counter. The complementary outputs (pins 7 and 6) of IC4 finally have the output signals of exactly 1/1000th of the input frequency and, just as importantly, it is a symmetrical square wave that is much more compatible with typical counter input circuits. The outputs of IC4 are again tied to ECL logic low level via 51Ω terminating resistors.

Since the outputs from IC4 are still switching between ECL levels (nominally +3V and +4V), the remaining step is to pass them through a level translation and output buffer/interface circuit, to provide buffered low impedance signals referenced to ground. This is done by transistors Q1 and Q2, connected as a differential switch. This has

therefore not self-resonant at frequencies below about 8GHz.

From the output of IC1 the boosted signal is fed to the clock input of IC2 via another 10nF capacitor. The value of the coupling capacitors at the input and output of IC1 determine the lowest operating frequency of the prescaler. The 10nF capacitors allow it to work down to below 50MHz. The reason larger values are not used to extend the range even lower is that larger value capacitors tend to self-resonate at frequencies below 4GHz that would lower the maximum frequency of operation.

IC2 is the first and most critical frequency divider, an ECL divide-by-4. It can operate at input frequencies up to at least 3.8GHz and has a propagation delay of less than 800ps. It even includes its own bias voltage source (Vbb, pin 4) that is used to provide the correct ECL bias for its two inputs (via the 2.2kΩ resistors). IC2 has complemen-

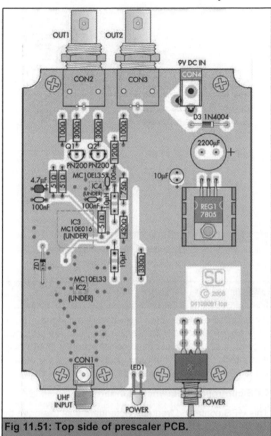

Fig 11.51: Top side of prescaler PCB.

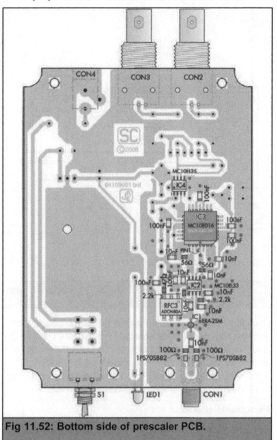

Fig 11.52: Bottom side of prescaler PCB.

the advantage that the prescaler has two independent outputs, so that it can drive either two different counters or perhaps a counter and an oscilloscope.

The prescaler circuitry operates from 5V DC. The power supply is very straightforward using a 7805 regulator, driven from an external 9V DC plug top power supply. The total current drain is about 190mA, giving a regulator dissipation of about 800mW, the regulator has a small heatsink so it keeps reasonably cool.

Construction

As shown in Figs 11.50 - 11.52 the prescaler is built on a double-sided PCB measuring 111 x 81mm, this is available from [10]. The board has rounded cut-outs in each corner so that it fits snugly inside a standard diecast aluminium instrument case, measuring 119 x 93.5 x 34mm. All the connectors, power switch S1 and the power

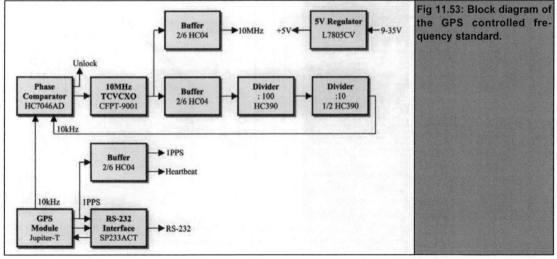

Fig 11.53: Block diagram of the GPS controlled frequency standard.

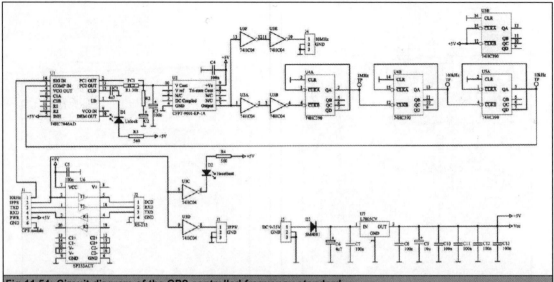

Fig 11.54: Circuit diagram of the GPS controlled frequency standard.

indicator LED are mounted on the top of the board, along with the regulator (on its heatsink), transistors Q1 and Q2 and the other leaded components. The surface mount ICs and other components are mounted on the underside of the board. The main divder chip has a heatsink made from a 12 x 12mm piece of aluminium under the PCB.

Functional checkout

The prescaler should be given a quick functional checkout before it's fitted into the box. To check it out, place the PC board assembly on a clean timber or plastic surface and connect a 9V DC supply. Turn on power switch S1 and check the +5V supply rail and the 3.1V across ZD1. Connect the output of the prescaler to the frequency counter. You may well find that the counter shows a reading even with no input signal. That is because IC2

tends to self-oscillate when there is no input signal. This is no cause for concern because as soon as a "real" signal is applied, it stops. Connect a known frequency input signal and check that the frequency counter reads the correct value. The prescaler can now be fitted into its housing.

GPS controlled frequency standard

This GPS controlled frequency standard was designed by Zeljko Bozic, S52ZB [11]. Most radio amateurs have frequency counters with reference oscillators that are not temperature compensated and they are made with bad quality crystals. A special problem is the ageing of crystals that can take up to 10 years. Because of this frequency counters can deviate by more than a hundred kHz at a frequency of 10GHz and are really only suitable for 100MHz or less. A simple and inexpensive solution is a

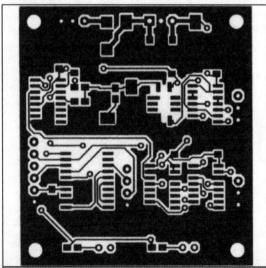

Fig 11.55: Top side of the PCB layout for the GPS controlled frequency standard. Available from [10].

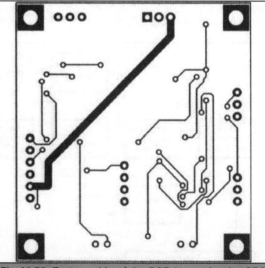

Fig 11.56: Bottom side of the PCB layout for the GPS controlled frequency standard.

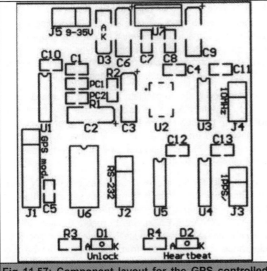

Fig 11.57: Component layout for the GPS controlled frequency standard.

Fig 11.58: The completed GPS controlled frequency standard.

GPS controlled frequency standard, often referred to as a GPSDO (GPS Disciplined Oscillator). It is a frequency standard that calibrates itself using GPS.

Circuit diagram

The block diagram of a GPS controlled frequency standard is shown in Fig 11.53. The circuit diagram of the GPS controlled frequency standard is shown in Fig 11.54. The circuit diagram is simple as it can be. The Navman TU60-D120-041 Jupiter-T GPS receiver [12] has a high accuracy 10kHz output synchronised to UTC. A 10MHz C-MAC TCVCXO CFPT-9001 [13] is divided down to 10kHz and phase locked to this GPS signal. Both outputs (10MHz and 1PPS) are buffered with inverters. The PLL filter components are designed for $\omega n = 0.239$ rad/s,

$\zeta = 0.707$ and Ko=67Hz/volt. R2 and C2 are not used. The GPS receiver can be controlled via the RS232 port and a 1PPS signal is available on DCD that can be used by a computer to keep precise UTC time to a few tens of ns.

Construction

The frequency standard is constructed on a double-sided PCB made from a 50.8mm x 55mm piece of 1.6mm thick FR4 laminate. It has plated through holes, solder resist and lead free tinning. The PCB layouts are shown in Figs 11.55 and 11.56, the component layout is shown in Fig 11.57 and the parts list in Table 11.10.

The GPS receiver used is a Navman TU60-D120-041 Jupiter-T which has both 1PPS and 10kHz outputs. It was designed especially for precision timing applications. In 2005 Navman discontinued manufacturing the Jupiter-T. Instead of the Jupiter-T you can use the standard Jupiter receivers TU30-D140-xxx and TU30-D410-xxx, which also have a 10kHz output. They are similar in size but the connector and pin out are different. These receivers are often available on eBay. Before purchase it is important to ensure that the firmware is v1.18 onwards. The firmware version is printed on a label and is also emitted at start up in an ASCII plain text NMEA message. The default protocol of the GPS receiver is Motorola UT+ "@@". Navman binary protocol and NMEA protocol are also available.

The GPS antenna is an external active antenna with 5V supplied through the coaxial cable. It is important that the GPS antenna has the fullest possible view of the sky. Getting the maximum number of satellites in view will get the best timing performance.

A better quality oscillator such as an OCXO can be used instead of the C-MAC TCVCXO but the PLL filter components must be recomputed. The oven-controlled oscillator has considerably better performance than a miniature SMD TCVCXO, but at the cost of greater power consumption and increased size. Good but big OCXOs can be found in old NMT base stations and also on eBay.

Table 11.10: Parts list for GPS controlled frequency standard.

R1	30k	0805
R2	-	0805, not used
R3, R4	560ohm	0805
C1	4n7	0805 C0G(NP0)
C2	-	SMD tantalum 35V, not used
C3	100u	SMD tantalum 35V
C4, C5, C7, C8, C10, C11, C12, C13	100n	0805
C6	4u7	SMD tantalum 35V
C9	10u	SMD tantalum 35V
D1	LED	Red 3mm
D2	LED	Green 3mm
D3	SM4001	MELF
U1	74HC7046AD	SO-16
U2	CFPT-9001	SMD 7 x 5 x 2mm, 10-pin
U3	74HC04	SO-14
U4, U5	74HC390	SO-16
U6	SP233ACT	SO-20 wide
U7	L7805CV	TO-220
J1	SIL socket	6-pin
J2	SIL socket	4-pin
J3, J4, J5	SIL socket	3-pin
PCB	-	50.8 x 55mm, FR4 1.6mm
Housing	-	Aluminium plate 1mm

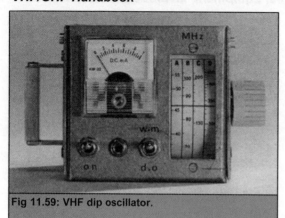

Fig 11.59: VHF dip oscillator.

The 10MHz output is square wave at HCMOS level, an output level of +15dBm. The PLL IC is a 74HC7046A [14] [15], it is an improved version of the familiar 74HC4046A. The PC3 function is replaced with an improved lock detector. The serial port driver IC is an SP233A [16], a low cost version of the familiar MAX233A.

The frequency standard status is shown by two LEDs. The green LED "Heartbeat" flashes at 1PPS and the red LED "Unlock" lights up when the PLL is unlocked. The value of the lock detector capacitor C1 is dependant on the PLL filter components. If the PLL filter components are changed, the value of C1 must also be changed.

The operating voltage of the frequency standard is 9 to 35V and the current consumption should be around 250mA including GPS receiver and GPS active antenna.

The frequency standard is built into a custom made housing 130mm wide, 110mm deep and 30mm high made from 1mm thick aluminium plate. Fig 11.58 shows the prototype GPS controlled frequency standard.

Results

First measurements of the frequency standard show that it has accuracy of 1 x 10^{-10} after 1 hour and about 1 x 10^{-11} after 24 hours. The test equipment was an Agilent PSA E4445A (1Hz resolution) spectrum analyser locked on a 10MHz frequency standard OSA 5230 from Oscilloquartz. Measurements with the spectrum analyser were on the 100th (1GHz), 200th (2GHz) and 500th (5GHz) harmonic. More accurate measurements were with an oscilloscope (Lissajous figure).

GPS satellites can be monitored using one of the NMEA 0183 data programs such as Tac32 [17] or VisualGPS [18]. These programs give a graphically display of specific NMEA sentences.

Help and support for this project came from; James Miller (G3RUH) [19], Robert Vilhar (S53WW) and Stojan Kuret (S51WI).

Dip oscillators

A dip oscillator (the valve versions were called grid dip oscillators) is an essential tool for the construction of VHF/UHF equipment.

In its simplest form it consists of a stable LC oscillator covering a wide range of frequencies. Depending on the actual range, the inductance will be cut to an appropriate size and will normally be a plug in type. Some form of indicator, such as a meter, is required to show when the dip oscillator is tuned to the circuit under test.

For VHF and UHF dip oscillators, FETs are normally used in a push pull circuit. With circuits of this type oscillators for use up to 500MHz are practical with careful mechanical layout so that connecting leads between the plug in coil and the tuning capacitor are short and of as low inductance as possible.

Plug in coils for the higher frequencies are usually made of sufficiently substantial material to be self supporting. If, however, any support is needed a low dielectric constant material such as PTFE should be used. Sockets for the coils should be mounted on similar material and adequate clearance for the sockets from the box should be provided. These precautions assist in the attainment of the highest frequencies.

The indicator may be either a low reading microammeter or a more robust instrument operated by a simple amplifier. The tuning control should for preference be driven by a slow motion dial, although a large diameter dial operated by the thumb has some merit in this type of instrument.

A VHF dip oscillator

This dip oscillator [20] is shown in Fig 11.59 covers 29 - 460MHz in four overlapping ranges with plug in coils. It is an old design but is still a very useful instrument. The ranges are:

- Range A 29 to 55MHz

- Range B 50 to 109MHz

- Range C 97 to 220MHz

- Range D 190 to 460MHz

Circuit description

The circuit is based around a Kalitron oscillator formed by two junction FETs TR1 and TR2; see Fig 11.60. The frequency determining components are the split stator capacitor C1 and the plug in coil L1. The resulting RF signal is then detected by a balanced diode detector D1 and D2, and used to drive meter amplifier TR3. The original design used either 2N5245 or TIS88 for TR1 and TR2 but these are no longer available. These can be substituted by a 2N3819, BF244A or similar N-channel junction FET.

The power can be turned off to convert the instrument to a sensitive absorption wavemeter, or when headphones are plugged into the jack J1 it becomes a modulation monitor. In this design the existence of spurious dips and "suck outs" in the various ranges is very much associated with the quality of the two RF chokes L2 and L3. These are each of 15µH. If troubles of this kind are experienced, other inductors can be tried. It is very difficult to find

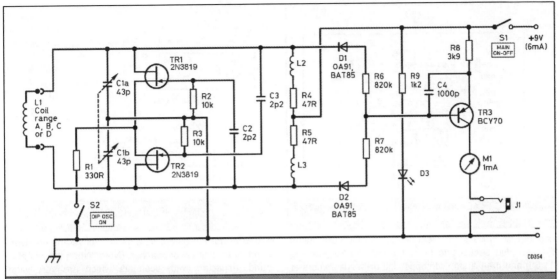

Fig 11.60: Circuit diagram for the VHF dip oscillator.

components with no strong resonance over the whole of a wide band, but nevertheless the prototype instrument using the inductors with the two series damping resistors R4 and R5 seemed to minimise the problem.

Power supply

This is normally provided by a PP3 battery the current drain being about 10mA (including the LED). A PP3 replacement mains supply could be substituted.

Construction

Construction can either be on tag strip (Fig 11.61) or using a PCB shown in Figs 11.62 and 11.63 with the parts list in Table 11.11. The most important points are to keep the leads to the tuning capacitor as short as possible, using copper strip to keep the inductance low. Also keep all other RF leads short, especially any that are associated with the sources of TR1 and TR2. The original version, as shown in the photograph, was constructed in an aluminium box forming about a 50mm (2in) cube and a

design for making this is given in Fig 11.64. Following this construction is, however, a matter of personal choice.

The tuning capacitor C1 with a tuning scale drum is driven by a 6:1 reduction drive. A homemade 22mm (0.875in) wide card or plastic scale is fitted to the drum. The coil socket and the coil mounting strips are made from 3mm (0.125in) thick PTFE sheet, although polythene or even polystyrene is acceptable (Fig 11.65). Two Belling Lee 4mm sockets (similar to O-Z pattern) are mounted on the socket strip.

Coil construction

The coil (see Table 11.12) for the lowest frequency range, A, is wound on a short piece of 12.5mm (0.5in) diameter polystyrene rod and then glued in place. Connecting and supporting legs (each 44.5mm or 1.75in long) are made from 14 SWG enamelled copper wire. The next range coil, B, is self supporting and wound directly with 14 SWG wire, also with connection pieces 44.5mm (1.75in) long. Range C has a simple rectangular loop of 13 SWG enamelled

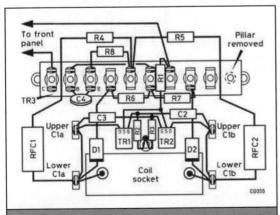

Fig 11.61: Tag board construction for the VHF dip oscillator

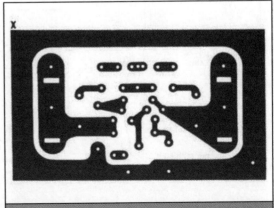

Fig 11.62: PCB layout for the VHF dip oscillator.

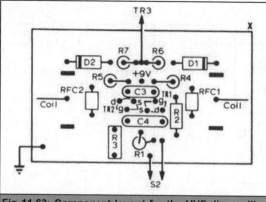

Fig 11.63: Component layout for the VHF dip oscillator.

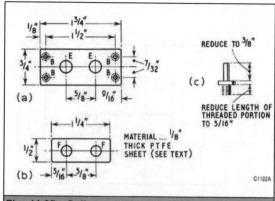

Fig 11.65: Coil mounting strips for the VHF dip oscillator.

copper wire, whilst the highest frequency range D requires the two plug sections to be further shortened (see Fig 11.65) and then a strip of copper foil or beryllium/copper sheet is soldered straight across their ends.

Calibration of dip oscillators

The easiest way to check the calibration of a dip oscillator

is to listen for the output on a general coverage receiver, an amateur receiver or scanner. (Note: When the signal is found, especially with scanners which are very wide bandwidth, check that there is no response at one half, one third or one fifth of the frequency in case the fundamental has not been found.)

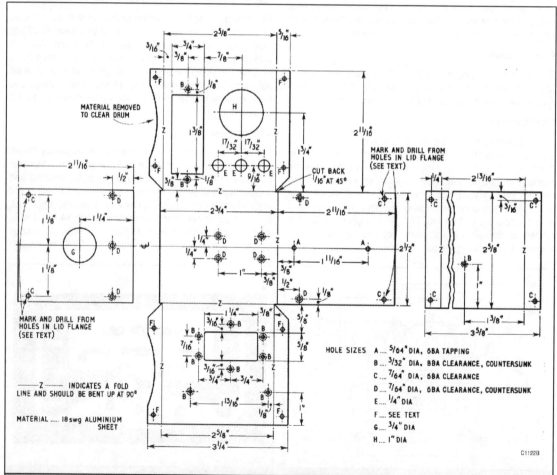

Fig 11.64: Construction details of the aluminium box for the VHF dip oscillator.

Table 11.11: Parts list for the VHF dip oscillator.

R1	330Ω
R2, 3	10kΩ
R4, 5	47Ω
R6, 7	820kΩ
R9	1.2kΩ
C1	43pF + 43pF variable
C2, 3	2.3pF ceramic
C4	1000pF ceramic
D1, 2	OA91, BAT85
D3	Low current LED
TR1, 2	2N3819 or similar
L1	see text
L2, 3	15µH
M1	1mA FSD meter
S1, 2	On/off switch
J1	Jack socket to suit
	PP3 battery connector
	Belling Lee 4mm OZ or similar plug and socket

Resistors are 0.25/0.5W ±5% unless stated otherwise

Table 11.12: Coil details for the VHF dip oscillator.

Range A 29 - 55MHz	12t 22 SWG enamelled copper wire on 12.5mm polystyrene rod 25mm long, 44.4mm legs 14 SWG
Range B 50 - 109MHz	8t 14 SWG enamelled copper wire wound on 9.5mm drill, 44.5mm legs
Range C 97 - 220MHz	16mm wide, 73mm long loop of 13 SWG enamelled copper wire
Range D 190 - 460MHz	8mm wide, 17.5mm long 26 SWG copper or beryllium copper strip soldered directly across plug ends

This probably allows a good check on the calibration into the VHF range. Additional points can be found by using the second channel response provided that the IF is known (the second channel response is 2 × IF removed from the normal response).

Another method is to use the resonances of lengths of feeder cables, providing that the velocity factor for the particular cable is known, so that the physical length corresponding to the wanted electrical half and quarter waves can be found.

Using the dip oscillator

Although the dip oscillator has a wide range of uses for measurements on both complete equipment and individual components, these all rely on its ability to measure the frequency of a tuned circuit. In use, the coil of the dip oscillator is coupled indirectly to the circuit under test with maximum coupling being obtained with the axis of the oscillator coil at right angles to the direction of current flow. Coupling should be no greater than that necessary to give a moderate change on the dip oscillator meter. These requirements are shown diagrammatically in Fig 11.66.

If the tuned circuit being investigated is well shielded magnetically (e.g. a coaxial line) it may be difficult to use inductive coupling. In such cases it may be possible to use capacitive coupling by placing the open end of the line near to one end of the dip oscillator coil. A completely enclosed cavity is likely to have some form of coupling loop and the dip meter coil can usually be coupled inductively by means of a low impedance transmission line such as a twisted pair with a coupling loop.

When used as an absorption wavemeter, the oscillator is not energised and the tuned circuit acts as a pick up loop. This arrangement is useful when looking for harmonic output of a multiplier or transmitter or for spurious oscillations.

Determination of the resonant frequency of a tuned circuit

The resonant frequency of a tuned circuit is found by placing the dip oscillator close to the circuit and tuning for resonance. No power should be applied to the circuit under test and the coupling should be as loose as possible consistent with a reasonable dip being produced on the indicating meter. The size of the dip is dependent on the Q of the circuit under test, a circuit having a high Q producing a more pronounced dip than one only having low or moderate Q.

Absorption wavemeter

By switching off the power supply in the dip oscillator and

Fig 11.66: Using the dip oscillator.

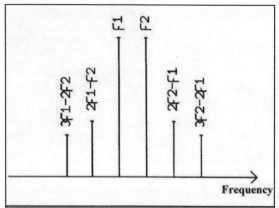

Fig 11.67: Diagram showing third and fifth order inter-modulation products

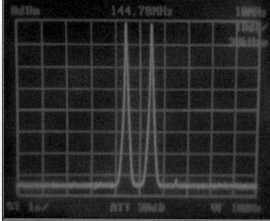

Fig 11.68: A screen shot of the output from the two-tone generator.

then using in the normal way, the instrument may be used as an absorption wavemeter. In this case power has to be applied to the circuit under test. Resonance is determined by maximum deflection on the meter caused by rectifying the received RF. The absorption wavemeter can also be used to check for harmonics and spurii.

Power amplifier measurement

The best way to measure the performance of a power amplifier is to use a two tone test with a high purity RF generator. Such a generator designed by Wolfgang Schneider, DJ8ES [21] for 144MHz is described in this section. Having injected the tones it is necessary to look at the output of the amplifier to measure the modulation products, Geoff Pike, GI0GDP has designed a neat narrow band spectrum analyser just for that purpose.

Two-tone generator for 145MHz

An RF amplifier stage is not only characterised by its amplification that is as high as possible but also for its signal quality measured by the inter-modulation behaviour. In practice, because of the gain slope, which is not completely linear, RF amplifiers are bound to produce distortion. A standard method for measuring this inter-modulation is the two-tone test.

In order to measure the inter-modulation behaviour of an amplifier, two signals of equal strength and with the frequencies f1 and f2 are applied to the input. The amplifier produces a spectrum of inter-modulation products from these signals. Particularly critical in practice are those of the third order (2 – f1 – f2; f2 – f1) and of the fifth order (3 – f1 – 2 – f2; 3 – f2 – 2 – f1). Fig 11.67 gives a

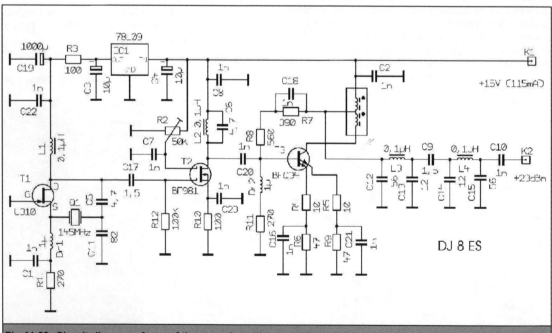

Fig 11.69: Circuit diagram of one of the crystal oscillators in the two-tone generator.

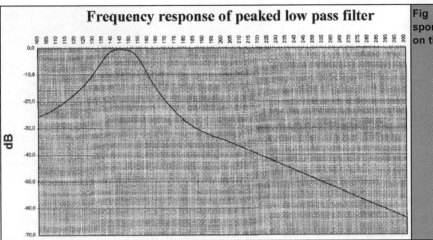

Frequency response of peaked low pass filter

Fig 11.70: Frequency response of the output filter on the two-tone oscillator.

representation of the position of these inter-modulation products.

The objective is to ensure that the third-order inter-modulation products are below -40dB in relation to the pure tone. Considerably stricter values apply to driver stages and mixers. Should these quality criteria not be taken into account in design, for an SSB transmitter this leads to poor modulation quality and a broad signal.

In order to measure the inter-modulation products, the two-tone generator itself must produce a high-quality signal. The equipment described here fulfils this requirement completely see Fig 11.68. The output level is +10dBm (10mW) for each pure tone. The selection of this signal level represents an acceptable compromise between cost and versatility. Should a higher output level be required, then a suitable power amplifier can be used such as the design by Carsten Vieland, DJ4GC [22].

The two frequencies, f1 = 144.850MHz and f2 = 145.150MHz, permit both the measurement of the third-order and fifth-order inter-modulation products using a spectrum analyser.

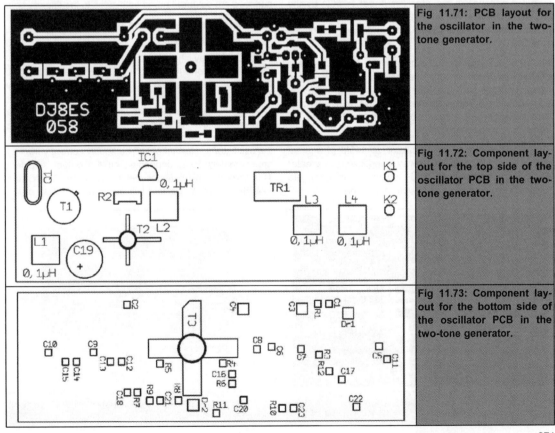

Fig 11.71: PCB layout for the oscillator in the two-tone generator.

Fig 11.72: Component layout for the top side of the oscillator PCB in the two-tone generator.

Fig 11.73: Component layout for the bottom side of the oscillator PCB in the two-tone generator.

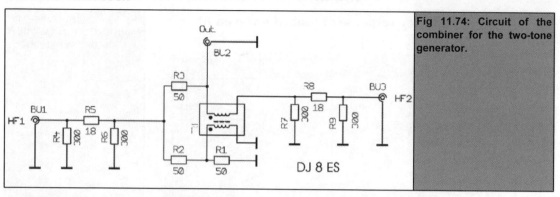

Fig 11.74: Circuit of the combiner for the two-tone generator.

Circuit description for crystal oscillator

The circuit diagram for the crystal oscillator is shown in Fig 11.69. The crystal oscillator uses a well-tried circuit with a U310 FET (T1). It has developed into a standard for VHF and microwave applications. What is new here is the additional low pass filter in the power supply. An RC filter consisting of R3 and C19 following the 78L09 regulator suppresses the voltage regulator noise and significantly improves the performance of the oscillator. The subsequent amplifier stage, with a dual gate MOSFET (T2), raises the oscillator signal to a maximum of + 7dBm (5mW). The amplification of this stage can be adjusted over a wide range, using the 50kΩ trimmer. The final amplifier uses a BFQ34 transistor (T3) to increases the output to a maximum of +24dBm (250mW). The input and output impedance of the amplifier is set to 50Ω by the feedback resistors. The current consumption for this stage is approximately 80mA (±15%), depending on the output level set.

The low pass filter on the output of the oscillator has a decisive influence on the spectral purity of the output signal at 145MHz. The insertion loss of the filter is approximately 1.3dB. The first harmonic at 290MHz is suppressed by more than 60dB. Fig 11.70 shows the frequency response of the low pass filter.

The output signal of the oscillator at 145MHz and an output of +23dBm (200mW) was investigated in greater detail by an Advantest R4131 spectrum analyser. No harmonic or spurious outputs were detectable.

Oscillator assembly instructions

The crystal oscillator is built on a 34mm x 108mm double-sided epoxy PCB shown in Fig 11.71, the component layouts are shown in Figs 11.72 and 11.73 and the parts list in Table 11.13. It fits into a commercially available 37mm. x 111mm x 30mm tinplate box. For the two-tone generator, two oscillator assemblies are required with identical components. The only difference is the crystal. Once the board has been drilled with a 0.8 or 1 mm. drill, the holes for non earth leads should be have a clearance cut using a 3mm drill on the component side. Connections to earth for components such as the filter capacitors are soldered on both sides of the PCB. Fit the SMA connectors and feedthrough capacitor into the box followed by the PCB, which should be as low as possible. The earth surfaces are soldered round both sides to the tinplate box.

Testing the crystal oscillator

Once the boards for the two oscillators have been fully assembled, they should first be checked for any faults. When all components are correctly inserted and soldered, the first oscillator can be put into operation. The supply voltage is +15V, with a current of approximately 100mA. The crystal oscillator (T1) should start to oscillate as the core of the coil is screwed in. The core should be positioned just below the point for maximum output, for the oscillator to start reliably. The supply current varies by approximately 15%, depending on the output selected. This level can be adjusted between +3dBm (2mW) and +24dBm (250mW) using the 50kΩ trimmer on G2 of the

Fig 11.75: PCB layout of the combiner for the two-tone generator.

Fig 11.76: A picture of the combiner for the two-tone generator.

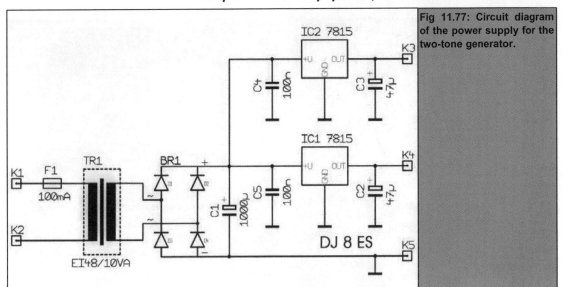

Fig 11.77: Circuit diagram of the power supply for the two-tone generator.

BF981 (T2). Pre-selecting the output to +20dBm (100mW) is best for subsequent use in the finished two-tone generator. To measure the power, a suitable mW meter can be connected at the output. The low pass filter at the output is then adjusted to give the maximum output level by repeated adjustment of coils L3 and L4. Finally adjust coil L2 for maximum output to complete the calibration procedure.

Combiner circuit description

The combiner adds the signals, f1 and f2, of the two crystal oscillators (Fig 11.74). The inputs each have a 3dB attenuator for better decoupling. The bifilar transformer, TR1, combines the two input signals. The circuit contains no active components, which would unnecessarily degrade the signal quality. Each signal branch contributes 10dB to the signal loss, 3dB for the attenuator and 7dB for the actual combiner. For an output of 2 x 100mW (+20dBm), the two-tone signal at the output is 20mW (+13dBm).

Combiner assembly instructions

The combiner assembly is constructed on a 34mm x 54mm double-sided epoxy PCB shown in Fig 11.75, a picture of the completed PCB is shown in Fig 11.76 and the parts list in Table 11.13. It fits into a commercially available 37mm. x 55.5mm. x 30mm tinplate box. Once the board has been drilled with a 0.8 or 1 mm. drill, the holes for non earth leads should be have a clearance cut using a 3mm drill on the component side. Connections to earth for components are soldered on both sides of the PCB. Fit the SMA connectors into the box followed by the PCB. The earth surfaces are soldered round both sides to the tinplate box. If the cost of special 50Ω resistors is prohibitive, 100Ω resistors in parallel (piggyback) can be used. To ensure symmetry, these resistors should be measured as precisely as possible in advance.

2 x 15V power supply

Each of the two crystal oscillators is powered by its own supply (15V, 100mA). The two regulators (IC1, IC2) keep

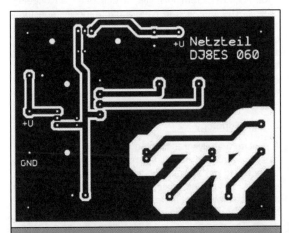

Fig 11.78: PCB layout of the power supply for the two-tone generator.

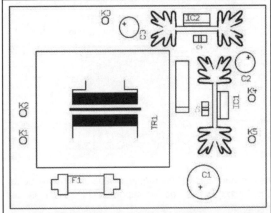

Fig 11.79: Component layout of the power supply for the two-tone generator.

Table 11.13: Parts lists for the two-tone generator.

Oscillator parts (two oscillators required)

T1	U310, transistor
T2	BF981, transistor
T3	BFQ34, transistor
IC1	78L09, voltage regulator
L1 - L4	BV5061 Neosid 0.1µH ready made coil
Q1	Crystal, HC-18/U, series, 7th overtone (e.g. 144.850MHz and 145.150MHz for the 2nd oscillator)
TR1	Bifilar transformer, 2 x 7 turns on ferrite core
R2	50kΩ trimmer, 64 W model
C19	1,000µF electrolytic capacitor, 16V, radial
C3, C4	10µF electrolytic capacitor, SMD, 1812 model
Dr1, Dr2	1µH choke, SMD, 1812 model
1 x	1nF, solderable feedthrough
1 x	SMA socket
1 x	Tinplate box 37mm x 111mm x 30mm
1 x	printed circuit board DJ8ES 058

All other components in SMD 1206:

C1, 2, 7, 8, 10, 16, 18, 20-23	1nF
C5, 6	4.7pF
C9	1.5pF
C11	82pF
C12, 15	56pF
C13, 14	12pF
C17	1.5pF
R1,11	270Ω
R3,10	100Ω
R4,5	10Ω
R6,9	47Ω
R7	390Ω
R8	560Ω
R12	100kΩ

Combiner parts list

R1-3	50Ω , SMD, model 1206
R4,6,7,9	300Ω , SMD, model 1206
R5, R8	18Ω , SMD, model 1206
TR1	Transformer, 7 turns, 0.2mm. enamelled copper wire, bifilar, on ferrite bead
3 x	SMA socket
1 x	tinplate box, 37mm x 55mm x 30mm
1 x	printed circuit board DJ8ES 059

Power supply parts

TR1	Transformer, 18V, 555mA, type 10VA
BR1	B40C1500, bridge rectifier
IC1, IC2	7815, 15V voltage regulator
C1	1,000µF electrolytic capacitor, radial, RM, 7.5mm
C2, C3	47µF electrolytic capacitor, radial, RM 5mm
C4, C5	100nF, ceramic, RM 2.5mm
F1	100mA fine wire fuse, delayed action, 5mm x 20mm
2 x	Heat sinks SK 104 38.1 STS, can be soldered in
1 x	fuse holder for printed circuit board mounting 5 x 1mm soldering studs
1 x	printed circuit board DJ8ES 060

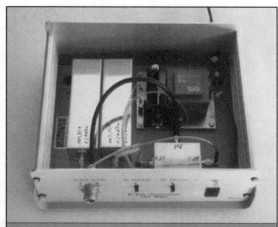

Fig 11.80: Picture of the completed two-tone generator.

layout in Fig 11.79 and the parts list in Table 11.13.

Putting into operation

Once all assemblies have been constructed ready for operation and positioned in a suitable housing as shown in Fig 11.80, the two-tone generator can be put into operation as a whole for the first time. The RF level for each oscillator is individually set at +10dBm (10mW), measured at the output socket. If both oscillators are switched on, the total signal measures +13dBm (20mW) or 40mW PEP.

The two-tone signal is now visible at 145MHz on a spectrum analyser. Fig 11.68 shows the good signal quality of this generator. It should be noted that most spectrum analysers are over modulated at such output levels and produce inter-modulation products themselves! Such signals can be measured only using a 20dB or 30dB attenuator.

Spectrum analyser

Geoff Pike, GI0GDP entitles this project "A 3 Band Spectrum Analyser for Intermodulation Measurements 1986 - 2007". From this title, it has been an ongoing project. The idea was to have a band specific spectrum analyser with >70dB dynamic range in a 1kHz spacing thus permitting intermodulation distortion in transmitters and 3rd order intercept points in LNA to be measured or at least compared. He decided to use 50, 70, and 144MHz as his specific bands, however the choice is your own and requires only a separate local oscillator and associated bandpass filter.

Design Topology

A spectrum analyser is nothing more than a receiver that has a logarithmic output applied to an oscilloscope as opposed to an essentially linear output applied to a speaker as in the case of the receiver. A notable difference also is that there is no gain in front of the mixer, in fact all the gain is after the mixer for the best dynamic range. The diagram in Fig 11.81 outlines the gain distribution and the general over view of the modules employed.

the voltage stable at the required value. In other respects, the circuit for the power supply in Fig 11.77 is self explanatory.

The power supply is built on a 100mm x 7 mm single-sided epoxy PCB as shown in Fig 11.78, the component

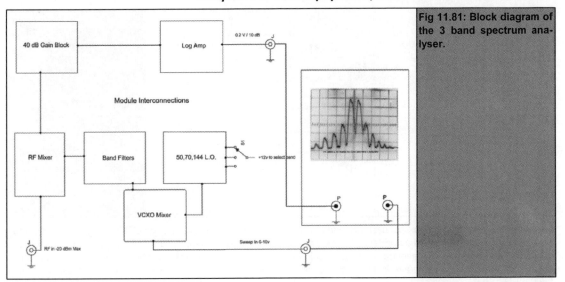

Fig 11.81: Block diagram of the 3 band spectrum analyser.

Prerequisites

As the sweep rate for displaying is normally of the order 50 - 100ms/div it is necessary to use an oscilloscope with a medium to long persistence tube. Also you need to use the narrowest CW filter that you can buy or make and really 500Hz is the absolute minimum with a 300Hz Yaesu filter used in the original. To make intermodulation tests you will need a two-tone RF or audio generator depending on your needs.

Circuit Description

This is essentially a high dynamic range receiver with a

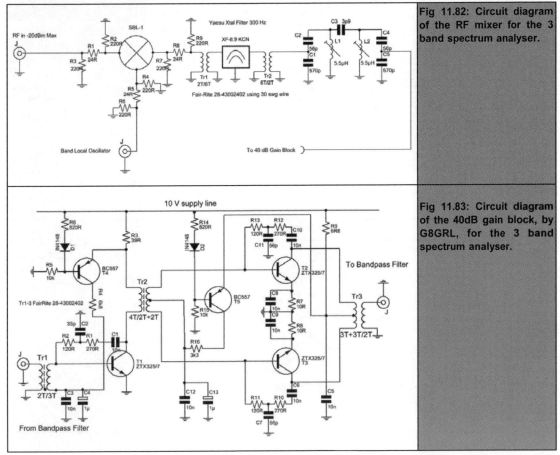

Fig 11.82: Circuit diagram of the RF mixer for the 3 band spectrum analyser.

Fig 11.83: Circuit diagram of the 40dB gain block, by G8GRL, for the 3 band spectrum analyser.

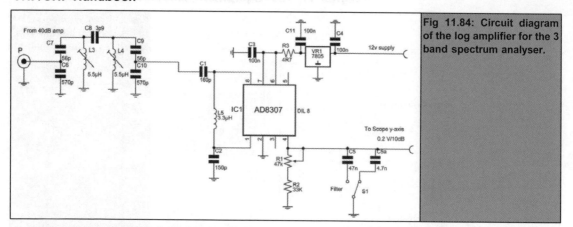

Fig 11.84: Circuit diagram of the log amplifier for the 3 band spectrum analyser.

maximum RF input of -20dBm applied to the input of the mixer, Fig 11.82. In the original a normal SBL-1 type mixer was used and obviously a better spec device could be substituted with a commensurate increase in LO drive level.

The IF path is through a 1:9 ferrite transformer to the crystal filter and then a 9:1 transformer into a 9MHz band pass filter before being applied to a push pull amplifier, Fig 11.83, with 40dB gain ahead of another bandpass filter. From here the signal is applied to the AD8307 log

amplifier, Fig 11.84. It is absolutely essential that no stray signals get in to the AD8307 at this point, as it will ruin the dynamic range that is available. Ideally the trace should sit about 1 or 2 divisions above ground with out any signal applied to the mixer input.

The local oscillator is essentially a three band switched affair and is mixed with a VCXO, Fig 11.85, which has a sweep range of about 50kHz depending on the varicap diode used.

The band oscillators, Figs 11.86 - 11.88 are switched with

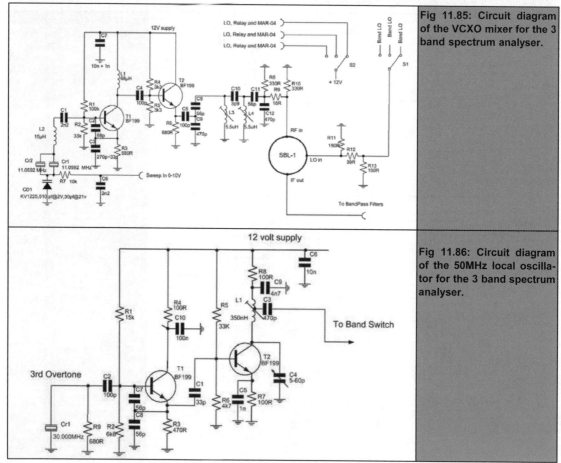

Fig 11.85: Circuit diagram of the VCXO mixer for the 3 band spectrum analyser.

Fig 11.86: Circuit diagram of the 50MHz local oscillator for the 3 band spectrum analyser.

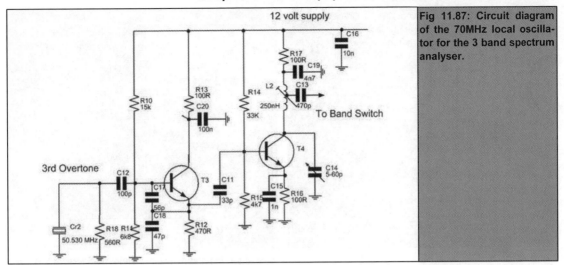

Fig 11.87: Circuit diagram of the 70MHz local oscillator for the 3 band spectrum analyser.

the appropriate bandpass filters, 11.89 and amplified to about 10dBm to drive the mixer. The band oscillators are mixed with a VCXO that is swept from the X output from the scope, typically 0 – 10V.

Under certain circumstances it may be better to have a separate sweep generator to drive the oscilloscope X axis and the VCXO input, this normally will give better centre frequency and width control. There are many suitable designs available e.g. JG1EAD [23] . This also has some varicap linearization built into the design.

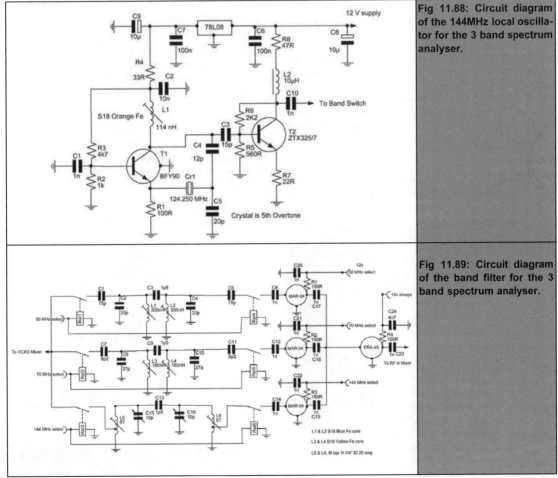

Fig 11.88: Circuit diagram of the 144MHz local oscillator for the 3 band spectrum analyser.

Fig 11.89: Circuit diagram of the band filter for the 3 band spectrum analyser.

Fig 11.90: Picture of the RF mixer for the 3 band spectrum analyser.

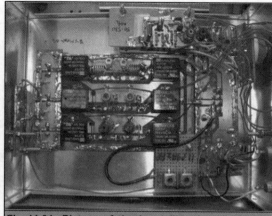

Fig 11.91: Picture of the band filter for the 3 band spectrum analyser.

Components

The only specialised part is the AD8307 log amplifier, the crystal oscillator frequencies are your choice, and also the VCXO crystals were to hand and perhaps weren't the best choice as some of the mixing products were close to the wanted signal.

The two hole Fair-Rite cores were wound with 30swg self fluxing wire. The cores are not critical. The main crystal filter really controls every thing but there is no reason why you could not make one from discrete crystals. The transformers for the bandpass filters are Toko KANK3334s but anything with the correct inductance will suffice. The KV1225 varicap diode was part of a 3 gang AM tuning diode. It maybe possible to get similar results from an LED or multiple reverse biased BD135 base - emitter junctions, a minimum VXCO swing of 20kHz would be needed for useful measurements.

Layout

It is essentially that all modules are screened and are interconnected with short coax interconnections with BNC or SMA connectors. I used separate diecast or aluminium

boxes for the input mixer, bandpass filters, 40dB gain block, the band pass filters / VCXO mixer and the AD8307 log amplifier. Figs 11.90 – 11.92 show the layout of the original with its interconnections and the relative positions to each other within the main enclosure.

No PCB layouts are offered as they are not critical and can be laid out in a schematic fashion on double-sided FR4 PCB material. The log amplifier was built dead bug fashion on a piece of scrap PCB and then fitted into an old Pye Telecoms low pass filter case.

The entire unit requires 12V and a separate 10V supply for the 40dB amplifier, this can be derived from the 12V supply with either a resistor or 3 diodes in series.

Operation

My oscilloscope is an old Cossor CDU150 that has a medium plus persistence and also a 10V output from the time base. This may not be available on your oscilloscope and therefore a sweep generator would need to be constructed and the example mentioned previously is a good start. It is important to select a time base or sweep speed that doesn't ring the filter, with my oscilloscope 50msec/div is almost as fast as the filter can take. The RF

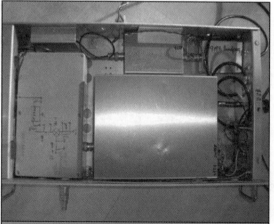

Fig 11.92: Picture of the completed 3 band spectrum analyser.

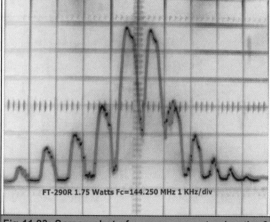

FT-290R 1.75 Watts Fc=144.250 MHz 1 KHz/div

Fig 11.93: Screen shot of a measurement using the 3 band spectrum analyser on an FT290R.

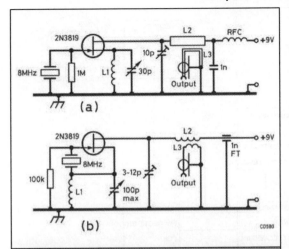

Fig 11.94: Two alternative simple VHF signal sources. Inductor details for (a) are: L1, 20t 8mm dia; L2, 120mm long by 3mm dia; L3, output coupling loop, 16 SWG wire; RFC, 35t 6mm dia. Inductor details for (b) are: L1, 28t 28 SWG wire, 6.5mm dia; L2, 4t 18 SWG wire, 12.7mm dia; L3, output coupling, 1t 18 SWG wire.

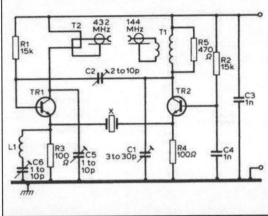

Fig 11.95: Circuit of a dual output signal source.

input should not exceed -20dBm for meaningful measurements. Of course the mixer will typically accept 0dBm and better mixers will be higher. The output from the log amplifier with no RF in should be about 0.4V, anything more than this suggests RF leaking into the detector, remember it works to 900MHz and beyond. It is important to reduce this offset by careful layout and supply decoupling.

At an input level of -20dBm the dynamic range is 70dB but as the input level increases this will get dramatically worse. This is something you will begin to understand when you make 3rd order intermodulation measurements.

Both Agilent [24] and Mini Circuits [25] explain the requirements to make 3rd order measurements so a search of their sites will produce the necessary information.

As a check on your measurements if you establish a trace and take results, then insert a 10dB attenuator into the incoming RF signal, all the products and parent tones will drop by 10dB. If however you are overloading the analyser and it is adding to the distortion then this will not be the case and the intermodulation products will fall by a value greater than the attenuator.

The results are shown in Fig 11.93 using a digital camera in manual mode, this shows my modified FT290R running 1.75W at a frequency of 144.250MHz and the tone spacing is approx 900Hz. The 3rd orders are about 28 - 30dB below the tones and the 5th, 7th, 9th and 11th visible and falling off at an acceptable rate. Non-linearity in the sweep is seen and this can easily be corrected.

To test a preamplifier you will need two RF tones and combiner, this is described in the Agilent and Mini Circuits notes. If you can, compare a dual gate MOSFET pream-

plifier of conventional design with a preamplifier with noiseless feedback and you will see a pleasant difference! but remember DO NOT OVERLOAD THE INPUT MIXER.

Receiver measurement

Signal sources

A reliable signal source is a useful adjunct for setting up receivers and converters. This is useful for both the setting of newly built equipment and the repair of equipment; both homebrew and "black box". Once the equipment has been aligned on a signal source it is worthwhile trying to tune to a distant beacon or repeater and again trying to optimise reception.

A simple signal source

Fig 11.94 shows two possible crystal oscillators with the appropriate tuned circuit, and both use 8MHz range crystals. The output should be checked with an absorption wavemeter to make sure that the correct harmonic of the crystal frequency has been selected. The possibility of error would be reduced if a higher frequency crystal were used; this would be particularly desirable if the output circuit were modified to give an output on 432MHz.

In construction it is desirable for the unit to be completely enclosed so that output is only obtained from the output socket; this will largely eliminate unwanted signals and also allow some control of the level. The power supply should be very well decoupled or a battery used in the same enclosure.

Dual output signal source

A useful signal source having outputs at 144 and 432MHz can be constructed readily using the familiar Butler crystal oscillator and multiplier circuit with a fifth overtone crystal of 103MHz - see Fig 11.95.

The circuit uses a series resonant crystal but the two different frequency output tuned circuits are connected to the respective collectors of the transistors in order to obtain the maximum output from the 432.6MHz side. A series resonant circuit (L1/C6) tuned to 288.4MHz is

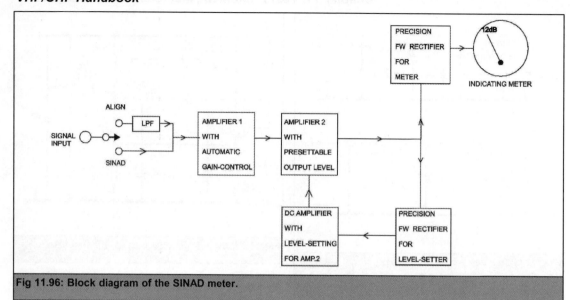

Fig 11.96: Block diagram of the SINAD meter.

connected in the emitter circuit of TR1. An output power of 30mW is obtainable on 144.2MHz and 10mW on 432.6MHz for an input power of 120mW.

The outputs are inductively coupled and suitably supported and adjusted. The transformer T1 for 144.2MHz output consists of four turns of 0.5mm wire wound with 7mm internal diameter, 9mm long and with a two turn link output coil. T2, the 432.6MHz output circuit, consists of 43mm lengths of wire formed into suitable loops. The 288MHz idler circuit (L1/C6) is formed of a coil of three turns of 0.5mm wire, 6mm internal diameter, 10mm long and tuned by a 1-10pF trimmer.

The transistors used are BFS17 or equivalent; types such as BSX20 will also be satisfactory, although somewhat lower output will be achieved.

SINAD meter

This easy to construct test meter by E. Chicken, G3BIK [26] simplifies measurement of the 12dB SINAD Sensitivity of an FM receiver. It connects to the receiver's loudspeaker terminals to automatically display the SINAD measurement. Power is from an external mains/dc unregulated 12V or 15V adaptor at 10mA, or from the receiver's dc supply.

When using the SINAD meter for measurement of a receiver, it must be used in conjunction with an FM signal generator of the type that has a modulating tone of 1kHz with adjustable deviation, and a voltage output control calibrated in microvolts RMS. That type of signal generator is fairly standard to those who are involved with FM radio equipment so should be reasonably available.

A very useful secondary feature of this SINAD meter, is that it can be used as a sensitive response indicator whilst tweaking for optimum sensitivity (maximum quietening) the RF, mixer, and local oscillator stages of an FM receiver. This is of particular advantage when re-tuning an ex PMR receiver for use on the amateur bands.

SINAD explained

The SINAD sensitivity of an FM receiver is expressed in microvolts RMS, and is derived from an internationally accepted method for determining the sensitivity of the receiver. SINAD is a ratio expressed in dB that relates the level of a 1kHz audio tone output from the loudspeaker, to distortion and noise generated within the receiver, using the formula:

$$\text{SINAD (dB)} = \frac{\textbf{SI}\text{gnal plus }\textbf{N}\text{oise }\textbf{A}\text{nd }\textbf{D}\text{istortion}}{\text{Noise and Distortion}}$$

Note that the term Signal refers to the 1kHz audio tone output from the loudspeaker, not the RF input signal!

The 12dB SINAD sensitivity figure that is expressed in microvolts RMS (not as SINAD dB), is the accepted standard of SINAD measurement against which to judge the sensitivity of an FM communications receiver. It is defined as that level of microvolts RMS (PD) RF signal into the receiver's antenna port that produces at the audio output a SINAD ratio of 12dB. At this sensitivity the receiver would give an intelligible voice signal on an acceptably quiet background. Any modern communications receiver will have a 12dB SINAD Sensitivity in the order of 0.5µV RMS or less.

Strictly speaking, the definitive method of SINAD measurement requires that:

- The RF signal being fed into the receiver's antenna terminal be frequency modulated by a 1kHz tone with deviation to 60% of the receiver's specified peak deviation

- The SINAD meter must incorporate a 1kHz band rejection filter

- The SINAD meter be connected across the receiver's loudspeaker or an equivalent load

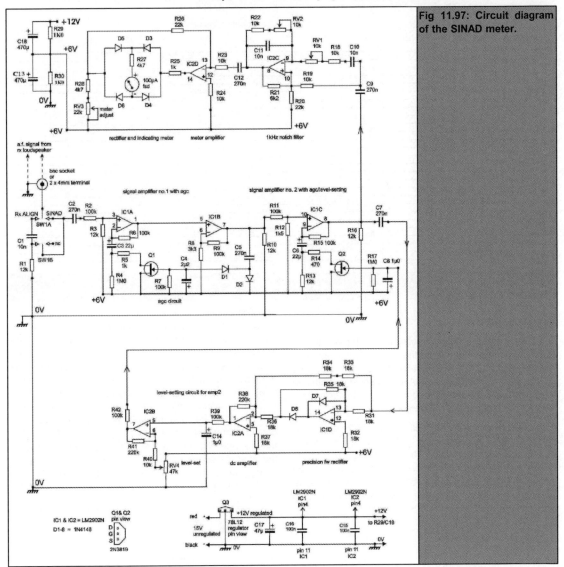

Fig 11.97: Circuit diagram of the SINAD meter.

- The audio output power should be at 50% of rated maximum when the SINAD meter indicates 12dB.

But, for the 5kHz peak deviation typical of today's amateur band receivers, that definitive method simplifies to become a 1kHz modulating tone at 3kHz peak deviation from the signal generator. Its microvolts RMS level will be in PD because the receiver's input impedance will in normal practice match that of the signal generator.

This design does incorporate the required 1kHz band reject filter, and for practical purposes, the SINAD meter can simply connect to the external loudspeaker terminals with the volume set to a comfortable listening level.

Bear in mind that (in simplistic terms) for a changing voltage level of tone modulated RF signal feeding into an FM receiver, the audio level of the receiver's output tone remains sensibly constant, but the noise level changes. As the level of the incoming RF signal decreases, the background noise increases to the point where the tone signal is totally swamped to inaudibility. As the level of the incoming RF signal increases, the noise level decreases until the tone signal is on a noise free background.

That latter feature is exploited in the design of this SINAD meter with its 1kHz rejection filter, to give a near zero reading on the meter in response to a noise free tone signal from the loudspeaker, and full-scale reading for a noise maximum inaudible tone signal. Between these two extremes, the intelligibility of a voice signal from the loudspeaker would vary from excellent to impossible. The meter response is acceptably linear, hence can readily be calibrated in dB intervals. By assigning a value of 0dB to full-scale deflection, and in the knowledge -12dB = x 0.25, then for a meter scale marked 0 - 100μA, FSD (100μA) = 0dB, 1/4 scale (25μA) = 12dB, minimum scale (approximately 10μA) = approximately 20dB. Once calibrated, only the 12dB marker is of real importance.

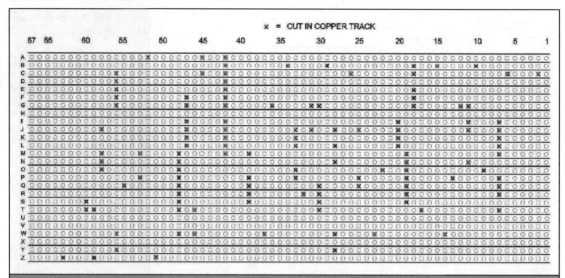

Fig 11.98: Stripboard cutting template for the SINAD meter.

Circuit description

The SINAD meter is fully automatic in use. It has one pair of input leads that connect to the receiver's loudspeaker. With its internal +12V dc regulator, it requires a single dc input of 13 – 15V at about 10mA, which could be obtained from a 12V or 15V unregulated mains/dc adaptor or from the receiver's nominal 13.5V supply.

Fig 11.96 shows the circuit in block diagram form, and the full circuit detail is given in Fig 11.97. The circuit consists of two audio frequency amplifiers in cascade that feed via a 1kHz reject filter into a fullwave rectifier, to drive an indicating meter calibrated in SINAD dB. Low cost quad op-amps are used rather than expensive VOGAD ICs.

The first amplifier formed by IC1A and IC1B incorporates its own automatic gain control (agc) circuit. This is used to feed a constant level of output signal voltage to the second amplifier, from an input signal level of between approximately 100mV and 3V RMS that is taken directly from the loudspeaker. The second amplifier IC1C incorporates a presettable gain/level set control RV4 that allows a degree of manual control to the overall agc. This combination of automatic and manual gain control ensures a constant preset level of audio signal being fed to the meter's precision fullwave rectifier circuit, irrespective of the level of input signal to the SINAD meter over the given range, hence allows the meter scale to be pre-calibrated in dB for fully automatic response in use. The level set

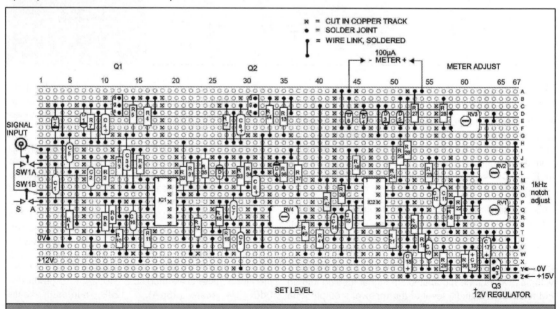

Fig 11.99: Component layout for stripboard version of the SINAD meter.

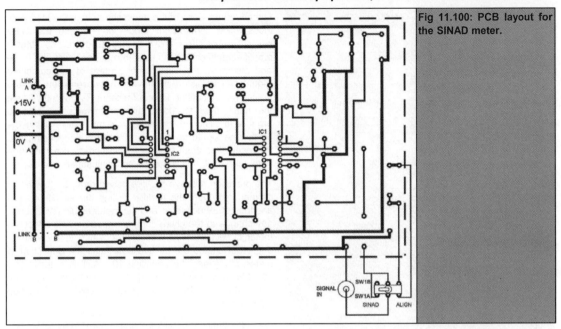

Fig 11.100: PCB layout for the SINAD meter.

control RV4 pre-sets the ac output level of IC1C, hence that into the IC2D meter amplifier/rectifier, to give a full-scale deflection on the meter for a totally noise signal i.e. the receiver on open squelch with no RF input signal .

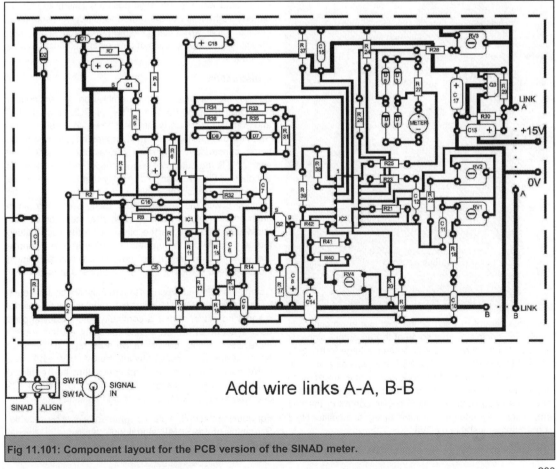

Add wire links A-A, B-B

Fig 11.101: Component layout for the PCB version of the SINAD meter.

Table 11.14: Parts list for the SINAD meter.

Semiconductors

IC1, IC2	Quad-Opamp ic type LM2902N
D1 - D8	Diode type 1N4148
Q1, Q2	FET type 2N3819
Q3	Voltage regulator 12V/100mA type 78L12

Preset resistor, carbon, min., horiz., pin spacing 10mm x 5mm

RV1, RV2	10kΩ
RV3	22kΩ
RV4	47kΩ

Capacitor, electrolytic, min.axial   16V

C8, 14	1.0µF
C4	2.2µF
C3, 6	22µF
C17	47µF
C13, 18	470µF

Capacitor, min.dipped, mylar/polyester film 100V dc

C1, 10, 11	10nF
C15, 16	100nF
C2, 5, 7, 9, 11	270nF

Resistor, metal film, 0.25W

R4	470Ω
R5, 25, 29, 30	1k0Ω
R12	1k5Ω
R8	3k3Ω
R27, 28	4k7Ω
R21	6k2Ω
R18, 19, 22, 23, 24, 40	10kΩ
R1, 3, 10, 13, 16	12kΩ
R31, 32, 33, 34, 35, 36, 37	18kΩ
R20, 26	22kΩ
R2, 6, 7, 9, 11, 15, 39, 42	100kΩ
R38, 41	220kΩ
RR4, 17	1M0Ω

Hardware

2	14pin dil socket
2	Terminal post, 4mm, small. One black, one yellow
1	Panel Meter, 100µA dc fsd , calibrated 0 -10 or 0 -100
1	Switch, dpdt toggle sub miniature, panel mounting
1	Stripboard, 0.1inch, copper, srbp, 170 x 75mm, 26 rows x 67 holes
1	Stripboard track cutting tool
1	Low cost plastic box with lid

The gain control in each of the two signal amplifiers is similar in principle, in that some of the ac output signal is rectified to be fed back as a dc control voltage to the gate of a field effect transistor. The FET then acts as a variable resistor in the negative feedback loop of the amplifier, to adjust the gain such as to hold the output signal constant at a prescribed voltage level. The gain control of the first amplifier is fully automatic, but that of signal amplifier No 2 is manually adjustable by RV4.

The amplified ac output signal from IC1C is a reasonably faithful reproduction of the audio signal from the receiver's loudspeaker terminal. It feeds via C9 into the 1kHz reject/notch filter formed around IC2C. Meter amplifier/rectifier IC2D is therefore fed only with the noise and distortion, the 1kHz tone content of the combined Signal+Noise+Distortion having been removed by the preceding reject filter. Preset resistors RV1 and RV2 tune the notch filter to 1kHz, and are simply adjusted to produce a minimum deflection on the meter, using the 1kHz tone signal from the signal generator feeding into the receiver at about 1000µV RMS to produce a noise free tone. Like RV4, this is a once only adjustment.

The precision fullwave rectifier based on IC2D has within its feedback loop, the rectifier bridge diodes D3, 4, 5, 6 and the 100µV dc meter, and the meter adjust RV3, hence any change to the given component values will affect the meter deflection. RV3 was only included to allow some degree of choice on the available full-scale deflection of meter, other than the specified 100µA. It is optional and could be replaced by a fixed 10kΩ resistor, because the level set control RV4 allows adequate control of full-scale deflection on the meter.

Also optional is the input low pass filter formed by C1/R1, and associated switch SW1ab. The switch has the legends SINAD and Align. In the SINAD position, the low pass filter is by passed. The filter is switched into the input signal path when in the Align position. This is to smooth out any slight flicker of the meter needle as it responds to receiver noise, whilst using the meter as a tuning aid when adjusting the tuned circuits of a receiver's RF/local oscillator stages.

Construction

Details are provided for assembly on either copper stripboard (Figs 11.98 and 11.99) or PCB (Figs 11.100 and 11.101), the parts list is shown in Table 11.14. Stripboard is perhaps the most convenient choice for the home constructor. The most critical part of stripboard assembly is the cutting of copper tracks, but the track cut template of Fig 11.98 should simplify that task. To use the template, fix a suitably sized photocopy of it to the stripboard with the image visible, using a drawing pin in each corner hole to locate it correctly, then secure with sticky tape and remove the pins. Use the track-cutting tool to partially cut through each marker in turn. Remove the template to reveal the now clearly visible cutting locations, and complete the cutting process at each hole.

Before installing components, carefully check that each track-cut is absolute! This is best done using a powerful magnifying glass, and/or a continuity test buzzer applied across each cut in turn. The time spent on this routine more than justifies the effort! Be sure also to check for absence of short circuits between the 0V, +6V, +12V, and +15V rails. Now apply dc and check that the regulated +12V is available. Disconnect the dc supply, insert IC1 and IC2, then set RV1, 2, 3, 4 to mid position.

For housing the unit, a plastic container would be suitable. Screening of the SINAD signal input leads is not necessary.

Setting-up and Calibration

This requires a low frequency sine wave source covering 300Hz - 3kHz with a variable 0 - 3V RMS output.

RV1, 2, 3, 4 are at mid position. Connect the SINAD meter's input leads to the low frequency source, with its output set to exactly 1kHz at 1volt RMS level. Reconnect the power supply to the SINAD meter, and observe some movement of the meter. Adjust RV1 and RV2 successively for minimum deflection on the meter, which should be near the 10µA reading. This proves that the 1kHz reject filter is functional. Swing the frequency either side of 1kHz, say to 300Hz and 3kHz, and the meter should rise towards full-scale deflection. With the frequency at 2kHz, adjust level setting control RV4 to give exactly full-scale deflection i.e. 100µA. Vary the output level of the low frequency source from zero to about 3V, and observe that the meter deflection remains sensibly constant for input variation from about 100mV to at least 2V RMS.

Finally, set up an FM receiver with an FM signal source connected to its antenna port. Set the signal generator to the receive frequency, with 1kHz tone modulation at 3kHz peak deviation, and with its output level at about 1000µV RMS. Adjust the receiver volume control to give a comfortable listening level for the 1kHz output tone, which will be on a completely noise free background. Connect the SINAD meter's input leads across the receiver's loudspeaker terminals, with the black lead to receiver chassis potential. The meter should be at or about minimum deflection. Re-adjust RV1 and RV2 to optimise the SINAD meter's reject filter to the RF signal generator's 1kHz modulating tone.

Disconnect the RF signal source from the receiver, and open the squelch to produce full noise output from the loudspeaker. Re-adjust RV4 to give full-scale deflection of exactly 100µA. This should remain sensibly constant when the volume control is varied.

Meter set control RV3 is still at mid position, and there it should remain. As stated earlier, it might only ever be needed if a meter of other than 100µA is used. Hence, RV1, 2, 3, 4 are now finally and forever set, and the SINAD meter becomes fully automatic in use.

The only thing left to do, is to mark "12dB" on the meter glass at its "one quarter full-scale" point i.e. at the 25µA position for a 100µA FSD meter. This is the 12dB SINAD sensitivity mark against which all future receiver checks will be made. Remember, the receiver's 12dB SINAD sensitivity is the µV RMS level from the signal generator that causes the SINAD meter to read 12dB, typically 0.5µV or thereabouts.

References

[1] Test Equipment for the Radio Amateur, 3rd edition, Clive Smith, G4FZH, RSGB, 1995

[2] Low power radio frequency wattmeter using an AD8362 detector, Wolfgang Schneider, DJ8ES, VHF Communications Magazine, 3/2005, pp 140 - 146

[3] Analog Devices, web: www.analog.com

[4] Display unit for the power detector by DJ8ES, Alexander Meier, DG6RBP, VHF Communications Magazine, 1/2007, pp 2 - 10. Alexander Meier web site: http://www.ame-engineering.de/

[5] Martin E Meserve web site: http://www.k7mem.150m.com/index.html

[6] Ron Taylor, G4GXO web site: http://www.g4gxo.cwc.net/index.htm
PIC counter page: http://www.g4gxo.cwc.net/new_page_12.htm
PCB layout download: http://www.g4gxo.cwc.net/images/Counter/counter6.brd
Software download: http://www.g4gxo.cwc.net/images/Counter/count_9.asm

[7] Cumbria Designs,The Steading, Stainton, Penrith, Cumbria, CA11 0ES, Tel: 07973 89 44 50, email: sales@cumbriadesigns.co.uk, web: http://www.cumbriadesigns.co.uk/

[8] Microchip Ltd, Microchip House, 505 Eskdale Road, Winnersh Triangle, Wokingham, Berkshire, RG41 5TU Tel: +44-118-921-5869 Fax: +44-118-921-5820 Email: euro.enquiry@microchip.com, web: www.microchip.com

[9] Silicon Chip Magazine, PO Box 139, Collaroy, NSW 2097 Australia, web: http://www.siliconchip.com.au/cms/A_107676/article.html

[10] PCB and front panel artwork for the prescaler are available on the Silicon Chip web site at: http://www.siliconchip.com.au/cms/attachments/show.htm l?year=2006&month=October. The PCB is available from: www.rcsradio.com.au

[11] A GPS controlled frequency standard, Zeljko Bozic, S52ZB, VHF Communications Magazine , 2/2007, pp 109 - 115

[12] Navman datasheet: Jupiter-T,web: http://www.jrmiller.demon.co.uk/projects/docs/10039C.PDF

[13] C-MAC datasheet: CFPT-9000 Series, web: http://www.farnell.com/datasheets/39552.pdf

[14] Philips datasheet: 74HC7046A, web: http://www.datasheetcatalog.com/datasheets_pdf/7/4/H/C/74HC7046A.shtml

[15] TI Application Note AN8823, web: http://focus.ti.com/lit/an/scha003b/scha003b.pdf

[16] Sipex datasheet: SP233A, web: http://www.sipex.com/productDetails.aspx?part=SP233A

[17] Tac32 software from CNS Systems Inc., web: http://www.cnssys.com/cnsclock/Tac32Software.html

[18] VisualGPS software from Visual GPS LLC. web: http://www.visualgps.net/VisualGPS/default.htm

[19] Simple GPS Stabilised 10 MHz Oscillator, James Miller, G3RUH, web: http://www.jrmiller.demon.co.uk/projects/ministd/frqstd.htm

[20] VHF Dip Oscillatotr, A L Mynett, RadCom, September 1970

[21] 2-Tone Generator for 145MHz, Wolfgang Schneider, DJ8ES, VHF Communications Magazine, 4/2002, pp 216 - 227

[22] Broadband, low inter-modulation, low output amplifier from 3 to 600MHz, Carsten Vieland, DJ4GC, CQDL, 11/88. pp 680 - 682

[23] JG1EAD's home page: http://www001.upp.so-net.ne.jp/jg1ead/e_toppage.html

[24] Agilent (ne Hewlette Packard), home page: http://www.home.agilent.com/

[25] Mini Circuits home page: http://www.minicircuits.com/

[26] A Sinadmeter, E Chicken, MBE, BSc, MSc, CEng, FIEE, G3BIK, VHF Communications Magazine 2/2001, pp 87 - 91

In this appendix :

- General data
- Designing resonant lines
- Combiners
- Fitting coaxial connectors

 his appendix contains reference information and useful formulae.

General data

Capacitance

The capacitance of a parallel plate capacitor is:

$$C = \frac{0.224KA}{d} \; picofarads$$

Where K is the dielectric constant (air = 1.0), A is the area of dielectric (in^2), and d is the thickness of dielectric (in). If A is expressed in cm^2 and d in cm, then:

$$C = \frac{0.0885KA}{d} \; picofarads$$

For multi plate capacitors, multiply by the number of dielectric thicknesses. The capacitance of a coaxial cylider is:

$$C = \frac{0.242K}{\log_{10}\left(\dfrac{D}{d}\right)} \qquad pF \; per \; cm$$

where D is the inside diameter of the outer and d is the outside diameter of the inner.

Capacitors in series or parallel

The effective capacitance of a number of capacitors in series is:

$$C = \frac{1}{\dfrac{1}{C_1} + \dfrac{1}{C_2} + \dfrac{1}{C_3} + ...}$$

The effective capacitance of a number of capacitors in parallel is:

$$C = C_1 + C_2 + C_3 + ...$$

Characteristic impedance

The characteristic impedance Z_0 of a feeder or transmission line depends on its cross sectional dimensions.

(i) Open wire line:

$$Z_0 = 276 \log_{10} \frac{2D}{d} \; ohms$$

where D is the centre-to-centre spacing of wires (in) and d is the wire diameter (in).

(ii) Coaxial line:

$$Z_0 = \frac{138}{\sqrt{K}} \log_{10} \frac{d_0}{d_1} \; ohms$$

where K is the dielectric constant of insulation between the conductors (e.g. 2.3 for polythene, 1.0 for air), d_0 is the inside diameter of the outer conductor and d_i is the diameter of the inner conductor.

Decibel

The decibel is the unit commonly used for expressing the relationship between two power levels (or between two voltages or two currents). A decibel (dB) is one tenth of a bel (B). The number of decibels N representing the ratio of two power levels P1 and P2 is 10 times the common logarithm of the power ratio, thus:

$$\text{The ratio} \qquad N = 10 \log_{10} \frac{P_2}{P_1} \; decibels$$

If it is required to express voltage (or current) ratios in this way, they must relate to identical impedance values, i.e. the two different voltages must appear across equal impedances (or the two different currents must flow through equal impedances). Under such conditions the power ratio is proportional to the square of the voltage (or the current) ratio, and hence:

$$N = 20 \log_{10} \frac{V_2}{V_1} \; decibels$$

$$N = 20 \log_{10} \frac{I_2}{I_1} \; decibels$$

Dynamic resistance

In a parallel tuned circuit at resonance the dynamic resistance is:

$$R_D = \frac{L}{Cr} = Q\omega L = \frac{Q}{\omega C} \; ohms$$

where L is the inductance, C is the capacitance, r is the effective series resistance, Q is the Q value of the coil and $\omega = 2\pi \times$ frequency.

Frequency – wavelength – velocity

The velocity of propagation of a wave is:

$$v = f\lambda \quad \text{cm per s}$$

where f is the frequency and λ is the wavelength.

For electromagnetic waves in free space the velocity of propagation v is approximately 3×10^8m/s and, if f is expressed in kHz and λ in metres:

$$f = \frac{300,000}{\lambda} kilohertz$$

$$\lambda = \frac{300,000}{f} metres$$

Free space $\quad \dfrac{\lambda}{2} = \dfrac{492}{MHz} feet$

Free space $\quad \dfrac{\lambda}{4} = \dfrac{246}{MHz} feet$

Note that the true value of v is 2.99776×10^8m/s.

Impedance

The impedance of a circuit comprising inductance, capacitance and resistance in series is:

$$Z = \sqrt{R^2 + \left(\omega L - \frac{1}{\omega C}\right)^2}$$

where R is the resistance, L the inductance, C the capacitance and $\omega = 2\pi \times$ frequency.

Inductors in series or parallel

The total effective value of a number of inductors connected in series (assuming no mutual coupling) is given by:

$$L = L_1 + L_2 + L_3 + \dots$$

If they are connected in parallel, the total effective value is:

$$L = \frac{1}{\dfrac{1}{L_1} + \dfrac{1}{L_2} + \dfrac{1}{L_3} + \dots}$$

When there is mutual coupling M, the total effective value of two inductors connected in series is:

$$L = L_1 + L_2 + 2M \quad \text{(windings aiding)}$$
$$L = L_1 + L_2 - 2M \quad \text{(windings opposing)}$$

Ohm's Law

For a unidirectional current of constant magnitude flowing in a metallic conductor:

$$I = \frac{E}{R} \qquad E = IR \qquad R = \frac{E}{I}$$

where *I* is the current, *E* is the voltage and *R* is the resistance.

Power

In a DC circuit, the power developed is given by:

$$W = EI = \frac{E^2}{R} = I^2R \quad \text{watts}$$

where E is the voltage, I is the current and R is the resistance.

Q

The Q value of an inductance is given by:

$$Q = \frac{\omega L}{R}$$

where L is the inductance, R is the effective resistance and $\omega = 2\pi \times$ frequency.

Reactance

The reactance of an inductance and a capacitance respectively is given by:

$$X_L = \omega L$$

$$X_C = \frac{1}{\omega C}$$

where L is the inductance, C is the capacitance and $\omega = 2\pi \times$ frequency.

The total reactance of an inductance and a capacitance in series is $X_L - X_C$.

Resistors in series or parallel

The effective value of several resistors connected in series is:

$$R = R_1 + R_2 + R_3 + \dots$$

When several resistors are connected in parallel the effective total resistance is:

$$R = \frac{1}{\dfrac{1}{R_1} + \dfrac{1}{R_2} + \dfrac{1}{R_3} + \dots}$$

Resonance

The resonant frequency of a tuned circuit is given by:

$$f = \frac{1}{2\pi\sqrt{LC}} \quad \text{Hertz}$$

where L is the inductance and C is the capacitance.

If L is in microhenrys (µH) and C is picofarads (pF), this formula becomes:

$$f = \frac{10^3}{2\pi\sqrt{LC}} \quad \text{Megahertz}$$

The basic formula can be rearranged thus:

$$L = \frac{1}{4\pi^2 f^2 C} \quad \text{Henrys}$$

$$C = \frac{1}{4\pi^2 f^2 L} \quad \text{Farads}$$

Since $2\pi f$ is commonly represented by ω, these expressions can be written as:

$$L = \frac{1}{\omega^2 C} \quad \text{Henrys}$$

$$C = \frac{1}{\omega^2 L} \quad \text{Farads}$$

See Fig A.1

Time constant

For a combination of inductance and resistance in series the time constant (i.e. the time required for the current to reach 1/e or 63% of its final value) is given by:

$$t = \frac{L}{R} \quad \text{seconds}$$

where L is the inductance and R the resistance. For a combination of capacitance and resistance in series, the time constant (i.e. the time required for the voltage across the capacitance to reach $1/\varepsilon$ or 63% of its final value) is given by:

$$t = CR \quad \text{seconds}$$

where C is the capacitance and R is the resistance.

Transformer ratios

The ratio of a transformer refers to the ratio of the number of turns in one winding to the number of turns in the other winding. To avoid confusion it is always desirable to state in which sense the ratio is being expressed, e.g. the "primary-to-secondary" ratio n_p / n_s. The turns ratio is related to the impedance ratio thus:

$$\frac{n_p}{n_s} = \sqrt{\frac{Z_p}{Z_s}}$$

where n_p is the number of primary turns, n_s is the number of secondary turns, Z_p the impedance of the primary circuit and Z_s the impedance of the secondary circuit.

Coil winding

Most inductors for tuning are single layer coils and they are designed as follows. Multilayer coils will not be dealt with here.

The inductance of a single layer coil is given by:

$$L(\mu H) = \frac{D^2 \times T^2}{457.2 \times D + 1016 \times L}$$

where D is the diameter of the coil, T the number of turns and L the length. Alternatively:

$$L(\mu H) = \frac{R^2 \times T^2}{9 \times R + 10 \times L}$$

where R is the radius of the coil, T is the number of turns and L is the length.

Note that when a ferrite or iron dust core is used, the inductance will be increased by up to twice the value without the core. The choice of which to use depends on frequency. Generally, ferrite cores are used at the lower HF bands and iron dust cores at the higher. At VHF, the iron dust cores are usually coloured purple. Cores need to be moveable for tuning but fixed thereafter and this can be done with a variety of fixatives. A strip of flexible polyurethane foam will do.

Designing inductors with ferrite pot cores

This is a simple matter of taking the factor given by the makers and multiplying it by the square of the number of turns. For example, an RM6-S pot core in 3H1 grade ferrite has a "factor" of 1900nH for one turn. Therefore 100 turns will give an inductance of:

$$100^2 \times 1900nH = 10000 \times 1900nH = 19mH$$

There is a large number of different grades of ferrite; for example, the same pot as above is also available in grade 3E4 with a "factor" of 3300. The manufacturers literature should be consulted to find these "factors".

Table A.1: Wire data.

Diameter	Approximate SWG	Turns/cm	Turns/in
1.5	16 - 17	6.6	16.8
1.25	18	7.9	20.7
1.0	19	9.9	25
0.8	21	12.3	31
0.71	22	13.9	35
0.56	24	17.5	45
0.50	25	19.6	50
0.40	27	24.4	62
0.315	30	30.8	78
0.25	33	38.5	97
0.224	34 - 35	42.7	108
0.20	35 - 36	47.6	121

Note: SWG is Imperial standard wire gauge. The diameters listed are those that appear to be most popular; i.e. they are listed in distributor's catalogues. The "turns/cm" and "turns/in" are for enamelled wire.

Table A.2: Colour coding for glass fuses.

Clour	Rating (mA)	Colour	Rating (A)
Green/yellow	10	Green	0.75
Red/turquoise	15	Blue	1.0
Eau-de-Nil	25	Light blue	1.5
Salmon pink	50	Purple	2.0
Black	60	Yellow and purple	2.5
Grey	100	White	3.0
Red	150	Black and white	5.0
Brown	250	Orange	10.0
Yellow	500		

Note that this coding does not apply to the ceramic bodied fuse commonly found in 13A plugs etc.

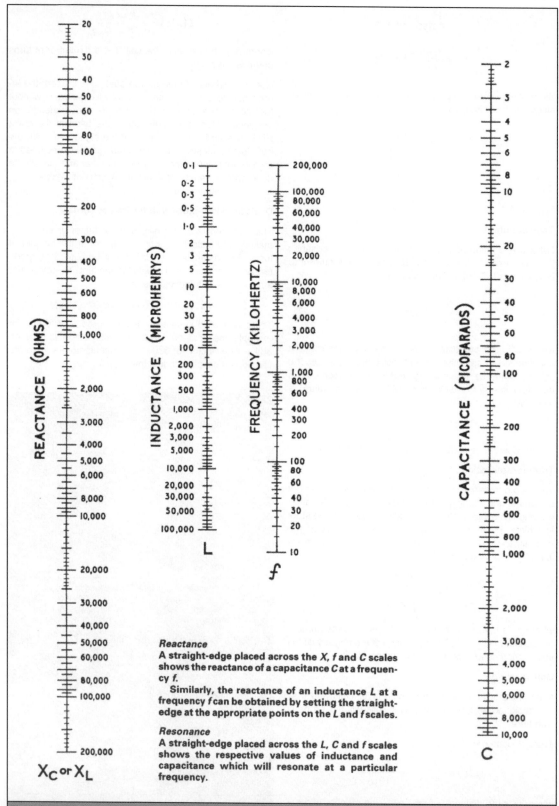

REACTANCE (OHMS)

X_C or X_L

INDUCTANCE (MICROHENRYS)

L

FREQUENCY (KILOHERTZ)

f

CAPACITANCE (PICOFARADS)

C

Reactance
A straight-edge placed across the X, f and C scales shows the reactance of a capacitance C at a frequency f.
   Similarly, the reactance of an inductance L at a frequency f can be obtained by setting the straight-edge at the appropriate points on the L and f scales.

Resonance
A straight-edge placed across the L, C and f scales shows the respective values of inductance and capacitance which will resonate at a particular frequency.

Fig A.1: Reactance and resonance chart.

Table A.3: Coaxial cables.

Type	Nominal impedance (Ω)	Outside diameter (mm)	Velocity factor	Capacitance (pF/m)	Maximum RF voltage (kV)	Attenuation per 10m of cable		
						10MHz (dB)	100MHz (dB)	1000MHz (dB)
CT100	75	6.65	0.84	56		0.2	0.6	2.1
HT100[1]	50						0.44	1.35
LDF4-50A[2]	50	16.0	0.88	75.8	8.0	0.07	0.224	0.77
LDF5-50A[3]	50	28.0	0.89	75	8.0	0.037	0.121	0.43
RA519[1]	50	10.3	0.80	84	5.0	0.10	0.35	1.25
RG58BU	50	4.95	0.66	100	3.5	0.5	1.7	5.6
RG58CU	50*	4.95	0.66	100	2.5	0.5	1.7	5.6
RG59BU	75	6.15	0.66	68	3.5	0.5	1.5	4.6
Min RG59	75	3.7	0.84	51		0.4	1.2	3.9
RG63AU	95	6.15	0.84	44		0.3	0.9	2.9
Min RG62	95	3.8	0.84	41		0.4	1.4	4.5
RG174AU	50*	2.8	0.66	101	2.1	0.3	0.9	2.9
RG178PE	50*	1.83	0.85	99		1.5	4.8	16
RG179PE	75*	2.54	0.85	69		1.2	4.0	13
RG213/URM67[1]	50	10.3	0.66	100	6.5	0.2	0.7	2.7
RG402U	50	3.58#						
RG405U	50	2.20#						
UR43	50	5.0	0.66	100	2.6	0.4	1.3	4.5
UR67	50*	10.3	0.66	100	6.5	0.2	0.68	2.5
UR70	75*	5.8	0.66	67	1.8	0.5	1.5	5.2
UR76	50*	5.0	0.66	100	2.6	0.5	1.6	5.3
UR95	50	2.3	0.66	100	1.3	0.9	2.7	6.9
UR202	75*	5.1	0.84	56		0.4	1.1	4.2
UR203	75	7.25	0.84	56		0.2	0.8	2.7
WF103	50	10.3	0.85	78	5.0	0.09	0.32	1.30
Aircom plus[4]	50	10.3	0.83	81	1.0	0.12	0.38	1.34
Aircell 7[4]	50*	7.3	0.83	75	1.0	0.22	0.63	2.15
Ecoflex 10[4]	50	10.2	0.85	78	1.0	0.12	0.40	1.42
Ecoflex 15[4]	50	14.6	0.86	77	1.55	0.09	0.28	0.98

* Indicates cable with flexible core. #Indicates cable with solid drawn outer, i.e. ridgid.

(1) Minimum bend radius is 60mm. Obtainable in The UK from W H Westlake Electronics [1]
(2) Minimum bend radius is 125mm. Obtainable in The UK from Diode Communications [2]
(3) Minimum bend radius is 250mm. Obtainable in The UK from Diode Communications [2]
(4) Obtainable in The UK from Diode Communications [2], full specification: http://www.diodecomms.co.uk/download/CCeng.pdf

Table A.4 Component colour codes.

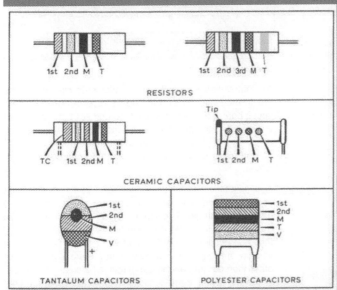

RESISTORS

CERAMIC CAPACITORS

TANTALUM CAPACITORS

POLYESTER CAPACITORS

Colour	1st	2nd	3rd	Multiplier	Tolerance ±%
Black	0	0	0	1	
Brown	1	1	1	10	1
Red	2	2	2	100	2
Orange	3	3	3	1000	
Yellow	4	4	4	10000	
Green	5	5	5	100000	0.5
Blue	6	6	6	1000000	0.25
Violet	7	7	7	10000000	0.1
Grey	8	8	8	100000000	0.05
White	9	9	9	1000000000	
Gold					5
Silver					10
No colour					20

Colour	Temp coeff. (TC) (parts/10^5/°C)	Voltage (Tantalum)	Voltage (Polyester)
Black	0	10	
Brown	-30		100
Red	-80		250
Orange	-150		
Yellow	-220	6.3	400
Green	-330	16	
Blue	-470	20	
Violet	-750		
Grey	+30	25	
White	+100 to -750	3	
Pink		35	

Units used are ohms for resistors, picofarads for ceramic and polyester capacitors and microfarads for tantalum capacitors. A pink fourth ring on resistors indicates "high stability"

Designing resonant lines

If this is for one frequency (e.g. for the output of a fixed frequency oscillator), they can be cut to a quarter or half a wavelength and trimmed carefully to resonance. Otherwise, they should be cut shorter and have a tuning or loading capacitor that can be calculated from:

$$\frac{1}{2\pi fC} = \frac{Z_0 \tan 2\pi L}{\lambda}$$

where f is the frequency, C is the tuning capacitance, λ is the wavelength, L is the length and Z_0 is the characteristic impedance, calculated as follows. For a coaxial line:

$$Z_0 = 138 \log_{10}\left(\frac{D}{d}\right)$$

where D is the inside diameter of the outer tube and d is the outside diameter of the inner tube or wire. For parallel lines:

$$Z_0 = 276 \log_{10}\left(\frac{2D}{d}\right)$$

where D is the interline spacing and d is the line diameter. See Figs A.2 – A.5. Fig A.6 gives a series of graphs for coaxial and parallel lines where f × L (in megahertz and centimetres) is plotted against f × C (in megahertz and picofarads) for a number of different values of r or D/d.

Helical resonators

These form high Q circuits and are roughly equivalent to quarter wave coaxial lines compressed. Fig A.7 shows the basic idea. They are used at VHF and UHF and can be tuned by a variable capacitor between the case and the upper end. They can also be cascaded by making slots in the side of the cases and bonding them together so that the resonators can "see" one another.

The unloaded Q is $50Df^{1/2}$, where D is the internal diameter of the case and f is the frequency. If the case is of square section, this must be multiplied by a correction factor of 1.2.

Fig A.8 shows a two component filter using helical resonators. To design one, the following formulae are used:

$$Pitch = \frac{D^2 f}{9.06}$$

where p and D are in millimetres.

$$Z_0 = \frac{386}{fD}$$

These assume that d/D = 0.55 and L/D = 1.5. Alternatively, the nomogram (Fig A.9) will give an accurate enough answer for all practical purposes. Note that the dimensions are given in inches. In order to maintain a high Q, it is desirable to plate the inside of the cavity and the outside of the wire with silver.

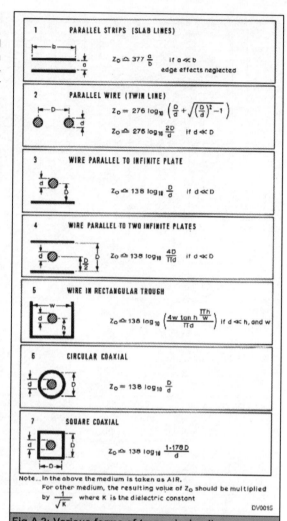

Fig A.2: Various forms of transmission line.

Microstrip circuits

At frequencies above 300MHz, microstrip circuits, which are formed directly on one side of double sided printed circuit board, are useful. Figs A.10 and A.11 show quarter wave and half wave microstrip lines with the position of the tuning capacitor. It is essential that the other side or ground plane is bonded to the "earthy" parts of the tuned circuit.

The dielectric should be as thin and of as low loss as possible. PTFE is ideal but expensive. Glass fibre is the next best material. The length is calculated in the same way as for a coaxial or trough line with modifications to take into account the different shape and the fact that the velocity of radio waves is lower where there is a dielectric other than air, just as the capacitance between two plates is greater when there is a solid dielectric present. The latter is greater by the dielectric constant that is about 2.1 for PTFE and about 5 for glass fibre reinforced epoxy resin.

The exact value, which depends on precisely which epoxy

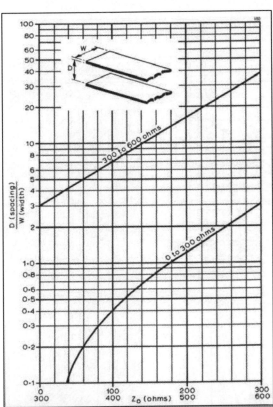

Fig A.3: Characteristic impedance of balanced strip transmission line.

is used, can be found by measuring the capacitance of a known area of double sided material:

$$e = 113 \times C \times \frac{t}{A}$$

where e is the dielectric constant, t is the thickness in millimetres, A is the area in square millimetres and C is the capacitance in picofarads.

The width of the element depends on the design impedance Z and is given by:

$$\log_{10} W = 0.874 + \log_{10} t - 0.005 \times Z \times \sqrt{e} + 1.14$$

where t is the thickness in millimetres, e is the dielectric constant and W is the width in millimetres.

Having found this, the length is calculated from:

$$l = l_0 \times V_f$$

where l is the element length, l_0 is the length (e.g. that of a half wavelength) in free space V_f is the velocity factor which is related to the dielectric constant by:

$$V_f = \frac{1}{\sqrt{0.475 \times (e + 0.67)}}$$

There are many Computer Aided Design (CAD) programs available to calculate microstrip and stripline circuits. Many of the expensive microwave CAD programs have "Student Versions" available to download free from the Internet. These generally have some restriction on their use but will perform many of the tasks needed by radio

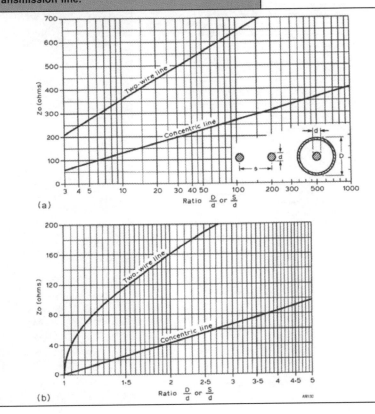

Fig A.4: Chart giving characteristic impedances of concentric (coaxial) and two wire lines in terms of their dimensional ratios, assuming air insulation. When the space around the wires is filled with insulation, the impedance given by the chart must be divided by the square root of its dielectric constant (permittivity). This ratio is called the velocity factor because the wave velocity is reduced in the same proportion.

amateurs. Two microwave CAD programs that are regularly used by radio amateurs are PUFF [3] and Ansoft Designer SV [5].

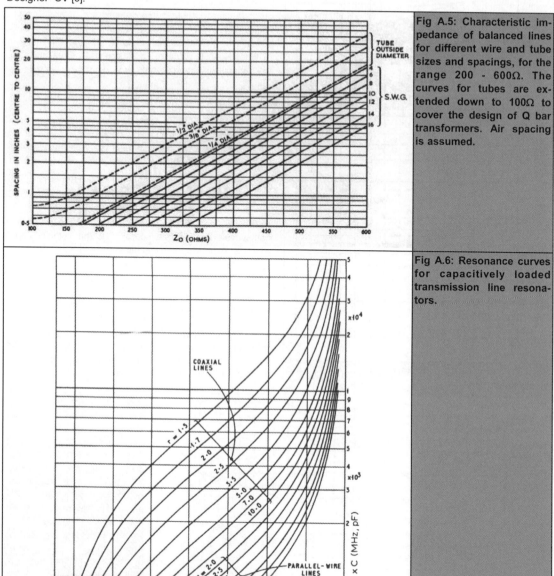

Fig A.5: Characteristic impedance of balanced lines for different wire and tube sizes and spacings, for the range 200 - 600Ω. The curves for tubes are extended down to 100Ω to cover the design of Q bar transformers. Air spacing is assumed.

Fig A.6: Resonance curves for capacitively loaded transmission line resonators.

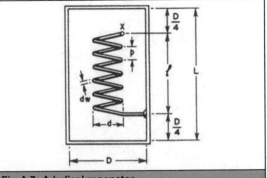

Fig A.7: A helical resonator.

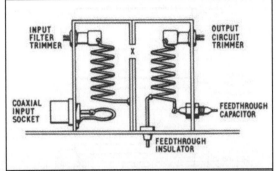

Fig A.8: A typical arrangement of helical resonators.

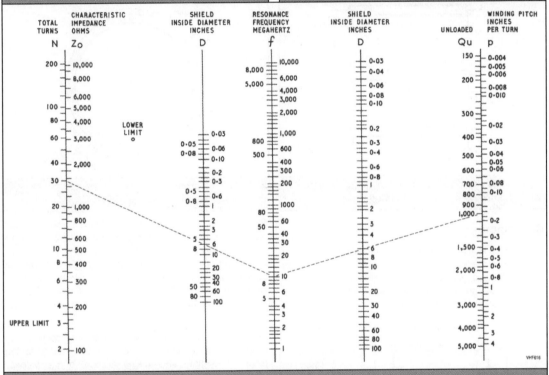

Fig A.9: Design chart for λ/4 helical resonators.

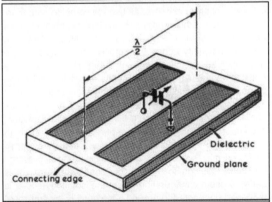

Fig A.10: General arrangement of a λ/4 microstripline circuit.

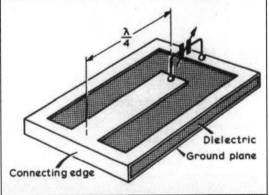

Fig A.11: General arrangement of a λ/2 microstripline circuit.

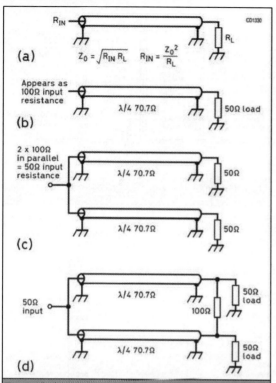

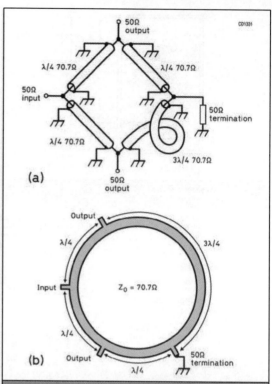

Fig A.12: (a - c) Coaxial splitter/combiner and derivation. (d) Wilkinson splitter/combiner.

Fig A.13: "Rat race" splitter/combiner. (a) Coaxial cable version. (b) Branch hybrid PCB form.

Combiners

A method of reaching higher power levels is to combine a number of complete amplifiers. Normally these amplifiers will be identical, with very similar gains. In these examples, it is assumed that each amplifier is designed to work at 50Ω input and load impedances.

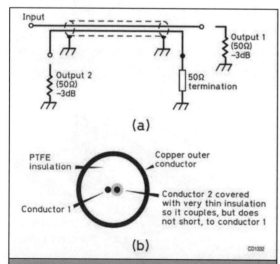

Fig A.14: Sage Wireline™. (a) Shown schematically. as a directional coupler. (b) Shown mechanically as a cross section through the cable.

Splitters and combiners are basically the same; a splitter has one input and two or more outputs. Used in reverse the same circuit becomes a combiner with two or more inputs and one output. The combiner might use different compo-nents to cope with the higher power, but the circuit will be the same as the splitter. For convenience, the term "combiner" is used here to cover both splitters and combiners.

In all of the examples discussed in this section, the lengths of cables and transmission lines relate to the electrical lengths, after taking account of the velocity factor.

The simple combiner in Fig A.12 can be made using λ/4 coaxial cable transformers, as used to combine antennas. While simple, this suffers from the disadvantage of offering no isolation between the amplifiers. This can result in instability and, if the amplifier characteristics are not absolutely identical, loss of output power. Adding a resistor between the divided points forms the Wilkinson combiner. This dissipates any imbalance and provides isolation between the two amplifiers; each one operates completely independently of the other. To get full isolation, it is important that the resistor is purely resistive and high power flange mounted components are usually used. At UHF and microwaves, the capacitance of these resistors becomes too high for use in this configuration and it is better to use a configuration where the isolating resistor is a 50 load connected to ground. One such is the "rat-race" (Fig A.13), so called because of its form if made with

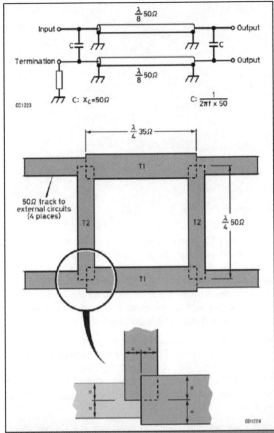

Fig A.15: Eighth wave splitter/combiner; coaxial cable and PCB version.

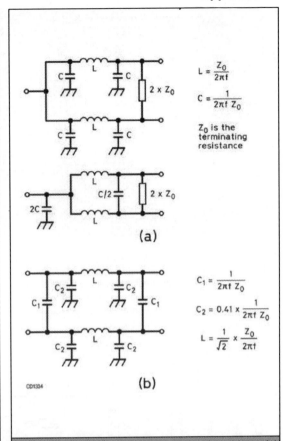

Fig A.16: Lumped component splitter/combiner. (a) Wilkinson. (b) Eighth wave.

printed transmission lines. This can be seen as an extension of the Wilkinson design. In these, the optimum impedance is 70.7Ω but in practice 75Ω coaxial cable works perfectly well.

Another family of combiners produce outputs that have a 90° phase offset. For this reason they are often called quadrature couplers. These have the advantage that, when used as a splitter, the input impedance is always 50Ω as long as the impedances at the two outputs are the same (whatever the actual impedances are). This is of great value when making wide band amplifiers but has limited importance in amateur applications.

The simplest, but most expensive, version is Sage Wireline™ (Fig A.14). This can be viewed as a directional coupler where the coupling is 3dB when the electrical length is λ/4; at this frequency half of the input power transfers to the coupled line. Wireline also has the advantage of wide bandwidth; typically the coupling varies by ±0.5dB (±12%) over a 2:1 frequency range.

Two other forms of quadrature couplers shown in Fig A.15 are the eighth-wave (or capacitively coupled hybrid) and branch hybrid designs. These have similar characteristics to Wireline, but operate over a narrower frequency range. The branch hybrid design is widely used at microwave frequencies as the whole combiner can be microstripline

without discrete components to introduce unpredictable parasitic elements. Additionally, the split and combining connections are on the same side that is very convenient for circuit layout.

The Wilkinson and eighth wave designs can be made using lumped components in place of the transmission lines (Fig A.16). The bandwidth is reduced, but is still adequate for amateur band coverage. This is especially useful for the lower VHF bands where the coaxial cable lengths become unwieldy.

Fitting coaxial connectors

Fitting coaxial connectors to cable is something we all have to do, and like most things there are probably more wrong ways of fitting connectors than right ones. The methods described are not necessarily the right ones, but they work. Although specific styles of connector and cable are mentioned, the methods are applicable to many others.

Cables and connectors

The main secret of success is using the right cable with the right connector. If you're buying connectors, it is important to be able to recognise good and bad types, and know what cables the good ones are for. Using the wrong connector and cable combination is sure to lead to

Table A.5: Some common coaxial connectors and equivalents.

Type	Pin	Clamp	Fits cable	MIL No.	RS Components	Greenpar
BNC Types						
Plug	C	P	URM43	UG88D/U	455-624	GE35070C10
Plug	F	I	URM43	UG88C/U		GE35018-10
Plug	F	O	URM43	UG83		GE35001-10
Angle plug	C	P	URM43		455-646	GE35002C10
Line socket	C	P	URM43	UG89C/U	455-652	GE35060C10
N Types						
Plug	C	P	URM43	UG536B/U	455-949	GE15055C10
Plug	C	P	URM67		455-753	GE15015C1
Plug	F	I	URM67	UG21E/U		
Angle plug	C	P	URM67	UG594/U	455-393	GE15003C1
Line socket	C	P	URM67	UG23D/U	455-775	GE15022C1

Pin types are: C - captive, F - free. Clamp types are: P - pressure, I - improved, O - original

disaster. Any information you can get, such as old catalogues, is likely to prove useful, especially if you can get the cable cutting dimensions and equivalents lists. Two further sources of dimensions and techniques are [5] and [6]. Some excellent general advice on cable and connector selection is contained in [7].

Cables commonly are of one of two families, the American 'RG' (Radio Guide MIL specification) types and the English 'UR' (UniRadio) series. For details of the most popular types see Table A.3. URM67 is equivalent to

RG213 it is 10.5mm in diameter and is the most common cable used with type N and PL259 connectors. URM43 (5mm OD) is one usually used with BNC connectors, although these also fit RG58 cable since both have similar dimensions. If there is any doubt about the quality of the cable, have a look at the braid. It should cover the inner completely. If it doesn't it is unlikely to be worth buying.

Having obtained your cable, the easy bit is over; now to select the connector. The three most popular connector types are the UHF, BNC and N ranges. These are covered in some detail, and a few others are mentioned later. If you can, buy connectors from a reputable manufacturer.

Some names that spring to mind are RS Components, Greenpar, Suhner, Radiall, Transradio, Kings and Amphenol, among many. There are some good surplus bargains about at rallies.

It cannot be too widely known that the iniquitous UHF connector is not good much beyond 200MHz, because the impedance through the plug socket junction is not 50Ω. The suitability of N and BNC connectors for use at UHF and beyond is due to them maintaining the system impedance (50Ω) through the connector. PL259 plugs, like the RG8 cable they were intended for, have a lot of nasty limitations. Beware of any that don't have PTFE insulation. They might be OK, but many cheap types are lossy and badly made. The plating should be good quality (silver solders best, although some proprietary plated finishes are just about as good), and there should be two or more solder holes in the body for soldering to the braid. There should be two small tangs on the outer mating edge of the plug that locate in the serrated ring of the socket and stop the body rotating. If you are going to use small diameter cable with these plugs, get the correct reducer. Often two types are available, one being for 75Ω cable. The 50Ω type is often called 'UG175'. Using the wrong one is certain disaster. Incidentally, buy your reducers at the same time, as some manufacturers use different reducer threads.

With BNC, TNC (like the BNC but threaded) N and C (like N but bayonet) types, life can be more complicated. All these connectors are available in 50Ω and 75Ω versions.

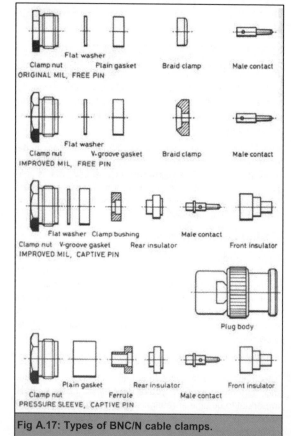

Fig A.17: Types of BNC/N cable clamps.

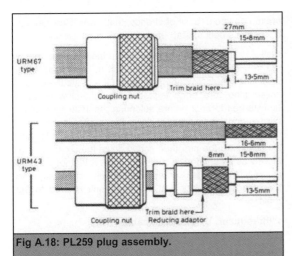

Fig A.18: PL259 plug assembly.

Be sure that you get the right one! To help those of you who are hunting for bargains at rallies, Fig A.17 shows some common designations. All of these connectors have evolved over the years, and consequently you will meet a number of different types. The variations are mostly to do with the cable clamping and centre pin securing method. The original cable clamp is usually called "unimproved MIL", the later modification the "improved" and the best for most uses is the "pressure-sleeve" type. If you are buying new then for normal use go for the pressure-sleeve type. It is much easier to fit. If you are fortunate enough to have some of the double braided PTFE dielectric cable such as RG142, you may find it easier to use the older clamp types, although the pressure-sleeve type will fit properly with care.

All original clamp types use a free centre pin that is held in place by its solder joint onto the inner conductor. Captive contact types have a two-part centre insulator between which fits the shoulder onto the centre pin. Improved MIL clamp types may have either free or captive contacts. Pressure-sleeve types have a captive centre pin. As an aid to identification, Table A.5 shows these types. Pressure-clamp captive-pin types are easy to spot; they have a ferrule or "top hat" that assists in terminating the braid, a two-piece insulator and a centre pin with a shoulder. Unimproved clamp types have a washer, a plain gasket, a cone-ended braid clamp and a single insulator, often fixing inside the body. Improved types have a washer, a thin ring gasket with a V groove and usually a conical braid clamp with more of a shoulder. There are variations, so if you can get the catalogue description it helps!

Tools for the job

To tackle this successfully, you really need a few special tools; while they may not be absolutely essential, they certainly help. First and foremost is a good soldering iron. If you never intend to use a PL259, then a small instrument type iron is sufficient. If you use PL259s, or intend to use some of the "dirty tricks" described later, something with a lot more heat output is required. Ideally a thermostatically controlled iron is best; as with most

tools, a little extra spent repays itself handsomely in the future.

A sharp knife is another must. A Stanley type is essential for larger cables, provided that the blade is sharp. For smaller cables, you can use a craft knife or a very sharp penknife or a scalpel. A word or two of warning is in order, however. Scalpels excel at the job they were designed for cutting flesh. Make sure it isn't yours! Use sharp blades, cut away from you, and keep the object you're cutting on the bench, not in your hand. Although sharp, the steel blades are brittle and will shatter if you apply excessive force or bend them. Dispose of used blades in a box or plastic jar. Model shops have a good range of craft knives that will also do an excellent job.

A pair of sharp small scissors is needed for cutting braids, and a blunt darning needle (mount it in a handle made from a piece of wood dowelling) is useful for un-weaving the braid; so too is a scriber. You will find a small vice a great help as well. For BNC, TNC and N type connectors, some spanners are essential to tighten the gland nuts. The BNC/TNC spanners should be thin 7/16in AF. Those for type N need to be 11/16 x 5/8in AF. BNC spanners are sold in pairs by RS Components and are 7/16 x 1/2in AF; the other end suitable for BNC line sockets. A junior hacksaw is needed to cut larger cables such as URM67. Finally, if you intend to put heat shrink sleeves over the ends of plugs for outdoor use, some form of heat gun helps, although the shaft of a soldering iron may work. (You probably have a heat gun already, thinly disguised as a hot air paint stripper).

Preparing cables

Fitting a plug requires you to remove various bits of outer sheath, braid and inner dielectric. The important knack to acquire is that of removing one at a time, without damaging what lies underneath. To remove the outer sheath, use a sharp knife or scalpel. Place the knife across the cable and rotate the cable while applying gentle pressure. The object of doing this is to score right round the cable sheath. Now score a line from the ring you just made up to the cable end. If you have cut it just enough, it should be possible to peel away the outer sheath leaving braid intact underneath. If this is not something you've tried before, practice on a piece of cable first. For some connectors, it is important that this edge of the sheath is a smooth edge at right angles to the cable, so it really is worth getting right.

Braid removal usually just requires a bit of combing out and a pair of scissors. Removal of the inner dielectric is most difficult with large diameter cables with laid multi strand inner conductors like URM67. Again, it is important that the end is a clean, smooth cut at right angles to the cable. Removing the bulk of the dielectric first, if necessary in several stages, and finally trimming the dielectric to length best achieves this. There is a limit to how much dielectric you can remove at one go; 1 - 2cm is about as much as can be attempted with the larger sizes without damaging the lay of the inner. For the larger cables, it is worthwhile to pare down the bulk of the unwanted material before trying to pull the remainder off the inner. If you can,

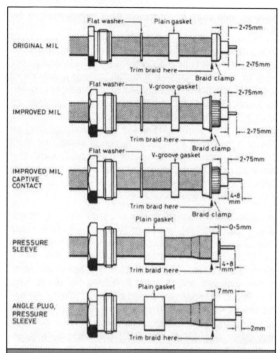

ORIGINAL MIL

Flat washer — Plain gasket
2·75mm
2·75mm
Trim braid here
Braid clamp

IMPROVED MIL

Flat washer — V-groove gasket
2·75mm
2·75mm
Trim braid here
Braid clamp

IMPROVED MIL, CAPTIVE CONTACT

Flat washer — V-groove gasket
2·75mm
Trim braid here
Braid clamp
4·8 mm

PRESSURE SLEEVE

Plain gasket
0·5mm
Trim braid here
4·8 mm

ANGLE PLUG, PRESSURE SLEEVE

Plain gasket
7mm
Trim braid here
2mm

Fig A.19: BNC dimensions, plug and line sockets.

fit one plug on short cables before you cut the cable to length (or off the reel if you are so lucky). This will help to prevent the inner sliding about when you are stripping the inner dielectric.

Fitting PL259 plugs

Without reducer, URM67 type cable

First make a clean end. For this large cable, the only satisfactory way is to use a junior hacksaw. Chopping with cutters or a knife just spoils the whole thing. Having got a clean end, refer to Fig A.18 for the stripping dimensions. First remove the sheath braid and dielectric, revealing the length of inner conductor required. Do this by cutting right through the sheath and braid, scoring the dielectric, then removing the dielectric afterwards. Next carefully remove the sheath back to the dimension indicated, without disturbing the braid. Examine the braid; it should be shiny and smooth. If you have disturbed it or it looks tarnished, start again a little further down. Now the tricky bit; with a hot iron, tin the braid carefully. The idea is to do it with as little solder as possible. Lightly tin the inner conductor also at this stage. Take a breather while the cable cools.

Now slide the coupling piece onto the cable (threaded end towards the free end). Examine the plug body. If it isn't silver plated, and you think it might not solder easily, apply a file around and through the solder holes. Now screw the body onto the cable, hard. When you've finished, the sheath should have gone into the threaded end of the connector, the inner should be poking out through the hollow pin, and the end of the exposed dielectric should be hard up against the inside shoulder of the plug. Look at the braid through the solder holes. It should not have

broken up into a mass of strands; that's why it was tinned. If it has, it's best to start again.

If all is well, lightly clamp the cable in the vice, then apply the iron to the solder holes. Heat it up and then apply solder. It should flow into the holes; if it stays there as a sullen blob, the body isn't hot enough. Now leave it undisturbed to cool before soldering the inner by heating the pin and feeding solder down the inner. Finally, when it's cool, cut any excess protruding inner conductor and file flush with the pin, then screw down the coupling ring. Merely as a confidence check, of course, test for continuity on both inner and outer from one end of the cable to the other, and check that the inner isn't shorted to the braid.

With reducer, URM43 type cable

First, slide the outer coupler and the reducer on to the cable. Next, referring to Fig A.19, remove the outer sheath without nicking the braid. Now, using a blunt needle, gently un-weave the braid a bit at a time until it is all straight and sticking out like a ruff around the cable. Remove the inner dielectric without nicking the inner conductor, so as to leave the specified amount of dielectric. Tin the inner conductor. Bring up the reducer until the end of it is flush with the end of the outer sheath. Fold the braid back so it lies evenly over the shank of the reducer, cut off the excess braid with scissors so that it is not in danger of getting trapped in the threads. Smooth it down once more, then offer up the plug body and, while holding the reducer and cable still, screw on the plug body until it is fully home. The only really good way of doing this is with two pairs of pliers. Now hold the assembly in the vice and ready the soldering iron. There has been a spirited discussion from time to time about the advisability of soldering the braid through the holes; the best information is that you should. If you don't, the cable will sooner or later fail. So, with a big iron, solder the braid through the holes. See the section above for advice. Finally, solder and trim the inner conductor and test the assembly as described earlier.

Fitting BNC and type N plugs

These are "constant impedance" connectors; that is, when correctly made up, the system impedance of 50Ω is maintained right through the connector. It is vital that the cable fits the connector correctly. Check that each part fits the cable properly after you prepare it. Refer to Fig A.19 for BNC dimensions and Fig A.20 for N types.

Original or unmodified clamp types

Slide the nut, washer and gasket onto the cable in that order. Using the sharp knife, score through the outer sheath by holding the knife and rotating the cable, without nicking the braid. Run the knife along the cable from the score to the end and peel off the outer sheath. Using a blunt needle, for example, start to un-weave the braid enough to enable the correct length of dielectric to be removed. Now slip the braid clamp on, pushing it firmly down to the end of the outer sheath. Finish un-weaving the braid, comb it smooth, then trim it with scissors so that it just comes back to the end of the conical section of the

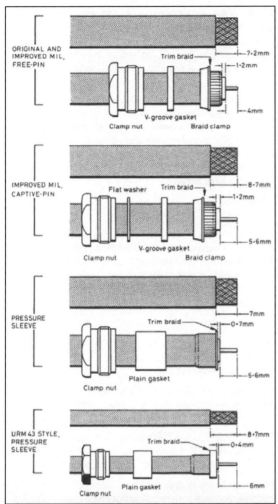

ORIGINAL AND
IMPROVED MIL.
FREE-PIN

Trim braid — 7·2mm
1·2mm
4mm
V-groove gasket
Clamp nut   Braid clamp

IMPROVED MIL.
CAPTIVE-PIN

Flat washer   Trim braid — 8·7mm
1·2mm
5·6mm
V-groove gasket
Clamp nut   Braid clamp

PRESSURE
SLEEVE

Trim braid — 7mm
0·7mm
5·6mm
Plain gasket
Clamp nut

URM 43 STYLE,
PRESSURE
SLEEVE

Trim braid — 8·7mm
0·4mm
6mm
Plain gasket
Clamp nut

Fig A.20: N type dimensions, plugs. angle plugs and line sockets.

Modified or improved clamp types

In general, this is similar to the technique for unmodified clamp types described above. There are some important differences, however. The gasket has a V shaped groove in it, which must face the cable clamp. The clamp has a corresponding V shaped profile on one side: the other side may be conical or straight sided, depending on the manufacturer. If the clamp end has straight sides, then the braid is fanned out and cut to the edge of the clamp only, not pushed down the sides. Some types have a small PTFE insulator that is fitted before the pin is put on (common on plugs for the small RG174 cable).

You now appreciate why having the assembly instructions for your particular plug is a good idea! Still, by using these instructions as a guide, it shouldn't be too difficult to get it right, even if it does not fit the first time.

One important point; if the plug has been assembled correctly and tightened up properly, the clamp will have (intentionally) cut the gasket. It is then rather difficult to re-use as a gasket, being thin, will not stand a second attempt. The thicker gasket types will often allow careful re-use.

Captive contact types

These have a small shoulder on the pin and a rear insulator that fits between the pin and the cable. Most types use a thick gasket and a ferrule, although some use a V grooved braid clamp and thin gasket. The ferrule type will be described, as these are the most commonly available and the easiest to fit.

First, slip the nut and gasket on to the cable. Refer to Fig A.19 or Fig A.20 for cutting dimensions, strip off the correct amount of outer sheath by rotating the cable, producing a neat scored circle. Score back to the end of the cable and peel off the unwanted sheath. Comb out the braid, and with it fanned out evenly around the cable, slide the ferrule (small end first) on to the dielectric covered inner conductor. Push it home so that the narrow portion of the ferrule slides under the braid, and the end of the outer sheath rests against the ferrule shoulder. Trim the braid with scissors to the edge of the ferrule. Slide up the gasket so that it rests gently against the ferrule shoulder, which will prevent the braid from being disturbed. Using the sharp knife, trim the dielectric back to the indicated dimension without nicking the inner conductor. Fit the rear insulator, which will have a recess on one side to accommodate the protruding dielectric. Incidentally, if you don't have the size for your particular plug, trim the dielectric until it fits but don't overdo it! Now trim the exposed inner conductor to length and check by fitting the pin, whose shoulder should rest on the rear insulator unless the inner has been cut too long. Tin the inner lightly, then fit the pin and solder it by applying the iron tip (cleaned of excess solder) to the side of the pin opposite from the solder hole and feed a small amount of solder into the hole. Allow cooling and removing excess solder with a fine file. Now fit the front insulator (usually separate from the body) and push the whole assembly into the body. Push down the gasket gently into the plug body with

clamp. Be sure that the braid wires aren't twisted. Now fit the inner pin and make sure that the open end of the pin will fit up against the dielectric. Take the pin off and lightly tin the exposed inner conductor. Re-fit the pin and solder it in place by placing the soldering iron bit (tinned but with the solder wiped off) on the side of the pin opposite the solder hole. Feed a small quantity of solder (22 SWG or so works best) into the hole. Allow it to cool and examine. If you've been careful enough, the dielectric should not have melted. Usually it does, and swells up, so with the sharp knife trim it back to size. This is essential as otherwise the plug will not assemble properly. Remove any excess solder from around the pin with a fine file. Now push the gasket and washer up against the clamp nut, check the braid dressing on the clamp then push the assembly into the plug body. Gently firm home the gasket with a small screwdriver or rod and then start the clamp nut by hand. Tighten the clamp nut by a spanner, using a second spanner to hold the plug body still; it must not rotate. Finally, check the completed job with the shack ohmmeter.

a small rod or screwdriver. Start the nut by hand, tighten fully with one spanner, using the other to prevent the body from rotating. Check with the ohmmeter, start on the other end, remembering to put the nut and gasket on first!

Variations

Angle plugs generally follow a similar pattern to the straight types, except that connection to the inner is via a slotted pin, accessed via a removable cap screw. Tighten the connector nut before soldering the inner. Line sockets are fitted in the same way as plugs.

Dirty tricks

Most of these were originally described in "The Golden Treasury of Connector Abuse" in the December 1985 issue of the VOWHARS newsletter. The author gratefully acknowledges the contributions by a number of connector abusers, who wish to remain anonymous.

We would like to use new connectors every time, but often a pressure-sleeve type can be re-used if the gasket is not too deformed. Get all the solder you can out of the pin and then carefully ream out the rest with a small drill, held in a pin chuck. The sizes to use are 1mm for URM43 style pins, and 2.6mm for URM67 ones.

Tarnished silver plated connectors can be made to shine by dipping the metal parts in Goddards "Silver Dip" silver cleaner. Rinse carefully afterwards and bake in a slow oven.

BNC connectors for URM67 cable can be rather hard to find. A standard captive-contact BNC plug can be fitted to URM67 in the following way. First discard the nut, gasket and ferrule, and prepare the rear insulator by removing the ridge from it with a sharp knife. Now prepare the cable by cutting with a knife, right through the jacket, braid and insulator about 5mm back from the end. Cut sufficiently deep so that you notch the inner conductor strands, and remove the remains. Carefully bend the six individual outer strands of the inner so they break off flush with the end of the dielectric, leaving one straight inner strand. Now remove sufficient outer jacket (about 2cm) such that when the body is pushed on the cable, some braid is still visible. Tin the braid and inner conductor lightly, then fit the rear insulator, pin and front insulator and push home the assembly into the plug body. With the big iron, heat the plug body and feed solder down the joint with the braid. After it has cooled, put some heat shrink adhesive lined sleeving over the plug and cable join to protect it. Testing of this trick with a TDR has shown it to be almost as good as the real plug, and certainly better than an adapter. This assembly will happily stand 100W of 1296MHz.

An N plug can be carefully pushed on to a BNC socket; OK for quick test equipment lash ups, but don't do it too often or too hard as you will eventually damage the socket. In a similar vein, the pin of a PL259 is about the same diameter as a 4mm wander plug; after all, what is a PL259 but a screened wander plug?

To make a PL259 to BNC adapter, solder a length of copper wire to the back of a BNC single hole socket. Drop it (without the nut) on to the top of a PL259 so that the wire pokes through the pin of the plug. With a big iron or a careful blowtorch, solder the body of the socket and plug together. After it has cooled, solder the inner wire to the pin. Not exactly a precision job, but good enough for a PL259!

Finally, to waterproof a connector cable joint and to provide added strength where flexing of the cable will occur, heat shrink a piece of adhesive lined heat shrink sleeving over the plug body and cable. For N connectors, a 19mm diameter variety (that shrinks to a minimum of 6mm, such as RS399-748) can be slid on to the cable and connector after assembly.

Conclusions

With a little practice, care and patience these notes should make the fitting of connectors a little less of a chancy business. Practice on some short leads (there is no such thing as too many spare short coaxial leads in any shack) and remember that the best time to put new connectors on the feeder isn't two minutes before the start of the contest!

References

[1] W H Westlake Electronics, "West Park", Clawton, Holsworthy, Devon, EX22 6QN, web: http://www.whwestlake.co.uk/

[2] Diode Communications, 19 Station Road, Wombwell, Barnsley, South Yorkshire, S73 0AH, Tel: 01226 754222, web: http://www.diodecomms.co.uk/index.php

[3] PUFF microwave CAD software available from K M Publications, 63 Ringwood Road, Luton, Beds, LU2 7BG, Tel/Fax: 01582 581051, web: www.vhfcomm,co.uk

[4] Ansoft Designer SV, web: http://www.ansoft.com/ansoftdesignersv/

[5] The Radio Amateur's Handbook (any edition), ARRL.

[6] Microwave Measurements and Techniques, T S Laverghetta, Artech House, 1976. (Good advice on cable, connectors and how to fit them. Much useful practical advice on many subjects, not just for microwavers!)

[7] The Buyer's Guide to Amateur Radio, Angus McKenzie, MBE, G3OSS, RSGB, 1986.

Index